Introduction to

The Commercial Fisheries of the United States and Canada

Illustrated 2012 Edition

Introduction to

The Commercial Fisheries of the United States and Canada

Illustrated 2012 Edition

Robin W. A. Rodger
Wyndylyn M. von Zharen

Illustrated by Minji Kim and Sherri Spurrell

Canadian Marine Publications

*CMP*_____ NS

Introduction to the Commercial Fisheries of the United States and Canada
By Robin W. A. Rodger and Wyndylyn M. von Zharen

Published by: Canadian Marine Publications
PO Box 34097, Halifax, Nova Scotia, Canada, B3J 3S1; E-mail: cmp@cmpPublications.com
Orders: 902-425-1320/1374 or consult http://www.cmpPublications.com/na_fisheries
Copyright ©2011 by Canadian Marine Publications (div. of Market Research Associates Ltd.)

Library and Archives Canada Catalogue Card Number C2011-905124-9; ISBN 978-0-9739494-1-4. Printed simultaneously in Canada and the United States of America.

Completely revised, new edition previously published as *The Fisheries of North America: An Illustrated Guide to Commercial Species*, by Canadian Marine Publications, Halifax, NS, 2006. Author Rodger, Robin W. A., Library and Archives Canada Catalog Card Number C2005-906582-6, Library of Congress Catalog Control Number 2006404221. ISBN 0-9693595-9-4 (S/Cover) ISBN 0-9739494-0-6 (H/Cover).

Interior illustrations of fishes and shellfishes by Minji Kim and Sherri Spurrell, copyright ©1991, ©2005 and ©2011 by Canadian Marine Publications.

United States fisheries and aquaculture statistics courtesy of The Fisheries Statistics & Economics Division of the Unites States National Marine Fisheries Service (NMFS). Canadian fisheries and aquaculture statistics reproduced, or adapted, from Fisheries and Oceans Canada with the permission of Her Majesty the Queen in Right of Canada, 2011.

Extreme care has been taken in the preparation of this work. However, authors and publisher make no warranty or representation, expressed or implied, with respect to accuracy, completeness, or utility of the information contained in this document; nor do the authors or publisher assume any liability with respect to the use of or reliance upon, or for damages resulting from the use of or reliance upon, any information, procedure, conclusion, or opinion contained in this document.

Library and Archives Canada Cataloguing in Publication

Rodger, Robin W. A.
    Introduction to the commercial fisheries of the United States and Canada / Robin W.A. Rodger, Wyndylyn M. von Zharen ; illustrated by Minji Kim and Sherri Spurrell. -- Illustrated 2011 ed.

Previously published as: The fisheries of North America.
Includes bibliographical references and index.
ISBN 978-0-9739494-1-4

    1. Fishery resources--Canada--Handbooks, manuals, etc. 2. Fishery resources--United States--Handbooks, manuals, etc. 3. Fishes--Canada--Handbooks, manuals, etc. 4. Fishes--United States--Handbooks, manuals, etc. 5. Shellfish--Canada--Handbooks, manuals, etc. 6. Shellfish--United States--Handbooks, manuals, etc. I. Von Zharen, Wyndylyn M. II. Kim, Minji III. Spurrell, Sherri IV. Rodger, Robin W. A. The fisheries of North America V. Title.

SH219.R63 2011   338.3'7270971   C2011-905124-9

<u>*Dedication*</u>

This book is dedicated to all the fishery researchers and scientists who are enhancing our capabilities to manage our fisheries more responsibly. It is their efforts that have made this book possible.

CONTENTS

Preface
Acknowledgements

PART 1 – INTRODUCTION

PART 2 - Fishes and Shellfishes (ILLUSTRATED)

MARINE FINFISHES (including diadromous species) 77

MARKET NAME	Featured Species Common Name	Scientific Name	Page
ALASKA POLLOCK OR POLLOCK	Walleye Pollock	Theragra chalcogramma	78
ALEWIFE OR RIVER HERRING	Alewife	Alosa pseudoharengus	80
AMBERJACK	Banded Rudderfish	Seriola zonata	82
ANCHOVY (& SARDINES)	Northern Anchovy	Engraulis mordax	84
BALLYHOO	Ballyhoo	Hemiramphus brasiliensis	86
BARRACUDA	Great Barracuda	Sphyraena barracuda	88
BASS, SEA	Black Sea Bass	Centropristis striata	90
BIGEYE	Bigeye	Priacanthus arenatus	92
BLUEFISH	Bluefish	Pomatomus saltatrix	94
BONITO	Pacific Bonito	Sarda chiliensis	96
BROTULA OR CUSKEEL	Bearded Brotula	Brotula barbata	98
BUTTERFISH	Butterfish	Peprilus triacanthus	100
CAPELIN	Capelin	Mallotus villosus	102
COBIA	Cobia	Rachycentron canadum	104
COD	Atlantic Cod	Gadus morhua	106
CROAKER	Atlantic Croaker	Micropogonias undulatus	108

PART 3 - Bibliography, References, Glossary, Index

Preface

This book is designed to be a comprehensive, user-friendly guide to understanding the fishing and aquaculture sectors (and associated recreational fisheries) in Canada and the United States (excluding Hawaii and other offshore territories), with a particular focus on the various species that make up the commercial catch. To that end, 147 different species have been chosen to represent the major seafood groups (e.g., cod, grouper, hake, trout, tuna, clam, crab, shrimp, etc.) and associated statistics that provide an overview of the entire industry. Using these chosen species, the book sheds light on more than 500 species that compose almost all the commercial species landed or farmed in the United States and Canada.

Although some commercial species presented herein are landed in Mexico and Mexican authorities also work closely with scientists in the United States and Canada on identification and other fisheries issues, inclusion of Mexican commercial fish species was not possible at the present time for two main reasons. Such inclusion would greatly increase the size and complexity of the book and would require additional language capabilities that we presently lack. Hawaii, Puerto Rica, and other offshore US territories have been excluded as well for much the same reasons. However, these may be the subject of future efforts.

Hence, the present book focuses only on species that account for almost 100% of the total value of marine and freshwater, finfish, and shellfish, landed in the continental United States, Alaska and Canada. Species identification includes "acceptable" market name(s), scientific common name, scientific name, many vernacular names (or aliases) as identified in the "The Seafood List," published by the United States Food and Drug Administration, as well as many international recognitions. This identification effort is aided by approximately 200 illustrations highlighting major distinguishing physical features and a comprehensive index of species names under naming various naming categories.

Featured species are described under key headings; for example, name recognition, physical identification and differentiation, habitat range, fishing methods, landing statistics and trends, commercial uses and forms, spawning behaviour, and life cycle. Where appropriate, the book also identifies real or potential threats to a fishery: conservation initiatives, aquaculture initiatives, impact of recreational fishing, government regulations or advisories, processing methods, under-utilized species, and unique species characteristics.

Conflicts and duplications in species' nomenclature are rife, particularly in the use of vernacular and market names. This hampers the integrity of both economic and scientific research efforts, as well as the transparency of commercial transactions. Like language itself, existing or local custom often prevails over standard conventions and some fish/shellfish nomenclature issues will never be entirely resolved to everyone's satisfaction. For example, it is unlikely that lake trout or brook trout will ever be widely known (or marketed) as "char" ["charr" in FishBase] even though this may be a more appropriate market name.

Many potential sources of nomenclature confusion abound. Pacific whiting, a regulated name in the US, is often otherwise known as Pacific hake. Other hakes (although not all), are more acceptably marketed as "whiting" as well. Atlantic Ocean pollock and Alaska pollock, are often reported together as "pollock" but are two very different species. Many rockfish are legally marketed as red snapper under state laws on the West Coast, while Greenland turbot (another regulated name in the US) is often called Greenland halibut outside the US. Species such as alewife (also known as gaspereau and kyak), dogfish (also known as northern shark and rock salmon), bluefish (also known as sunfish and snapping mackerel), blackback flounder (also known as winter flounder) and gray sole (also known as witch flounder) are just a few examples where vernacular names are often found in place of the correct scientific common name. Some species of shellfishes (e.g., whelks, sea urchins) have no generally recognised scientific common name at all.

The book tackles these identification issues head-on. To accomplish "cradle to grave" species identification, the authors' approach was to match (where possible) the preferred market names and the common names of fish/shellfish species, as identified in "The Seafood List" to the most recently designated scientific names of the species as verified in the Integrated Taxonomic Information System (ITIS). In most cases, species' scientific names in "The Seafood List" are the same as the ITIS name; however, if there was a difference, (or if the species was not listed in "The Seafood List") the ITIS or other source designation was used and noted.

The United States-sponsored ITIS database for scientific names, as with the "The Seafood List," is based on North American-wide input. Hence, the species identification terminology used in this book is compatible with the most recently approved usage in North America, but may not equate with other conventions. For example, species of finfish and shellfish were cross-referenced with the "FishBase" and "SeaLifeBase" databases; and many differences in nomenclature, particularly in common names, were noted and included here. As well, multi-lingual names are included in the text.

The book makes a serious effort at clarifying issues of species identity so that the reader can quickly appreciate and connect issues of larger importance. Market information is often deficient without clear identification and understanding of the species being discussed. Similarly, scientific information on species often lacks important perspectives on economic impact and market presentation. The integrated approach taken in this book facilitates a quick, comprehensive, and detailed understanding of the state of the major commercial fisheries in the United States and Canada.

An introductory section provides a perspective on the historical impact of the fisheries and key Fisheries Management Frameworks:

- Overfishing Issues
- Additional Anthropogenic Stressors on Fish Biomass

- Key Management Issues
- The Impact of Aquaculture
- The Social-Economic Impact of Fisheries Today

The above is supplemented with illustrations and information on fishing methods and common terms used to describe fishes' physical attributes to enable the reader to easily follow the text. A glossary of the scientific terms used is also included.

Now in its 3rd edition, the book has proven to be valuable tool to industry and government decision-makers, as well as researchers and educators involved in the North American fisheries.

About the Authors

Dr. Wyndylyn von Zharen is Regents Professor in Marine Sciences at Texas A&M University. She also holds graduate appointments in the departments of Marine Biology, Oceanography, and Wildlife and Fisheries Sciences. Her research and teaching interests include management strategies for resilient fisheries, eco-system perspectives for coastal and marine stewardship, and anthropogenic stressors on the marine ecosystem. Her work in environmental impact assessment modeling includes endangered species, invasive species, habitat loss, and pollution control. Her legal background also lends itself to legal perspectives on ocean management and to the decision, risk, and management science fields. She has published several books on environmental management systems as well as numerous articles on this and related topics.

Robin W. A. Rodger, MBA, CMC is a certified management consultant specializing in the economic analysis and marketing of seafood products. Early in his career, he was instrumental in spearheading a drive to find new scallop resources on the Grand Banks of Newfoundland and in implementing fuller utilization of scallop products. Together with Maritime Ocean Resources he produced the first *Canadian Fish and Shellfish Exporters Guide* for the Canadian Department of Foreign Affairs and International Trade. In 1991, he authored the first "Fish Facts" book for Van Nostrand Reinhold, NY, NY, which led to the current series. More recently, he has been a team member and/or project leader on major international studies focused on the lobster, shrimp, and saltfish sectors. Mr. Rodger resides in Halifax, NS.

Acknowledgements

This book owes its existence to the contributions of many people, but especially to the fisheries researchers and research organizations that have been cited in the Appendix and elsewhere. Foremost among these, the authors acknowledge the key contributions of the researchers and scientists developing the _Integrated Taxonomic Information System (ITIS)_, _FishBase, SeaLifeBase,_ and _The Seafood List_ databases, which are used extensively in this work.

We would also thank Warren Jardine for his original work on _Fish Facts_ (the first book in this series); particularly, in the book's organization, glossary, and index that have been updated, but whose format is carried through to this edition. We would also like to thank Kera McAllister for her assistance in formatting this edition as well as Sherri Spurrell who completed many of the fish, and especially shellfish, illustrations for this book, starting originally with the publication of _Fish Facts_. Sherri is now joined by Minji Kim who produced many fine new fish illustrations for the present edition.

Other researchers who contributed much to this edition were Bharat Joshi (who helped greatly with the statistical analysis), Kerry Mellett (who assisted with naming changes), and Alyson Azzara and Mara Nery who both helped "break the ice" on new species added in this edition.

We would also like to acknowledge the statistical information provided by the US National Marine Fisheries Service and the Canadian Department of Fisheries and Oceans.

Finally, we also appreciate the assistance of all past and present book reviewers whose contributions have added greatly to the present volume. A list of some of these reviewers, and their review topics, is found in the Appendix.

Introduction and Overview

If the ancients had known what the earth was really like,
they undoubtedly would have named it Oceanus.
The Matchless Phenomenon of the Sea[1]

The global fishery is not in great shape. Although total exploitation has stabilized at around 90 million tonnes per year, the Fisheries and Agriculture Organization of the United Nations (FAO) estimates that in 2008, only about 15% of the world's fisheries were underexploited (versus 40% in the mid -1970s). "In contrast, the proportion of overexploited, depleted or recovering stocks increased from 10% in 1974 to 32% in 2008."[2] Moreover, a 2003 study estimated that large predatory fish biomass is about 10% of pre-industrial levels, suggesting the baseline level of fisheries exploitation is even higher than usually reported.[3]

In North America, groundfish stocks decimated on the East Coast and salmon stock declines on the West Coast in recent decades have come to symbolize the impacts of commercial overfishing. Many more stocks, particularly freshwater species, have been damaged through destruction of habitat, pollution, the introduction of exotic and/or invasive species and through less than optimal fisheries and/or aquaculture practices.

In North America, the US National Marine Fisheries Service (NMFS) reports 203 fish stocks or stock complexes had a known **overfished** status in 2009 and 46 stocks or stock complexes (23%) were designated as overfished. A further 250 stocks or stock complexes had a known **overfishing** status in 2009 and 38 stocks or stock complexes (15%) had a fishing mortality rate that exceeded the overfishing threshold (i.e., were found subject to overfishing).[4] In Canada, with a smaller number of species to review, about 10 species of commercial fishes are presently identified as being at risk, or under concern, including abalone and sturgeon populations and a number of very important salmon, cod and other groundfish stocks.[5]

The purpose of this book is to present an overview of the state of commercial fisheries in the oceans surrounding the continental United States, Alaska and Canada, and also the state of freshwater fisheries and aquaculture production. Based on observations and analysis from the above, the authors suggest new strategies to help improve fisheries management beyond current sustainability practices. The ultimate goal is the development of robust and resilient fisheries at all levels. Such an ambitious goal requires the input of many more critical factors than are typically applied under current fisheries management plans.

The new strategies suggested here are cognizant of many factors. First, current stewardship (if one can call current strategies "stewardship"), is usually based on a series of regimes directed at the various parts rather than the whole and, therefore, is often ineffective.

---

[1] *See* Leonard Engel, The Sea (1969) 9.
[2] FAO, "The State of World Fisheries and Aquaculture 2010, page 35". *Also see* John Charles Kunich, "Losing Nemo: The Mass Extinction Now Threatening The World's Ocean Hotspots," 30 Colum. J. Envtl. L. 1 (2005):22-23.
[3] Ransom A. Myers and Boris Worm, "Rapid Worldwide Depletion of Predatory Fish Communities," 423 Nature 280, (2003):282.
[4] NMFS, "2009 Status of US Fisheries" <http://www.nmfs.noaa.gov/sfa/statusoffisheries/sos_full28_press.pdf> (last visited August 15, 2011)
[5] Government of Canada, "Species at Risk Public Registry" <http://www.sararegistry.gc.ca/sar/listing/schedules_e.cfm?id=1> (last visited August 15, 2011)

Secondly, research presented here suggests stewardship must be supported through an interdisciplinary, adaptive, interdependent and interconnected approach encompassing the views of all representative stakeholders. That is, the approach must embrace the human dimension, including individuals as well as communities. Thirdly, the existence of uncertainty must be recognized and acknowledged; fisheries must be managed using imperfect, complex information about the biology of the fishery and its habitats, the interdependency of other ecosystems, and associated risk. Fourthly, the strategy must move past sustainability to encompass the dual goals of a resilient and robust fishery. Fifthly, the application of an environmental strategy such as the international environmental management system strategy, ISO 14001, with a focus on environmental efficiency, may be an effective first step in a global and/or North American effort to steward living marine species. This is particularly true for reef associated and migrating species, many of which are not well covered under international conventions.

Finally, and perhaps most importantly, marine stewardship requires a globally integrated strategy that embraces scientific, economic, social and ethical dimensions based on continual tracking of the marine ecosystem, in particular, and the larger environment, in general.

Part 1 of the book is divided into nine sections and provides in-depth background information on fisheries and aquaculture practices in North America. The objective is to provide the reader with a complete picture of fisheries activities from harvesting to socio-economic impacts, while identifying key fisheries policy considerations in the process. The first six sections provide an overview of historical and current fisheries exploitation and, in particular, how various policies and regulations have impacted overfishing.

Section One provides a brief historical overview of the decline of the North American fishery. The purpose is to reflect on the devastation of fish populations resulting from the problem of too many fishers chasing too few fish. *Section Two* provides examples of complex, multiple stressors that disturb the ecosystem upon which fish depend. *Section Three* canvasses a few examples from the plethora of the most ambitious legal regimes, management theories, and codes aimed at regulating fishing and managing fish populations; most of which have proven to be inadequate, and thus, ineffective. *Section Four* offers a management strategy that goes beyond mere sustainability: an adaptive, holistic strategy aimed at creating a resilient and robust fishery; one that is harmonious with major international templates, and provides for long-term fisheries policy development. The strategy takes account of human social involvement and suggests that once this basis is formed, the possibility of creating an effective global initiative for stewardship of fish and their habitat is greatly enhanced. *Section Five* presents information on aquaculture processes and species common to North America. *Section Six* provides pertinent data on the socio-economic impacts of fisheries and aquaculture.

The last three sections of Part 1 provide technical information. *Section Seven* identifies and illustrates common fishing capture methods and gear used in the North American fishery. *Section Eight* identifies common fish terminology for identification purposes. *Section Nine* provides further details on interpreting and understanding fish data information.

Part 2 of the book provides two-page entries highlighting key information on almost all the individual species and/or stock complexes commercially fished in North America. Following Part 1 and Part 2 are an index, glossary and bibliographic information.

Caught Off Guard:
A Brief Historical Review of the Fisheries and Overfishing

The men were astonished at the numbers of salmon in the river, mostly dying after the spawn and therefore inedible. The water was so clear that, no matter how deep the river, the bottom was plainly visible.
From the Journals of Captain Meriwether Lewis and William Clark
(October, 1805)

Fishing is one of North America's oldest industries.[6] Moreover, fishing played a central role in the European settlement of North America.[7] Even before Europeans arrived, Native Americans fished using nets made from natural fibers and hooks made from bones.[8] With the development of seaworthy vessels, Europeans -- Basque, British, Norse, and Vikings amongst other European people -- sought out Atlantic Ocean waters in pursuit of abundant fish populations.[9] For example, in 1497, the experiences of Italian explorer John Cabot in Canadian waters off Newfoundland were thus described: "[Fish could] be taken not only with the net but in baskets let down with a stone so that they sink in the water."[10] A century later, British skippers reported the existence of great banks of oysters as large as shoes and twenty-pound lobsters.[11]

Along with improved shipbuilding came improved navigation techniques and fishing gear. With the progression of improvements came more and more fishers as news of fisheries' abundance spread. By the early 1500s, thousands of fishers were sailing to the Grand Banks of Newfoundland and New England.[12] The development of Newfoundland fisheries took pressure off the fishing grounds of Europe and provided an alternative fishing ground to the North Sea and Iceland fisheries. Cod became the staple product in trade for two reasons: it was the most abundant fish and it preserved well, better than many other fish. Salting preserved fish better and for longer periods of time than the alternatives of smoking and/or drying.

With its ice-free winters, the New England fishery flourished. New England merchants exported fish, particularly salted cod. In the early 1600s, settlers moved to the area now known

---

[6] *See*, e.g., Pews Oceans Commission, "Socioeconomic Perspectives on Marine Fisheries in the United States" (2003) <http://www.pewtrusts.org/uploadedFiles/wwwpewtrustsorg/Reports/Protecting_ocean_life/environment_pew_oceans_socioeconomic_perspectives.pdf> (last visited Marcy 4, 2011).

[7] *Id.*

[8] Chester D. King, "Evolution of Chumash Society: A Comparative Study of Artifacts Used for Social System Maintenance in the Santa Barbara Channel Region before A.D. 1804" (1991): 80-81.

[9] See, e.g., Innis, Harold A. "The Cod Fisheries. The History of an International Economy" (1978):12; and Marguerite Ragnow, "Cod, Driven to Discover," University of Minnesota <http://www.lib.umn.edu/bell/tradeproducts/cod> (last visited March 28, 2011).

[10] Raimondo di Soncino, Milan's envoy in London, wrote this description in a letter dated December 18, 1497, to the duke of Milan, who financed Cabot's expedition. *See* Mark Kurlansky, "In Cod We Trust," THE GUARDIAN (LONDON) (Jan. 31, 1998):20.

[11] "A Run on the Banks: How 'Factory Fishing' Decimated Newfoundland Cod," E/The Envtl. Mag. (Mar.-Apr. 2001) <http://www.emagazine.com/view/?507> (last visited March 4, 2011).

[12] The Grant Banks of Newfoundland are underwater plateaus southeast of Newfoundland on the North American continental shelf. Here, the cold Labrador Current mixes with the warm Gulf Stream. Add to this the shape of the ocean bottom and the results are nutrients that help to create an unusually rich fishing ground.

as Cape Cod and established fishing ports. Estimates are that by 1640, fishers were bringing in 300,000 cod per year.[13] European fishing fleets were also having their own significant impact on cod stocks.[14] For example, it was estimated that by 1660, English fishers were drying and salting 150 shiploads of cod per year.[15]

By the eighteenth century, the New England fishery was "world status." The fish trade, especially cod, provided great wealth to the new colony and created a "codfish aristocracy" in Boston. Mansions were built and decorated with symbols of codfish. Early US coins, tax stamps, state seals and company crests were issued with an emblem of the "mighty" codfish.[16] During the same time, the Newfoundland cod trade focused on Mediterranean markets. Thus, "the pope became the toast of Newfoundland fishermen."[17] Significant catches of other fish -- haddock, halibut, ocean perch, and yellowtail flounder -- were dietary staples, particularly before the era of productive farming. New industries were created around this enterprise: boatbuilding, salt mining, and ice harvesting, as well as fertilizer and oil production.

As the population grew, local fisheries were developed throughout North America: freshwater fish in the Great Lakes, shellfish in the mid-Atlantic, reef fish (e.g., snapper and grouper), mackerel, shrimp and sponges in Florida and the Gulf of Mexico, and sardines and salmon on the Pacific coast became large fisheries in themselves. In the 18th and 19th centuries, whitefishes, perches and alewives provided some of the largest catches in the Great Lakes and, when salted or smoked, provisioned much of the developing land before widespread farming took place. Fisheries for industrial uses developed as well and menhaden became the largest species landed in terms of quantity for many years.

The U.S. markets for salted cod continued to increase through the 1800s due, in part, to an increase in European immigration to North America including a large Catholic population that, in general, consumed fish. Salted cod was a staple of the Union Army in the Civil War.[18] New fishing methods and technologies provided a boost to the fishing industry.[19] Steamboats and powered winches initiated the era of the offshore dragger in the late 1800s. Rather than sailboats with lines and jiggers, new "steamers" could now chase fish and catch them in large nets. By 1900, North American markets were demanding fresh fish, now made possible by cold storage. Haddock, pollock, ocean perch, hake, and flatfishes eventually began to replace cod in many markets. Frozen fillets were developed in the 1920s[20] and within 25 years, freezer technology and refrigerated transport were perfected and became widely available throughout

---

[13] David Barber, "History of Commercial Cod Fishing," eHow Contributor <http://www.ehow.com/about_6744836_history-commercial-cod-fishing.html> (last visited March 12, 2011).

[14] A stock "describes characteristics of semi-discrete groups of fish with some definable attributes which are of interest to fishery managements." GA Begg et al. (1999) "Stock identification and its role in stock assessment and fisheries management: an overview." Fisheries Research, 43:1–8.

[15] Barber, *supra* note 13.

[16] For a more complete discussion of the impact of fisheries in the development of North America, *see* Mark Kurlansky's *Cod: A Biography of the Fish That Changed the World* (1997) [hereinafter Kurlansky].

[17] D.A. Farnie, "The Commercial Empire of the Atlantic, 1607–1783," The Economic History Review, 15 (1962):205–218.

[18] Kurlansky, *supra* note 16.

[19] Kurlansky provides a prescient anecdote: Until the 1930s, the traditional mode of catching cod was from a dory that, when filled with a certain mass of cod, became unseaworthy; thus, fishers were limited in their catch by vessel "technology," Kurlansky, *supra* note 16 at 114. *See also* Jeremy B.C. Jackson et al., "Historical Overfishing and the Recent Collapse of Coastal Ecosystems," Science, vol. 293, no. 5530 (2001):629-637.

[20] Clarence Birdseye is credited with inventing in 1924 the quick freezing method. "Everyday Mysteries" Library of Congress <http://www.loc.gov/rr/scitech/mysteries/frozenfood.html> (last visited March 15, 2011).

North America. These changes facilitated shipments of fish to inland destinations and the increased demand was met with increased fishing. More sophisticated gillnets and draggers came into use in the 1920s and cod catches increased throughout the 1950s as the fishing grounds became more competitive.[21] These landings included the larger, older, more fertile female cod as opposed to younger females, a destructive practice indeed.

Throughout the 1960s, fleet sizes increased, aided by new technologies for finding and catching even more fish. Distant water fleets from up to two dozen nations competed for fish. The largest trawl nets, with a circumference of some 2,048 meters and producing a mouth opening area of 22,900 square meters, could encircle more than a dozen jumbo jets.[22] These factory trawlers can be longer than a football field "and capable of catching and processing up to 200 tons [180 tonnes] of fish daily."[23] Coupled with unregulated high seas "free for all," 80% of the world's marine catch was produced by only twenty fishing nations.[24]

A collapse was inevitable. The impact of fisheries collapse can be devastating, as evidenced by the Newfoundland cod crash of 1992, in which 18,000 direct jobs were lost,[25] fishing towns shrank in population by up to 20%, and the Canadian taxpayer spent billions of dollars to deal with the aftermath of the collapse. In 1993, a moratorium on cod fishing on the Eastern Scotia Shelf was declared. So also ended one of the most lucrative fisheries for Nova Scotia; however, the collapse of the Atlantic cod fishery brought about a renewed worldwide attention to the need for fisheries conservation efforts. That the cod fishery was depleted, a staple product that had fed much of Europe for almost 500 years while fostering New World expansion, was a shock. "If one of the largest fisheries in the world, exploited continuously for 500 years, could not be sustained by a nation with an advanced research, monitoring, and management capacity, it left little hope for success elsewhere. Big laws -- international conventions, 200 mile limits and a host of state-imposed technical legislation regulating fishing activity -- had failed to prevent the crisis of small catches, with profound consequences for the economy and society of maritime Canada."[26]

Overfishing on the Grand Banks was not a novel phenomenon, but rather, a global one. Approximately 47% of the major fisheries are fully fished or overfished, and fishing fleets have the capacity to catch many more fish than the maximum sustainable yield.[27] Added to the pressure of overfishing is the issue of by-catch. By-catch represents the millions of tonnes of non-targeted and economically undesirable fish that are caught in nets set for other species of

---

[21] Barber, *supra* note 13.

[22] "Amazing Facts About the Global Fisheries Crisis," Greenpeace Archive <http://archive.greenpeace.org/comms/fish/amaze.html> (last visited May 26, 2011)

[23] *Id.*

[24] *Id.*

[25] "Overfishing," Greenpeace International <http://www.greenpeace.org/international/campaigns/oceans/overfishing/> (last visited May 27, 2011).

[26] E.H. Allison, "Big Laws, Small Catches: Global Ocean Governance and the Fisheries Crisis," Journal of International Development 12 (2001):993.

[27] "Taking Stock of Coastal Ecosystems," World Research Institute <http://pdf.wri.org/wr2000_coastal_2.10_takingstock.pdf> (last visited May 27, 2011).

fish.[28] Globally, between 18 and 40 million tonnes are discarded annually by commercial fisheries; the ecological impact is severe: it can alter the structure of marine ecosystems.[29]

In a recent study using more than 200 marine ecosystem models from around the world and extracting more than 68,000 estimates of fish biomass from 1880-2007, scientists found that predatory fish -- cod, tuna, and groupers, for example -- have declined by two-thirds during the past 100 years, while small forage fish such as sardines, anchovy and capelin have more than doubled over the same period; 54% of the decline in predatory fish population took place in the last forty years: "If the fishing-down-the-food-web[30] trend continues, our oceans may one day become a 'farm' to produce feeds for the aquaculture industry. Goodbye, Wild Ocean!"[31]

In another study, data from more than 230 populations revealed a median reduction of 83% in breeding population size from known historic levels. "Few populations recover rapidly; most exhibit little or no change in abundance up to 15 years after a collapse. Reductions in fishing pressure, although clearly necessary for population recovery, are often insufficient. Persistence and recovery are also influenced by life history, habitat alteration, changes to species assemblages, genetic responses to exploitation, and reductions in population growth attributable to depensation. Heightened extinction risks were highlighted recently when a Canadian population of Atlantic cod (*Gadus morhua*) was listed as endangered on the basis of declines as high as 99.9% over 30 years."[32]

To manage what fisheries are left and to restore fish populations, attempts have been made to restrict fishing efforts. Deciding on which strategy is most effective is problematic: each has its benefits and drawbacks. Examples of specific management techniques to lessen or halt the decline of fish include:

---

[28] *See* Danielle Knight, "US Environmentalists Against Overfishing," The Independent (June 15, 1998).

[29] *See* M. Barange, "Ecosystem Science and the Sustainable Management of Marine Resources: from Rio to Johannesburg," Frontiers in Ecology and the Environment 4 (2003):194; *see also* "By-catch and Discard Impacts, A Global Assessment of Fisheries By-catch and Discards," FAO Corporate Document Repository (explaining the impact of discards on the ecosystem, e.g., impact of discards on non-target populations versus target species, marine mammals, turtles, sharks, ad other species) <http://www.fao.org/DOCREP/003/T4890E/T4890E04.htm> (last visited May 4, 2011).

[30] When catches of larger, longer-lived species (e.g., tuna and cod) are exhausted, fishers concentrate on catching smaller, shorter-lived, plankton-eating species (e.g., squid, sardines, and invertebrates) which are nearer the bottom of the food chain; thus, the removal of significant numbers of predatory fish create a problem for the remaining predators: they must feed on lower trophic level species which typically have fluctuating seasonal abundance. When these lower trophic level species are also fished, the entire ecosystem for both predator and prey, as well as their ecosystems are in danger.

[31] "Predatory Fish in Sharp Decline, UBC researchers say," Vancouver Sun (February 18, 2011) <http://www.vancouversun.com/technology/Predatory+fish+sharp+decline+researchers/4308870/story.html#ixzz1N xUX338q> (last visited May 27, 2011).

[32] Jeffrey A. Hutchings and John D. Reynolds, "Marine Fish Population Collapses: Consequences for Recovery and Extinction Risk," BioScience 54(4) (2004):297-309; *see also* Nancy L. Shackell, et al, "Decline in Top Predator Body Size and Changing Climate Alter Trophic Structure in an Oceanic Ecosystem," Proceedings of the Royal Society Biological Sciences, Proc. R. Soc. B 7 May 2010 vol. 277 no. 1686 1353-1360 <http://rspb.royalsocietypublishing.org/content/277/1686/1353> (last visited May 7, 2011). *See also* International Earth System Expert Workshop on Ocean Stresses and Impacts," IPSO, IUCN, WCPA (June 20th, 2011) (stating that the health of the world's oceans is declining much faster than originally thought -- under siege from pollution, overfishing, and other human-made stressors) <http://www.stateoftheocean.org/pdfs/1906_IPSO-LONG.pdf> (last visited June 21, 2011).

- seasonal restrictions - however, such restrictions act to induce fishers to increase fishing efforts when the season is open.[33]
- licensing program - but there remain the problems of fairness of issuance and overfishing by licensees.[34]
- gear restrictions - but such restrictions increase costs to fishers and enforcement entities (difficulty with detection) and perhaps endangerment of non-targeted species[35]
- total allowable catch/setting maximum catch allowed for species/areas/times - but there remain the problems of determining allowable catch and who gets to fish.[36]

The latter option, total allowable catch (TAC), is a biologically-based method that sets the maximum amount of fish that could be taken from each stock without depleting it and is based on the concept of Maximum Sustainable Yield (MSY); i.e., the maximum amount of fish that could be taken from a stock without depleting it. Unfortunately, when a TAC is announced, fishers usually race for the fish and continue fishing until the TAC is reached, creating new problems -- a glut of (often low quality) fish that must all be processed at once.

Alternatively, the TAC could be determined and then allocated among fishers so that the sum of each of the fishers' quotas equals the TAC. This individual fishing quota (IFQ) allocation is often based on prior catch history[37] When fishers fish with an individual quota their access to common stocks is secure and individual fishing effort can be allocated to maximize quality, supply and prices. Often the fisher can also trade or sell these quota rights, called individual transferable quota (ITQ).

Another problem that contributes significantly to overfishing is subsidies. Many countries subsidize their commercial fishing fleet. For example, Canada funded the expansion and modernization of Atlantic fleets to compete with growing pressure from European fishers beginning in the 1960s.[38] Canadian subsidization of its Atlantic fishing industry contributed to overexploitation. A comprehensive study of subsidies that expand commercial capacity estimates that from 1995 through 2005, globally, some $30 to 34 billion were dispersed in subsidies, e.g., vessel construction and re-fits, operating costs, construction of fishing ports and processing plants, payment for foreign access agreements, and marketing support; and the global fleet "is estimated to be two and a half times greater than needed to catch" what the ocean can sustainably produce.[39] "This represents close to 20% of the total value of marine

---

[33] *See* Anthony D. Scott, Conceptual Origins of Rights Based Fishing, in Rights Based Fishing 11, 24 (Philip A. Neher et al. eds., 1989).

[34] *Id.*

[35] *Id.*

[36] *See, e.g.,* "Towards Sustainable Fisheries: Economic Aspects of the Management of Living Marine Resources," Organisation for Economic Co-operation and Development ("OECD") (2003).

[37] Suzanne Iudicello Michael Weber, and Robert Wieland, Fish, Markets and Fishermen: The Economics of Overfishing (1999):110-14.

[38] *Id.* at 61.

[39] Brooke Glass-O'Shea, "Watery Grave: Why International and Domestic Lawmakers Need to Do More to Protect Oceanic Species From Extinction," 17 Hastings W.-N.W. J. Env. L. & Pol'y 191 (2011):200 (citing Charles Clover, The End of the Line: How Overfishing is Changing the World and What We Eat, 104-06 (2006):137-9) [hereinafter Glass-O'Shea]. See also, "Hooking the Reader," Columbia Journalism Review (2011) <http://www.cjr.org/the_observatory/hooking_the_reader.php?page=all> (last visited December 5, 2011); and Eric A. Bilsky, Symposium: Territory Without Boundaries: Colonizing Natural Resources: Conserving Marine Wildlife Through World Trade Law, 30 Mich. J. Int'l L. 599, 601 (2009).. *But see* Rashid Sumaila, "The role of Subsidies in Overfishing Cannot Be Over-emphasized" Common Fisheries Policy Online, CFP-reformwatch.EU (May 25, 2011) (estimating the number at $16 billion globally each year)

catch. ... [P]ast subsidies are partly to blame for the need to go farther and deeper now. ...[M]ore subsidies now will only result in fishers having to go even farther and deeper later, until there is nowhere else to go."[40]

The joint World Bank/FAO report argues that the world's capture fishery resources are non-performing assets with rates of return, or yields, not exceeding zero, costing the world economy an estimated $50 billion per year in foregone resource rent.[41] According to a 2010 FAO report, this happened because:

> By the middle of the twentieth century, fishery managers in industrialized countries, realizing that stocks were being overexploited, attempted to improve the design and enforcement of resource management measures. However, it became apparent that introducing harvest controls through the implementation of total allowable catches (TACs), or the equivalent thereof alone, generally led to the emergence of excess fleet capacity and severe economic waste. Subsequently, TACs were complemented with "limited entry schemes." However, even if the numbers of vessels were effectively controlled, technological advances in fishing technology meant that fishing capacity increased and resource depletion, economic waste (in the form of excess vessel capital) and lost economic rents (the result of exploiting standing stocks much below optimal stock sizes) continued to grow, exacerbated by fishery subsidies. The extension of economic zones in the 1980s, followed by the 1995 United Nations Fish Stocks Agreement (UNFSA), did not improve the institutional framework for resource management to such an extent that resources investment occurred and economic waste disappeared, in part because of the problems associated with shared stocks.[42]

In Canada, "conservation measures are set up to fail...because insurance allows fishermen to maintain oversized fishing fleets, creating constant pressure to raise allowable catches."[43] Yet, encouraging commercial fishing pushes fishers to continue catching fish to depletion, far beyond the point where fishing is merely unprofitable. Subsidies are not needed to jump start commercial fishing enterprises. For almost a century, we have had too many fishers going after too few fish.

For terrestrial-based resources such as minerals, governments, in general, require payment for access; but governments do not require payment for access to fisheries and yet, like minerals, fish represent the common property (even as stewardship property). The result is that not receiving payment for use of the resource translates into still another government subsidy. The only rational government subsidy would be to subsidize the training that would allow fishers to switch successfully to another profession.

<http://www.cfp-reformwatch.eu/2011/01/the-role-of-subsidies-in-overfishing-cannot-be-over-emphasized/> (last visited May 11, 2011) [hereinafter Sumaila].

[40] *Id.* Sumaila.

[41] "The Sunken Billions: The Economic Justification for Fisheries Reform," FAO and the World Bank (2011):120 <http://siteresources.worldbank.org/EXTARD/Resources/336681-1224775570533/SunkenBillionsFinal.pdf> (last visited May 4, 2011).

[42] "Part 3, Highlights of Special Studies," The State of World Fisheries and Aquaculture, 2010, FAO (2010):120-121.

[43] Glass-O'Shea, *supra* note 39 (citing Charles Clover, "The End of the Line: How Overfishing is Changing the World and What We Eat" [2006]:133-4).

Section Two

Oceans of Abuse:
Additional Examples of Anthropogenic Stressors on Fish Biomass

The majority of the world's 170 million fishers and those dependent on the fishing industry (including families) live in areas that are exposed to other multiple anthropogenic stressors that can have a debilitating effect on fisheries. Each stressor can have a significant impact; at the same time, seemingly insignificant impacts can be deleterious depending on the cumulative impact of a stressor or stressors. One of the difficulties with grasping what is happening to fish populations is that for most humans, it is difficult to "see." Unlike terrestrial flora and fauna, marine life lives "in" the element rather than "on" it. An imaginative challenge is posed for a typical person in an industrialized nation to visualize the extent of the problem when the seafood shelf of the grocery store is lined with choices of fish and other marine delicacies. "Where's the problem?" asks the consumer. Only when schools of fish blacken blue water, or shrimpers pull in their nets, for example, is one reminded of what lies within the oceans. Similar to what has happened on land, the oceans have been systematically clear-cut.[44]

In addition to systematic overfishing and subsidization of the industry, there are myriad reasons for the decline of fish populations, including several primary human activities: disruption of the coastal and marine ecosystems through pollution and the blight of uncontrolled coastal development.

Disruption of the Coastal and Marine Ecosystems through Pollution. Degrading of the oceans first captured global attention through the explorations of Thor Heyerdahl.[45] In 1947, he and five crew members sailed a raft across what was then a comparatively pristine ocean, from Peru to Tahiti.[46] In 1970, he crossed the Atlantic and "'reported seeing far more oil lumps than fish, and alerted the world about the enormous quantities of trash, oily wastes and plastic debris he observed in the sea.'"[47] Forty or so years later, the degradation is even more apparent.

Coastal invasion and destruction of marine habitat are equally pervasive contributors to the deterioration of the ocean ecosystem.[48] A brief look at the sobering statistics and issues depicting but a few of the multiple stressors provides a clear indication that Heyerdahl's second travel portended gloom. The oceans have been called "our global garbage can."[49] Pollution sources are varied: "The National Research Council estimates that as many as 8.8 million tons [8 million tonnes] of oil enter the ocean each year as a result of human activity."[50] In the 2011

---

[44] *See* Carl Safina, "The World's Imperiled Fish," Sci. Am. Presents: The Oceans (1998):58, 59.

[45] *See* Kieran Mulvaney, "A Sea of Troubles: In the International Year of the Ocean, Are We Reaching the Limits?" E: Envtl. Mag. (Jan. 11, 1998):28.

[46] *Id.*

[47] *Id.* (citing a letter from Dr. Claude Martin, Director General of the World Wide Fund for Nature, and Dr. Thor Heyerdahl, which appeals to the United Nations to effectuate a plan to preserve the oceans).

[48] *Id.*

[49] *Id.* at 31.

[50] *See id.* (citing National Research Council statistic); *see also* Nancy Lord, "Our Only Ocean; Care for the Oceans," Sierra (July 17, 1998):34 (citing National Research Council statistic). Tar balls also can be a naturally occurring phenomenon; and "Taking Care of Our Oceans and Beaches," EcoMall: A Place to Help Save the Earth: <http://www.ecomall.com/greenshopping/esocean.htm> (last visited May 4, 2011).

Report, *Tracking Trash: 25 Years of Action for the Ocean*, volunteers with the Ocean Conservancy have helped to rid coasts and waterways of harmful trash; in twenty-five years, it has tallied and removed some 166 million pieces of trash including 7,825,319 plastic bags, 1,248,892 balloons, 52,907,756 cigarette butts and filters, and 979,468 tires, as well as food wrappers, rope, straws, caps and lids, cup and plates, and beverage cans. This debris entangled amphibians, birds, corals, fish, invertebrates, mammals, and reptiles.[51]

In a 2009 report jointly produced by the UN Food and Agriculture Organization (FAO) and UN Environment Programme (UNEP), it is estimated that abandoned, lost or discarded fishing gear (ALDFG) in the oceans makes up around 10% (640,000 tonnes) of all marine litter and is a problem that is increasingly of concern.[52] The impacts of ALDFG include continued catching of target and non-target species, alternations to the benthic environment, navigational hazards, beach debris/litter, introduction of synthetic material into the marine food web, introduction of alien species transported by ALDFG, and a variety of costs related to clean-up operations and impacts on business activities. "In general, gillnets and pots/traps are most likely to 'ghost fish' while other gear, such as trawls and longlines, are more likely to cause entanglement of marine organisms, including protected species, and habitat damage."[53]

In addition to ALDFG, vessel source pollution also can include a wide range of pollutants; e.g., sound pollution, exhaust emissions, oil spills, sewage and other wastes as well as invasive species. Noise pollution from ships is increasing; the noise can travel long distances and fish that rely on sound for spawning, navigation, etc. during their life history can be harmed by this pollution.[54]

Shipboard engines are among the world's highest polluting combustion sources per tonne of fuel consumed.[55] Large ships are often run on low quality fuel oils such as bunker oil which are highly polluting and have been shown to be a health risk.[56] As well, a majority of pollutants attributable to persistent continental pollution comes from vessels.[57]

The CMU study[58] found that worldwide shipboard nitrous oxide (NO_x) emissions from diesel engines are equal to nearly half the total emissions from the U.S.; 42% of NO_x emissions from North America; and 74% of emissions from the entire Organization for Economic Cooperation and Development (OECD). For sulphur oxide (SO_x) emissions from steam engines, shipboard emissions are equal to nearly 43% of the total emissions from the United States, 35% of SO_x emissions from North America, and 53% of emissions from the OECD.[59]

---

[51] "2011 Report: Tracking Trash –25 Years of Action for the Ocean," The Ocean Conservancy, (2011):25 <http://www.oceanconservancy.org/news-room/collateral/icc2011report__global_final.pdf> (last visited May 25, 2011).

[52] Graeme Macfadyen, Tim Huntington, and Rod Cappell, "Abandoned, Lost, or Otherwise Discarded Fishing Gear," UNEP Regional Seas Reports and Studies 185, FAO Fisheries and Aquaculture Technical Paper 523 (2009):1 <http://www.fao.org/docrep/011/i0620e/i0620e00.htm> (last visited May 30, 2011).

[53] *Id.* at iv.

[54] *See* Alan Khee-Jin Tan, "Vessel-Source Marine Pollution: The Law and Politics of International Regulation," Cambridge University Press (2005); and "Human Noise Pollution in Ocean Can Lead Fish Away from Good Habitats and Off to Their Death," Science Daily (August 13, 2010) <http://www.sciencedaily.com/releases/2010/08/100803212015.htm" (last visited March 7, 2011).

[55] *See* James Corbett and Paul Fischbeck, "Emissions from Ships," Science, vol. 278 (1997):823-825.

[56] Adrian Burton, "Air Pollution: Ship Sulfate an Unexpected Heavyweight," Environ. Health Perspect. 116(11) (2008):A475 < http://www.ncbi.nlm.nih.gov/pmc/articles/PMC2592288/> (last visited May 15, 2011).

[57] *Id.*

[58] Corbett, *supra* note 55.

[59] *Id.* at 823-824.

Vessel source operational pollution accounts for 12% of marine pollution while land-based and atmospheric sources account for 77%. Vessel-related marine oil pollution stems primarily from two types of spills: 1) operational discharges; and 2) spills from oil cargo carriers, "tanker accidents." Operational discharges occur during loading and unloading. It has been estimated that two thirds of vessel-source oil pollution results from operational discharges. Operational discharges for tankers also result from such routine operations as ballast and tank-cleaning processes for dry-docking and changing cargoes.[60] Unless discharging occurs away from ports and harbours (as in the lightering of vessels); spills, though small, can be deleterious because of their proximity to the shore, the closed-in demographics of the fouled water, and the undiluted property of the oil.

Tanker accidents, representing the second type of spill, are potentially more devastating: Crude oil contains polycyclic aromatic hydrocarbons (PAHs) that are difficult to clean up and last for years in the coastal and marine environment.[61] Remarkably, accidental oil spills from tankers this decade have been at record low levels—one third of the previous decade and one tenth of the 1970s—at a time when oil transported has more than doubled since the mid 1980s.[62] Oil spills can also include releases of crude oil from offshore platforms (such as the 2010 release in the Gulf of Mexico), drilling rigs, as well as well as spills of refined petroleum products and their by-products, and heavier fuels used by large vessels, e.g., bunker fuel. (Natural seepage into the marine environment is estimated to be 600,000 tons [500,000 tonnes] per year.)[63] According to the United States Coast Guard, 35.7% of the volume of oil spilled in the United States from 1991 to 2004 came from tank vessels (ships/barges), 27.6% from facilities and other non-vessels, 19.9% from non-tank vessels, 9.3% from pipelines, and 7.4% from mystery spills.[64]

Sewage and other vessel wastes are significant. The cruise line industry, for example, dumps 255,000 gallons of "graywater" and 30,000 gallons of "blackwater" into the sea every day.[65] As much as 75% of solid waste -- e.g., glass, paper, cardboard, aluminum, steel cans, and plastics -- is incinerated on board and the ash discharged at sea. The remaining solid waste, however, can entangle fish and other marine species.[66] The largest driftnets for commercial fishing can be more than 50 kilometers (30 miles) in length, extending to a depth of 30 meters (one hundred feet) from the surface.

---

[60] W.M. von Zharen, "Marine Transportation: Major Oil Pollution Prevention and Compensation Regimes: Jurisdictional Issues in Oil Pollution," Natural Resources Law, Richard Fink (ed.), American Bar Association (1994):91-11.

[61] L.E. Panetta (Chair), "America's Living Oceans: Charting a Course for Sea Change," Pew Oceans Commission (2003) <http://www.pewtrusts.org/uploadedFiles/wwwpewtrustsorg/Reports/Protecting_ocean_life/env_pew_oceans_final_report.pdf> (last visited March 4, 2011)

[62] "Pollution Analysis - Level of Oil Spilled in 2006 Was One of the Lowest for Over 35 Years," International Association of Independent Tanker Owners (May 18, 2007) <http://www.intertanko.com/templates/Page.aspx?id=42166> (last visited May 24, 2011).

[63] "Oil in the Sea III: Inputs, Fates, and Effects," Ocean, National Research Council (2003) <http://www.nap.edu/catalog.php?record_id=10388> (last visited May 3, 2011).

[64] "Cumulative Spill Data and Graphics," United States Coast Guard (2007) <http://www.allcountries.org/uscensus/390_oil_spills_in_u_s_water.html> (last visited May 26, 2011). More stringent regulations by nation-states, increased media attention, and potential liability have contributed to this decline.

[65] See Michael Herz and Joseph Davis, "Cruise Control, A Report on How Cruise Ships Affect the Marine Environment," The Ocean Conservancy (2002):13 <http://act.oceanconservancy.org/site/DocServer/cruisecontrol.pdf?docID=141> (last visited April 3, 2011).

[66] Id.

A vessel's bilge water is another potential pollutant. Fuel, oil, on-board spills, and waste water from engines and other machinery collect in the bilge, an area located at the bottom of a vessel's hull. The biological breakdown of petroleum products, e.g., dissolved solids, oil, and other chemicals, can poison fish even in minute concentrations. A typical cruise ship generates an estimated 25,000 gallons of oily bilge water on a one-week voyage.[67]

Ballast water, seawater pumped into compartments in the hull of a vessel to stabilize the vessel, is necessary for safe operation. As a ship unloads cargo or burns fuel, the vessel becomes lighter; ballast water must be taken on board where it is pumped into large holding tanks. Vessels may take on additional ballast water to pass under bridges, or may discharge ballast water to allow the vessel's keel to clear shallow areas. However, this discharge represents yet another anthropogenic stressor on fish and their habitats.

In addition to potential introduction of hazardous chemicals, ballast water discharges are believed to be the leading source of invasive species in U.S. marine waters.[68] Invasive, non-indigenous or exotic species, as they are called, have been dubbed the "corporate raiders of nature"[69] and the "darkest cloud yet in the invasion biology of North America."[70] Ballast water is frequently taken on in one region and then discharged in another, often resulting in the introduction of non-native, nuisance species that can cause extensive negative impacts to the ecology of aquatic ecosystems, including fish habitat. The discharge typically contains various plants, animals, and pathogens, as well as dormant stages of microscopic toxic aquatic plants that can cause harmful algal blooms after their release.[71]

With the expansion of international trade, the potential increases for the introduction of alien, invasive species. As vessels travel faster, the survival rates of species carried in ballast tanks have increased. The Atlantic comb jelly, a United States east coast native, was introduced by ballast water into the Black and Azov Seas in the early 1980s. By 1988, it had become the dominant species in the Black Sea, leading to the collapse in fish stocks and an estimated $250 million of lost fisheries revenue.[72]

Biologists report that exotics are thought to have played a role in 70% of the native aquatic species extinction in this century in the United States alone.[73] The problem gained public attention in the mid-1980s when the prolific zebra mussel *(Dreissena polymorpha)*, thought to originate in Eastern Europe, arrived in the Great Lakes in ballast water.[74]

Non-indigenous species can be introduced in ways other than through ballast-water discharge. For example, Florida is plagued by exotic tropical fish that are raised for the aquarium industry

---

[67] Kira Schmidt, "Cruising for Trouble: Stemming the Tide of Cruise Ship Pollution," United Nations Environment Programme (2000):8 <http://www.cep.unep.org/publications-and-resources/databases/document-database/other/rep-ss-cruise-trouble-1.pdf> (last visited March3, 2011).

[68] Statement of Catherine Hazlewood, The Ocean Conservancy, "Ballast Water Management: New International Standards and NISA Reauthorization," Hearing, House Transportation and Infrastructure Subcommittee on Water Resources and Environment, 108th Cong., 2nd sess.(March 25, 2004).

[69] Jim Hiney, "Hostile Takeover," Texas Shores (Summer 1998):3. No universal term for these invaders has been agreed upon by regulators, conservationists, and researchers. Monikers to describe the species as a generic group include: aquatic exotics, nonindigenous, transplants, and aliens.

[70] Dan Terlizzi, "Foreword," Maryland Sea Grant: Zebra Mussels and the Mid-Atlantic (1993):3.

[71] See "The International Environmental Agenda: Toxic Paints, Emissions, and Ballast Water," Int'l Ship Registry Rev. (Aug. 1998):1,2.

[72] See Mulvaney, *supra* note 45 at 28.

[73] See Hiney, *supra* note 69 at 6.

[74] See Patrick Baker, "Criteria for Predicting Zebra Mussel Invasions in the Mid-Atlantic Region," Maryland Sea Grant: Zebra Mussels and the Mid-Atlantic (1993):9.

and pet trade and then are either intentionally let go or escape, e.g., during a hurricane.[75] One of the most recent invaders is the lionfish (*Pterois volitans*), native to coral reefs in the South Pacific and Indian Oceans. They are presently found in the their "adopted" environment of the Atlantic Ocean; as ambush predators, they are believed to pose high risks to local reef communities and are capable of disrupting the balance of these communities.[76]

Recreational boaters who move their boats from one state or one country to another may unknowingly have various organisms attached to the bottom of the vessel. Intracoastal waterways and drainage basins such as the Mississippi River, which drains into the Gulf of Mexico, also provide a means for these species to migrate.[77] In the United States, for example, 78% of all the goods imported move through ports. Thus, coastal fisheries can be particularly exposed to the threat of invasive species. Since 2004, all vessels equipped with ballast water tanks must have a ballast water management plan.[78]

Atmospheric deposition, pollution entering the water from the atmosphere either as a precipitation or in dry form, is another source of pollution. Heavy metals and chemical compounds, such as polychlorinated biphenyls (PCBs),[79] dichlorodiphenyltrichloroethane (DDT),[80] and dioxin have been associated with a wide range of impacts on marine wildlife.[81]

Rising carbon dioxide emissions could also have a significant impact on the world's fish populations. According to recent research, juvenile fish may become an easy choice for predators if the world's oceans become more acidic due to CO_2 fallout. As carbon levels rise and ocean water acidifies, the behaviour of baby fish changes dramatically in ways that decrease their chances of survival by 50-80%.[82] "As CO2 increases in the atmosphere and dissolves into the oceans, the water becomes slightly more acidic. Eventually, this reaches a point where it significantly changes the sense of smell and behaviour of larval fish; instead of avoiding predators, they become attracted to them. They appear to lose their natural caution and start taking bigger risks, such as swimming out in the open – usually with lethal consequences."[83]

Uncontrolled Coastal Development. The coastal regions represent the interface between the marine and land environments. These regions provide many species with habitats for breeding, feeding, and shelter. The vast majority of all marine life inhabits the intertidal zone and shallow

---

[75] *See id.* at 4-5.
[76] "The Lionfish Invasion," NOAA Ocean Service Education
<http://oceanservice.noaa.gov/education/stories/lionfish/lion04_biology.html> (last visited April 2, 2011).
[77] *See Id.*
[78] "Ballast Water Management," United States Coast Guard <http://www.uscg.mil/hq/cg5/cg522/cg5224/bwm.asp> (last visited March 20, 2011).
[79] PCBs are any of a group of organic compounds that were once widely used as liquid coolants and insulators in industrial equipment. They are toxic to animals. *See* "Proceedings of the Subregional Awareness Raising Workshop on Persistent Organic Pollutants (POPs), Bangkok, Thailand," *United Nations Environment Programme* (November 25-28th, 1997) <http://www.chem.unep.ch/pops/POPs_Inc/proceedings/bangkok/FIEDLER1.html> (last visited Nov. 30, 2010).
[80] *Id.* DDT is an insecticide toxic to animals when swallowed or absorbed through the skin. It has been banned for most uses in the United States.
[81] *Id.* (providing a general overview of DDT, PCBs and dioxins).
[82] "Carbon Emissions Threaten Fish Populations," Science Daily (July 27, 2010) (citing Phili L. Munday, et. al., "Replenishment of Fish Populations is Threatened by Ocean Acidification," PNAS [July 6, 2010] DOI: 10.1073/pnas.1004519107).
[83] *Id.*

seas bordering the continents.[84] One-third of the world's marine fish species are found on coral reefs,[85] referred to as the "rain forests of the oceans," as they are the most productive coastal ecosystems of all.[86] Ninety percent of the world's fish catch is made within two hundred nautical miles of the coast, and the majority of that catch is within the first five miles.[87]

Aquaculture has doubled in production since 1990; capture fisheries and aquaculture supplied the world with about 142 million tonnes of fish in 2008. Of this, 115 million tonnes were used as human food providing an estimated per capita supply of about 36 pounds (17 kg).[88] Aquaculture accounted for 46% of total apparent food fish supply in 2008, which represents a continuing increase from 43% in 2006.[89] While aquaculture accounts for almost 50% of fish consumed by humans, and this share is expected to increase further to meet future demand,[90] aquaculture also accounts for significant deterioration and loss of wetland and other coastal habitats. "Industrial-scale aquaculture production magnifies environmental degradation... This is true even when farming operations implement the best current marine fish farming practices."[91] For example, the total global production of farmed shrimp reached 2.5 million tonnes in 2005, some 42% of the total shrimp production that year.[92] Consequently, the industry's rapid expansion is "exacting a serious toll on wetland habitats found in these areas; mangrove forests, which lie in the intertidal zone, have been particularly impacted."[93]

As coastal ecosystems such as estuaries, wetlands, shallow bays, mangroves, coral reefs, and sea-grass beds decline, their pollutant-filtering capacity also declines. An estimated 80% of ocean pollution comes from land-based sources such as runoff pollution; e.g., septic tanks, cars, trucks, boats, and larger sources such as farms, ranches, and forest areas.[94] For example, agricultural runoff contains nitrogen and phosphorous, two primary nutrients that can come from fertilizer or sewage. These nutrients nourish algae in water and, in turn, create eutrophication –the "algal bloom" of phytoplankton in the water (sometimes known as green tides or brown tides).[95] This causes hypoxia, the depletion of oxygen in the water, which can

[84] *See* Engel, *supra* note 1, at 14.
[85] *See* Mulvaney, *supra* note 45; *see also* Rita Ariyoshi, "Halting a Coral Catastrophe," Nature Conservancy (Jan.-Feb. 1997):20, 22 ("Indonesia's waters alone are home to more than 400 hard coral species . . . . [Its reefs] support 2,500 species of fish, nearly 35% of the world's fish species.").
[86] *See* Mulvaney, *supra* note 45.
[87] *See* Martin I. Glassner, Neptune's Domain (1990):73.
[88] State of World Fisheries and Aquaculture, *supra* note 42 at 3.
[89] *Id.*
[90] *Id.* at 117.
[91] "Large-Scale Fish Farm Production Offsets Environmental Gains, Assessment Finds," Science Daily (Oct. 28,2010) <http://www.sciencedaily.com/releases/2010/10/1010270992201.htm> (last visited May 23, 2011).
[92] *See* "The State of World Fisheries and Aquaculture" (2008):124 <ftp://ftp.fao.org/docrep/fao/011/i0250e/i0250e.pdf>; *see also*, "Shrimp Farming and the Environment. A Consortium Program to Analyse and Share Experiences on the Better Management of Shrimp Aquaculture in Coastal Areas," Synthesis Report, World Bank, Network of Aquaculture Centres in Asia-Pacific, World Wildlife Fund and Food and Agriculture Organization of the United Nations (2002) <http://library.enaca.org/Shrimp/Publications/DraftSynthesisReport-21-June.pdf> (last visited May 3, 2011).
[93] Coralie Thornton, Mike Shanahan, and Juliette Williams, "From Wetlands to Wastelands: Impacts of Shrimp Farming," Environmental Justice Foundation, SWS Bulletin (March 2003):48 < http://www.ejfoundation.org/pdf/wetlands_to_wastelands.pdf> (last visited May 28, 2011).
[94] "Ocean Facts on Runoff Pollution, International Year of the Ocean –Fact Sheet," National Oceanic and Atmospheric Administration (1998) < http://www.yoto98.noaa.gov/facts/pollut.htm> (last visited April 8, 2011).
[95] *See* "Coastal Eutrophication: Linking Nutrient Sources to Coastal Ecosystem Effects and Management –The Intersection of Several UNESCO-IOC Programmes Related to Nutrients," UNESCO (2008) <http://www.jodc.go.jp/info/ioc_doc/INF/160489e.pdf> *(last visited May 22, 2011).*

lead to biological "dead zones."[96] Some 375 hypoxic coastal zones have been identified globally. [97] Loss of these natural coastal areas can also lead to a decline and loss of biodiversity.[98]

Thirteen of the world's 20 largest cities are located on the coast, and 40% of the world's population lives within 100 kilometres of a coastline, an area that accounts for only about 20% of the world's land mass.[99] In the United States, a staggering 53% of the nation's total population currently live in coastal counties (17% of the total land area excluding Alaska) and an 8% increase in U.S. coastal county population is expected by 2020.[100] Population increases and conversion of coastal lands for development, agriculture, and aquaculture are reducing, at an alarming rate, estuaries, wetlands, marshes, shallow bays, mangroves, seagrass areas, and coral reefs. These coastal ecosystems play a major role in the life cycle of many fish and other marine organisms by providing breeding, nursery, and feeding grounds. Rapid coastal development and human population growth place heavy demands on ecosystems. For example, oceans are equivalent to superhighways for moving commerce. This takes an ecological toll on the marine ecosystem. Not only do vessels themselves create varying types and quantities of pollution, but the infrastructure needed to host these vessels in ports and waterways makes additional demands on coastal and main ecosystems.

Ports require large areas of coastal land for both construction and modification, as well as operation.[101] As ports are built and existing facilities expanded, the construction and reclamation accounts for significant habitat loss, changes in water currents and circulation, turbidity and sediment load; in turn, these have an impact on benthic communities.[102] Many of the same problems are associated with the construction and expansion of marinas. Breakwaters, quays, groins, slips, and similar structures require large areas of land and water. The impacts to already sensitive areas are compounded by dredging, including maintenance dredging, soil excavation, soil replacement or backfilling, surface sealing, water drainage and high ground loads.[103]

Tourism triggers its own set of issues with hotels, airports, roads, and vacation homes causing negative impacts to coastal and marine ecosystems.[104] For example, seagrasses appear to be relatively hardy, but when subjected to typical shoreline development -- excess siltation, turbidity, shading, and water pollution -- they can be severely damaged.[105] Seagrasses play a

---

[96] *Id.*

[97] *Id.*

[98] *See* "A Guide to World Resources 2000-2001: People and Ecosystems: The Fraying Web of Life," United Nations Development Programme, World Bank, World Resources Institute (2000) <http://pdf.wri.org/world_resources_2000-2001_people_and_ecosystems.pdf> (last visited April 5, 2011).

[99] *See* Lauretta Burke, Yumiko Kura, Ken Kassem, Carmen Revenga, Mark Spalding, Don McAllister, "Pilot Analysis of Global Ecosystems: Coastal Ecosystems," World Resources Institute (2001) <http://pdf.wri.org/page_coastal.pdf> (last visited May 23, 2011).

[100] "NOAA'S State of the Coast," National Oceanic and Atmospheric Administration <http://stateofthecoast.noaa.gov/population/welcome.html> (last visited May 3, 2011).

[101] "Physical Alteration and Destruction of Habitat: A Backgrounder for the GPA Online Dialogue," Stakeholder Forum Briefing Paper Series, UNEP's Global Programme of Action (GPA) <http://www.stakeholderforum.org/fileadmin/files/Physical_Alteration_and_Destruction_of_Habitat_Briefing.pdf> (last visited May 23, 2011).

[102] *Id.*

[103] *Id.*

[104] *Id.*

[105] *Id.*

particularly important role in maintaining sediment stability and water quality, roles that are critical to the sustainability of commercial and recreational fisheries. They provide shelter and food to fish species as well.

Anthropogenic stressors may also be contributing to climate change. Ozone depletion has a direct effect on the amount of UVB radiation absorbed by the atmosphere, potentially affecting all life forms, and ozone depletion is also linked to climate change and global warming.[106] The composition, geographic distribution, and productivity of many ecosystems are predicted to shift as individual species respond to changes in climate:

> Global climate change is impacting and will continue to impact marine and estuarine fish and fisheries. Data trends show global climate change effects ranging from increased oxygen consumption rates in fishes to changes in foraging and migrational patterns in polar seas, to fish community changes in bleached tropical coral reefs. Projections of future conditions portend further impacts on the distribution and abundance of fishes associated with relatively small temperature changes. Changing fish distributions and abundances will undoubtedly affect communities of humans who harvest these stocks. Coastal-based harvesters (subsistence, commercial, recreational) may be impacted (negatively or positively) by changes in fish stocks due to climate change. Furthermore, marine protected area boundaries, low-lying island countries dependent on coastal economies, and disease incidence (in aquatic organisms and humans) are also affected by a relatively small increase in temperature and sea level....[107]

In another study, scientists calculated the likely impact of climate change on the distribution of more than 1,000 species of fish around the globe.[108] The model predicts what might happen under different climate scenarios to the distribution of commercially important species including cod, herring, sharks, groupers, and prawns. The findings suggest (in part) that:

- There could be large-scale re-distribution of species, with movement towards the Pole(s)
- On average, fish are likely to shift their distribution by more than 40 km per decade and there will be an increasing abundance of more southern species
- Nordic countries such as Norway could see increased catches
- In the North Sea, the northward shift of Atlantic cod could reduce its abundance by more than 20%, while European plaice, a more southerly fish, may increase by more than 10%

---

[106] *See* Mulvaney, *supra* note 45 at 32-33.

[107] Julie M. Roessig, Christa M. Woodley, Joseph H. Cech, Jr., and Lara J. Hansen, "Effects of Global Climate Change on Marine and Estuarine Fishes and Fisheries," World Wide Fund for Nature (2005):3 <http://www.wwf.de/imperia/md/content/klima/ST_Meeresfisch_und_Klima.pdf> (last visited March 28, 2011); *see also* "Dramatic Climate Change-Driven Impacts Documented Across Marine Life Spectrum," Scripps News, Scripps Institute of Oceanography (April 30, 2009) (finding that warming causes shifts in habitats of open-ocean fishes using global models for implementing the worldwide initiative) <http://scrippsnews.ucsd.edu/Releases/?releaseID=985> (last visited May 23, 2011).

[108] "Climate Change and Fisheries: U.S. Atlantic Cod Population to Drop by Half by 2050," Science Daily (February 16, 2009) (citing William Cheung, Vicky Lam, Jorge Sarmiento, Kelly Kearney, Reg Watson, and Daniel Pauly, "The Capacity and Likelihood of Climate Change Adaption in the World's Fisheries," Fish and Fisheries [February 13, 2008]).

- In the U.S., there may be a 50% reduction in the number of some cod populations on the east coast by 2050
- Some species could face a high risk of extinction including striped rock cod in the Antarctic and St. Paul rock lobster in the Southern Ocean(s)
- The invasion of non-native/alien species and local extinction of species may disrupt some marine ecosystems and biodiversity.[109]

Summary

Sharp increases or decreases in numbers of fish species are characteristic indicators of destabilized ecosystems.[110] Subjecting populations of living marine species to anthropogenic stressors results in an unstable marine ecosystem that, in turn, impacts on all life forms. With these facts in mind, it is distressing to note that only 1.17% of the world's oceans have been designated as protected.[111] This grim overview illustrates the repercussions caused by failed attempts at stewarding living marine species. Those in power and other stakeholders have neither kept pace in addressing the onslaught of increased human activity surrounding these species, nor have they tackled these complex issues from an ecosystem perspective.

The sections above provided a brief glimpse at some of the more pressing issues related to anthropogenic stressors on fish populations and other marine biota. The next section provides an overview of the most ambitious, albeit ineffective, attempts to halt the decline of marine fish populations.

---

[109] *Id.*

[110] *See generally,* Eugene P. Odum, Fundamentals of Ecology 242 (3rd ed. 1971).

[111] *See* C. Toropova, I. Meliane, D. Laffoley, E. Matthews, and M. Spalding, M. (eds.), "Global Ocean Protection: Present Status and Future Possibilities," International Union for Conservation of Nature and Natural Resources (2010):32 <http://data.iucn.org/dbtw-wpd/edocs/2010-053.pdf> (last visited May 3, 2011).

Section Three

Stemming the Tide of Fisheries Declines
Policy Frameworks and Selected Legal Regimes

With over 100 multilateral, regional, and bilateral treaties that weave the ocean governance fabric, fourteen United Nations agencies and nineteen Intergovernmental Organizations with "ocean responsibilities," sorting out international legal regimes and associated agencies can be a numbing task.[112] The following selected international theories and international and regional agreements may encourage the development and application of an adaptive, flexible, and holistic management tool (discussed in *Section Four*).

International Tenets

Applicable to Canadian and U.S. legal regimes are common tenets found within customary international law and those laws addressing jurisdiction over the seas.[113] They form the basis for addressing issues such as under whose jurisdiction fish species fall, whether there are duties to protect the marine environment, and the role of individual nations in exploiting the world's oceans. The following is an overview of these principles.

Customary International Law. The basis for customary international law is the practice of states which reflects common activity throughout the international community and, as such, has the force of law.[114] Disputes between two states may be referred to international tribunals such as the International Court of Justice (ICJ) if all parties accept this jurisdiction.[115] Without express treaty provisions, the judgment of the ICJ has no binding force except between the parties and only in respect to that particular case.[116] Application of customary international law may be particularly appropriate for issues involving fisheries. For example, although there is no general obligation imposed on states to negotiate under customary international law in all situations, there are two decisions of the ICJ in which the court held that states are under such an obligation in certain situations.[117] In the *Fisheries Jurisdiction* case,[118] the ICJ held that conservation measure must be taken into account when fishing on the high seas. The ICJ's pronouncements in the *Gulf of Maine (Canada and the U.S.)* delimitation of maritime boundary case contributed significantly to recognition of a 200-mile zone as part of customary international law. In that case, the ICJ Chamber pointed out that Canada and the United States

---

[112] *See* Allison, *supra* note 26.

[113] For an overview of environmental regimes governing the oceans, see W.M. von Zharen, "Environmental Governance of the Seas, the Coastal Zone, and Their Resources," 9 Nat. Resources & Env't (1995):3.

[114] *See generally* Joseph G. Starke, "Introduction to International Law," International Law (Barry E. Carter and Phillip R. Trimble eds., 1995): 141, 142.

[115] *See, e.g.,* W.M. von Zharen, "An Eco-Policy Perspective for Sustaining Living Marine Species," *Ocean Development and International Law,* vol. 30, no.1 (1999):1-42. [hereinafter Eco-Policy].

[116] *Id.*

[117] Fisheries Jurisdiction Case (U.K. & N. Ireland v. Iceland), 1974 I.C.J. 3, 32 (July 25); North Sea Continental Shelf Cases (F.R.G. v. Den.; F.R.G. v. Neth.), 1969 I.C.J. 3, 47 (Feb. 20).

[118] *Id.*

had traditionally and successfully resolved fisheries management issues jointly through international agreement.[119]

Global commons. The global commons refers to areas that are outside the generally recognized sovereign territory of any nation.[120] Included in the commons are the high seas and the denizens therein.[121] Fishing rights were the issue in the *Fisheries Jurisdiction* case[122] (noted previously) in which the ICJ enjoined the parties to conduct their negotiations on the basis that "each must in good faith pay reasonable regard to the legal rights of the other, thus bringing about an equitable apportionment of the fishing resources based on the facts of the particular situation."[123] Fish, when part of the global commons, can be sustained only through global stewardship of the global marine ecosystem.

Jurisdiction over the Seas. Hugo Grotius, respected as the "father of international law," provided in his 1608 *Mare Liberum*[124] a summation of a centuries-old argument concerning a fundamental principle of the law of the sea: "Every nation is free to travel to every other nation, and to trade with it."[125] The high seas, then, were the common property of all or the property of no-one, *res nullius.* This pronouncement formed the basis of the aggressive, possessionary stance of coastal states in the 20th century asserting their right to fish under the freedom of the high seas mentality. This "catch as catch can" attitude began to shift with the creation of a legal order for the seas including sovereign rights of all nations under the 1958 Geneva Law of the Sea Conference.[126] Out of this conference came the Convention on the High Seas,[127] Article 2, which qualifies the rights of states to fish on the high seas, while maintaining a duty to conserve living resources. The idea of conservation of fish and other living marine species in the oceans was reinforced by the United Nations Convention on the Law of the Sea, (1982)[128] (discussed below) some thirty years in the making, which recognizes the right of a coastal nation to assert sovereign rights over fisheries within a 200-mile zone, the exclusive economic zone (EEZ), an area beyond and adjacent to the territorial sea and in which the coastal state exercises exclusive jurisdiction and control over its natural resources.[129] The provisions call for coastal states to

---

[119] Delimitation of the Maritime Boundary in the Gulf of Maine Area (Can./U.S.), 1984 ICJ REP. 246 (Judgment of Oct. 12). Interestingly, maritime boundaries and rights were the focus in 1812 when the United States declared war on Britain, the only major war, other than native wars, fought on Canadian soil.

[120] Eco-Policy, *supra* note 115 at 5.

[121] *See, e.g.,* Christopher D. Stone, "Mending the Seas through a Global Commons Trust Fund," Freedom for the High Seas in the 21st Century: Ocean Governance and Environmental Harmony 171 (Jon. M. Van Dyke, Durwood Zaelke, and Grant Hewison eds., 1993).

[122] Fisheries Jurisdiction (U.K. v. Ice.), *supra* note 117.

[123] *Id.*

[124] Hugo Grotius, The Freedom of the Seas (Mare Liberum) Ralph Van Deman Magoffin trans., 1916 (1608).

[125] *Id.* at 7.

[126] Twenty-two ratifications or accessions were required to bring this convention into force. However, since the adoption of the United Nations Convention on the Law of the Sea, no state has ratified this treaty. 1958 Geneva Law of the Sea Conference, A/CONF.13/L.58, 1958, UNCLOS, Off. Rec. vol. 2, 146 <http://untreaty.un.org/cod/avl/ha/gclos/gclos.html> (last visited May 14, 2011).

[127] Convention on the High Seas, 1958, U.N.T.S. No. 6465, vol. 450, pp. 82-103, Art. 2 <http://sedac.ciesin.columbia.edu/entri/register/reg-021.rrr.html> (last visited May 2, 2011).

[128] United Nations Convention on the Law of the Sea, *opened for signature* Dec. 10, 1982, U.N. Doc. A/CONF.62/122, 21 I.L.M. 1261 (1982), *reprinted in* United Nations, Official Text of the United Nations Convention on the Law of the Sea With Annexes and Index, U.N. Sales No. E.83.V.5 (1983) <http://www.un.org/Depts/los/convention_agreements/texts/unclos/closindx.htm > (last visited May 23, 2011) [hereinafter UNCLOS III]

[129] *Id.* art. 61(1).

conserve living marine species within their jurisdiction[130] The Convention entered into force in 1994. Canada ratified the Convention in 2003.[131] The United States has not ratified the treaty but the EEZ was established by Presidential Proclamation 5030[132] in 1983 and later codified in the Magnuson Fishery Conservation and Management Act (Magnuson Act) (discussed later in this Section).[133]

Major International and Regional Regimes[134]

Major international and federal fishery protection and conservation[135] law offers, in general, direct protection of fish populations or indirect protection through general environmental proclamation although the two categories often contain cross-over provisions.

The two international bodies responsible for fishery conservation are the United Nations (UN) and its agency, the International Maritime Organization (IMO). Prior to 1972, the UN passed few international environmental agreements.[136] In 1972, however, the UN declared that it was committed to environmental issues,[137] and subsequently, a number of conventions addressing the marine environment were enacted.[138] The IMO, formerly called the Intergovernmental Maritime Consultative Organization (IMCO), was established by a convention adopted at a 1948 conference in Geneva and began functioning in 1958 when the convention entered into

---

[130] Conservation is emphasized in Article 61 of UNCLOS III as well as other articles, e.g., Articles 63, 65, 66, and 67.

[131] *See, e.g.,* J. Richard MacDougall, Wendell Sanford, and Jacob Verhoef, "Ice and No Ice: The Canadian UNCLOS Bathymetric Mapping Program," Proceedings of the Canadian Hydrographic Conference and National Surveyors Conference (2008):1 <http://hydrography.ca/assets/files/2008conference/session_2A/2A-4_MacDougall_et_al.pdf> (last visited May 23, 2011).

[132] Proclamation No. 5030, 48 Fed. Reg. 10,605 (1983), reprinted in 1983 U.S.C.C.A.N. 28.

[133] Magnuson Fishery Conservation and Management Act (MFCMA), 16 U.S.C. 1801-1882 (1994).

[134] A discussion of specific international treaties to reduce or eliminate pollution and other anthropogenic stressors is beyond the scope of this section. However, mention should be made of an example of an international attempt to reduce certain pollutants from vessels: The International Convention for the Prevention of Pollution by Ships, 1973 [done in London, 2 November 1973, reprinted in 12 I.L.M. 1319 (1973)]. This Convention and its modification by a Protocol adopted by the International Conference on Tanker Safety and Pollution Prevention (TSPP Conference) in 1978 [done in London, 17 February 1978, 17 I.L.M. 546 (1978)], is referred to as MARPOL 73/78. Its six annexes are intended to regulate pollutants as follows: Annex I – Oil; Annex II – Noxious Liquid Substances carried in Bulk; Annex III – Harmful Substances carried in Packaged Form; Annex IV – Sewage; Annex V – Garbage; and Annex VI – Air Pollution. A state that becomes party to MARPOL 73/78 must accept Annex I and II. Annexes III-VI are voluntary. As extensive as MARPOL 73/78 appeared to be in prescribing technical advances and preventative schemes for preventing oil and other marine pollutants, it avoids altogether the issues of a coastal state's power of enforcement and the prosecution of flag-state violations.

[135] The term "protection" is used generically to describe those regimes that emphasize conservation and/or sustainability and applies to this section only.

[136] An exception is the International Convention for the Regulation of Whaling (ICRW) signed in 1946 (International Convention for the Regulation of Whaling, with Schedule of Whaling Regulations, Dec. 2, 1946, 62 Stat. 1716, 161 U.N.T.S. 72 [entered into force Nov. 10, 1948]).

[137] *See* Report of the United Nations Conference on the Human Environment, June 5-16, 1972, 27th Sess., U.N. Doc. A/Conf. 48/14 (1972).

[138] *See, e.g.,* U.N. Environment Program, Register of International Treaties and Other Agreements in the Field of the Environment, U.N. Doc. UNEP/GC15/INF4 (1993).

---

force.[139] Originally, it promulgated accident avoidance schemes; more recently, however, it began to address pollution problems.[140]

United Nations Convention on the Law of the Sea, (1982) (UNCLOS III)[141]

This comprehensive convention has been called a "constitution for the oceans."[142] In particular, it attempted to resolve the age-old jurisdictional squabbles about "who owns what" and "who has jurisdiction over what."[143] As noted earlier, UNCLOS III declares that the coastal states' sovereignty extends twelve nautical miles from shore (its territorial sea)[144] and the coastal state has jurisdiction over its 200 mile EEZ. Provisions include protection of living marine species on the high seas in general,[145] as well as an agenda for conservation of fish populations specifically within the EEZ[146] and fish populations specifically in the high seas.[147] For example:

> Coastal states and states fishing for straddling stocks are directed to agree on the proper allocation of straddling stocks both within the EEZ and beyond and distant to it in Article 63.[148] States fishing for highly migratory species must cooperate in order to conserve these fisheries and optimize utilization according to Article 64. Article 116 ensures the right to fish on the high seas subject to treaty obligations[149] while Article 119 addresses maximum sustainable yields for fish stocks and the requirement of considering the special needs of developing nations.[150,151]

UNCLOS III delineates rights but also imposes responsibilities. Article 61 requires each coastal state to set the allowable catch for fished species within its EEZ and to use "the best scientific evidence available to it" to prevent over-exploitation in its EEZ.[152] While Articles 117 and 118 require coastal states to adopt conservation measures for their citizens and to cooperate with other coastal states in the conservation of living resources, these articles do not provide specifics other than the establishment of regional fisheries bodies. Only Article 119 provides any real conservation "punch": conservation measures (including determination of the allowable catch) should be designed "to maintain or restore populations of harvested species at levels which can produce the maximum sustainable yield, as qualified by relevant environmental and economic factors."[153]

---

[139] *See* W.M. von Zharen, "Ocean Ecosystem Stewardship," 23 Wm. & Mary Envtl. L. & Pol'y Rev. 1 (1998):237 [hereinafter Ecosystem Stewardship].

[140] *Id.*

[141] UNCLOS III, *supra* note 128.

[142] Lakshman Guruswamy, International Environmental Law in a Nutshell (2nd ed. 2003):392.

[143] UNCLOS III has been ratified by 158 countries.

[144] *See, e.g.,* A. Charlotte De Fontaubert, David R. Downes, & Tundi S. Agardy, "Biodiversity in the Seas: Implementing the Convention on Biological Diversity in Marine and Coastal Habitats," 10 Geo. Int'l Envtl. L. Rev. 753 (1998):758.

[145] See UNCLOS III, *supra* note 128, arts. 117-18.

[146] *Id.* arts. 55-75.

[147] *Id.* arts. 86-120.

[148] *Id.* art. 62(2).

[149] *Id.* art. 116.

[150] *See id.* art. 119 (1) (2).

[151] Ecosystem Stewardship, *supra* note 139 at 63.

[152] *See* UNCLOS III, *supra* note 128, art. 61.

[153] *Id.* arts. 117-19.

Although UNCLOS III represents a solid first step in articulating rights and duties of states and providing a general framework for conservation, that specific context is found only in reference to those areas that a coastal state "owns." Beyond that jurisdiction, free access is the rule. Even with the admonishment that fisheries must be conserved, these provisions are vague and have little strength. The fisheries management obligations are ambiguous. With no enforcement mechanism of even these basic rules, UNCLOS III fell woefully short of providing the direction and muscle to halt the decline of fish populations.

Convention on Biological Diversity (Biodiversity Convention), 1992, 1993.[154]

The Biodiversity Convention was first signed at the 1992 Conference on Environment and Development -- the Earth Summit -- in Rio de Janeiro. It entered into force in 1993 and as of 2011, 192 States and the European Union are parties.[155] While its title bodes impressive contents, it is essentially another toothless treaty in its failure to assign binding obligations on nations. Like so many other associated conventions, this one is a "framework" treaty with aspirational text.

The threefold goals of the Biodiversity Convention -- conservation of biodiversity, sustainable use of biodiversity, and fair and equitable sharing of the benefits arising from the use of genetic resources[156] -- are superseded by the deferential approach it takes to national sovereignty and discretionary directives. Nations are encouraged to adopt the "precautionary principle" or approach (Preamble: "Where there is a threat of significant reduction or loss of biological diversity, lack of full scientific certainty should not be used as a reason for postponing measures to avoid or minimize such a threat."[157]). "States have ... the sovereign right to exploit their own resources pursuant to their own environmental policies" as long as these actions do not cause harm beyond their boundary.[158] As with so many other international treaties, implementation is left up to the discretion of each signatory nation with no consequence for inaction or ignoring the provisions.

Driftnets.

Although a subset of general fish conservation laws, the driftnet resolution passed by the United Nations called for the reduction of driftnet fishing:

The United Nations General Assembly Resolution on Large-Scale Pelagic Driftnet Fishing and its Impact on the Living Marine Resources of the World's Oceans and Seas (Pelagic Driftnet

---

[154] United Nations Conference on Environment and Development: Convention on Biological Diversity, *opened for signature* June 5, 1992, 31 I.L.M. 818 (entered into force Dec. 29, 1993) [hereinafter Biodiversity Convention] <http://www.biodiv.org/convention/convention.shtml> (last visited March 9, 2011).

[155] The United States did not sign the Biodiversity Convention at the Earth Summit. Convention on Biological Diversity <http://www.cbd.int/> (last visited May 23, 2011).

[156] *Id.* CBD Fact Sheets; for general information, *see also*, Montserrat Gorina-Ysern, "World Ocean Public Trust: High Seas Fisheries After Grotius - Towards A New Ocean Ethos?," 34 Golden Gate U. L. Rev. 645, 660 (2004):660.

[157] Text of the Convention, *supra* note 154.

[158] *Id.* art. 3; *see also* Tamara Mullen, "The Convention on Biological Diversity and High-Seas Bottom Trawling: The Means to an End," 14 U. Balt. J. Envtl. L. 135 (2007):145.

Fishing I), 1989[159] and *The United Nations General Assembly Resolution on Large-Scale Pelagic Driftnet Fishing and its Impact on the Living Marine Resources of the World's Oceans and Seas (Pelagic Driftnet Fishing II), 1991*[160]

In 1989, the U.N. adopted Pelagic Driftnet Fishing I, with the goal of reducing driftnet fisheries in the Pacific and halting expansion of driftnet fishing in other areas.[161] Large-scale pelagic driftnet fishing was described as "a method of fishing with a net or combination of nets intended to be held in a more or less vertical position by floats and weights, the purpose of which is to enmesh fish by drifting on the surface of or in the water."[162] A moratorium was called for on all large-scale pelagic driftnet fishing by June 30, 1992, with exceptions as necessary.[163] After scientific review found that driftnet fishing had an adverse impact on the conservation and sustainable management of living marine resources (and in violation of UNCLOS III provisions that place an obligation on nations to protect and preserve the marine environment[164]) in 1991, the U.N. adopted Resolution 46/215, Pelagic Driftnet Fishing II, which called for a more general moratorium on driftnet fishing even if the moratorium would cause adverse socio-economic consequences.[165] Multinational cooperation is essential in enforcing conservation of fisheries and cooperation among the U.S., Russian, and Chinese authorities has achieved a steep drop in illegal driftnet fishing in the North Pacific.[166]

The Agreement for the Implementation of the Provisions of the United Nations Convention on the Law of the Seas of 10 December 1982 Relating to the Conservation and Management of Straddling Stocks and Highly Migratory Fish Stocks, 1995 (Straddling Stocks Agreement).[167]

Unlike so many international protection agreements, this one takes a refreshingly new approach. This agreement was spurred by an explosive clash of economic and environmental pressures: Canada, with the world's longest coastline and second largest continent shelf, has vital interests in its border oceans:

> In the Atlantic, large foreign fishing vessels, including those from Spain, routinely fished the Grand Banks just outside Canada's 200-mile limit. In 1995, Canada complained that Spanish fishing vessels had violated international quotas designed to

---

[159] The United Nations General Assembly Resolution on Large-Scale Pelagic Driftnet Fishing and its Impact on the Living Marine Resources of the World's Oceans and Seas, G.A. Res. 225, U.N. GAOR 2d Comm., 44th Sess., Supp. No. 49, at 147-48, U.N. Doc. A/RES/44/225 (1989), *reprinted in* 29 I.L.M. 1555 (1990).

[160] United Nations General Assembly Resolution on Large-Scale Pelagic Driftnet Fishing and its Impact on the Living Marine Resources of the World's Oceans and Seas, G.A. Res. 215, U.N. GAOR, 46th Sess., U.N. Doc. A/Res/46/215 (1992), *reprinted in* 31 I.L.M. 241 (1992).

[161] *See generally, id.*

[162] *See id.* at 147, 29 I.L.M. at 1556.

[163] *See id.*

[164] *See* UNCLOS III, *supra* note 128.

[165] *See id.*

[166] *See* John Davis, "How International Enforcement Cooperation Deters Illegal Fishing in the North Pacific," (2006) < http://www.illegal-fishing.info/uploads/US-Coastguard-iuu-enforcement.pdf> (last visited May 23, 2011).

[167] The Agreement for the Implementation of the Provisions of the United Nations Convention on the Law of the Seas of 10 December 1982 Relating to the Conservation and Management of Straddling Stocks and Highly Migratory Fish Stocks, 6th Sess., U.N. Doc. A/CONF.164/37 (1995), *reprinted in* 34 I.L.M. 1542 [hereinafter Straddling Stocks Agreement]. The United States was one of the first to ratify the agreement and it came into force in 2001. <http://www.un.org/Depts/los/convention_agreements/convention_overview_fish_stocks.htm> (last visited May 23, 2011).

protect turbot.[168] These fish stocks straddled the jurisdictional lines of Canada's exclusive fishing zone. As with jurisdictional stocks (those stocks that lie within the jurisdictional water of coastal state), these straddling stocks declined after years of inefficient management by the coastal states. An intense competition developed for what remained of straddling stocks and highly migratory species, the latter of which also showed rapid declines.[169] In March 1995, Canada acted on its threat to police overfishing on the high seas: it seized a Spanish vessel, the *Estai*, fishing for turbot beyond the Canadian 200-mile zone. Some environmental groups praised Canada for the action. The European Union, initially backing Spain, condemned Canada's action as "piracy," and the Turbot War was in full swing. On board, investigators asserted that 70% of the *Estai's* capture was young, small fish, caught illegally.[170] According to newspaper reports, some of these were stored in false bulkheads.[171] Canada made its grievance known globally: its then-Fisheries Minister, Brian Tobin, vented his outrage at the plunder of "the seeds of the future."[172] Positioned near the UN headquarters in New York against a backdrop displaying the *Estai's* gigantic green and gray net recovered from the North Atlantic (and featuring the net's small holes, the dimensions of which contravened specifications permitted under international agreement), Tobin hyperbolized: "We're down now finally to one last, lonely, unattractive little turbot clinging on by its fingertips to the Grand Banks, saying: 'someone reach out and save me in this 11th hour.'"[173]

Subsequent to this and other jurisdictional incidents, participants in the 1992 Earth Summit (noted previously), agreed to address the specific issue of straddling and highly migratory fish stocks.[174] Fish stocks may "straddle" the boundary between domestic and international waters (e.g., cod and pollack). Highly migratory species (most tuna species, swordfish, marlin and other billfish, and some sharks) migrate through both the coastal state's EEZ and the high seas during their life span.[175] Migration is cyclical, and therefore predictable. Who has control over these fish is particularly problematic: fish do not carry passports and don't observe ocean boundaries.

UNLCOS III, Articles 63 and 64, inadequately address how jurisdiction over these stocks is determined. The Straddling Stocks Agreement attempts to fill in the gaps of UNCLOS III provisions which deal with these so-called straddling fish by emphasizing: cooperation, conservation, enforcement, and compulsory dispute settlement.[176]

---

[168] Eco-Policy, *supra* note 115 (citing Lisa Anderson, "Depleted Fish Stocks Spark Canada's Turbot War with Spain," *Chi. Trib.*, [Mar. 19, 1995]:C4.)

[169] Eco-Policy, *supra* note 115 (citing Peter Weber, "Abandoned Seas: Reversing the Decline of the Oceans" Worldwatch Paper 116 [1993]).

[170] Id. (citing Tony Bartelme, "Technology, Competition Swamp Fisheries," Post & Courier [Charleston, SC [June 24, 1996]:1; and "Save the Lonely Turbot," S.F. Chron. (Mar. 31, 1995):A24.

[171] *Id.*

[172] *Id.*

[173] *Id.*

[174] Report of the United Nations Conference on Environment and Development, Rio de Janeiro, June 3-14, 1992, at 145-46, U.N. Doc. A/CONF.151/26 (Vol. II). The resolution to hold the conference was adopted Jan. 29, 1993, G.A. Res. 47/192, 47th Sess., 93rd mtg., U.N. Doc. A/RES/47/192 (1993).

[175] The Agreement on High Seas Fishing: An Update, Earth Summit+5 (1997) <http://www.un.org/ecosocdev/geninfo/sustdev/fishery.htm> (last visited May 23, 2011).

[176] *See supra* note 167, e.g., Article 5 (stating that the goal is conserving and managing straddling fish stocks); Articles 9 and 10 (duty to collect and exchange information); Article 19 (special attention given to the interests of developing countries and coastal states dependent on regulated fish stocks); Article 5 and Annex II, para. 2 (state

The requirement of cooperation frequently forms the basis of the obligations delineated. Examples are provided of what constitutes cooperation.[177] The enforcement provisions are unusually strong for an international environmental agreement and are specific. Parties must either cooperate with a regional fisheries management organization or negotiate directly with one another to establish conservation programs;[178] non-flag states who are parties to the Agreement have the authority to board vessels of other parties fishing on the high seas to ensure compliance with sub-regional or regional initiatives;[179] and sanctions must be imposed when a state detects a violation by a vessel flying its flag; these sanctions must be "adequate in severity to be effective in securing compliance...and shall deprive offenders of the benefits accruing from their illegal activities."[180]

In other words, parties are allowed to inspect each other's vessels on the high seas, secure evidence, and if a flag state fails to respond or take action once being notified of an apparent violation, bring the offending vessel to port. This is indeed a change from other agreements in which, typically, deference is given to states. Interestingly, Canada and the European Union have entered into a bilateral treaty which involves satellite tracking of vessels and the placement of fisheries inspectors on each other's vessels.[181]

Regional and sub-regional organizations are charged with developing the substantive strategy for halting the diminution of fish populations.[182] What may be one of the most critical provisions in the agreement is the call for both coastal and inland states to "apply the precautionary approach widely to conservation, management and exploitation of straddling fish stocks and highly migratory fish stocks in order to protect the living marine resources and preserve the marine environment."[183] When there is scientific uncertainly about a future harm, the precautionary approach (also referred to as the precautionary principle) lowers the burden of proof required for taking action against proposed or existing activities that may have serious long-term harmful consequences. The compulsory dispute settlement provision holds that unresolved disputes may be submitted to a third-party dispute settlement tribunal, either established by the parties as they see fit or provided in the mechanisms of the 1982 Law of the Sea Convention (which is incorporated by reference).[184]

In addition to echoing the principles of conservation and cooperation found in the 1982 Law of the Sea Convention, the addition of enforcement and sanctions, and compulsory dispute settlement, the Straddling Stocks Agreement is also designed to protect non-targeted, non-

---

must develop precautionary "reference points" including both a limit reference point and a target reference point); Annex II, para. 7 ("the fishing mortality rate which generates maximum sustainable yield should be regarded as a minimum standard for limit referent points: Article 6(4) (states must take measures so that these limits are not exceeded); and Article 5(k) (states must "promote and conduct scientific research and develop appropriate technologies in support of fishery conservation and management"). For provisions on compulsory dispute settlement, see Articles 5-7.

[177] *Id.* art. 5.

[178] *Id.* art. 8(1).

[179] *Id.* art. 14 (port States are authorized to board and inspect vessels voluntarily entering their ports); art. 17 (port States may maintain control over a suspected vessel while the port State's authorities inform the ship's respective flag State).

[180] *Id.* art 19(2).

[181] Canada-European Community: Agreed Minute on the Conservation and Management of Fish Stocks (Apr. 20, 1995), *reprinted in* 34 ILM 1260 (1995).

[182] *See id.* arts. 19-23.

[183] *Id.* art. 6.

[184] *Id.* art. 30.

commercial valued species. The Straddling Stocks Agreement requires states to minimize the catch of non-targeted species harvested with commercially valued fish,[185] to protect endangered species to "the extent practicable,"[186] and to also assess activities other than fishing on these non-targeted species.[187] As a result, seizures of fishing vessels have increased significantly including seizures on the high seas. Thanks to Canada's unilateral action, a treaty is in place that actually works.

Although novel and comparatively forceful as the Straddling Stocks Agreement seems to be, serious flaws remain, with two in particular: 1) the majority of fish are caught within a country's EEZ, thus restricting application to within a country's jurisdiction[188] and 2) the document does not address a major cause of fishery depletion: subsidization of the world's fishing fleets.

The Kyoto Declaration and Plan of Action on the Sustainable Contribution of Fisheries to Food Security (Kyoto Declaration), 1995.[189]

Under the Kyoto Declaration, parties are committed to enact national laws and regulations to promote sustainable fisheries. Parties are encouraged to adhere to the FAO's 1995 Code of Conduct for Responsible Fisheries (discussed later in this section). Parties must also consider becoming parties to UNCLOS III, the 1993 FAO Compliance Agreement,[190] and the 1995 Fish Stocks Agreement.[191] A precautionary approach is also encouraged.[192] Still, the picture is clear: there are no enforcement mechanisms or sanctions; another toothless tiger was born.

The following are provided merely as descriptive examples of agreements aimed at protecting specific fish populations:

The Convention for the Conservation of Anadromous Stocks in the North Pacific Ocean, 1992, 1993.[193]

With a goal of conserving benefits for states-of-origin anadromous fish,[194] those fish that ascend rivers during certain seasons for purposes of breeding (e.g., salmon and steelhead trout) but spend most of their lives in the high seas of the North Pacific Ocean,[195] this agreement is aimed at conserving these stocks for coastal countries to fish within their 200-mile EEZ.[196] The Convention established the North Pacific Anadromous Fish Commission (NPAFC) to promote the conservation of salmon in the North Pacific[197] and to oversee oceanic research and

---

[185] *Id.* art. 5(f).

[186] *Id.*

[187] *Id.* art. 5(d).

[188] *See* Straddling Stocks Agreement, *supra* note 167, art. 6.

[189] U.N. ESCOR, Commission on Sustainable Development, 4th Sess., E/CN.17/1996/29 (1996).

[190] Food and Agriculture Organization: Agreement to Promote Compliance with International Conservation and Management Measures by Fishing Vessels on the High Seas, *approved on* Nov. 24, 1993, 33 I.L.M. 968 (1994).

[191] U.N. ESCOR, Commission on Sustainable Development, 4th Sess., para. 5, E/CN.17/1996/29 (1996).

[192] *See id.* para. 10.

[193] Convention for the Conservation of Anadromous Stocks in the North Pacific Ocean, Feb. 11, 1992, S. Treaty Doc. No.102-30 (1992).

[194] *Id.* art. III.

[195] *Id.* art. I. "Anadromous Fish" are defined as "the fish of anadromous species . . . which migrate into the Convention Area." *Id.* art. II.

[196] *Id.* pmbl.

[197] *Id.* art. VIII.

international cooperation on fishing issues.[198] For vessels fishing illegally in a nation's waters, parties may bring those vessels into the enforcing country's ports and turn the violators over to the appropriate authorities in their home country for prosecution.[199] The Convention prohibits trafficking in illegally caught salmon[200] and the re-flagging of vessels under a non-signatory country's flag to avoid the ban on high seas fishing.[201]

Pacific Salmon Treaty, 1985,[202] (amended/revised in 1999 and 2009)

As with the Turbot War noted earlier, salmon also shared the limelight of controversy and confrontation. For example:

> In the spring of 1997, Canadian and United States representatives of the Pacific Salmon Commission[203] walked away from the table without deciding the issue of the annual permitted catch.[204] Canadian commercial fishers claimed that in the absence of limits, Alaskan fishers harvested more than five hundred thousand sockeye salmon, as they swam through Alaskan waters on their way south to Canada to spawn.[205] This was more than three times the amount ever allowed under the Pacific Salmon Treaty. In an attempt to protect their own share of the salmon, Canadian fishers responded first with public protests and threats of violence.[206] Then, on July 19, 1997, the fishers took action.[207] A flotilla of Canadian fishing boats blockaded an Alaska-bound United States ferry with three hundred aboard as it left its port in Prince Rupert, British Columbia.[208] Only after three days of intense negotiations was the ferry finally permitted to depart.[209] The incident provides an acute example of each nation's attempt to ensure sustainability of marine species. At the same time, such drama illustrates the exigency for significant change in the stewardship of and attitude towards living marine species. The incident also exemplifies the frustrations of coastal nations over their apparent inability to check overfishing.[210]

Obviously, the goal of the Pacific Salmon Treaty -- cooperation in the management, research, and enhancement of Pacific salmon stocks of mutual concern -- was not met. The treaty attempts to prevent overfishing and provide for optimum production with both countries receiving benefits equal to the production of salmon originating in their water. The treaty called

---

[198] *Id.* arts. VIII-IX.

[199] *Id.* art. V.

[200] *See id.* art. III(3).

[201] *See id.* art. IV(3). The agreement replaced the International Convention for the High Seas Fisheries of the North Pacific Ocean, May 9, 1952, 4 U.S.T. 380, 205 U.N.T.S. 65, which terminated in 1993

[202] Treaty Concerning Pacific Salmon, Jan. 28, 1985, U.S.-Can., T.I.A.S. No. 11,091 [hereinafter Pacific Salmon Treaty].

[203] Eco-system Stewardship, *supra* note 139 at 29 (stating that the Pacific Salmon Treaty of 1985 established the Pacific Salmon Commission to manage activities in the salmon fisheries within two hundred miles of the western coasts of Canada and the United States.)

[204] *Id.* (citing Anthony DePalma, "Canadians End Blockade in Salmon-Fishing Dispute," N.Y. Times [July 22, 1997]:A6).

[205] Id. (citing Timothy Egan, "Salmon War in Northwest Spurs Wish for Good Fences," N.Y. Times [Sept. 12, 1997]: A26).

[206] *Id.* (citing Egan).

[207] *Id.* (citing DePalma, *supra* note 203).

[208] *Id.* (citing Egan, *supra* note 204).

[209] *Id.* (citing DePalma, *supra* note 203).

[210] Eco-System Stewardship, *supra* note 139 at 30.

for the establishment of the Commission to "advise the Parties on any matters relating to the Treaty."[211] It includes one Canadian Section and one U.S. Section, each of which has one vote.[212] The Commission oversees the efforts of three geographically-based fishery management panels, reviews their reports, and makes recommendations.[213]

When the original fishing arrangement in the 1985 treaty expired, the Canadian and the United States governments were not able to reach agreement on a comprehensive arrangement; through subsequent and oftentimes tumultuous negotiations, a long-term renewal of fishing arrangements was culminated in 1999. The successful outcome may have been due, in part, to the fact that Pacific salmon listings under the U.S. Endangered Species Act threatened to close U.S. fisheries if negotiations under the Treaty failed.[214] The 1999 Agreement included: the creation of the Transboundary Panel and Committee on Scientific Cooperation; the inclusion of habitat provisions in the Treaty; a move from fisheries based on negotiated catch ceilings to abundance-based management of fisheries; and the establishment of the Northern and Southern Restoration and Enhancement funds.[215]

In 2008, the Pacific Salmon Commission recommended "a new bilateral agreement of the conservation and harvest sharing of Pacific salmon to the Government of Canada and the United States... and represents a major step forward in science-based conservation and sustainable harvest sharing of the salmon resource between Canada and the United States of America...; the new fishing regimes are in force from the beginning of 2009 through the end of 2018."[216] The new strategies are found in Annex IV of the treaty and address: 1) trans-boundary rivers; 2) northern British Columbia and Southeast Alaska Boundary Areas; 3) chinook salmon; 4) Fraser River sockeye and pink salmon; 5) Coho salmon; and 6) southern British Columbia and Washington State Chum salmon.[217]

The Convention for the Conservation of Salmon in the North Atlantic Ocean, 1982, 1983.[218]

The convention's goal is to promote the conservation, restoration, enhancement, and rational management of salmon stocks in the North Atlantic Ocean through international cooperation. The Convention requires member nations to make decisions based on the best available information provided by the International Council for the Exploration of the Sea (ICES).[219] The ICES is pivotal in ensuring a cooperative approach to protecting and enhancing Atlantic salmon.

---

[211] Pacific Salmon Treaty, supra note 202, art. II, para 8.

[212] *Id.* art. IV para. 1, art. II para 6.

[213] *Id.* art. II para 18, art. IV para 5.

[214] *See, e.g.,* Austin Williams, "The Pacific Salmon Treaty: A Historical Analysis and Prescription for the Future," 22 J. Envtl. Law and Litigation (2007):153.

[215] "The Pacific Salmon Treaty – 1985" <http://www.psc.org/about_treaty.htm> (last visited May 26, 2011).

[216] *Id.*

[217] *Id.*

[218] Convention for the Conservation of Salmon in the North Atlantic Ocean, *opened for signature* Mar. 2, 1982, 35 U.S.T. 2284, 1338 U.N.T.S. 33.

[219] *See id.* art. 9, 35 U.S.T. at 2290, 1338 U.N.T.S. at 37-38.

International Commission for the Conservation of Atlantic Tuna (ICCAT)[220] and its Convention for the Conservation of Atlantic Tunas (Atlantic Tuna Convention)[221]

Established in 1966, the ICCAT is responsible for the conservation of some thirty tuna or tuna-like species in the Atlantic Ocean including, for example, the Atlantic bluefin, skipjack, yellowfin, albacore, bigeye and other smaller tuna, as well as swordfish and some billfish.[222] ICCAT adopted the International Convention for the Conservation of Atlantic Tunas. The convention was formed by those countries interested in protecting Atlantic tuna and other tuna-like species to allow for maximum sustainable catch.[223] As with other conventions that build upon previous agreements, the Atlantic Tuna Convention was built upon the High Seas Fishing Convention and the need to protect these highly valued fisheries. ICCAT can also recommend to its member states that they refuse to import tuna from the suspected non-member "free-rider," a non-member state who stands to potentially gain from the conservation efforts of ICCAT.[224]

Unfortunately, again like many international agreements, this one fell short of solving the tuna depletion dilemma because of its limited jurisdiction. Instead of protecting these species within the entire Atlantic basin and adjacent areas to which they may migrate, the area is limited to areas outside a state's territorial control.[225] To add insult to injury, satellite tracking devices have shown that (at least some of) these fish migrate into the eastern Mediterranean, which is outside ICCAT's jurisdiction to limit the pressure from international fishing vessels.[226] Another shortfall is the data reviewed by panels to determine the health of a particular species: a major portion of the data is derived from commercial fishers who, in turn, have a protected interest in maximizing their profits.[227]

---

[220] *See* International Commission for the Conservation of Atlantic Tunas, <http://www.iccat.int/en/introduction.htm> (last visited Feb. 15, 2010).
[221] International Convention for the Conservation of Atlantic Tunas, May 14, 1966, 20 U.S.T. 2887, 673 U.N.T.S. 63 [hereinafter Atlantic Tuna Convention].
[222] *See* International Commission for the Conservation of Atlantic Tunas, <http://www.iccat.int/en/introduction.htm> (last visited March 12, 2011).
[223] *Id.* at pmbl.
[224] NAFO uses that technique to assist in eliminating the free-rides. *See, e.g., infra* note 232.
[225] *See, e.g.*, Karen L. Smith, "Highly Migratory Fish Species: Can International and Domestic Law Save the North Atlantic Swordfish?", 21 W. New Eng. L. Rev. 5, (1999):21.
[226] Barbara A. Block, Heidi Dewar, Charles Farwell, and Eric D. Prince, "A New Satellite Technology for Tracking the Movements of Atlantic Bluefin Tuna," 95 Proc. Nat'l Acad. Sci. USA (1998):9384 <http://www.ncbi.nlm.nih.gov/pmc/articles/PMC21347/> (last visited May 30, 2011).
[227] *See, e.g.*, Mort Rosenblum, "Bluefin Tuna Losing Battle for Survival" (July 19, 2004) (pointing out that a single bluefin may be worth as much as $150,000 on the Tokyo market) <http://www.msnbc.msn.com/id/5428979/> (last visited March 11, 2011).

The Convention on Future Multilateral Cooperation in the Northwest Atlantic Fisheries[228] and the Northwest Atlantic Fisheries Organization (NAFO)

NAFO was founded in 1979 as an intergovernmental fisheries science and management body and was the successor to the International Commission of the Northwest Atlantic Fisheries (ICNAF) (1949-1978). NAFO's main goal is to promote and contribute, through consultation and cooperation, conservation of the fishery resources of the Convention Area.[229] The Convention applies to most fishery resources of the Northwest Atlantic except salmon, tunas/marlins, whales, and sedentary species. NAFO consists of 1) the Fisheries Commission responsible for the management and conservation of the fishery resources of the Regulatory Area (waters outside the EEZs); 2) the Scientific Council which gives advice upon request on the status of fish stocks in the Convention Area; 3) the General Council who is responsible for international affairs and external relations; and 4) the Secretariat (NAFO headquarters), located in Dartmouth, Nova Scotia, Canada.[230]

Each year, NAFO establishes TACs that are divided into quotas allocated to its member states;[231] NAFO inspectors can board member vessels and check for compliance. This set-up is the type of organizational structure referred to in the Straddling Stocks Agreement. NAFO is hindered by the free-rider issue (those non-member states that benefit from the conservation efforts of member states).[232] In an attempt to address this problem, NAFO makes the presumption that any non-member fishing in the regulated area is circumventing NAFO's regulatory conservation strategy; if that non-member tries to enter the port of a member state, the member state may prohibit landing until the potentially offending state agrees to an inspection.

The Agreement to Promote Compliance with International Conservation and Management Measures by Fishing Vessels on the High Seas (FAO Compliance Agreement), 1994.[233]

This is considered an integral part of the non-binding 1995 United Nations FAO's International Code of Conduct for Responsible Fisheries[234] (a voluntary instrument adopted by the FAO Conference in 1995 and noted later) and builds upon the legal framework established by UNCLOS III[235] including the Straddling Stocks Agreement.[236] The Compliance Agreement

---

[228] The Convention came into force in 1979 with seven signatories: Canada, Cuba, the European Economic Community, German Democratic Republic, Iceland, Norway, and the Union of Soviet Socialist Republics. This Convention established the Northwest Atlantic Fisheries Organization (NAFO). In 2009, NAFO has 12 Members from North America, Europe, Asia, and the Caribbean including four coastal members bordering the convention area: Canada, the U.S.A., Denmark (in respect of Faroe Islands and Greenland), and France (in respect of St. Pierre et Miquelon). The Convention has been amended three times – 1980, 1987, and 1996 - by modifications of its Annex III (boundaries). <http://www.nafo.int/about/frames/con-index.html> (last visited May 22, 2011).

[229] *See* <http://www.nafo.int/about/frames/activities.html> (last visited May 22, 2011).

[230] *Id.*

[231] The Northwest Atlantic Fisheries Organization ("NAFO") has seventeen member states. NAFO Contracting Parties <http://www.nafo.ca/about/STRUCTURE/CPs.html> (last visited January, 2011).

[232] *See* R.R. Churchill & A.V. Lowe, The Law of the Sea (1988):224-27, 231-32.

[233] Agreement to Promote Compliance with International Conservation and Management Measures by Fishing Vessels on the High Seas, *adopted* Nov. 24, 1993, 33 I.L.M. 968 (1994) [hereinafter FAO Compliance Agreement].

[234] FAO Compliance Resolution 15/93, para. 3. The Code developed out of Agenda 21, adopted by the 1992 United Nations Conference on Environment and Development at Rio de Janeiro, Brazil, June 13, 1992. U.N. Doc. A/CONF. 151/26 (1992).

[235] *See* FAO Compliance Agreement, *supra* note 233, pmbl., 33 I.L.M. at 969. *See* 1982 Law of the Sea Convention, *supra* note 128.

coupled with the Straddling Stocks Agreement and the Code of Conduct for Responsible Fisheries provide the framework for actions concerning, in particular, high seas fishing. Because they were negotiated at approximately the same time, there is a good deal of consistency between the provisions.

The compliance agreement is designed to clarify and expand the rights and duties of states whose vessels fish on the high seas;[237] states whose vessels fish on the high seas are obligated to ensure that those vessels fish in a manner that is consistent with conservation and management efforts.[238] States must implement a licensing program or another form of authorization for their vessels to fish on the high seas.[239] The authorization can only be granted if the state can effectively exercise its responsibilities under the agreement with respect to each of its vessels.[240] There are clear reporting requirements. Parties are obligated to maintain detailed records on the vessels they authorize to fish on the high seas;[241] the information must be submitted to the FAO for inclusion in a global registry of high seas fishing vessels;[242] and if a party has reason to believe that the vessels of another state are fishing in a manner that undermines the effectiveness of international conservation and management measures, it must report such information to the flag state.[243] Information may also be reported to the FAO.[244]

Examples of Non-legal International Regimes

In response to global attention focusing on the general need for conservation of fisheries through a broader, ecosystem approach, several voluntary regimes have emerged: the Code of Conduct for Responsible Fisheries (1995), the ISO 14001 Environmental Management Standard, and the Marine Stewardship Council.

International Code of Conduct for Responsible Fisheries[245]

This non-binding agreement established by the FAO in 1995 addresses a wide range of issues involved in the sustainable development of the ocean fisheries such as fishing operations and capture, processing and trade, post-harvest practice, scientific research, and aquaculture,[246] setting out "principles and international standards of behaviour for responsible practices."[247] Unlike many stewardship regimes, this one specifically echoes a theme of ecosystem management: measures should ensure conservation of species "belonging to the same ecosystem or associated with or dependent upon the target species."[248]

---

[236] Straddling Stocks Agreement, *supra* note 167.

[237] *See* FAO Compliance Agreement, *supra* note 233, pmbl., 33 I.L.M. at 969-70.

[238] *Id.* art. III (1)(a), 33 I.L.M. at 971.

[239] *Id.* art. III (2), 33 I.L.M. at 972.

[240] *Id.* art. III (3), 33 I.L.M. at 972.

[241] *Id.* art. IV, 33 I.L.M. at 973.

[242] *Id.* art. VI, 33 I.L.M. at 974-76.

[243] *Id.* art. VI (8)(b), 33 I.L.M. at 975-76.

[244] *Id.*

[245] Code of Conduct for Responsible Fisheries, U.N. Food and Agriculture Organization (1995) [hereinafter Code of Conduct] <http://www.fao.org/docrep/005/v9878e/v9878e00.htm> (last visited January 7, 2011).

[246] *See generally, id.*

[247] *Id.*

[248] *Id.* art. 6.2.

The Code encourages integration of fisheries management with coastal management. It emphasizes long term sustainability: fisheries management should "promote the maintenance of the quality, diversity and availability of fishery resources in sufficient quantities for present and future generations,"[249] one that would make a substantial contribution to world food security and employment opportunities.[250] Phrases and terms in the Code clearly articulate the values and principles of the Code including the concept of sustainable utilization of fishery resources in harmony with the environment;[251] the use of capture and aquaculture practices which are not harmful to ecosystems, resources and their quality;[252] the incorporation of added value to such products through transformation processes meeting the required sanitary standards;[253] and the conduct of commercial practices so as to provide consumers access to good quality products.[254] The emphasis on the complex marine environment as a whole is reflected in sections dealing with aquatic ecosystems,[255] endangered species,[256] biodiversity,[257] critical fisheries habitats,[258] the impact of fisheries,[259] and the impact on environment.[260] By-catch and other wastes are addressed, noting that living marine species have sustainability limits:[261] selectivity[262]—the ability to harvest target species with non-target fish, juveniles, and other by-catch escaping unharmed—is an integral part of responsible fishing[263] as is the use of environmentally safe fishing gear,[264] safe practices, and the avoidance of discarding or losing gear.[265]

The focus is not only on direct fish protection but indirect protection through ecosystem management.[266] The Code embraces the precautionary principle (or approach).[267] It considers human factors such as the necessity of food,[268] the nutritional value and safety of products,[269] and the consideration of economical and social factors,[270] in addition to natural resource conservation. The issues of poverty,[271] employment,[272] and fishers' rights[273] are considered. Responsibilities for sustainable fisheries are shared between fishing industries and states including special responsibilities given to Flag States and Port States.[274] Safe working conditions and safety in general are also addressed[275] as is the use of internationally agreed

---

[249] *Id.*
[250] *Id.* art. 7.2.
[251] *Id.* art. 6.3.
[252] *Id.*, art. 6.6.
[253] *Id.*
[254] *Id.* art. 6.16.
[255] *Id.* arts. 6.1; 6.4.
[256] *Id.* art. 7.6.9.
[257] *Id. art.* 6.6.
[258] *Id.* art. 6.8.
[259] *Id.* arts. 6.7; 7.4; 7.6.4; 7.6.9.
[260] *Id.* art. 6.7; *see also, id.* arts. 7.4.2; 10.2.4.
[261] *Id.* art. 7.6.9.
[262] *Id.* arts. 7.6.9, 8.
[263] *Id.* art. 7.6.9.
[264] *Id.* arts. 6.6; 7.6.9.
[265] *Id.* art. 7.6.9. This gear can entangle or trap aquatic species.
[266] Id. arts. 6.1, 6.6, 6.8.
[267] Id. arts. 6.5, 7.5.s
[268] *Id.* art. 6.2; 6.18.
[269] *Id.* art. 6.7.
[270] *Id.* arts. 6.4; 7.4.2; 7.4.5.
[271] *Id.* art. 6.2.
[272] *Id.* art. 6.18.
[273] *Id.* arts. 6.18; 10.1.3.
[274] *Id.* arts. 8.1; 8.2; 8.3.
[275] *Id.* art. 6.17.

standards for statistics, measurements, and assessment;[276] the importance of monitoring, control and surveillance of all fishing activities;[277] and conflicts[278] resulting from intensive fishing with each operator or community using its own methods.

In an effort to include all stakeholders, the Code includes the issue of subsistence fisheries,[279] with fisheries carried out by local communities with traditional, customary fishing practices given priority.[280] The management strategy should include the concepts of transparency, timeliness, consultation, and participation of stakeholders.[281] Canada has developed its own code, The Canadian Code of Conduct for Responsible Fishing Operations, using the international code as a template. However, the Canadian code was developed by fishers for fishers, a grassroots effort that may be unique in the world. As of 2004, the Canadian code "had been ratified by over 80 fish harvester organizations from all regions and fishing sectors throughout the country, accounting for over 90% of the commercially harvested fish and seafood in Canada."[282] The United States has adopted the International Code.

Marine Stewardship Council (MSC)[283]

A specific environmental management systems (EMS) certification module is the Marine Stewardship Council (MSC), an alliance initially formed between the World Wildlife Fund (WWF) and Unilever, one of the world's largest buyers of fish,[284] but MSC is now working independently. In this market-based solution to protecting the world's declining fish population, the MSC promotes voluntary, independent certification and eco-labelling of performance standards for fisheries management to ensure that fishing is sustainable. MSC works with fisheries, seafood companies, scientists, conservation groups, as well as the public to promote the environmental choice in seafood.[285]

MSC's core theory for changing the way fish are harvested is through market incentives. Although assessment of sustainability is complex, the idea is simple: "current catch should be at levels that ensure fish populations and the ecosystems on which they depend remain healthy and productive for today's and future generations' needs."[286] Products must come from fisheries that are not exhibiting signs of overfishing, and only fisheries meeting these standards will be eligible for certification and the eco-label.[287] The MSC uses third-parties to assess fisheries against the standard in deciding whether to certify the product.[288] Certification on biological, environmental, economic, and social criteria may be carried out by independent firms.

---

[276] *Id.* arts. 6.17; 7.4.4; 7.4.6.

[277] *Id.* arts. 6.10; 7.1.7.

[278] *Id.* art. 6.15.

[279] *Id.* art. 6.18.

[280] *Id.* arts. 7.6.6; 10.1.3.

[281] *Id.* arts. 7.1.2; 7.1.6.

[282] "Fisheries and Ocean Canada" <http://www.dfo-mpo.gc.ca/media/back-fiche/2003/hq-ac26b-eng.htm> (last visited January 2011).

[283] "Marine Stewardship Council: Certified Sustainable Seafood" [hereinafter MSC] <http://www.msc.org/> (last visited May 23, 2011).

[284] *See* Unilever website <http://www.wbcsd.org/Plugins/DocSearch/details.asp?DocTypeId=24&ObjectId=MjA5MjY> (last visited May 23, 2011).

[285] *See* MSC, *supra* note 283.

[286] "Our Theory of Change," < http://www.msc.org/business-support/theory-of-change> (last visited May 26, 2011).

[287] *See id.*

[288] *See id.*

From 1999 to 2009, MSC has certified 42 individual fisheries, 2,000 products, and close to 2.5 million tonnes of sustainable seafood that carried the MSC eco-label.[289] "There are over 8,000 MSC-labelled products on sale, from prepared seafood meals to fresh fish."[290] MSC poses the question: Does certification make a fishery more sustainable, or does it simply reward best practice that exists already? Its answer is that although many fisheries have been fishing sustainably for longer than the MSC has been in existence, "measurable improvements have occurred under MSC certification,"[291] with multiple benefits: environmental, economic, and social.

The requirements vary with the specific fishery. For example, MSC can require a fishery to record by-catch more systematically than under existing regulations. "Chain of custody" certification can be used in which all seafood carrying the MSC logo is "traceable all the way back to the certified fishery," e.g., requiring an "entire catch to be weighed, box by box, under government control …to ensure buyers and consumers that the certified catch does not come from vessels fishing illegally…."[292] These examples illustrate different approaches to maintaining an EMS. Each shares the same elements: motivated stakeholder involvement; evaluation of an activity's impact on the environment; establishing objectives and targets; developing and implementing an action plan; and continually evaluating, monitoring, and adapting.

MSC maintains that the main beneficiaries with price premiums have been "smaller-scale, artisanal fisheries;"[293] e.g., the American Albacore Fishing Association (AAFA) Pacific tuna fisheries in the United States "saw its prices increase from $1,700 to $2,250 a ton [$1,870 to $2,475 a tonne] as soon as it became MSC certified in August 2007."[294] Social benefits may also accrue. "If fishery resources are managed sustainably, this should improve the security of the livelihoods of the fishing communities who depend upon them,"[295] as well as through community empowerment, resulting in increased government attention and therefore improved essential services.[296]

The MSC is not without its detractors. Some have accused the MSC of "duping" consumers by giving its eco-label to fisheries where stocks are tumbling. "It recently celebrated the 100th award of its eco-label…but a series of decisions allowing controversial fisheries to be granted the prized MSC label has prompted severe criticism of the organization…"[297] including an award to a fishery which is "still regarded by scientists and the industry as an exploratory fishery." The species in question, the Antarctic toothfish fishery, "is so little understood that

---

[289] Andrew Purvis, "Sea change: 10 years of the Marine Stewardship Council," <http://www.msc.org/documents/fisheries-factsheets/net-benefits-report/net-benefits-introduction-web.pdf> [last visited February 26, 2011].
[290] "MSC certified 'Fish to Eat'" <http://www.msc.org/cook-eat-enjoy/fish-to-eat> (last visited February 26, 20111).
[291] Purvis, *supra* note 289 at 4.
[292] *Id.*
[293] Purvis, *supra* note 289 at 5.
[294] *Id.*
[295] *Id.*
[296] *Id.*
[297] Lewis Smith, "Sustainable Fish Customers 'Duped' by Marine Stewardship Council," The Guardian (Jan. 6, 2011) < http://www.guardian.co.uk/environment/2011/jan/06/fish-marine-stewardship-council> (last visited May 23, 2011).

researchers still do not know even basics such as where the fish spawns."[298] Other rulings have been criticized as well; e.g., "krill in the Antarctic, tuna and swordfish off the U.S. coast, pollock in the Eastern Bearing Sea (where stock levels fell 64% between 2004 and 2009), and Pacific whiting (hake) that suffered an 89% fall in biomass since 1989."[299] MSC has responded to these pronouncements by insisting that all assessments were "'scientifically robust' ... to ensure the 'biological and ecological' components of each fishery are not compromised. Moreover, it introduces better levels of protection to stock levels than might otherwise be found in fisheries."[300] As with the cornerstone of the next management strategy to be discussed, ISO 14001, continual improvement of the management system may be an element on which the MSC needs to focus.

ISO 14001-- Environmental Management Standard[301]

Another model that requires motivated stakeholder involvement; evaluation of an activity's impact on the environment; establishing objectives and targets; developing and implementing an action plan; and continually evaluating, monitoring, and adapting, is ISO 14001.[302] As an international voluntary standard[303] applicable to all organizations, ISO 14001 may provide further and perhaps more extensive demonstrable evidence of a commitment to environmental protection throughout an organization's activities, products, and services.[304] The standard addresses many of the necessary conditions for the greening of an organization, from acquisition to production, to marketing, to disposal. The fishing industry is diverse, encompassing multitudinous activities with widely different practices and scales of operation. Thus, it requires a flexible, adaptive strategy which is the core value of ISO 14001.

ISO 14001 goes a few steps further. To be certified, an organization must meet strict criteria including:

- an organization demonstrates its commitment to environmental management
- an environmental policy must be developed and communicated to all levels of the organization and to the public
- a system must be in place to identify all applicable legislative and regulatory requirements

---

[298] *Id.*

[299] *Id.*

[300] *Id.*

[301] *See* "ISO 14000 Essentials" < http://www.iso.org/iso/iso_14000_essentials> (last visited May 19, 2011).

[302] *See* von Zharen, ISO 14000: Understanding the Environmental Standards 15 (1996) [hereinafter von Zharen ISO 14000).

[303] *See* Ecosystem Stewardship, supra note 139 (noting that ISO 14001 is the specification document, the only "standard." Thus, it is prescriptive. It is a "management" standard, not a legal standard. ISO 14001 may be used to replace the traditional piece-meal regulatory approach to stewarding ocean species).

[304] W.M. von Zharen, ISO 14001: Positioning Your Organization for Environmental Success 45 (2001) [hereinafter von Zharen, 14001] (explaining that the International Organization for Standardization, commonly referred to as ISO, is an international, non-governmental federation of "standards" bodies and is based in Geneva, Switzerland. It was founded in 1946 with the aim of promoting standardization and related activities to facilitate international exchange of goods and services. The impetus for the ISO 14000 series can be traced to the United Nations Conference on the Environment and Development (UNCED) and its Global Environmental Initiative in Rio de Janeiro in 1992 in which agreement was reached on the need for further development of international environmental management programs. The UNCED petitioned the ISO to consider developing the standards and, in response, Technical Committee 207 was formed with Canada as the secretariat. Specifically, the Committee could not set environmental performance levels, test methods for pollutants, and standardization of products; instead, its focus was on developing an environmental management standard rather than a performance standard.)

- environmental aspects associated with the organization's activities, products, and services that may have an impact—positive or negative—on the environment must be analyzed and prioritized
- an effective management process must be in place to develop and meet objectives and targets aimed at reducing the negative impact on the environment
- employees must be trained to recognize environmental impacts of their activities
- management reviews and audits must identify areas for continued improvement of environmental performance through effective environmental management
- communication with internal and external interested parties must be maintained and
- appropriate financial and human resources must support the system to ensure the success of the strategy[305]

This proactive strategy provides a generic blueprint for all segments of the marine sector, from a single fishing trawler to a seafood processor, to a seafood restaurant, to a local fish stand. As with MSC, implementing ISO 14001 is not only a means to demonstrate that an organization is "green," it can also reduce costs and potential liabilities, leading to greater profitability.

Marine Protected Areas (MPAs) offer a template for the potential application of ISO 14001. MPAs have been recognized as key components in the recovery and sustainability of marine ecosystems.[306] Current global marine targets are to protect 10-30% of marine habitat by 2013, but there has been little assessment of just how this will be achieved.[307] As noted previously, only 1.17% of global oceans are designated as MPAs.[308] An assessment of the effectiveness of the management strategy requires adaptation of an effective management strategy. Yes, that is correct. Because ISO 14001 has proven to be a global leader in environmental management standards, it is an appropriate mechanism for planning and developing a management plan; covering all the critical components, e.g., structure, training and awareness, communication, documentation, document control, operational control, checking and corrective action through monitoring and measurement, and stakeholder involvement; management review; and continual improvement. The ISO 14001 standard is based on consensus from a broad range of stakeholder groups. With MPAs constantly subjected to anthropogenic and natural changes, ISO 14001 provides the required flexibility and adaptability.[309]

The standard represents unprecedented market-place and scientifically-based consensus initiatives. By design, it is generic and thus could apply to all components of maritime activities, including fisheries management and management of marine ecosystems.

---

[305] *See id.* at 105.
[306] *See,* e.g., L.J. Wood, L. Fish, J. Laughren, and D. Pauly, "Assessing Progress Towards Global Marine Protection Targets: Shortfalls in Information and Action." Oryx 42(3) (2008): <http://www.bipindicators.net/LinkClick.aspx?fileticket=c0ZrnqIYa8Y%3D&tabid=71&mid=519> (last visited May 18, 2011).
[307] *Id.*
[308] *See* C. Toropova,et al,, supra note 111.
[309] *See* Frank J. Gable, "A Large Marine Ecosystem Voluntary Environmental Management System Approach to Fisheries Practices." NOAA Technical Memorandum NMFS-NE-195 (2005).

Brief Overview of the Major Federal Fishery Protection Law of Canada[310] and the United States[311]

We have a long history of bilateral cooperation on species migrating between the United States and Canada. In fact, discussions about issues concerning migratory species go back to the founding of the U.S./Canada relationship and to the Treaty of Paris (1783). Yet, despite our long history, we had a relatively poor track record when it comes to managing our impacts on migratory organisms with which we share the North American eco-region. For it is the environmental boundaries, and not the arbitrary political boundaries, that birds, fish, and other migratory species recognize and respect.
Dorinda Dallmeyer[312]

Canada

The Oceans Act

The Department of Fisheries and Oceans (DFO) and its head, the Minister of Fisheries and Oceans, was established by the Department of Fisheries and Oceans Act, 1985.[313] Among other duties, its role was to integrate fisheries management with other regulated ocean activities. However, the Oceans Act,[314] 1997, is the most comprehensive law for conservation of fisheries. The act expanded the role of the DFO to include application of sustainability development, integrated management, and the precautionary approach to its management strategy.[315] The Act also sets out to define Canada's continental shelf, its exclusive economic zone, its jurisdiction, and its sovereign rights (as consistent with UNCLOS III) and duties including the protection and preservation of the marine environment.[316] Although its overall tenor is anything but aggressive, it does embrace an ecosystem management approach.

Fisheries Act

Fish and fish habitat are protected under the Fisheries Act[317] in which the Department of Fisheries and Oceans (DFO)) plays a pivotal role. This act addresses issues relating to fishery leases and licenses[318] and general fish habitat protection and pollution prevention,[319] among

---

[310] For a list of regulations and legislation that govern Canada's marine fisheries, *see* Fisheries and Ocean Canada <http://www.dfo-mpo.gc.ca/acts-loi-eng.htm> [last visited April 2011].

[311] For an overview of the various U.S. laws that may help in protecting marine species, e.g., protection against aquatic invasive species, protection of marine mammals, etc., *see* Eco-system Stewardship, *supra* note 139.

[312] Dorinda Dallmeyer, "Fish and Other Migrating Species in the Canada/U.S. Context: Introduction," 28 Can.-U.S. L.J. (2002):377.

[313] Department of Fisheries and Oceans Canada Act, R.S.C., ch. F-15 (1985) (Can.), available at http://laws.justice.gc.ca /en/F-15/47477.html (last visited February 23, 2011).

[314] Oceans Act, R.S.C., ch. 31 (1996) (Can.) [hereinafter Oceans Act], available at http://laws.justice.gc.ca/en/O-2.4/index.html (last visited March 2, 2011).

[315] *Id.* 30.

[316] *Id.* 13-14.

[317] R.S.C. 1985 c. F-14 [Fisheries Act].

[318] *Id.* 7, 8.

[319] *Id.*,34.

others. Canadian fisheries waters include all waters in the fishing zones of Canada, all waters in the territorial sea of Canada, and all internal waters of Canada.[320]

Coastal Fisheries Protection Act

The Coastal Fisheries Protection Act[321] is the principal act dealing with foreign fishing in Canadian water. Its amendments in 1999[322] empower the government to enforce conservation measures beyond Canada's EEZ-200 mile limit. These measures stem from the Northwest Atlantic Fisheries Organization (NAFO)[323] and apply to specific situations and vessels of specific states. Rather than a traditional management strategy, this legislation stresses enforcement rules such as use of force, arrest, seizure, and forfeiture of vessels and catch.[324]

The Canada Shipping Act

The Canada Shipping Act,[325] 2001,[326] 2007,[327] is the principal legislation focusing on shipping and navigation, marine transportation, and protection of the marine environment, among others. This is the law that addresses vessel-source pollution. It applies to Canadian vessels operating in all waters, as well as to all vessels operating in Canadian waters. The Pollution and Response[328] and the Pollution Prevention[329] sections address fines for various pollution related offenses. Under Miscellaneous,[330] are provisions that deal with danger to the environment and risk of death or harm to persons. The Coastal Fisheries Protection Act and the Canada Shipping Act provisions reflect the amendments that occurred when the Straddling Stocks Agreement was adopted.

United States

Magnuson-Stevens Fishery Conservation and Management Act

The most comprehensive law addressing fishery conservation is the Magnuson-Stevens Fishery Conservation and Management Act (MFCMA). Originally enacted as the Fishery Conservation and Management Act of 1976,[331] the MFCMA has been amended many times. The most recent amendments were the Sustainable Fisheries Act of 1996[332] and the present Magnuson-Stevens Fishery Conservation and Reauthorization Act of 2006.[333] The present Act institutes a more

---

[320] *Id.* 2.

[321] Coastal Fisheries Protection Act, R.S.C. 1985, c. C-33.

[322] Canada: Coastal Fisheries Protection Act as Amended in 1994, 33 I.L.M. 1383 (1994) [hereinafter CFPA].

[323] NAFO was established by the Convention on the Future Multilateral Co-operation in the Northwest Atlantic Fisheries, done in Ottawa, 24 October 1978, reprinted in Official Journal of the European Communities, No. L 378 (1978).

[324] *See, e.g., CFPA, supra* note *322* at section 7-15.

[325] Canada Shipping Act (R.S.C., 1985, c. S-9) (repealed).

[326] Canada Shipping Act, 2001 (S.C. 2001, c.26) [hereinafter CSA].

[327] On July 1, 2007, the Canada Shipping Act, 2001 (CSA 2001) replaced the Canada Shipping Act (CSA) which, at over one hundred years of age, was one of Canada's oldest pieces of legislation.

[328] CSA, Part 8, *supra* note 326.

[329] *Id.* Part 9.

[330] *Id.* Part 12.

[331] U.S. Public Law 94-265.

[332] U.S. Public Law 104-297.

[333] 16 U.S.C. 1801-1883 (2006).

aggressive federal management of the nation's fish populations[334] and consolidates control of territorial waters. Under the MFCMA are eight regional councils to manage fish stocks. The Act currently focuses on the following seven principles:

- to take immediate action to conserve and manage the fishery resources
- to support and encourage the implementation and enforcement of international fishery agreements
- to promote domestic commercial and recreational fishing under sound conservation and management principles
- to provide fishery management plans to achieve and maintain the optimum yield
- to establish Regional Fishery Management Councils to steward fishery recourse
- to encourage the development of fisheries which are currently underutilized or not utilized
- to promote protection of essential fish habitats[335]

The act also calls for the reduction of by-catch and establishing monitoring systems. The Regional Management Councils (RMC) are created by and derive their authority from the Act. Members are appointed by the National Marine Fisheries Service (NMFS), under the Secretary of Commerce. These councils develop and implement the Fishery Management Plan(s) (FMP). The Act requires the council to prepare a FMP for each fishery within its region where conservation management is needed; otherwise, that fishery is open to unrestricted assess. An FMP can contain measures for protecting habitat, reducing by-catch, imposing gear restrictions, and requiring observers.[336]

The MFCMA has its drawbacks. For example, it does not require a specific level of scientific scrutiny before exploitation can occur, but rather that the management measures "prevent overfishing while achieving, on a continuous basis, the optimum yield from each fishery for the Untied States' fishing industry."[337] Optimum yield is defined as the "maximum sustainable yield from the fishery"[338] while maximum sustainable yield is defined as "the largest long-term average catch or yield that can be taken from a stock or stock complex under prevailing ecological and environmental conditions."[339]

Another potential obstacle to ensuring conservation of fisheries is that the councils have substantial discretion to determine what is practicable. Since councils represent commercial and recreational interests,[340] decisions may be made based upon financial and recreational gains of the council members, a potentially clear conflict of interest.

---

[334] *See* Statement on Signing the Sustainable Fisheries Act, Pub. Paper RGS (Oct. 11, 1996).
[335] Magnuson-Stevens Fishery Conservation and Management Act
<http://www.nmfs.noaa.gov/msa2005/docs/MSA_amended_msa%20_20070112_FINAL.pdf> (last visited March 26, 2011).
[336] *Id.* at 1853.
[337] *Id.* at 1851(a)(1).
[338] *Id.* at 1802(28)(b).
[339] 50 C.F.R. 600.310(1) (2009).
[340] *See,* e.g., Thomas A. Okey, "Membership of the Eight Regional Fishery Management Councils in the United States: Are Special Interests Over-Represented?" 27 Marine Pol'y (2003):193.

Strategies Required for an Ecologically Resilient and Robust Fishery
Beyond Conservation and Sustainability – Stewardship through Adaptive Ecosystem Management

We're fishing down the food web,[341] where we take lower and lower trophic levels of fish, so that what our grandparents called fish bait we now call calamari.
Dorinda Dallmeyer[342]

As noted throughout this part, fish populations at large have experienced a significant decline or extirpation. Overfishing, by-catch, and habitat destruction are just part of the problem. A study by the United Nations Environment Programme provides sobering facts:

- there are 35 million fishers and more than 20 million boats actively engaged in fishing
- fisheries directly and indirectly support 170 million jobs and $35 billion in incomes to fishing household annually
- if post-fishing activities are factored in, along with an assumption that one fisher has three dependents, then about 520 million people or eight % of the global population are supported by fishers
- mismanagement, lack of enforcement, and subsidies totalling over $27 billion annually have left close to 30% of fish stocks classed as "collapsed"
- of the $27 billion worth of subsidies, only $8 billion can be classed as 'good' with the rest classed as contributing to over-exploitation of fisheries
- only 25% of commercial stocks - mostly of low-priced species -- are considered to be in a healthy or reasonably healthy state
- some researchers estimate that virtually all commercial fisheries will have collapsed by 2050 unless urgent action is taken to bring more intelligent management to fisheries[343]

Added to that mix are the other critical factors: chemical and nutrient pollution; introduced alien and invasive species including disease from aquaculture; selective fishing for apex predators; and ocean conditions possibly becoming warmer and more acidic. With a backdrop of such dramatic and drastic stressors primarily caused by anthropogenic activities, what can be done to create an ecologically resilient and robust fishery, one that can reduce its vulnerability and keep functioning when disturbed? How, then, should we humans steward fisheries and the ecosystems in which they, and we, exist? Why have humans been able to clear-cut the oceans while the equivalent activity on land is excoriated? Because the oceans are immense? Because, shortly after a factory ship leaves to strip yet another area, little evidence is left? Because,

---

[341] Daniel Pauly, Villy Christensen, Johanne Dalsgaard, Rainer Froese, and Francisco Torres, "Fishing Down Marine Food Webs," 279 Science (1998):860 <http://www.seafriends.org.nz/issues/fishing/pauly1.htm> (last visited May 1, 2011). In contrast to this tenet, *see*, e.g., T. Branch, R. Watson, E. Fulton, S. Jennings, C. McGilliard, G. Pablico, D. Ricard, and S. Tracey, "The Tropic Fingerprint of Marine Fisheries, Nature 468 (2010):431-435.
[342] Dallmeyer, *supra* note 312 at 377-78.
[343] "Turning the Tide on Falling Fish Stocks: UNEP-led Green Economy Charts Sustainable Investment Plan" <http://www.unep.org/Documents.Multilingual/Default.asp?DocumentID=624&ArticleID=6566&l=en> (last visited June 20, 2010).

"unlike a denuded forest visible for decades, the ocean leaves no trace of the transgression"?[344] Because bounteous seafood is stacked on ice in the "seafood" section of the grocery - so where's the problem?

The problem is multi-faceted. There has been an industrialization of global fisheries along with other anthropogenic stressors such as unbridled growth of the human population and its demand on the marine environment, from food to coastal development, to pollution. The problem is that the issues require an overriding focus by all nations. The complexity of the challenge transcends the ability of any one nation to solve the problem. Collectively, humans need to think about the source of their food, as well as the process used to attain it, from a stewardship prospective. Stewards of the marine ecosystems, "the carers and the keepers," must take a global perspective to see the interconnectivity and interdependence of the system.

Determining a more effective regime for stewarding fisheries may be ascertained by asking several questions.[345] "First, in order to sustain a population, how many members of a species, and up to what size, may be harvested, or none at all? The answer demands an analysis of complex factors such as the carrying capacity of the oceans, climatic alternations, environmental inputs and stressors affecting the ocean's ecosystem, and ethical concerns.

The second question, regarding the proper allocation among various stakeholders, depends on how the first is answered. The final two questions reflect how the word 'stakeholder' is defined."[346] Does the term include fish themselves? If the answer to this question is yes, then should their inherent interests, their entitlements, be taken into account when developing a stewardship policy? Assessing the attitude of those humans involved in deciding the level of human impact on fish and their ecosystems reveals what ultimately will be the guiding principles of stewardship. Effective stewardship demands attention, at a minimum, to a number of pragmatic requirements. A baseline has been established through such regimes as the Straddling Stocks Agreement, the Code of Conduct for Responsible Fisheries, and the ISO 14001 standard and may provide near-term solutions. What is called for, then, is an integrated, informative, adaptive eco-system stewardship strategy that goes beyond sustainability to promote and maintain resilient and robust fisheries.

What is resiliency and robustness in the context of healthy fisheries? In ecology, a system is said to be resilient if it is able to "tolerate disturbance without collapsing into a qualitatively different state that is controlled by a different set of processes. A resilient ecosystem can withstand shocks and rebuild itself when necessary."[347] When a fishery loses resilience, it becomes vulnerable to changes that could have been tolerated if it were in a resilient state. A robust system is one that remains relatively balanced in the face of uncertainty and instability.

What must be crucially noted is that uncertainty exists. Fisheries must be managed using imperfect, complex information about the biology of the fishery and its habitats, the interdependency of other ecosystems, and associated risk. A successful management strategy by

---

[344] *See* Eco-system Stewardship, *supra* note 139 at 84.
[345] *Id.*
[346] *Id.* at 28-29.
[347] "Resilience Alliance" <http://www.resalliance.org/index.php/resilience> (last visited May 28, 2011); *see also* B. Walker, C.S. Holling, S.R. Carpenter, and A. Kinzig, "Resilience, Adaptability and Transformability in Social-Ecological Systems," Ecology and Society vol. 9, no. 2 (2004).

necessity must be robust, one that is less sensitive to the existing informational vagaries and precariousness that plague dynamic systems such as the coastal and marine ecosystem.

Some fisheries are surviving. What factors contribute to their resilience, to their robustness? What can be done to assist those fisheries that are suffering? Myriad management strategies have been tried and most have failed. There have also been successes.[348]

Ecological resilience and robustness must be built into any ecosystem management strategy. A resilient marine community has the ability to absorb, resist, or recover from disturbances, as well as to adapt to changes while continuing to maintain essential functions and processes. In a resilient marine community, vulnerability is reduced.

As the previous section revealed, the legal regimes aimed at conserving fish populations are varied, forming a patchwork quilt of sometimes fragmented and sometimes overlapping laws that often look at the individual rather than the whole. What is needed, then, is a broadening of the scope of fishery management. To begin with, the conventional concept of management itself requires a re-tooling. If the scope is broadened to include not only the fish and fleet, but immediate and far-reaching habitat, the interconnectivity with other species and their habitat, as well as the human dimensions involved in the fishery, the individual and the community, then stewardship is the more appropriate term.

The conceptual module, then, goes beyond the traditional environmental management systems articulated by the International Standards Organization's ISO 14001 and the Marine Stewardship Council's certification and eco-labeling standards. The module builds upon these concepts but adds significant dimensions to the overall strategy to address the unique equilibrium that a resilient and robust fishery requires: one which minimizes instabilities, is as uncertainty-averse as possible, incorporates unequivocally the precautionary approach, and provides the opportunity for participatory co-management throughout the process. The command-and-control bureaucracy that, by its very nature, has difficulty dealing with uncertainty, with shocks or perturbations, is replaced by a flexible system that can be tailored to specific needs and outcomes, and shared by the social network. Uncertainty and complexity can also involve conflict. Uncertainty can be the result of a sudden event or it can be the result of the cumulative effect of piece-meal processes. Both require an adaptive, flexible approach in addressing uncertainty. As well, with uncertainty, the precautionary approach aids in guiding decisions in fishery management.

The first step is to view stewardship of the fishery as an integrated system of fish, humans, and their environment within multiple dimensions. It must be recognized that the fishery exists within a socio-ecological setting. Avoiding the human construct of parsing out individual components requires development of a socio-ecological consciousness capable of seeing the ecosystem from multiple, shifting perspectives. As Jan C. Smuts explained in coining the term "holistic," "every organism, every plant or animal, is a whole, with a certain internal organization and a measure of self-direction and an individual specific character of its own.... [A]ll the parts appear in a subtle indefinable way to subserve and carry out the main purpose or idea."[349] Stewardship requires innovative thinking and analysis on a deeper level, recognizing

---

[348] The conservation of reef fish spawning aggregations, although highly susceptible to over-fishing, has become a model for resilience. *See, e.g.*, <http://www.reefresilience.org/Toolkit_FSA/F2_Basics.html> (last visited May 30, 2011).

[349] Jan C. Smuts, Holism and Evolution (1973):98.

that human activity has a profound effect on the environment. Humans have the tools to significantly reduce degradation of the marine environment and be stewards thereof.

Subsequent steps build upon this view of stewardship, one that expands the constructs of a typical environmental management system such as ISO 14001. For simplicity, this will be referred to as an environmental stewardship strategy (ESS). Because the focus of ISO 14001 is on a management ecosystem,[350] many of its tenets will be incorporated into the ESS protocol, e.g., commitment to environmental performance; integration of ecological and human dimensions; building trust through collaboration; forecasting of likely consequences of stewardship and management actions; process orientation; review of environmental impacts; formulation of objectives; synoptic monitoring and evaluation, as well as learning from the results; fostering adaptive responses to changes and stressors; and continual improvement of the ESS. Figure 1 provides an overview of many of the elements of an ESS.

Figure 1 - ESS Flow Chart

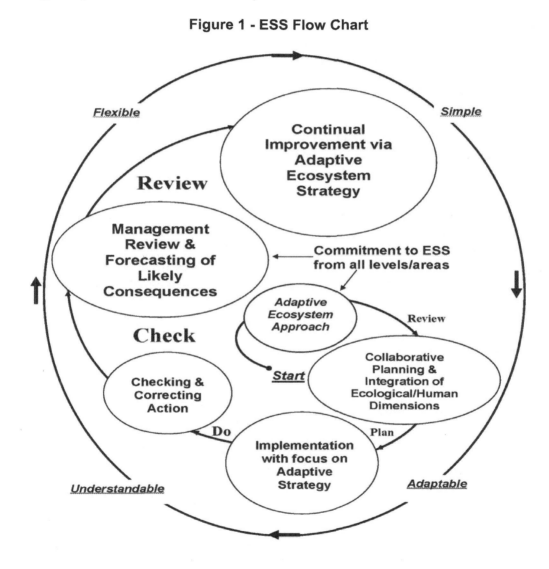

[350] See von Zharen, ISO 14001, *supra* note 304.

The ESS focuses on the organization and its people, using a collaborative approach to address the multifaceted issues in a fishery. The ESS is adaptive and relies on an integration of co-management to address scientific as well as social uncertainty.[351]

ISO 14001-type strategies can be adapted to all sizes and types of marine industry and organizations, whether they are vessel specific, fish processing plants, or artisanal fishers. The latter is of particular importance since worldwide, the evolving fisheries are small-scale but represent a significant portion of the catch and employ a majority of the world's fishers.

At the outset, a commitment to the ESS is axiomatic. The maturation process of this concept can be telling. It parallels the four stages humans often go through before embracing a revolutionary idea: First: *This is nonsense; don't waste my time.* Second: *This is interesting – but not important.* Third: *I always said this was a good idea.* Fourth: *I thought of it first.*[352] Ideally, this would be the attitude of those working as stewards. The idea of stewardship applies throughout an organization. Equally universal in its application is the idea of commitment. Each person must be committed to developing and maintaining a resilient and robust fishery. Involvement of fishers is critical for increasing their sense of ownership and responsibility for management. The players must also be committed to co-management, learning from each other, learning from the system itself. That commitment can be demonstrated through development and dissemination of an environmental policy, a step that should galvanize the organization. Other elements of the ESS flow from it. The environmental policy is not intended to be an amalgam of empty slogans. Goals should be concrete and substantive and should be the result of "a tremendous amount of thoughtful analysis."[353] It should strive to achieve adaptive and holistic management for ensuring robust and resilient fisheries.

An adaptive and flexible plan comes next. A thorough analysis of the *aspects* of activities (e.g., trawl fishing), products (e.g., seafood processors), and services (e.g., charter boats) that may have an *impact* on the fishery should be made. *Aspects are the causes;* cause relates to operations. Aspects can include bottom trawling, gear loss and discard, and reduction in plant capacity, for example. *Impacts are the effects,* the changes to the environment, adverse or beneficial, wholly or partially resulting from an organization's activities, products, or services – an organization's aspects. By-catch is an example of the impact of gillnet fishing. Impacts can be indirect as well as direct. Aspects and impacts can be significant or marginally significant. Systematic identification of the level of significance allows for effective prioritizing. Figure 2 (over) provides an overview of the steps used in determining how an organization interfaces with the environment.

The following is another, positive example of an aspect and its impact: An aspect significant to an organization may be safe vessel operation. The impacts include a reduction in injuries to humans and the environment. Table 1 (over) provides a hypothetical determining the significance of an aspect. When making an analysis of aspects and impacts, keep in mind that the definition of fishery used herein includes the human dimension, the fish populations, as well as the coastal and marine ecosystems.

---

[351] *See,* e.g., Derek R. Armitage, et al, "Adaptive Co-Management for Social-Ecological Complexity," Frontiers in Ecology and the Environment, volume 7, issue 2 (2009)95-102.
[352] *See* von Zharen, 14001, *supra* note 304 (citing Leonard P. Pasculli, "Life in Environmental Law: Waste Not, Want Not." New Jersey Lawyer [May 10, 1999]:7).
[353] *Id.* at 121.

Figure 2
Steps in Determining How an Organization Interfaces With the Environment

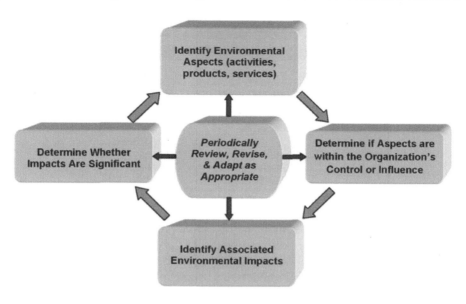

Figure 3
Hypothetical: Considerations in Determining The Significance of an Aspect*

ASPECT: Disposal of Product Packaging in Fish Plant	
Considerations	**Significance & Rationale** **Rating 1- 3** (1 = High; 2 = Medium; 3 = Low; N/A = Not Applicable)
What is the geographical extent of the impact?	1 – Landfill
Are abnormal or emergency conditions taken into account?	N/A
What are the likely severity, scale, and duration of the impact?	2 – Landfill
Is it direct (can it be controlled internally)?	2 – Disposal contractor – require in contract to recycle 2 – Contact government agency and/or knowledgeable person to determine availability of alternative or if it can be made environmentally friendly
Is it indirect at point of disposal (over which the organization can be expected to have influence)?	2 – Requirement for take-back and/or recycling in vendor contracts 2 – Educate consumers
What is the frequency with which the aspect or impact occurs? (probability and duration)	1 – Packaging waste generated daily
Does the aspect have community and/or stakeholder impacts?	2 – Neighborhood impacted by garbage trucks used for disposal; landfill use
Is it regulated?	3 – Not regulated
What are the financial considerations?	1 – Significant disposal costs

*Adapted from von Zharen, W.M., *ISO Positioning Your Organization for Environmental Success*, Roman & Littlefield Publishers & Government Institutes Press, 2001, 550 pp. (ISBN: 0865878196)

Figure 4
Hypothetical Aspects and Impacts: Fishing Vessel

Hypothetical Aspects and Impacts: Fishing Vessel**		
Activity, Product, Service	Aspect	Potential Impact
Activity: Handling of Boat Fuel	Potential for spill	Contamination of water
	Potential for emissions of volatile organic compounds	Increase in ground level ozone
Product: Wood Decking for Mooring	Use of natural resource: wood/forests	Natural resource reduction: forests
Service: Boat Painting	Generating toxic wastes from use of paint	Contamination of water; increased use of landfills

**Adapted from von Zharen, W.M., *ISO Positioning Your Organization for Environmental Success*, Roman & Littlefield Publishers & Government Institutes Press, 2001, 550 pp. (ISBN: 0865878196)

The planning phase includes establishment of objectives and targets. Objectives are what an organization wants to do; targets are how and when it is going to do it. Objectives and targets assist in translating "purpose into action." They can be derived from the policy goals, identification of significant aspects and impacts, and stakeholders' views. An objective could be to reduce by-catch; a target is to reduce by-catch by substituting gillnet fishing for long-line fishing by the year X. Or the objective could be to reduce fish habitat destruction from trawling. The target could be to substitute trawl fishing with Y (an innocuous or less destructive method) by the year X. It is important to foster a social-ecological dialogue in which objectives and targets are explored. This process should result in improving the adaptive capacity of the fishery, to be able to accommodate change, expand or modify variability as change requires, and adapt in order to build resiliency.

Once the planning is complete, the focus turns to implementation and operation of the plan. This begins with the identification of the structure of the organization and the responsibilities of those employee/participants. These people must be accountable within the scope of their responsibilities. Knowledge, skills, and training are necessary to achieve an organization's objectives. Employees/participants must be trained to recognize the environmental impacts of their activities. In the quest for a resilient and robust fishery, awareness training is particularly important. Does the employee/participant know the impact on fisheries of a discharge of motor oil into marine waters? Of its cumulative effects? Of discarded or lost fishing gear? Of plastics tossed overboard? Of the cumulative effects of air emissions from a flotilla of boats? Of by-catch, non-targeted species? Of catch-and-release? This awareness training is crucial to develop a holistic ESS, one that is proactive rather than reactive.

Because of the nature of the fishery, competency training for those activities that may have a significant impact on the fishery and its ecosystem is also important. Is the stakeholder/employee/participant competent to handle nets? To navigate in inclement weather? To know when to return to shore? To fuel the boat safely with no discharge? To use fish processing machinery safely? To identify and avoid spawning areas in season? Do people in the organization know of additional safety issues? Have suggestions? Are they prepared for uncertainties? Training should also emphasize emergency preparedness and response with procedures identifying potential accidents and emergencies and appropriate responses including mitigation of environmental damage. Time should be spent on proactive risk reduction initiatives so that potential vulnerabilities are forecast and addressed. Also critical to the operation of the plan is communication. A successful ESS requires a concerted effort augmented by communication about the ESS. Through such dialogue, adaptive capacity is built.

The ESS should be a roadmap indicating the interrelationships among the various social, ecological, and system elements. This is evidenced through documentation. Documentation assists participants in understanding what is required under the ESS. An important element in documentation is timeliness: the document must be up-to-date, with obsolete documents removed from the general system. They must also be available to those who need them. Finally, the mechanisms in an ESS for managing processes related to the organization's impact on the environment are operation control procedures, the detailed instructions for processes such as waste management and storage of hazardous chemicals. Therefore, each operation and activity associated with significant environmental aspects should be identified and managed in accordance with the ESS's policy, objectives and targets.

To continually improve the ESS, its effectiveness must be verified. There should be systems for measuring and monitoring activities and operations that can have a significant impact on the environment and implementing corrective and preventive action. The monitoring and measuring phase is intended to let an organization know how its ESS is performing, controlling, and improving its environmental performance. Monitoring and measurement should be made to keep track of activities associated with environmentally significant aspects. The ESS should identify areas of root causes so that corrective action and improvement of the ESS can take place. This identification should be on-going. Objectives and targets should also be tracked to determine areas of success, as well as to identify those areas that require corrective action and improvement. It is helpful to develop a set of indicators that are objective, verifiable, and reproducible, e.g., percentage reduction in fuel consumption, BTUs of energy consumed, percentage of solid waste recycled, and volume of raw material purchased. No system is perfect. When deficiencies are found through measurement and other activities, the root causes should be identified and corrective action taken to resolve the problem.

Another key to continual improvement and one that is critical to an adaptive, flexible, holistic, fishery is the review of the ESS. Periodic review ensures that the appropriate participants are actively engaged in keeping the ESS functioning properly, looking at the system to assure that it is, and will remain, suitable and effective. Because the ESS is adaptive and flexible, the importance of frequent review of where changes are necessary cannot be overstated. The intent of the review is to improve the ESS. Typically, this is done by "management," but in an ESS, a broader scope of participation may be appropriate. Input from crews, for example, can provide valuable information about the effectiveness of safety objectives and targets. The emphasis is on whether the ESS is suitable, adequate, and effective.

An ESS may also center on an eco-market, value driven strategy which results in increased efficiency, improved employee/participant morale, and added value to the bottom line. Environment performance initiatives such as energy efficiency and waste management can be environmentally preferable and profitable. This strategy requires appropriate allocation of environmental costs, savings, and benefits. Ultimately, there should be no conflict among the goals of economic development, the preservation and enhancement of a healthy marine environment, and a resilient, robust fishery.

In the short term, there may be costs to the business and costs to the consumer. In the long-term, positive environmental impacts can result in overall reduction of costs, improved quality of products, and reduced exposure to risks and liability. There are also less tangible benefits such as greater commitment on the part of personnel, improved relationships with stakeholders, and competitive advantages.

Environmental performance is often viewed as a single topic. However, the environmental performance of an organization is the result of many different management choices, each with its own financial implications. Three types of costs may be associated with an organization embracing an ESS: costs that directly affect a company's bottom line and the only one to which a company may be accountable; costs that are associated with nature and the environment; and costs to society. But environmental costs can often be reduced or avoided through pollution prevention practices such as product design, process redesign, and improved operational and maintenance practices. Understanding environmental cost accounting – transforming these seemingly external costs into specific, internal measurements as a basis for evaluating an organization's environmental performance – can result in environmental costs being significantly reduced or eliminated. Examples include implementation of energy-saving devices and decreased consumption of non-renewable resources.

There are prospective costs, expenditures that will occur at a point in the future, such as reducing pollution from future operations. Another cost would be contingent costs that may or may not materialize. They are probabilistic. Prevention offers greater environmental protection from pollution at a lower cost. Examples include the costs of compensating for future environmental damage, accidental releases of contaminants into the ocean, and future fines.

Finally, there are intangible costs, those that are part of a global commons that do not require payment in terms of societal accounting. As social awareness continues to develop, the latter costs become even more important. Consider the costs of navigating a fishing trawler from point A to point B. Traditional cost factors may include: gasoline, oil, wear and tear on the vessel, provisions, payments on any loans on the vessel, fishing licenses, crew costs, insurance, and taxes. Factored into the price of the gas and oil, for example, is the cost associated with traditional costs of exploration, production, marketing, and taxes (those factors typically included in a price per gallon/liter cost) or the indirect costs of exploration and production (hazardous wastes, erosion, chemical manufacturing, for example) or the environmental costs of marketing the gas (prints, dyes, and raw materials for advertising), or those direct costs associated with health care required as a result of a pollution-based disease or some measure of degradation to the atmosphere and, in turn, the ocean, as well as direct degradation of the ocean.

The costs associated with the trawler could also include prospective costs such as potential liability for a spill. Costs associated with the trawling that could affect the bottom line could also include lost revenue associated with loss of customer confidence after, say, an environmental accident. There may also be costs associated with the actual fishing activity of trawling; e.g., significant by-catch and fish habitat destruction. In other words, an ESS assessment should include an overall account of costs including reduction in costs of operations traditionally and in the pursuit and achievement of an environment stewardship strategy.

An ESS can promote resilient and robust fisheries by focusing on what is critical to the particular entity and fostering participatory co-management so that the fishing community is recognized as the central reference point. This proactive strategy provides a generic blueprint for all segments of the marine sectors, from artisanal fishers to seafood processors to eco-labeling of products. If this flexible, adaptive, globally appropriate environmental stewardship strategy is adopted, one that stresses commitment to developing and maintaining a resilient and robust fishery through a long-term strategy that emphasizes co-management of a fishery, then there is hope for the oceans' fisheries.

Finally, stewardship of fisheries must be based on an ethical foundation, a dimension in which living marine species are perceived as vulnerable to the impacts of human activities. The process involves each person, each business, and each organization, looking carefully at their actions, the products they produce or use, the services they give or receive, and determining the effects on the ocean and its inhabitants. This ethical dimension questions whether it makes any difference if one more mangrove forest is replaced by a shrimp farm; one more fish species becomes extinct; one more plastic bag floats on the waves; one more trawl net scrapes the bottom; or one more dead or dying non-targeted fish is thrown overboard.

Nearly 100 years ago, the late Robert Benchley returned from one of his strenuous undergraduate weekends on Monday morning to face a Harvard quiz asking him to "discuss the North Atlantic Fisheries Treaty from the point of view of the United States." His paper began: "I am not competent this morning to discuss this treaty from the point of view of the United States. I shall, therefore, discuss this treaty from the point of view of the fish." *Cod speed.*

The Contribution of Aquaculture/Mariculture to Global Fishery Resources

Fish and shellfish provide about 1/6 of the animal protein consumed by humans worldwide.
Coastal Ecosystems, World Resources Institute[354]

Aquaculture/Mariculture and Related Terms

Aquaculture (also known as aquafarming), is commonly defined as "the active cultivation (maintenance or production) of marine and freshwater aquatic organisms (plants or animals) under controlled conditions."[355] Water, fresh or salt, is the common medium for cultivation.

The terms aquaculture and mariculture are often used interchangeably. However, the terms have distinct meanings. Aquaculture is a more general term and refers to the production of plants or animals in water in which the producer controls a minimum of one life stage; whereas in mariculture, the producer controls a minimum of one life stage in saltwater and uses organisms commonly found in oceans and estuaries (i.e., a marine environment). (Note that saltwater includes brackish water; i.e., water of low salinity). Fish farming is also used as a synonym for aquaculture and involves raising fish commercially in tanks or enclosures.

A fish hatchery is a facility that farms and releases juvenile fish into the wild for recreational fishing or for increasing natural population numbers of a species. Fish ranching refers to a more limited type of fish farming in which the fish/shellfish is cultivated in captivity only at an early stage of its life cycle before being released into the natural environment. The fish feeds itself in its natural habitat and is harvested when it returns to spawn. This practice is used most commonly with anadromous fishes like salmon, as these fish return to the location of their birth to spawn.

Sometimes fish ranching is also used to describe the capturing of fish in the wild and then cultivating them for market. Tunas, eels and groupers are sometimes caught and "ranched" this way. However, a more accurate term for this type of cultivation is capture-based aquaculture (CBA). Fish or shellfish enhancement is similar to fish ranching; however, in this case, species are released into the natural environment at an even earlier stage, when they are just fertilized eggs or larvae, and are not expected to stay at, or return to, their release point.

In 2009, global production of fish, crustaceans, and mollusks increased to 145.1 million tonnes. While capture production has stayed around the 90 million tonne level since 2001, aquaculture production has continued to show strong growth, increasing at an average annual growth rate of 5.3% from 41.9 million tonnes in 2004 to 55.1 million tonnes in 2009. The value of aquaculture production was estimated at USD 98.5 billion in 2008.[356] With rising global demand for

---

[354] Lauretta Burke, Yumiko Kura, Ken Kassem, Carmen Revenga, Mark Spalding, Don McAllister, "Coastal Ecosystems," World Resources Institute Archive (2000) <http://archive.wri.org/page.cfm?id=1013&z=?> (last visited March 4, 2011).

[355] "Aquaculture Operations," Agriculture, U.S. Environmental Protection Agency < http://www.epa.gov/agriculture/anaquidx.html> (last visited June 18, 2011).

[356] Fishery and Aquaculture Statistics, FAO Yearbook, 2008 (publ 2010) < http://www.fao.org/docrep/013/i1890t/i1890t.pdf> (last visited June 18, 2011) (hereinafter, FAO).

seafood, coupled with stagnant growth in wild catches, the volume of aquaculture/mariculture has been increasing significantly and this growth is expected to continue for decades to come.[357]

TABLE 1 World Fisheries Landings and Aquaculture Production (million tonnes)						
PRODUCTION	**2004**	**2005**	**2006**	**2007**	**2008**	**2009**
MARINE						
Capture Landings	83.8	82.7	80.0	79.9	79.5	79.9
Aquaculture	16.7	17.5	18.6	19.2	19.7	20.1
Subtotal (Marine)	**100.5**	**100.1**	**98.6**	**99.2**	**99.2**	**100.0**
FRESHWATER						
Capture Landings	8.6	9.4	9.8	10.0	10.2	10.1
Aquaculture	25.2	26.8	28.7	30.7	32.9	35.0
Subtotal (Fresh)	**33.8**	**36.2**	**38.5**	**40.6**	**43.1**	**45.1**
Total capture	92.4	92.1	89.8	89.9	89.7	90.0
Total aquaculture	41.9	44.3	47.3	49.9	52.6	55.1
Total world fisheries	**134.3**	**136.4**	**137.1**	**139.8**	**142.3**	**145.1**

Note: Excluding aquatic plants. Source: FAO

TABLE 2 World Fisheries Utilization (million tonnes)						
UTILIZATION	**2004**	**2005**	**2006**	**2007**	**2008**	**2009**
Human consumption	104.4	107.3	110.7	112.7	115.1	117.8
Non-food uses	29.8	29.1	26.3	27.1	27.2	27.3
Total world fisheries	**134.2**	**136.4**	**137**	**139.8**	**142.3**	**134.2**
Population *(billions)*	6.4	6.5	6.6	6.7	6.8	6.8
Per capita food fish supply *(kg)*	16.2	16.5	16.8	16.9	17.1	17.2

Note: Excluding aquatic plants. Source: FAO

---

[357] *See,* e.g., Amir Neoria, Thierry Chopinb, Max Troell, Alejandro H. Buschmanne, George P. Kraemerf, Christina Hallingd, Muki Shpigela, Charles Yarish, "Integrated aquaculture: rationale, evolution and state of the art emphasizing seaweed biofiltration in modern mariculture," Aquaculture 231 (2004) 361-391.

As Table 1 indicates, global capture production has remained relatively constant at about 90 million tonnes in recent years, while aquaculture production is increasing. Aquaculture now accounts for almost 40% of all fish production and almost 50% of all human fishery-related consumption (Table 2). The *FAO 2010 Yearbook, Fishery and Aquaculture Statistics*, highlights these data:

- In 2008, China accounted for 62% of world aquaculture production (32.7 million tonnes). Other countries producing over one million tonnes in 2008 were India (3.5 million tonnes), Vietnam (2.5 million tonnes), Indonesia (1.7 million tonnes), Thailand (1.4 million tonnes) and Bangladesh (1 million tonnes)
- Carps are the most cultured species in the world with 39% of production by volume. Other major groups cultured include shellfishes (shrimps and prawns, oysters, clams, mussels and scallops) and freshwater fishes (especially tilapias, catfish and salmon)
- At the single species level, white leg shrimp generated the highest value (USD 9 billion) in 2008, followed by Atlantic salmon (USD 7.2 billion), grass carp (USD 4.8 billion), and silver carp (USD 4.8 billion)
- Aquaculture production has maintained its steady growth with the average annual growth rate of 6.2% for 2003-2008[358]

Along with this economic growth, however, come strong environmental concerns. Briefly, a few of these can be categorized as follows:

- **Pressure is maintained on Wild Stocks.** Aquaculture doesn't always take pressure off wild fisheries and can even exacerbate the problem. This is because the diet of many farmed fish (e.g., salmon) is dependent on fish meal and fish oils from wild stocks. Even if the wild stock is a by-catch, or from stocks not normally consumed by humans (e.g., Peruvian anchovies), the loss can still place stress on natural food webs (including birds). However, shellfishes and herbivorous fishes (e.g., tilapia, carp and catfish) that are not meat-eaters can allay these concerns.

- **Feed Pollution.** In fish farming (as opposed to mollusk farming), many species depend on a diet of feed in pellet form. These pellets are broadcast onto the surface of the water and may be consumed as they settle to the bottom. Food which is not consumed lands on the bottom where it is decomposed by microorganisms or eaten by other organisms living on the bottom of the water column (benthos). This interaction can significantly alter the natural food web; e.g., microbial decomposition can deplete oxygen, thus affecting sedentary species.

- **Effluent and Sound Pollution.** Heavy concentrations of fish feces (as well as uneaten food and other organic debris) flushed into rivers or coastal waters can combine with nutrients to cause algal bloom and, when these die, their decomposition can deplete the oxygen causing eutrophication. Some species benefit from this process, but it is toxic to others. The build up of fecal matter (and unused food) in sea cages and/or in land-based ponds or tanks that dispose sludge or fecal matter, can pollute surrounding environments. Acoustic harassment devices (AHDs) to ward off predators can affect fish migrating and spawning patterns and are another form of environmental pollution.

---

[358] FAO, *supra* note 354 at xvi.

- **Antibiotics and Other Chemicals.** The use of drugs and other food additives to combat disease, as well as the use of chemicals to inhibit fouling of cages and nets, can negatively affect non-targeted species and marine environments. For example, arthropod species, such as lobster, can be very sensitive to chemical insecticides used in aquaculture. Chemicals and coloring agents to enhance productivity and/or product quality may also impinge on product safety in human consumption.

- **Fish Escapes.** Fish escaping from fish farms can breed with native fish resulting in fish populations that may not have the characteristics critical to surviving in the wild. Escaped fish can also spread disease and parasites (e.g., sea lice in salmon farming) as well as compete with native species for food and territory. Genetic engineering to increase growth rates (e.g., Atlantic salmon) is an added concern in terms of potential impacts on wild stocks.

- **Habitat Destruction and Altered Coastal Ecosystems.** Aquaculture, and, in particular, the shrimp industry, is taking a serious toll on wetland habitats. For example, mangrove forests, which lie in the intertidal zone, have been particularly affected along with wetlands and estuaries. The decline of coastal ecosystems results in a loss of pollutant-filtering capacity, storm and erosion protection and critical nurseries for wild fish.

- **Excessive Economic Costs.** Aquaculture requires energy for its fish pellets, cages, boats, equipments, etc. For example, for feed, it is estimated that some 10-15% of all fishmeal goes to aquaculture feed and it takes roughly 2 kilograms of fishmeal to produce a kilogram of farmed fish or shrimp, a net loss of fish protein.[359]

- **Invasive Species.** Importing non-native populations for culture can also have a significant, negative impact including introduction of disease and other organisms.

Some of the above concerns can be mitigated. Closed containment farms that have little contact with other environments are certainly preferable to pens in the open ocean. Moreover, farmed herbivorous species are generally less invasive to the environment. Many fishery enhancement projects are also viewed as being of net benefit to wild stocks. Purely organic pollution will often disseminate naturally (over time) and is not always a major contaminant. The criticisms of aquaculture may also reflect the growing pains of a new industry. New methods to control sea lice, diseases, predators and feed contaminants are in constant development. Fish meal used to feed salmon is viewed by some as highly efficient conversion of non-edible protein that would otherwise be used as fertilizer or processed only for its oil (as long as stocks are not overfished).

Some aquaculture is already demonstrating that it can be less expensive than traditional fishing. One irony of the success of worldwide salmon and shrimp farming is that prices often out-compete and inhibit the wild fishery. Hence, pressure on some wild stocks has declined and perhaps aquaculture could become a victim of its own success. If not, perhaps it will achieve more credit in the future for helping to rebuild wild populations, rather than threatening them.

---

[359] "Environmental Impacts of Aquaculture," World Resources Institute < http://www.wri.org/publication/content/8383> (last visited June 23, 2011).

The Socio-economic Framework and Impact of the Fisheries

Sometimes the more important a thing is, the more it is taken for granted, as if its very grandeur cancels out better judgment...like the ocean.
The Cousteau Society[360]

That the fisheries were of major importance in the colonization and early development of North America is without question. However, it is not always easy to see the impact today, especially if one doesn't live near the water. Nevertheless, fisheries and aquaculture efforts still exert major socio-economic impacts on North American society.

For example, many people are employed at sea to catch the fish and on land to process it. Trucks, trains and ships are needed to transport products to market, where distributors and retailers are employed to market the fish. Table 3 (below) illustrates that direct employment in the industry numbers in the hundreds of thousands. In fact though, as a primary industry, the fishing industry "kick-starts" employment in many other secondary industries and exerts a pervasive influence on society at large. This effect is often overlooked.

TABLE 3 Overview of US and Canadian Fisheries and Aquaculture Industries (2008-2009)		
	United States	**Canada**
Number of Harvesters (Part or Fulltime)	135,466	52,107
Number of Vessels (> 5 tons US; > 35 feet Cda)	*20,000	8,141
Number of Boats (< 5 tons US; < 35 feet Cda)	*17,000	7,851
Number of Primary Fish Processing Plants	858	*610
Number of Primary Fish Plant Workers	37,397	27,641
Number of Wholesale Fish Plants	2,342	N/A
Number of Wholesale Fish Plant Workers	23,293	N/A
Number of Aquaculture Workers (Direct Employment)	10,519	4,510
Seafood Domestic Consumption (FAO-2007)	7.4 million tonnes	783,671 tonnes
Per Capita Consumption FAO-2007 (round weight)	24.05 kg	23.8 kg
Exports of edible fish - 2010	$US 4.1 billion 1.2 million tonnes	$Cda 3.9 billion 656,016 tonnes
Imports of edible fish - 2010	$US 14.8 billion 2.5 million tonnes	$Cda 2.4 billion 502,845 tonnes

Source: NMFS, DFO, FAO and estimates* by author based on information supplied by NMFS and DFO.

For example, in order to fish, boats must be built and maintained; and a large segment of the boat and shipbuilding industries in North America exists only for this reason. The boats are equipped with expensive motors, machinery, electrical and communications equipment, safety gear, etc.; often produced far away. Wharves, docks, holding tanks, aquaculture ponds and pens and processing facilities must be also built and equipped, often using specialized materials and machinery produced inland. Ocean charts must be made and buoys and other navigational aids are set and maintained. Government vessels must inspect the fishing grounds and thousands of

---

[360] Cousteau Society, "*1998: International Year of the Ocean,*" Calypso Log, Mar.-Apr. 1998: 18.

biologists, statisticians, researchers and administrators are employed to monitor and manage the industry. Nets, ice, salt, fish pellets, packaging equipment and supplies, food, fuel, paint, specialized clothing and other consumables are needed to maintain production. In addition, more billions of dollars are spent on recreational fisheries, at least doubling the economic impact of nominal commercial landings in Canada and perhaps tripling it or more in the US.

In 2008, global (edible and industrial) commercial fishery landings and aquaculture production totaled 142.3 million metric tonnes. The FAO also reported global export trade in all fish/shellfish products was $US 102 billion (55 million tonnes) in 2008, growing at about 8% per year by value (1.5% by volume).

US 2009 landings, including 2008 aquaculture, totaled 3.93 million tonnes and represent approximately 2.7% of world 2008 production (see Table 4). Canadian 2009 landings and production (1.1 million tonnes), was approximately 0.7% of world production (see Table 5). Canadian landings tend to be more concentrated in high-valued shellfish species, versus large US landings of lower-valued finfish (e.g., Alaska pollock, arrowtooth flounder and menhaden).

United States: In the 2005-2007 period, the US was the third largest consumer of seafood products (after China and Japan); however, it has now moved into second place, replacing Japan. (This reflects declining consumption in Japan more so than increased consumption in the US.) In 2009, US per capita consumption of *edible* fishery products (including imports and exports) was 15.8 pounds (or 7.2 kg).[361] Fresh and frozen finfish accounted for 84% of the total landings, but only 47% of the value. The value of domestic production of edible fishery products was $7.6 billion and the value of industrial products was $554.4 million in 2009. Fully $75.5 billion was spent by US consumers for seafood products. The 2009 total includes $50.3 billion in expenditures at food service establishments (restaurants, carry-outs, caterers, etc.); $23.8 billion in retail sales for home consumption; and $1.4 billion for industrial fish products.[362]

In 2009, the US also became the largest importer of fish and fishery products, overtaking Japan that was the top importer for the previous 30 years. Imports of edible seafood products was 5.2 billion pounds valued at $13.1 billion; while imports of non-edible (i.e., industrial) products was $8.7 billion. In 2009, the total US seafood export value was $19.6 billion, consisting of 2.5 billion pounds of edible products valued at $4.0 billion and non-edible products valued at $15.7 billion.

The top five US domestic landed species by weight in 2009 were Alaska pollock (23%), menhaden spp. (17%), salmon spp. (9%), flatfish spp. (7%) and cod spp. (6%). Crabs, as a group, rated highest in value at $485.4 million, followed by scallops spp., shrimp spp., salmon spp. and lobster.

Catfish farming ($390 million) dominates aquaculture value, but with good showings in crawfish ($127 million), clams ($88 million), oysters ($80 million) and trout and salmon ($95 million). Tilapia production is still relatively small at $34 million. Total aquaculture production was relatively constant from 2006 to 2009, valued at approximately $1.2 billion.

---

[361] Note that US seafood consumption is based on edible weight, rather than the FAO use of round weight as expressed in Table 3.
[362] *Fisheries of the United States*, 2009, NMFS, MD.

TABLE 4
US Fisheries Landings 2009 and Aquaculture Production 2008
(50 States) (Nominal Values)

	Tonnes	Value ($US 000)
Landings (2009)		
Fish	2,996,197	1,847,808
Shellfish	580,681	2,051,936
Other (plants, urchins, etc.)	N/A	N/A
Subtotal	3,576,878	3,899,744
Aquaculture (2008)		
Fish	280,997	587,785
Shellfish	70,010	308,099
Other (e.g., aquarium fish)	N/A	298,775
Subtotal	351,007	1,194,659
Total	3,927,885	5,094,403

Note: Shellfish bivalves and univalves reported as meat weight.
Source: Adapted from Fisheries Statistics Division, F/ST1, NMFS

TABLE 5
Canada Fisheries Landings 2009 and Aquaculture Production 2009
(Nominal Values)

	Tonnes	Value ($Cdn 000)
Landings (2009)		
Fish	487,769	365,524
Shellfish	420,215	1,264,141
Other (plants, roe, etc.)	16,774	11,805
Subtotal	924,758	1,641,470
Aquaculture (2009)		
Fish	108,861	641,345
Shellfish	31,683	60,481
Subtotal	154,169	793,926
Total	1,078,927	2,435,396

Note: All shellfish are reported as live weight.
Source: Adapted from Fisheries and Oceans Canada, Statistics Division
Data Above includes confidential data as reported by provinces.

North Atlantic trawl fish landings in 2009 of butterfish, Atlantic cod, cusk, flounders (winter/blackback, summer/fluke, yellowtail and other), haddock, red and white hake, whiting (silver hake), ocean perch and pollock (combination of New England, Middle Atlantic, and Chesapeake Regions) were more than 97.4 million pounds valued at nearly $101.8 million. Landings of menhaden along the Atlantic coast were almost 401.7 million pounds valued at more than $28.4 million. Gulf region landings were 1 billion pounds valued at almost $60.6 million. Massachusetts with over 31.3 million pounds and New Jersey with over 10.3 million pounds accounted for more than 81% of the total landings of Atlantic mackerel.

US landings of Atlantic and Pacific halibut were almost 59.7 million pounds valued at more than$139.4 million. The Pacific fishery accounted for 59.6 million pounds of the 2009 total halibut catch.

Massachusetts had landings of ocean quahog at almost 18.7 million pounds valued at almost $10.7 million while New Jersey production was more than 12.4 million pounds valued at $6.9 million. Together, Massachusetts and New Jersey accounted for 89% of total ocean quahog production in 2009. Surf clams yielded almost 50.6 million pounds of meats valued at $34.1 million. New Jersey was the leading state landing surf clams with nearly 32.9 million pounds, followed by New York, nearly 8.8 million pounds and Massachusetts, 4.6 million pounds.

The hard clam fishery produced 5.7 million pounds of meats valued at nearly $40.9 million. Landings of hard clam in the New England region were 1.6 million pounds of meats; Middle Atlantic, more than 1.4 million pounds; Chesapeake, 1.8 million pounds; and the South Atlantic region, 769,000 pounds. Soft clams yielded 3.9 million pounds of meats valued at over $20.3 million. Maine was the leading state with 1.9 million pounds of meats, followed by Massachusetts, more than 1 million pounds, and Washington, 681,000 pounds.

The U.S. oyster landings yielded almost 35.6 million pounds valued at more than $136.5 million. The Gulf region led in production of oyster landings with 22.1 million pounds of meats, over 62% of the national total; followed by the Pacific Coast region with over 11.3 million pounds (32%), principally Washington, with nearly 9.5 million pounds (more than 84% of the region's total volume); and the South Atlantic region with 927,000 pounds (3%).

Hard blue crab landings were nearly 153.9 million pounds valued at $149 million. Louisiana landed 33% of the total U.S. landings of hard blue crab landings followed by: Maryland, 20%; North Carolina, nearly 19%; and Virginia, more than 15%. Hard blue crab landings in the Chesapeake region were almost 54.6 million pounds; the South Atlantic with over 36.3 million pounds; and the Gulf region with 59.1 million pounds increased nearly 26%. The Middle Atlantic region with 3.9 million pounds valued at $5.8 million.

Dungeness crab landings were more than 63.4 million pounds valued at over $131.2 million. Oregon landings of Dungeness crab was nearly 21.8 million pounds led all states with more than 34% of the total landings. Washington landings were almost 20.7 million pounds or almost 33% of the total landings. California landings were over 15.2 million pounds and Alaska landings were 5.6 million pounds.

Maine led in American lobster landings for the 28th consecutive year with 78 million pounds valued at almost $228.6 million. Massachusetts, the second leading producer, had landings of almost 11.6 million pounds valued at nearly $41.9 million. Together, Maine and Massachusetts produced more than 92% of the total national landings. Florida, with landings of spiny lobster at 4 million pounds valued at almost $12.5 million, accounted for nearly 85% of the total catch and over 61% of the value.

Sea scallop landings were 58 million pounds valued at over $382.2 million. Massachusetts and New Jersey were the leading states in landings of sea scallops with nearly 29.8 million and 14 million pounds of meats, respectively, representing almost 76% of the national total.

US landings of shrimp were 301.1 million pounds valued at over $370.2 million. Gulf region landings of shrimp were the nation's largest with 241 million pounds and 80% of the national total. Louisiana led all Gulf States with nearly 109.8 million pounds; followed by Texas, almost 89.7 million pounds; Alabama, almost 21.7 million pounds; Mississippi, 10.1 million pounds; and Florida West Coast, 9.7 million pounds. In the Pacific region, Oregon had landings of 22 million pounds; Washington had landings of 7.6 million pounds; and California, 3.6 million pounds.

U.S. commercial landings of squid were over 266.3 million pounds valued at $85 million. California was the leading state for landings of squid with almost 203.6 million pounds (more than 76%) and was followed by New Jersey with almost 24.7 million pounds (over 9% of the national total). The Pacific Coast region landings were 205.1 million pounds; followed by Middle Atlantic, over 32.2 million pounds; followed by the New England region with 28.1 million pounds; followed by the Chesapeake region with 764,000 pounds; and the South Atlantic region with 71,000 pounds.

The US landings of Pacific trawl fish (Pacific cod, flounders, hake, Pacific ocean perch, Alaska pollock, and rockfishes) were over 3.2 billion pounds valued at $546 million in 2009. Landings of Alaska pollock were 1.9 billion pounds followed by Pacific cod at 491.1 million pounds; Pacific hake (whiting) landings at 253.1 million pounds; and rockfishes at over 35.3 million pounds.

US commercial landings of salmon were over 705.2 million pounds valued at $370.1 million. Alaska accounted for 95% of total landings of salmon; Washington, more than 4%; California, Oregon, and the Great Lakes accounted for less than 1% of the catch.

Alaska salmon landings were 671.2 million pounds valued at almost $344.7 million. The distribution of Alaska salmon landings by species in 2009 was: pink, nearly 276.8 million pounds (41%); sockeye, 256.1 million pounds (38%); chum, almost 106.5 million pounds (16%); coho, almost 26.7 million pounds (4%); and chinook, nearly 5.1 million pounds (1%). Washington salmon landings were almost 31.6 million pounds valued at nearly $21.8 million. The biennial fishery for pink salmon was 17 million pounds in 2009. Washington landings of chum salmon were 5.9 million; followed by coho, over 5.2 million pounds; chinook, 3.4 million pounds; and sockeye, 44,000 pounds. Oregon salmon landings were nearly 2.3 million pounds valued at $3.5 million. Chinook salmon landings were almost 1.3 million pounds valued at over $2.2 million; coho landings were over 1 million pounds valued at $1.3 million; sockeye landings were 4,000 pounds valued at $6,000; pink and chum landings were both less than 500 pounds valued at less than $500. California salmon landings were 1,000 pounds valued at $6,000. Chinook salmon were the principal species landed in the state.

Landings of sablefish in Alaska were 27 million pounds valued at $94.2 million. Landings in Washington were nearly 3.5 million pounds and $8.7 million. The 2009 Oregon catch was over 7.2 million pounds, and nearly $15.9 million California landings of nearly 5.1 million pounds and $9.8 million. Alaska landings of Pacific sea herring accounted for 98% of Pacific coast landings with 87 million pounds valued at over $29.3 million.

California accounted for nearly 99% of the U.S. landings of jack mackerel in 2009. Total landings were 265,000 pounds valued at $18,000. Landings of chub mackerel were over 11.2 million pounds valued at nearly $1.1 million; California accounted for 100% of the total landings.[363]

Canada: In 2008 (most recent detailed data), total landings from marine commercial fishing in Canada were valued at $1.89 billion (932,000 tonnes). This represented a $70 million (4%) decrease compared to 2007, mainly due to decreases in the landed value of herring, mackerel and shrimp, respectively on the Atlantic coast and (with the exception of sockeye) of salmon species on the Pacific coast. The value of freshwater fisheries decreased $59 million in 2008, 7% lower than in 2007.

In 2008, Canadian aquaculture production increased by $40 million to reach a total of $801 million, which represented an increase of 5% over 2007. This was mainly due to a 6% increase in the production value of farmed salmon and trout. The gross revenue of the seafood processing industry fell to $3.9 billion in 2008 from 2007.

Canada was ranked 22nd by the FAO in terms of the global volume of fish landings in 2008; this represents just over 1% of the world total. Since 2007, Canada has ranked 8th worldwide among seafood exporting countries in terms of total export value, behind the United States and Chile, among others. However Canada does have a significant share of worldwide exports of some products. These include smoked herring (63% of worldwide exports of this product are Canadian), lobster (51%), frozen crab (39%), fish livers and roes (26%), Atlantic and Pacific halibuts (including Turbot or "Greenland halibut" - 13%) and fresh haddock (14%).

Approximately 85% of Canadian seafood production was exported in 2008, mostly to the United States (63%). Total exports of Canadian fish and seafood was valued of $3.88 billion in 2008. The most valuable Canadian exports in 2008 were 1) lobster, 2) farmed salmon, 3) snow crab and 4) shrimp. The combined value of these species represented 60% of the total value of Canadian seafood exports during the year. Lobster, salmon, and snow crab accounted for 65% of the total exports to the US. Other exports to the EU, Japan and China accounted for 13%, 7.5% and 6.7% of the total export value, respectively.

---

[363] NMFS "Fisheries of the United States – 2009" Silver Spring, MD, 2010

Canada imports far less fish and seafood than it exports, and was ranked 16th highest seafood importer in the world in 2008. United States and Japan were the top two major fish and seafood importers in 2008 and they accounted for 27% of the worldwide value of imports. Canadian imports reached a total value of $2.24 billion in 2008. The main imported species were shrimp, lobster, wild salmon, tuna as well as groundfish species such as cod, haddock and halibut.[364] In 2008, 36.7% of the total value of Canadian imports of fish and seafood came from the United States, for a total of $820 million. Thailand was second with 14.9% of the total value ($333 million), followed by China with 14.6% ($326 million).

Overall aquaculture production was valued at $801 million in Canada in 2008. This value can be attributed to increases in the value of salmon and trout in recent years. The aquaculture production value of mussels and oysters decreased by 19% for both species, while trout production increased by 71%. 2008. The production value of salmon accounted for about 78% of the total aquaculture production value in Canada.

British Columbia continues to dominate Canadian aquaculture production, accounting for over half of Canada's total. In 2008, New Brunswick reported the second highest farmed production, primarily from finfish (especially salmon). Newfoundland and Labrador ranked third in value of production, primarily from finfish. Nova Scotia ranked fourth in value of production in 2008 and finfish accounted for 69% of the total value of $35.6 million.

Canadian Provincial Highlights

Marine commercial fishing occurs in six of the ten Canadian provinces and three territories. Approximately 27% (255,000 tonnes) of the total volume of commercial marine fisheries in Canada in 2008 was landed in Nova Scotia, for a total of $677 million, or 36% of the total Canadian landed value. The key species were lobster (54%), scallops (13%) and snow crab (10%) as well as cod, hake and halibut, which accounted for 8% of the landed value.

The total landed volume in Newfoundland and Labrador in 2008 fell to just under 338,000 tonnes, valued at $530 million. While the value of landings decreased for lobster, seals and pelagic species, these were offset by increased landed value for shrimp, crab and other crustaceans. Newfoundland and Labrador's share of the total landings in Canada has increased modestly from 25% of the total landed value in Canada in 2006, to 28% in 2008. Key species by value in 2008 were shrimp (35%) and crab (34%).

The total landed volume in British Columbia was 150 thousand tonnes, valued at 247 million in 2008. British Columbia contributed 13% of the total fishing value in Canada coming 3rd in total landings. Based on landed value, the key species harvested were crab (15%), flounder, halibut and sole (14%), and clam, cockles and arkshells at 13%.

In 2008, the landed value in New Brunswick was $170 million, with Quebec at $142 million, both representing 16.5% of the total landed value in Canada. They came in 4th and 5th place respectively in terms of total landings. Prince Edward Island was in sixth place with respect to

---

[364] Note that Canada is a large exporter of coldwater shrimp, but all warm-water species are imported; also Canada processes upwards of 50% of all US-landed American lobster due to soft-shell conditions. Canada also exports snow crab and various groundfish to China that may be processed and exported back to Canada and/or other countries.

the value of marine commercial fishing in Canada. In 2008, 6.6% or $124 million of the total value of catches in Canadian waters was landed in this province.

In 2008, commercial freshwater fisheries accounted to 3% of the commercial fishing value and 3% of the total volume in Canada. The landed volume of freshwater species was 31,063 tonnes, valued at $59 million. The main freshwater species fished commercially in Canada are yellow pickerel, whitefish and perch. Landings of these three species represented close to 82% of the total landings of freshwater species in Canada.

Freshwater commercial fishing is the most important fishery in Ontario and Manitoba, with respective landed values of $27 million and $25 million in 2008. Fish landings in these two provinces represented 88% of the overall landed value of freshwater commercial fisheries in Canada.

Recreational Fisheries

United States: The US 2009 Recreational Fishing Statistics Program conducted by the NMFS reported that approximately 10 million anglers made almost 75 million marine recreational fishing trips in the continental US, Alaska, Hawaii, and Puerto Rico. The estimated total marine recreational catch was nearly 391 million fish, of which nearly 56% were released alive. Statistics indicated the recreational catch of finfish in these states accounted for about 8% of the total harvest of finfish in these same states. The estimated total weight of the harvested catch was 96,162 tonnes. Nationally, 65% of the recreational catch came from inland waters, 26% from state territorial seas, and 9% from offshore (the EEZ). The majority of trips also fished primarily in inland waters. [365]

The Atlantic coast accounted for the majority of trips (59%) and catch (51%) nationally. East Florida accounted for over 23% of the Atlantic trips, with most other states making a strong showing. The most commonly caught non-bait species (in numbers of fish) were summer flounder, Atlantic croaker, bluefish, black sea bass, and spot (seatrout). The largest harvests by weight were striped bass, bluefish, dolphinfish, summer flounder, and Atlantic croaker. Over the last ten years, the total annual catch of black sea bass decreased overall from 19 million fish in 2000 to 12 million fish in 2009. In 2009, black sea bass catch was more than 13% below the 10-year average of nearly 14 million fish. From 2000 to 2009, total annual catch of summer flounder has averaged more than 23 million fish. Black sea bass, summer flounder, Atlantic cod, dolphinfish, and bluefish were the largest catches in federally managed waters.

The Gulf coast (excluding Texas), accounted for 31% of the trips (67% of this from West Florida) and 44% of the national catch. The most commonly caught non-bait species (in numbers of fish) were spotted seatrout, red drum, sand seatrout, Atlantic croaker, and gray snapper. The largest harvests by weight were for spotted seatrout, red drum, sheepshead, red snapper, king mackerel, and black drum.

The Pacific coast accounted for 7% of trips (93% of this in California) and 3% of the national catch. The most commonly caught non-bait species (in numbers of fish) were Pacific sardine, black rockfish, coho salmon, kelp bass, and barred surfperch. The largest harvests by weight were coho salmon, black rockfish, albacore, lingcod, Pacific halibut, and California halibut.

---

[365] Data may not be all inclusive; *see* http://www.st.nmfs.noaa.gov/st1/fus/fus09/03_recreational2009.pdf

Canada: Except for British Columbia (BC), most of the Canadian recreational fishery is in inland waters. In 2005, over 3.2 million anglers participated in recreational fishing. This was 10% lower than the estimate of 3.6 million in 2000. These anglers are estimated to have spent approximately $7.5 billion.

In 2005, there was 215 million fish of all species caught and nearly 72 million were retained. More than half were caught in Ontario (115 million), followed by Quebec and the three Western provinces. Walleye ranked first and represented nearly a quarter of the total catch, followed by trout, perch and bass. It was the first time walleye surpassed trout since the survey was first conducted. A dominant species caught by resident anglers continued to be brook trout, particularly in the eastern provinces and Quebec. The Territories had significant catches of lake trout, arctic grayling and northern pike.

Anglers spent $5 billion in the form of investments and major purchases of durable goods related to recreational fishing activities. $2.5 billion was spent on trip expenses such as accommodation, food, transportation, supplies and services. The government of BC estimates its recreational fishery returns 70 times more than its commercial fishery, on a pound for pound basis. Many recreational fisheries are likely to show similar returns.

Fish Capture Methods and Gear

Technological advances and innovations have made it possible to capture more fish at lower cost. The introduction of powered gear has improved the efficiencies of many fishing methods. Global positioning systems, gear monitoring sensors, and fish location equipment have helped fishers increase efficiency while avoiding catches of unwanted species.

More than 300 species of seafood are captured in North America, reflecting the huge size and diversity of the fishery resources. Many different types of fishing gear are used to catch these fish including purse seines, trawl nets, longlines, gillnets, dredges, trolling gear, and pots. The gear is usually specialized to catch certain species, or to use in certain locations.

Trawls

Otter Trawl

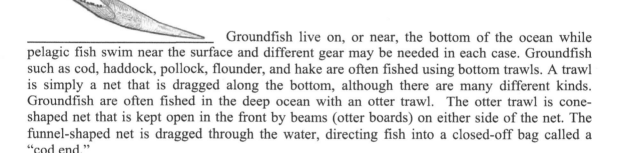

Groundfish live on, or near, the bottom of the ocean while pelagic fish swim near the surface and different gear may be needed in each case. Groundfish such as cod, haddock, pollock, flounder, and hake are often fished using bottom trawls. A trawl is simply a net that is dragged along the bottom, although there are many different kinds. Groundfish are often fished in the deep ocean with an otter trawl. The otter trawl is cone-shaped net that is kept open in the front by beams (otter boards) on either side of the net. The funnel-shaped net is dragged through the water, directing fish into a closed-off bag called a "cod end."

After towing and hauling the net, the catch is released on deck from the cod end. The fish are sorted, cleaned, and packed on ice, or in brine, for the return trip. Sorting may be necessary to separate by-catch, i.e., unmarketable, illegal, or undersized species. By-catch often has to be thrown back, usually dying or dead, but research initiatives to improve gear are decreasing unwanted species and new markets for under-utilized species are also being continually investigated to eliminate waste.

Trawl nets can also drag the middle depths of the ocean and these trawls are called mid-water trawls. Mid-water trawls are similar to bottom trawls except weights used in the net, or the speed of the boat, are adjusted to keep the net off the bottom. Often these trawls are used to catch ocean perch, shrimp and squid, but sometimes groundfish are caught as well. Other variations of trawling include stern trawling and side trawling. These refer to the position of the net on the boat during setting and hauling. Pair trawling uses two boats to spread the mouth of the net open. Trawling may be regulated through limiting entry to a particular fishery, closed areas, and/or seasons and by mesh size requirements, or other methods.

As noted earlier, pelagic fish refer to such species as mackerel and herring that are found near the surface. These fish are more suited for catch in nets that float, or are dragged, near the surface. This includes seines, purse seines, and gill nets.

Seine

_____ A seine net is a very long net, with, or without, a bag in the centre that is used to encircle fish. Unlike trawling, it is the encircling action, rather than the towing action, that catches the fish. The seine is set either from the shore, or from a boat, to surrounding schools of fish and is operated with two long ropes at its ends for hauling the fish.

Purse Seine

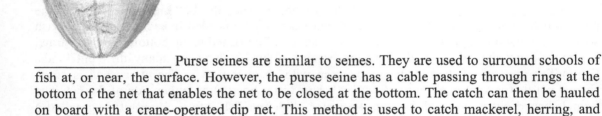

_____ Purse seines are similar to seines. They are used to surround schools of fish at, or near, the surface. However, the purse seine has a cable passing through rings at the bottom of the net that enables the net to be closed at the bottom. The catch can then be hauled on board with a crane-operated dip net. This method is used to catch mackerel, herring, and other pelagic schooling species.

Gillnet

_____ Gillnetting is a passive fishing method that uses a fixed net held in place with weights at the bottom and floats at the top and usually anchored at each end. Fish swim through the almost invisible netting and are trapped when their gills become entangled in the net mesh. Gillnets are suspended either at, or under, the surface and can be used for both pelagic and groundfish fishing. Gillnetting is often characterized by small boats making day trips and landing limited amounts of fish such as herring, mackerel, monkfish, and bluefish. The fishers regularly haul the nets into their boats, remove the fish and return the nets to the water to continue fishing. Gillnet fisheries are managed through limited entry, closed seasons and restrictions on net length and mesh sizes.

Longlining

Longlining is a method of setting long lines, often as log as fifty miles, of baited hooks that can be left in the water to fish. The number of hooks used is increased by hanging shorter lines with many hooks (called gangions or leaders) from the main line. The line can be anchored at the bottom in areas too rough for trawling, or suspended by floats for surface fishing. The lines, often miles long, can be hauled daily and re-baited. Manually hauling and baiting of longlines is labour intensive, but is also non-destructive to fish habitat and produces a quality catch because, in general, targeted species are efficiently captured and by-catch can be removed live from the hook. Automated baiting systems are also available for longlining. Longlines are often used to fish swordfish, tuna, and shark on the surface and groundfish and flatfish on the bottom; but they can be used to catch almost any type of fish. The longline fisheries are managed through a variety of measures, primarily quotas, seasonal closures and limits on the number of boats.

Fish Traps, Poundnets and Weirs

Fish Weir

A weir is a passive fishing method consisting of fences or posts permanently attached to the bottom. A straight fence from the shoreline, called a "leader," acts as a barrier to fish so that they follow the leader into the trap. The enclosure is shaped so that the fish tend to swim in circles and cannot easily find their way out. Often the weir has built-in "pockets" or other small enclosures that trap the fish further (not shown above). A seine or purse seine is then used to remove the fish from the pocket.

Poundnets and fish traps are similar to weirs, but are constructed with netting or wire and are often designed to float where bottom terrain prohibits stakes or pilings. Floating traps are held in place with anchors and the bottom of the trap is covered with netting. Traps like these are valued as they do not require bait, require little use of fuel, and are relatively inexpensive to acquire. Cod, scup, sea herring, menhaden, squid, bluefish, and mackerel are some of the species caught in such traps on the Atlantic Coast.

Shellfish Harvesting Methods

Dredge

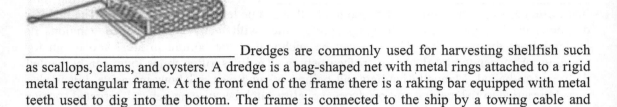

_____ Dredges are commonly used for harvesting shellfish such as scallops, clams, and oysters. A dredge is a bag-shaped net with metal rings attached to a rigid metal rectangular frame. At the front end of the frame there is a raking bar equipped with metal teeth used to dig into the bottom. The frame is connected to the ship by a towing cable and dragged along the bottom.

Scallops: After a tow the dredge is hauled onboard, the bag is emptied and the catch sorted. Usually the scallops are "shucked" onboard, with only the white meat (adductor muscles) being retained and the shell and other waste thrown back. The waste shells provide a surface for new "spat" to collect for new scallop growth. (In Europe, the whole scallop is generally consumed, except for the liver, and scallop meats are usually served with the roe attached.) A small, but growing market exists for roes and scallops in-the-shell in North America and boats will sometimes keep part of the catch unshucked to supply it.

Clams: Hydraulic dredges are similar to mechanical dredges, but with nozzle attachments that direct pressurized water into the bottom. This allows the dredge rake to penetrate the bottom to capture burrowed clams and quahogs. Suction dredges use pumps to suction shellfish into the boat through a pipe.

Other Harvesting Methods

Smaller Traps and Pots

Small traps and pots are box-like structures used to catch fish or shellfish. They are usually baited and equipped with funnel openings that confuse prey and prevent easy exit. They are weighted to rest on the bottom, with marker buoys at the surface, and are sometimes attached to other traps or pots in a long trawl line to make them quicker to retrieve. The traps range in size from small inshore crab pots to large offshore lobster and crab traps set in hundreds of feet of water. Trap caught fish and shellfish are of the highest quality as they are usually still alive when landed and often kept that way so consumers can buy them fresh.

The trap fishery is regulated through quotas, seasonal and area closures, and through trap exits that allow immature fish or shellfish to escape. Traps now have doors that automatically open after being submerged for a certain time to prevent "ghost fishing" by lost traps.

Trotlines

A trotline is a simple device that uses a baited line without hooks to attract crabs that crawl up the line and are caught.

Rakes

Different kinds of rakes are often used to harvest clams and seaweed. Simple hand rakes are like large garden rakes, but with longer, curved teeth. Other rakes have basket attachments or telescopic handles for operating from a boat.

Handlining and Jigging

Traditionally, hand-lining and jigging are the oldest forms of fishing, but are still used today. Hand-lining is simply using a line and baited hook. In deeper water the line is weighted to take it to the bottom quickly so no time is wasted. Jigging is using a line with a baited hook or lure that is continually jerked up and down in the water. This is done by hand or with an automated jigging machine. Fish are attracted by the motion and take the hook. Hand-lining and jigging are often used to catch groundfish, although squid and pelagic species are sometimes caught.

Harpoons

Harpoons were used extensively for whaling in the old days and are still used today to catch swordfish, shark and tuna. Harpoons are usually tipped with a barb that is attached to a long line with a buoy at the end. The fish are free to run and are followed until they tire and can be hauled aboard. The harpoon can be thrown by hand or shot by a mounted gun.

Trolling

Trolling is just the towing of fishing lines behind a moving boat. It is sometimes used for swordfish, tuna and shark fisheries and extensively in some salmon fisheries.

Dip Net or Scoop Net

Large, power-operated dip nets, or "brail nets" are used to remove fish from weirs and purse seines. Smaller hand-held dip nets are used in sport fishing.

Lift Nets

Lift net are lowered into the water, left for a while and then lifted rapidly to the surface. They are often used by fishermen for catching schooling river fish.

Cast Nets

Cast nets are thrown by hand and sink to the bottom, covering fish. The net is gathered by drawing ropes attached to the net. Striped mullet have been caught this way in Florida.

Fyke Nets and Hoop Nets

These are cone-shaped or cylindrical nets or traps often used in rivers or estuaries to catch eels, but can be used for catching a variety of fish and shellfish. Usually they are held open by hoops and can be joined together to form a long net system with an internal cone-shaped net or nets to prevent fish from escaping. These nets are often collapsible as well.

Common Fish Descriptive Terminology

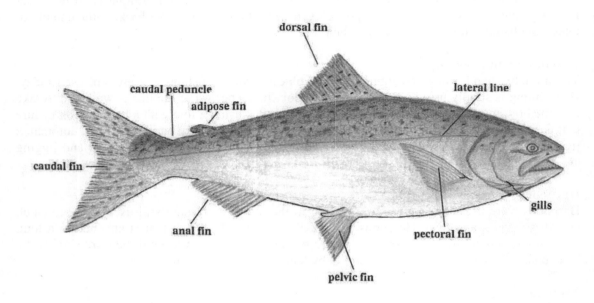

adipose fin: a small fleshy fin with no rays, located between the dorsal and caudal fins
anal fin: a vertical fin positioned on the underside of the abdomen behind the anus
caudal fin: the most posterior fin located behind the caudal peduncle; also tail fin
caudal peduncle: the fleshy end of the body located between the anal and tail fins
dorsal fin: the fin located on the back of fishes, and in front of the adipose fin, if it is present
gills: the respiratory organs for underwater breathing of fishes and other aquatic vertebrates
lateral line: a thin horizontal series of pore like openings positioned along each side of the abdomen that act as a sensory organ
pectoral fins: anterior and uppermost of the paired fins, positioned behind the gills
pelvic fins: posterior paired fins, located in the abdominal position or towards the rear

Note: Please refer to the Glossary for additional terms.

How to Use Part 2 of this Book

MARKET NAME

COMMON NAME

Common Name, *Scientific Name*

GENERAL

The **American shad** is a member of the family Clupeidae (herrings, river herrings, menhadens, sardines). The genus *Alosa*, subfamily Alosinae, includes many of the shads and other river herrings (about 23 species in *ITIS* and 24 in *FishBase*, not including subspecies). *The Seafood List* identifies 9 species of shad, several of which are common on the Atlantic East Coast. These include the American shad, the hickory shad (*A. mediocris*), the Alabama shad (*A. alabamae*), the gizzard shad (*Dorosoma cepedianum*), and the threadfin shad (*D. petenense*). The alewife and blueback herring also share the *Alosa* genus. (Also see alewife and menhaden entries in this book.)

Like the river herrings, at one time shad swarmed the rivers of eastern North America and approximately 23,000 tonnes of American shad was landed in the US and Canada in 1896. However, as in the case of other anadromous species (e.g., salmon, alewife) dams, pollution and perhaps overfishing have long since curtailed catches of that magnitude.

PHYSICAL DESCRIPTION

Max length: 76.0 cm TL male/unsexed; (Ref. 6885); 61.7 cm SL (female). Common length: 50.0 cm SL male/unsexed; (Ref. 188);
Max. published weight: 5,500 g (Ref. 7251);
Max. reported age: 13 years (Ref. 72462)
Length at first maturity: 305 - 485 cm

American shad is moderately compressed with a distinct keel. The coloration is silver with either blue or green-metallic luster on dorsal side. The shoulder has a dark spot often followed by several more and occasionally by a second row. Teeth are small and weak and the adipose eyelid is well developed. It is often confused with the blueback herring. *A. aestivalis* and the alewife, *A. pseudoharengus* (which has a steeply rising jaw not present in American shad) as well as and hickory shad, *A. mediocris* (where coloration is more green to black than silver).

Aliases
Atlantic Shad/
Potomac Shad/
Northern Silver
Shad

FishBase Name
American shad

International Recognitions
Spain—Sábalo
americano
France—Alose
savoureuse
Italy—
Allaccia
Germany—
Amerikanische
Finte

LANDINGS AND VALUES

American shad is multi-faceted traveller and can be found in oceanic to brackish and fresh water environments at various depths up to 250 meters deep. It is distributed throughout the Atlantic from Newfoundland and the St. Lawrence River basin to central Florida. It was introduced to the Pacific in the 1870s and is now found from Alaska to Baja, California. The US American shad catch was 275 tonnes, valued at $616,000 in 2008 (see table). The Canadian marine catch in 2008 was only 5 tonnes, valued at $5,000 (see table). The Canadian catch was increased by freshwater landings of 15 tonnes, valued at $12,000 in 2008 (see table). The US gizzard shad accounted for almost 70% of total US shad landings, while the American shad accounted for about 30% of the value (see table). American shad are caught commercially in weirs, traps and gillnets while spawning and occasionally at sea. They are also a gamefish in many areas. **Endangered Status:** Alabama shad is a Species of Concern (US).

COMMERCIAL USES

Marketed fresh, frozen, salted or smoked. The flesh is white and flaky and the fish is also known for its excellent roe.

LIFE CYCLE

The American shad is mostly oceanic, but returns to freshwater streams in the spring. Males arrive in the river first and after females arrive spawning timing is temperature dependent (12°C – 18.3°C). Spawning occurs in the evening at night with each female accompanies by several males. Eggs are released in open water where they are fertilized by the males. Approximately 20,000 to 150,000 eggs or more can be released (numbers are independent of female size). Individual fertilized eggs (2.5mm – 3.5mm diameter; transparent pink or amber color) slowly sink to the bottom and are carried along in the current. The larvae hatch after 8-12 days and the spent fish return to sea where they travel in schools. Juveniles are found in rivers during the summer and as they mature form schools and stay in groups to move downstream. After entering the ocean in the fall they remain there until they return to spawn. They feed on plankton, small copepods and mysids and occasionally on smaller fish. They are preyed upon by seals, but adults have few predators.

American Shad US Landings by Year – Nominal Data Value in $US (000); Quantity in tonnes; (NMFS)				
	2004	2005	2006	2007	2008
Value	846	780	658	790	616
Quantity	678	575	340	426	275

American Shad Canada Marine Landings by Year – Nominal Value in $Cdn (000); Quantity in tonnes; (DFO)				
	2004	2005	2006	2007	2008
Value	27	27	18	7	5
Quantity	41	43	27	11	5

American Shad Canada Freshwater Landings by Year – Nominal Value in $Cdn (000); Quantity in tonnes; (DFO)				
	2004	2005	2006	2007	2008
Value	2	2	2	12	12
Quantity	2	2	2	14	15

Gizzard Shad US Landings by Year – Nominal Data Value in $US (000); Quantity in tonnes; (NMFS)				
	2004	2005	2006	2007	2008
Value	789	563	693	200	407
Quantity	1,870	1,081	731	656	1,187

Hickory Shad US Landings by Year – Nominal Data Value in $US (000); Quantity in tonnes; (NMFS)				
	2004	2005	2006	2007	2008
Value	49	57	21	13	15
Quantity	114	103	38	24	35

156

157

SPECIES IDENTIFICATION

Each two-page entry usually generally focuses on one species. The preferred **MARKET NAME** of the species is found at the top of the left-side page. The **Common Name** and *Scientific name* are found near the bottom right of the illustration on the left-side page. Note that a market name may include more than one species. For example, the **market name** "SHAD" includes species with the **common names** of American shad, gizzard shad, hickory shad and others. Other species associated with the featured species through taxonomy, physical appearance, or similar market or common names are discussed, and distinguishing characteristics are highlighted.

The use of **aliases** (or vernaculars) is generally not recommended as this can create additional identity and market confusion, but some aliases are included to assist in referencing. Because of the existence of many aliases and duplication in market names and common names, *Scientific Names* are used to help identify species. *FishBase* and *SeaLifeBase* common names, often different from North American sources, are also included for references purposes. If a species name the reader is looking for is not in the index, it may be because it is not a significantly, commercially-valuable species in the US or Canada.

All featured species market names, common names and scientific names used in this book have been referenced to the *ITIS* database and *The Seafood List* as of October 1, 2011. Illustrations are meant to reflect general species characteristics and should not be considered accurate in detail.

American Shad, *Alosa sapidissima*

GENERAL

The **American shad** is a member of the family Clupeidae (herrings, river herrings, menhadens, sardines). The genus *Alosa*, subfamily Alosinae, includes many of the shads and other river herrings (about 23 species in *ITIS* and 24 in *FishBase*, not including subspecies). *The Seafood List* identifies 9 species of shad, several of which are common on the Atlantic East Coast. These include the American shad, the hickory shad (*A. mediocris*), the Alabama shad (*A. alabamae*), the gizzard shad (*Dorosoma cepedianum*), and the threadfin shad (*D. petenense*). The alewife and blueback herring also share the *Alosa* genus. (Also see alewife and menhaden entries in this book.)

Like the river herrings, at one time shad swarmed the rivers of eastern North America and approximately 23,000 tonnes of American shad was landed in the US and Canada in 1896. However, as in the case of other anadromous species (e.g., salmon, alewife) dams, pollution and perhaps overfishing have long since curtailed catches of that magnitude.

PHYSICAL DESCRIPTION

Max length: 76.0 cm TL male/unsexed; (Ref. 6885); 61.7 cm SL (female); Common length: 50.0 cm SL male/unsexed; (Ref. 188);
Max. published weight: 5,500 g (Ref. 7251);
Max. reported age: 13 years (Ref. 72462)
Length at first maturity: 305 - 485 cm

American shad is moderately compressed with a distinct keel. The coloration is silver with either blue or green-metallic luster on dorsal side. The shoulder has a dark spot often followed by several more and occasionally by a second row. Teeth are small and weak and the adipose eyelid is well developed. It is often confused with the blueback herring, *A. aestivalis* and the alewife, *A. pseudoharengus* (which has a steeply rising jaw not present in American shad) as well as hickory shad, *A. mediocris* (where coloration is more green to black than silver).

Also Known As
Atlantic Shad/
Potomac Shad/
Northern Silver
Shad

FishBase Name
American shad

International Recognitions
Spain—Sábalo americano
Franco—Alose savoureuse
Italy—Alloccia americana
Germany—Amerikanische Finte

LANDINGS AND VALUES

American shad is multi-faceted traveller and can be found in oceanic to brackish and fresh water environments at various depths up to 250 meters deep. It is distributed throughout the Atlantic from Newfoundland and the St. Lawrence River basin to central Florida. It was introduced to the Pacific in the 1870s and is now found from Alaska to Baja, California. The US American shad catch was 275 tonnes, valued at $616,000 in 2008 (see table). The Canadian marine catch in 2008 was only 5 tonnes, valued at $5,000 (see table). The Canadian catch was increased by freshwater landings of 15 tonnes, valued at $12,000 in 2008 (see table). The US gizzard shad accounted for almost 70% of total US shad landings, while the American shad accounted for about 30% of the landings, but 60% of the value (see table). American shad are caught commercially in weirs, traps and gillnets while spawning and occasionally at sea. They are also a gamefish in many areas. **Endangered Status:** Alabama shad is a Species of Concern (US).

COMMERCIAL USES

Marketed fresh, frozen, salted or smoked. The flesh is white and flaky and the fish is also known for its excellent roe.

LIFE CYCLE

The American shad is mostly oceanic, but returns to freshwater streams in the spring. Males arrive in the river first and after females arrive spawning timing is temperature dependent (12°C –18.3°C). Spawning occurs in the evening at night with each female accompanies by several males. Eggs are released in open water where they are fertilized by the males. Approximately 20,000 to 150,000 eggs or more can be released (numbers are independent of female size). Individual fertilized eggs (2.5mm – 3.5mm diameter; transparent pink or amber color) slowly sink to the bottom and are carried along in the current. The larvae hatch after 8-12 days and the spent fish return to sea where they travel in schools. Juveniles are found in rivers during the summer and as they mature form schools and stay in groups to move downstream. After entering the ocean in the fall they remain there until they return to spawn. They feed on plankton, small copepods and mysids and occasionally on smaller fish. They are preyed upon by seals, but adults have few predators.

American Shad US Landings by Year – Nominal Data Value in $US (000); Quantity in tonnes; (NMFS)					
	2004	2005	2006	2007	2008
Value	846	780	658	790	616
Quantity	678	575	340	426	275

American Shad Canada Marine Landings by Year – Nominal Value in $Cdn (000); Quantity in tonnes; (DFO)					
	2004	2005	2006	2007	2008
Value	27	27	18	7	5
Quantity	41	45	27	19	5

American Shad Canada Freshwater Landings – Nominal Value in $Cdn (000); Quantity in tonnes; (DFO)					
	2004	2005	2006	2007	2008
Value	2	2	2	12	12
Quantity	2	32	1	14	15

Gizzard Shad US Landings by Year – Nominal Data Value in $US (000); Quantity in tonnes; (NMFS)					
	2004	2005	2006	2007	2008
Value	788	561	693	200	407
Quantity	1,870	1,081	731	656	1,187

Hickory Shad US Landings by Year – Nominal Data Value in $US (000); Quantity in tonnes; (NMFS)					
	2004	2005	2006	2007	2008
Value	49	57	21	13	15
Quantity	114	193	38	24	35

PHYSICAL DESCRIPTION

Finfish physical descriptions are mostly sourced from www.*FishBase*.org where TL = total length, SL = standard length, FL = forked length and Ref. cites the *FishBase* reference source. See the glossary for additional information on terms used. Referenced lengths and weights may differ from other sources and, in a few cases; other noted sources were used instead of *FishBase*. Shellfish physical descriptions come from a variety of sources, including *SeaLifeBase* (see new references).

LANDINGS AND VALUES — A Note on the Tables

1. US statistical data refer to the contiguous United States and Alaska and do not include Hawaii, Puerto Rico and other offshore USA territories, unless otherwise noted.

2. All US landed values are presented in United States dollars ($US) and all Canadian landed values are expressed in Canadian dollars ($Cdn.). The dollar value is current for the year reported and not adjusted for inflation/deflation. Users can use the Consumer Price Index (CPI) or the Producer Price Index (PPI) to convert these nominal landing values into constant $ values.

3. All landed quantities are expressed in metric tonnes (MT). Quantities landed refer to live (round) weight, except for US univalve and bivalve (e.g., clams, mussels, oysters and scallops) that are reported as meat weight.

4. Value and quantity data in the tables have been rounded to the nearest thousand dollars and the nearest metric tonne, respectively. Species with landings of less than $500 are therefore reported as N/A (or - -), or zero (0) if there were no values. Similarly, species with landings of less than 0.5 metric tonnes are therefore reported as N/A (or - -) or zero (0), if there were no quantities.

5. Generally, data refer to fish or shellfish that were sold only as a result of commercial fisheries landings or aquaculture production. Some fish/shellfish that were caught recreationally, or used for bait, may not be reported. Fish reported under the category of "other," "miscellaneous" or "unclassified" may also not be reported, but generally, these represent very small landings.

6. Some of the entries include comparative 1989 landing information when many North American fish stocks were reaching harvesting peaks (especially groundfish on the East Coast and salmon on the West Coast). It is expected this information will provide useful insights on how some major species stocks are recovering from the collapses of the early 1990s.

7. All marine and freshwater commercial fisheries statistical information has been provided by the US National Marine Fisheries Service (NMFS) and the Canadian Department of Fisheries and Oceans (DFO), except where noted.

8. For US landings, all table statistical data were accurate as of November 1, 2011. All Canadian table statistical data were accurate as of November 1, 2010 for East Coast landings and September 1, 2010 for West Coast landings. Canadian freshwater landings were accurate as of December 1, 2010. All statistical data are subject to revision.

9. US Aquaculture Statistics were sourced from Fisheries Statistics Division, F/ST1, NMFS and Census of Aquaculture, USDA, published in the *Fisheries of the United States – 2009*. Canadian Aquaculture Statistics were sourced from *Aquaculture Statistics 2009* Catalogue no. 23-222-X, published Nov., 2010 by Statistics Canada. All statistical data are subject to revision.

10. US recreational fisheries statistics were sourced from the *Fisheries of the United States – 2009*. Canadian recreational fisheries statistics were sourced from the *Survey of Recreational Fishing 2005*, published in 2007 (DFO) Catalogue No. Fs23-522/2005E.

11. Some species reported on in this book may be indigenous to waters deeper than 200 meters, and therefore not found in the "Common and Scientific Names of Fishes from the United States, Canada and Mexico," published by the American Fisheries Society (Special Publication 29).

REFERENCES AND RATIONALE FOR SPECIES IDENTIFICATION SOURCES

All species scientific names used herein have been referenced as valid and verified (unless otherwise noted) in the *ITIS* database as of November 1, 2011. Most acceptable market names and scientific common names are referenced to *The Seafood List (TSL)* as of the same date. In a few cases simple inaccuracies or apparent spelling errors were identified, or the species was not listed in the *TSL* or *ITIS* with a common name. These cases are noted in the text. In some species, the market name and the scientific common name are the same. In a few cases, market names and/or common names are also set by regulations. Finally, common names used in *The Seafood List* may be different from the common names used by *FishBase* and these differences are identified for all featured species.

Main Sources of Species Information and Names Used in this Book								
Source	**Finfish Names**				**Shellfish Names**			
	Scientific Name	Market Name	Common Names/ Aliases	Preferred Common Name	Scientific Name	Market Name	Common Names/ Aliases	Preferred Common Name
ITIS	X		Some		X		Some	
FishBase	X		X	X				
SeaLifeBase					X		Many	Many
The Seafood List	X	X	X	X	X	X	X	X

Key: X means the information is usually reported by the source.

The Integrated Taxonomic Information System (*ITIS*) and *The Seafood List* (*TSL*) were chosen as the major references sources for species market-common-scientific names for a number of reasons. Both databases reflect significant input from recognized Canadian and US sources (as well as Mexico) as these relate to the proper naming of North American fish and shellfish species. *The Seafood List* was mainly used to identify preferred market and common names, but also to provide correct scientific names as referenced to credible sources. *TSL* also provides various vernacular names and aliases that species are known under; however, the purpose here is not to promote these competitive names, but to aid in identification. *TSL* is however, a somewhat limited source of fish and shellfish information, focusing mainly on commercial species. *ITIS* was used as a check on scientific names and correct spelling, but mainly to round out species taxonomic relationships and systematic identification issues. It also helped in providing common names for species not listed on the *TSL*. The *ITIS* database states the following:

> "(*ITIS* provides) authoritative taxonomic information on plants, animals, fungi, and microbes of North America and the world. We are a partnership of U.S., Canadian and Mexican agencies (ITIS-North America); other organizations; and taxonomic specialists. ITIS is also a partner of Species 2000 and the Global Biodiversity Information Facility (GBIF). The ITIS and Species 2000 Catalogue of Life (CoL) partnership is proud to provide the taxonomic backbone to the Encyclopedia of Life

(EOL)." *ITIS* was established in the mid-1990s as a cooperative project among several US federal agencies to improve and expand upon taxonomic data maintained by the National Oceanographic Data Center (NODC), National Oceanic and Atmospheric Administration (NOAA). Partners now include the US Department of Commerce (NOAA), Department of Agriculture, Department of Interior – Fish and Wildlife (USGA), Environmental Protection Agency, Smithsonian Institution (NMNH), National Biological Information Infrastructure, Nature Serve, National Park Service; Agriculture and Agri-food Canada and Conabio (Mexico). The mission is to create a scientifically credible database of taxonomic information, placing primary focus on taxa of interest to North America, with world treatments included, as available.

The Seafood List (*TSL*) references both *ITIS* and *FishBase* as sources of scientific information as well as a number of other sources for common and market names of fishes. It may be worth noting that the use of one designated common name for a species, while problematic at times, also assists greatly in fish identification and is supported at the highest scientific levels. "History confirms that common names are often more stable than scientific names (this is often not appreciated)… There is clear need for standardization and uniformity in vernacular names not only for sport and commercial fishes, but as trade (market) names, for aquarium fishes, in legal terminology, and as substitutes for scientific names in popular or scientific writing. The Committee (on Names of Fishes) believes it desirable to establish a common name for each species of fishes occurring naturally or through introduction in the waters of Canada, the United States, and Mexico."[366]

The Seafood List represents an effort to clarify fish names (in English), with unique scientific common name and preferred market name designations, associated with the correct scientific name. The *TSL* was originally developed by the US National Marine Fisheries Service (NMFS) and the US Food and Drug Administration (FDA) in conjunction with Canadian and other international authorities. Data sources cited by the publication include the following:[367]

1. Food and Drug Administration, "*Fish and Fishery Products Hazards and Controls Guidance, Third Edition*[22]," Chapter 3. 2001.
2. Joseph S. Nelson, Edwin J. Crossman, Hector Espinosa-Perez, Lloyd T. Findley, Carter R. Gilbert, Robert N. Lea, and James D. Williams, "*Common and Scientific Names of Fishes From the United States, Canada and Mexico,*" American Fisheries Society, Sixth edition, 2004.
3. Donna Turgeon et al., "*Common and Scientific Names of Aquatic Invertebrates from the United States and Canada: Mollusks,*" American Fisheries Society, Second Edition 1998.
4. Williams et al., "*Common and Scientific Names of Aquatic Invertebrates from the United States and Canada: Decapod Crustaceans,*" Publication 17. American Fisheries Society, 1989.

---

[366] Joseph S. Nelson, Edwin J. Crossman, Hector Espinosa-Perez, Lloyd T. Findley, Carter R. Gilbert, Robert N. Lea, and James D. Williams, "Common and Scientific Names of Fishes From the United States, Canada and Mexico," American Fisheries Society, Sixth edition, 2004, page 10.

[367] <http://www.fda.gov/Food/GuidanceComplianceRegulatoryInformation/GuidanceDocuments/Seafood/ucm113260.htm>

5. R. Robins et al., *"World Fishes Important to North Americans Exclusive of Species from the Continental Waters of the United States and Canada,"* American Fisheries Society, Publication 21; 1991.
6. Willibald Krane, *"Five-Language Dictionary of Fish, Crustaceans and Molluscs,"* Van Nostrand Reinhold, 1986.
7. Organization for Economic Co-operation and Development, *"Multilingual Dictionary of Fish and Fish Products,"* Fourth Edition, Fishing News Books, New York 1995.
8. Austin Williams, *"Lobsters of the World, an Illustrated Guide, Lobsters of the World in U.S. Trade,"* Osprey Books, 1988.
9. J. McClane, Holt, Rinehart and Winston, *"The Encyclopedia of Fish Cookery,"* First Edition Canada 1977.
10. Integrated Taxonomic Information System[23]: ITIS on-line database (accessed 12/03/2009).
11. FishBase[24][25]: A Global Information System on Fishes, Froese, R., Bailly and D. Pauly, Editors (accessed 12/03/2009).

FishBase is a detailed database that provides global information on more than 32,200 species of fish, including 295,600 common names and 46,500 references. Unlike *ITIS, FishBase* is dedicated only to fishes and has more of a worldwide focus. As such, it is a great source of fisheries information. However, it supports the use of different common names for many North American fish species and differs in some major fish families' systematics, thereby rendering it less useful in the context of North American fisheries. However, it provides referenced information on individual species not found elsewhere (e.g., size, distribution, biology, international recognitions, etc.). The authors sourced almost all of the physical dimensions (i.e., size, weight and age data) used in species descriptions in this book from *FishBase* and (to a lesser extent *SeaLifeBase*, see below) as denoted by referenced source numbers in the text. In addition, some of the international recognitions for fishes were also sourced from *FishBase*. A more detailed description of *FishBase* follows:

> *FishBase* is a comprehensive fish taxonomy database project developed at the International Center for Living Aquatic Resources Management (ICLARM) in collaboration with the Food and Agriculture Organization (FAO) of the United Nations and many other partners. *FishBase* contributors include a consortium of museums, fisheries research institutes and international organizations with a fisheries mandate. The founding members of this consortium include: Swedish Museum of Natural History (Stockholm), Royal Museum for Central Africa (Tervuren), Muséum National d'Histoire Naturelle (Paris), Institute of Marine Research (Kiel), Fisheries Centre of the University of British Columbia (Vancouver), FAO (Rome) and ICLARM (Los Baños). The database presently encompasses "practically all fish species known to science" and is in the public domain (www.*FishBase*.org). *FishBase* has been funded mainly through sequential grants from the European Commission.

SeaLifeBase (SLB) started up in early 2006, as a joint initiative of the Sea Around Us Project (Fisheries Centre, UBC, Vancouver, Canada) and the FishBase Consortium. It is a searchable online information system modelled after *FishBase* that provides key information on scientific and common names, distribution, ecology and life history data for "all multi-celled marine organisms of the world's oceans." Unlike *FishBase,* it focuses on marine life other than finfish.

However, at this early stage of its development, and considering the number of species and massive task it has taken on, much of the present data on shellfishes is often incomplete. Nevertheless it is one of the few sources of referenced information on various shellfish species that was used in this present work.

The Canadian Food Inspection Agency (Agriculture and Agri-Food Canada) is another source of fish names in North America; however this source is less definitive than *ITIS* for scientific names and *The Seafood List* for market and preferred common names. It does, however, provide many species names in French for bi-lingual purposes in Canada.[368]

In summary, *The Seafood List* as it is presently constructed is an excellent vehicle for aiding researchers and lay persons alike in identifying commercial fish and shellfish species landed and/or traded in North America, including many imported species. Species information is based on North American input for preferred common and market names; and scientific names and taxonomies are also based on North American participation as reported by *ITIS*.

NAME DESIGNATION PROTOCOL

Scientific identification follows the convention of designating family, genus and species name. However, often only the genus and species names are used, as this usually represents unique identification. The example below shows the taxonomic classifications of the Chinook salmon from *ITIS*, together with its market and common names from *The Seafood List*.

Chinook Salmon

Kingdom	Animalia — Animal
Phylum	Chordata — chordates
Subphylum	Vertebrata — vertebrates
Superclass	Osteichthyes — bony fishes
Class	Actinopterygii — ray-finned fishes, spiny-rayed fishes
Subclass	Neopterygii — neopterygians
Infraclass	Teleostei
Superorder	Protacanthopterygii
Order	Salmoniformes — salmons
Family	Salmonidae — salmonids, salmons, trouts
Subfamily	Salmoninae
Genus	*Oncorhynchus* — Pacific salmon
Species	***Oncorhynchus tshawytscha***
Scientific Common Name:	**Chinook salmon**
Preferred Market Name(s):	**Salmon, Chinook <u>or</u> King <u>or</u> Spring**

(For additional information on North American salmon, trouts and chars, see the Salmonidae Table.)

---

[368] See http://www.inspection.gc.ca/english/fssa/fispoi/product/comnome.shtml

Index to Part 1
(also see Index to Part 2)

Marine Finfishes

Listed Alphabetically

ALASKA POLLOCK OR POLLOCK

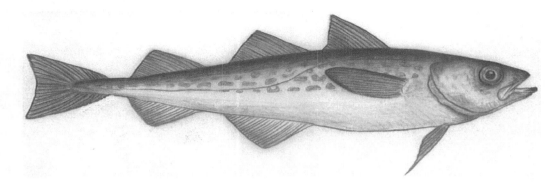

Walleye Pollock, *Theragra chalcogramma*

GENERAL

Commercially known as the Alaska pollock, **walleye pollock** is a member of the cod family, Gadidae. A species almost unheard before the early 1980s, walleye pollock is now one of the world's largest fisheries. In 1987, it became the largest US catch in terms of quantity landed; replacing menhaden. These two species are still the largest US catches, but landings are down for both over previous years. Still, worldwide catches of Alaska pollock can account for 40% of all global whitefish landings. Its snow-white, somewhat bland flavor and relatively low price has made it highly valued as substitute for other quality whitefish in less supply and as an imitation shellfish (surimi) product.

The walleye pollock should not be confused with the Atlantic Ocean pollock (*Pollachius virens*), a different species that is darker, oilier and has a "fishier" flavor. (Often the landings for walleye pollock are reported together with *P. virens* as if they were one species.) The name may also be confused with the freshwater walleye, another very different species and member of the perch family Percidae. It is also different from the whiting (*Merluccius* spp.) although this species is also a source of whitefish for surimi products.

Also Known As
Pollock/ Pacific Pollock
Whiting/ Pacific Tomcod/ Pacific

FishBase Name
Alaska Pollock

International Recognitions
Spain— Colin de Alaska
France— Lieu de l'Alaska
Italy— Merluzzo dell'Alaska
Japan— Suketôdara
Germany— Pazifischer Pollack

PHYSICAL DESCRIPTION
Max. length: 91.0 cm TL male/unsexed; (Ref. 2850)
Max. published weight: 3,850 g (Ref. 56335) Max. reported age: 15 years (Ref. 1371)

The walleye pollock is a slim fish with a projecting lower jaw. It has three dorsal fins, which are well separated, and a slightly forked caudal. The two anal fins are also well separated. The scales of the walleye pollock are roundish and small. It is olive green to brown on the dorsal surface, frequently blotched or mottled, with silvery sides. The fins are dusky to black. The lateral line is continuous to about the end of the first dorsal-fin base. The young have two narrow bands along their sides, and occasionally, a short third band.

LANDINGS AND VALUES

The range of this species is thought to be from central California, north to the Bering Sea and west to the Sea of Japan. Schools are found near the surface to depths of about 1,200 feet. It is primarily a Russian and Alaskan fishery, but is also an international fishery. However a 1993 moratorium on fishing in international waters has failed to rebuild stocks. It is caught by mid-water and bottom trawls, with the largest commercial catches taken from the more northerly regions. The US catch has risen dramatically from 1983, when only 1,254 tonnes was landed (not shown), to recent years when more than 1 million tonnes is common, valued at $US 323 million in 2008 (see table). By comparison, the Canadian catch is relatively small at only 5,798 tonnes in 2008, valued at approximately $4.8 million (see table).

Walleye Pollock US Landings by Year — Nominal Data Value in $US (000); Quantity in tonnes; (NMFS)					
	2004	**2005**	**2006**	**2007**	**2008**
Value	271,630	306,972	329,879	297,461	323,212
Quantity	1,521,080	1,547,359	1,542,598	1,391,002	1,032,452

Pollock Canadian Landings by Year — Nominal Data Value in $Cdn (000); Quantity in tonnes; (DFO)					
	2004	**2005**	**2006**	**2007**	**2008**
Value	4,221	4,560	3,509	5,352	4,789
Quantity	8,777	8,082	4,895	6,944	5,798

The species was the largest single fishery worldwide in the mid-1980s, with more than 6 million tonnes harvested in 1985, or about 7.5% of the total world catch. It still ranks as the second largest catch in the world (about 3.0% of total landings) after the Peruvian anchoveta (8.2%), now the largest fishery for many years, but used entirely for industrial purposes.

COMMERCIAL USES

Alaska pollock is available in both fresh and frozen fillets. It is also used in fish sticks and other secondary products. The flesh is lean, firm and white and can be poached, baked, broiled, steamed, sautéed, or deep-fried. The roe is also salted. Most Alaska pollock is processed into blocks for use as surimi (imitation shellfish) or fillets. Surimi blocks are made when the fish is extruded as a paste. Fillet blocks are made by placing fillets in a tray and freezing them under hydraulic pressure.

LIFE CYCLE

On the middle part of the continental shelf in the southeast Bering Sea (in the northern part of their range), walleye pollock spawn between April and June. This area provides many physical and biological advantages for the survival, growth and distribution of the eggs and larvae. As a result of changing egg and larvae buoyancy associated with their stages of development, the eggs and larvae are stratified in the subsurface layers of the water. It is believed that the depth of the water plays an important role in the survival rate of the young fish. The incubation period varies with the water temperature, ranging from 25 to 27 days at 36°F to only 14 days at 43°F. After the eggs hatch, absorption of the yolk sac takes six to seven days at 43°F. However, this too varies with the water temperature. Very young yolk sac larvae and post-larval pollock feed mainly on euphausiids (krill), but also copepods (i.e., tiny shrimp-like crustaceans) that are either in their beginning larvae stage (nauplii) or later larval stages (copepodid and adult). Larger pollock feed mainly on shrimp and fish. They are a relatively fast growing, short-lived species, maturing at age 3-4; and females are able to produce up to 2 million eggs.

ALEWIFE OR RIVER HERRING

Alewife, *Alosa pseudoharengus*

GENERAL

The **alewife** is a member of the herring, or Clupeidae, family that also includes shad and menhaden. Alewife is an anadromous species (i.e., spawning in fresh water, but maturing at sea). It can be found in lakes, rivers and estuarial waters when spawning, but behavior at sea is not fully understood. Some research suggests ocean-schooling alewife stay close to their native rivers. However, fish tagged and released in the Saint John River in New Brunswick, Canada have been found as far away as North Carolina. Some alewives are also landlocked and, in this case, migrate from deep water lakes to shallow water beaches and rivers to spawn.

The term alewife usually includes two very similar species: *Alosa pseudoharengus* (alewife) and *Alosa aestivalis* (blueback herring). Both species are also known correctly as river herring. They are similar to the menhaden and closely related to the shad, both of which are also anadromous species. (Also see shad and menhaden entries in this book.)

Also Known As
Gaspereau/
River Herring/
Branch Herring/
Gray Herring
Kyak

FishBase Name
Alewife

International Recognitions
Spain—
Pinchagua
France— Alose
gaspareau
Italy— Alosa

PHYSICAL DESCRIPTION
Max length: 40.0 cm SL male/unsexed; (Ref. 7251);
Common length: 30.0 cm SL male/unsexed; (Ref. 7251);
Max. published weight: 200 g (Ref. 7251); max. reported age: 9 years (Ref. 72462)

The alewife is a laterally compressed fish with a deep belly. It has a greyish-green back, shading to a silver sheen on the sides, and a very pale belly. It has a single dark spot behind the gills at eye level. The alewife may also have a variety of dark stripes running high along its sides. Those caught at sea may have a slightly brassy sheen. The only easily discernible difference between alewife and blueback herring is the color of the body cavity lining. In alewife it is a pinkish white, while in the blueback herring it is a sooty black. The flesh of both species is firm, white, sweet and, similar to the shad, quite bony. The alewife is smaller than the shad and menhaden and has the distinct spot on its shoulder. The menhaden is the only one of the three which is not usually eaten, as the flesh is quite oily and sometimes gives off an unpleasant odor.

LANDINGS AND VALUES

Anadromous alewife spends most of its life in the northwest Atlantic ranging from Newfoundland and the Gulf of St. Lawrence in the north to North Carolina in the south. Harvesting normally occurs in the spring when returning to fresh water to spawn. In estuaries and river mouths alewife is often caught with weirs and large trap nets, while dip nets and gillnets are more commonly used in rivers and lakes. The largest catches are usually in Maine, which often accounts for 50% to 80% of the total. Other states - Virginia,

Alewife US Marine/ Freshwater Landings by Year — Nominal Data Value in $US (000); Quantity in tonnes; (NMFS)					
	2004	**2005**	**2006**	**2007**	**2008**
Value	300	211	124	198	292
Quantity	639	357	137	414	642

Alewife Canadian Marine Landings by Year — Nominal Data Value in $Cdn (000); Quantity in tonnes; (DFO)					
	2004	**2005**	**2006**	**2007**	**2008**
Value	1,473	1,386	2,197	3,276	1,500
Quantity	5,123	4,287	5,263	4,321	3,079

North Carolina, Maryland and Wisconsin often account for the balance of the catch. US landings reflect both marine and (very small) freshwater landings and report 642 tonnes of alewife landed in 2008, valued at $292,000 (see table). In Canada, the marine catch of 3,079 tonnes, valued at approximately $1.5 million was larger than the fresh water catch in 2008. Alewife occurs landlocked in many parts of North America, especially the Great Lakes. In addition to the marine catch, Canada reported 941 tonnes of alewife landed in freshwater in 2008, valued at $207,000 (see tables). **Endangered Status:** Alewife and blueback herring are candidates for Species of Concern (US).

COMMERCIAL USES

Alewife is used as a food fish, as bait in the lobster and crab industries and as fertilizer and pet food. Most of the Great Lakes catch is used for pet food. As a food fish, alewife is marketed fresh or salted. Haiti, in the Caribbean, has traditionally been a market for pickled alewife.

Alewife Canadian Freshwater Landings by Year — Nominal Data Value in $Cdn (000); Quantity in tonnes; (DFO)					
	2004	**2005**	**2006**	**2007**	**2008**
Value	256	256	256	207	207
Quantity	1,164	1,164	1,164	941	941

LIFE CYCLE

Spawning takes place in estuaries and sluggish areas of freshwater streams, after which the adults return to the sea. The eggs hatch in three to six days and the young stay in the river until late summer or early fall. Most migrate seaward in August or September and spend the next few years at sea. It is believed that they school in large numbers near the shore, but they have been found far out to sea at great depths, and there is a possibility that they may undertake large summer/winter migrations. The males generally mature after four years, the females after five years. Then they return to their natal streams to begin the cycle anew. Most alewives will spawn two or three times before they die or are caught. The females can release anywhere from 60,000 to 200,000 eggs. Landlocked alewives grow less large and produce fewer eggs than their relatives at sea. The adults spawn in shallow water and then return to deeper water. The young alewives stay close to shore, but migrate to deeper water as they grow larger and then repeat the spawning cycle.

AMBERJACK

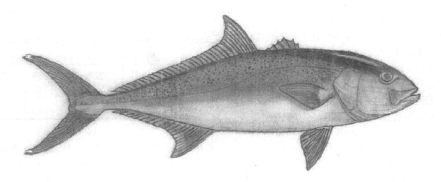

Banded Rudderfish, *Seriola zonata*

GENERAL

Amberjacks are members of the jack family, Carangidae, which also includes pompano and crevalle jacks. This is a large family of about 30 genera and more than 150 species. There are 9 *Seriola* spp., but frequently mentioned in North America are 5 species — **banded rudderfish,** along with greater amberjack (*S. dumerili*), lesser amberjack (*S. fasciata*), the almaco jack (*S. rivoliana*) and the yellowtail (*Seriola lalandi*). Amberjacks can often be confused with samsonfish and kingfish. (Also see entries on jack and jack mackerel in this book.)

PHYSICAL DESCRIPTION
Max length: 75.0 cm TL male/unsexed; (Ref. 5217); Common length: 50.0 cm TL male/unsexed; (Ref. 5217); Max. published weight: 5,200 g (Ref. 3277); Species of *Seriola* lack scutes (Ref. 37816).

Other than size (greater amberjacks are larger), different amberjacks can be difficult to distinguish; however, banded rudderfish juveniles have 6 distinct dark side bands running vertically across their body, which disappear as they get older. An adult rudderfish can be identified by its white tipped tail lobes. The amalco jack has long lobes on its second dorsal and anal fins.

Amberjacks are more slender than most jacks and also have a distinctive horizontal amber band on the sides that angle from the eye to the caudal fin. The tail fin is lunate or moon shaped. They do not have finlets and the keel at the base of the tail is slight and soft. The back is bluish purple to olive green; the sides are yellowish—white and the underside is silver. Occasionally, there is an amber or pink tint to the body. Although most amberjacks average about 20 pounds or less, some species marketed under this name can weigh in at 150 pounds or more. The Texas record is 115 pounds and 66.5 inches in 1994.

Also Known As
Amberjack/ Jackfish/ Banded Mackerel

FishBase Name
Banded rudderfish

International Recognitions
Spain— Medregal guaimeque, Serviola
France— Sériole guaimeque
Italy— Ricciola

LANDINGS AND VALUES

Banded rudderfish are regionalized to the Western Atlantic and landed mostly along the coast of South Carolina and Florida (east and west), but various amberjacks are found along the US east coast from New York south to the Gulf of Mexico and Brazil. (Almaco jacks are also landed in this region and in Hawaii.) Adult rudderfish are pelagic or epibenthic and primarily found in coastal waters.

Banded Rudderfish US Landings by Year — Nominal Data Value in $US (000); Quantity in tonnes; (NMFS)					
	2004	2005	2006	2007	2008
Value	24	25	28	25	29
Quantity	16	18	16	16	18

The lesser amberjack is also found in the Eastern Atlantic (Europe), while the greater amberjack is circumpolar. These fishes tend to occupy natural or manmade reefs, rock outcrops, wrecks and oil rigs and are voracious predators. Amberjacks are fished commercially with long lines. Commercial catches are relatively minor with larger (greater) amberjacks showing the highest landings with 487 tonnes in 2008, at a value of approximately $1.1 million (see table). As amberjacks are often difficult to distinguish, some landings are also recorded as Amberjack spp. (see table). Amberjack is not a commercial fishery in Canada. **Recreational fishery:** 1,126 tonnes of amberjack were landed in the US recreational fishery in 2008.

Lesser Amberjack US Landings by Year — Nominal Data Value in $US (000); Quantity in tonnes; (NMFS)					
	2004	2005	2006	2007	2008
Value	74	56	51	39	33
Quantity	31	23	20	14	11

Greater Amberjack US Landings by Year — Nominal Data Value in $US (000); Quantity in tonnes; (NMFS)					
	2004	2005	2006	2007	2008
Value	1,466	1,290	1,095	1,145	1,146
Quantity	747	640	467	491	487

COMMERCIAL USES

Smaller fish, averaging 15 pounds, are preferred. They have a firm, white meat with a mild flavor and are considered to be an extra lean fish. They can be substituted for fish similar in flavor and texture such as dolphinfish (mahi mahi), tilefish, mullet, grouper and shark. As with other reef fish, amberjack can be exposed to organisms that create the ciguatera toxin and can be toxic to humans when consumed. Amberjack is marketed fresh or frozen and is a commercial product in the United States,

Amberjacks (Spp.) US Landings by Year — Nominal Data Value in $US (000); Quantity in tonnes; (NMFS)					
	2004	2005	2006	2007	2008
Value	162	149	145	172	157
Quantity	105	98	82	94	87

but also consumed in Japan as sushi. The fish is valuable commercially, as a sports fish and is up and coming in aquaculture (i.e., another species, *S. quinqueradiata* is farmed extensively in Japan and somewhat in Korea).

LIFE CYCLE

Amberjacks are a reef associated ocean species. They prefer depths from the surface to 100 meters. In the Americas, they generally range from Nova Scotia to Brazil. They prey mostly on small juvenile fishes associated with floating plants or debris as well as other reef associated species such as squid and crustaceans. Juvenile amberjack tend to form small schools while adults are more solitary. Larger adults are generally female that live longer than males. Eggs are pelagic. Spawning offshore begins at 2–3 years of age and is believed to occur year-round.

ANCHOVY (& SARDINES)

Pacific Sardine

Northern Anchovy, *Engraulis mordax*

GENERAL

Small fish, big landings: it might seem natural to assume that anchovies, sardines, pilchards and other small fishes would not have a major impact on total world fish landings, but the truth is just the opposite — these fishes often account for up to 25% of all world fisheries by weight. The Peruvian anchoveta (*Engraulis ringens*) fishery alone has accounted for 10% of total world landings by quantity in recent years. There are at least 14 species of the anchovy family (Engraulidae) in North American waters. Ten are found on the Atlantic coast and four on the Pacific, but allowing for occasional landings of other species, the Pacific **northern anchovy** has traditionally been the main species reported as commercially fished. Other major anchovy species in North America include the slough anchovy (*Anchoa delicatissima*), the deep body anchovy (*Anchoa compressa*) and the east coast bay anchovy (*Anchoa mitchilli*) — some of which are used as bait in other fisheries. Another small fish (very different species) that competes, and interacts curiously, with the northern anchovy in its native habitat is the Pacific sardine (*Sardinops sagax*, family Clupeidae), made famous in Steinbeck's novel "Cannery Row."

PHYSICAL DESCRIPTION

Max length : 24.8 cm SL male/unsexed; (Ref. 27436); common length : 15.0 cm TL male/unsexed; (Ref. 9988)

Max. published weight: 68.0 g (Ref. 56527); max. reported age: 7 years (Ref. 6884)

The small silvery anchovies are characterized by large eyes, a bulbous snout, a mouth with a distinctly recessed lower jaw, large scales, a single dorsal fin located mid-body, abdominal pelvic fins, but no adipose fin and scales on the side of the tail fin. The head is devoid of scales and there is no lateral line. The northern anchovy is a round, rather than compressed, species and is also distinguished by an anal fin that begins directly below the rear of the dorsal fin. The northern anchovy has distinct, broad, silvery bands along its sides. Anchovies are distinguished from their close relatives, the sardines and small herrings, by a "weak" lower jaw that is set far back on the underside of the head. Most anchovies are quite small; depending upon the species, they may range in size from 4 inches (bay anchovy) to up to 9 inches (the northern anchovy).

Also Known As
North Pacific Anchovy/ California Anchovy

FishBase Name
Californian anchovy

International Recognitions
Spain— Anchoa del Pacifico
France— Anchois du Pacifique
Italy— Accluga del nord pacifico
Germany— Amerikanische Sardelle

LANDINGS AND VALUES

Anchovies are found mainly in marine waters, in estuaries, and shallow bays or sounds, though some species do venture into fresh water for a short time. They are harvested in large quantities by surface-fishing purse seiners. The large northern anchovy, one of the most commonly caught Pacific species, ranges from British Columbia, to Baja, California. The bay anchovy is found on the Atlantic coast, off New England and south to the Gulf of Mexico. Another east coast species, the striped anchovy (*Anchoa hepsetus*), is found from Nova Scotia to the Caribbean and farther south. The

Northern Anchovy US Landings by Year — Nominal Data Value in $US (000); Quantity in tonnes; (NMFS)					
	2004	2005	2006	2007	2008
Value	819	1,127	1,335	1,137	1,657
Quantity	7,019	11,414	12,952	10,541	14,620

Pacific Sardine US Landings by Year — Nominal Data Value in $US (000); Quantity in tonnes; (NMFS)					
	2004	2005	2006	2007	2008
Value	10,072	10,199	9,291	13,256	14,579
Quantity	89,275	86,452	84,810	126,463	86,379

northern anchovy fishery is presently increasing and 14,620 tonnes were landed in the US in 2008, valued at approximately $1.7 million (see table). Meanwhile, Pacific sardine landings have been relatively stable. Landings of Pacific sardine were 86,379 tonnes in 2008, valued at $14.6 million (see table). US (Florida) landings of the Spanish sardine (*Sardinella aurita*) are much lower and totaled 980 tonnes, valued at $438,000 in 2008 (not shown). Small amounts of anchovies (bay and unspecified) were caught on the East coast from New York to Florida.

The northern anchovy often shares the same habitat on the north Pacific coast as the Pacific sardine. Some studies suggest alternate cycles of abundance of approximately 40-60 years, while others suggest a more moderate correlation in abundance with anchovy populations fluctuating over 80-100 years and sardines recovering within 30 years after collapse. This recurring phenomenon is believed due to changing climatic factors (e.g., water temperature and atmospheric changes, etc.) and perhaps biological interactions (e.g., competition for food) and is expected to re-occur in the future even without human intervention. In other words, overfishing may not have caused previous collapses, especially as attributed to the sardine industry.

COMMERCIAL USES

The majority of the anchovy catch is used for bait, with only a small quantity converted to oil, or used for animal feed or human consumption. Almost all edible anchovies in North America are imported; however, northern anchovies are noted for having a fine, delicate flavor. The fresh northern anchovy, when fried in olive oil, compares favorably with the Pacific herring. The processing of Mediterranean anchovies is an art. The latter are often individually hand-filleted and specially salted and cured before being canned; a process that accounts for their high price.

LIFE CYCLE

Anchovies, like many sardines and small herrings, migrate, feed and breed in huge schools. Anchovies feed by scooping up tiny floating plants and animals. During feeding, the anchovy's lower jaw opens wide and its head almost seems to separate from its body—an amazing sight when an entire school is feeding simultaneously. As it swallows large amounts of plankton-rich water, the anchovy strains the food from the water by passing it through the gill openings. The strained food is covered with mucous secretion before ingestion. Larger anchovy, like the northern anchovy also feed on smaller fish. In turn, they are a food source for larger fish, such as mackerel, salmon and tuna, as well as birds and marine mammals.

BALLYHOO

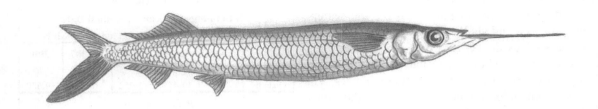

Ballyhoo, *Hemiramphus brasiliensis*

GENERAL

The **ballyhoo*** (or bally), is a baitfish of the halfbeak family (Hemiramphidae). This family is closely related to the flying fishes. The species is similar to the Balao halfbeak (*Hemiramphus balao*). Ballyhoo is frequently used as cut bait and for trolling purposes by saltwater sportsmen. *Ballyhoo* is also used in colloquial American English to refer to "brashness" or "flamboyance."

[*The taxonomic status is listed as valid and verified in ITIS, but the species (not surprisingly) is not found in FDA's *The Seafood List* as it is primarily used as bait.]

Also Known As
Bally

FishBase Name
Ballyhoo
halfbeak

International Recognitions
Spain— Agujeta
brasileña
France—
Demi—bec du
Brésil

PHYSICAL DESCRIPTION

Max length : 55.0 cm TL male/unsexed; (Ref. 2683);
Common length : 35.0 cm TL male/unsexed; (Ref. 3633);
Max. published weight: 200 g (Ref. 5217)

The Ballyhoo has an overall silver coloration with a greenish black back, silver flank and underside and dark fins. The beak of the Ballyhoo is relatively short, only 16 to 20 percent of the body length. The species is characterized by a ridge before the eyes, a deeply forked caudal fin with larger lower lobe and unscaled anal and dorsal fins. The tip of lower jaw and upper lobe of the caudal fin is orange red. It has short pectoral fins. The pelvic fins extend past the beginning of the dorsal fin.

It can be confused with six other halfbeaks: the California Halfbeak, *Hyporhamphus rosae* (the back is not black and there is a ridge before the eye); the Choelo Halfbeak, *Hyporhamphus gilli* (short beak with a red tip with the distance from the pelvic fins to the caudal fin greater than the distance from the pelvic fins to the eye pupil); the Longfin Halfbeak, *Hemiramphus saltator* (a black long lower beak, a caudal fin that is deeply forked and no ridge before the eyes); the Naos Halfbeak, *Hyporhamphus naos* (long beak with a red fleshy tip with the anal fin origin directly under the dorsal fin origin); the Ribbon Halfbeak, *Euleptorhamphus viridis* (long slender body with disproportionately large anal, dorsal and pectoral fins); and the Silverstripe Halfbeak, *Hyporhamphus unifasciatus* (distance from eye to origin of anal fin equal to distance from anal fin to base of caudal fin).

LANDINGS AND VALUES

The Ballyhoo is a coastal pelagic species associated with near shore reefs. It is found on both sides of the Atlantic Ocean. In North America, distribution extends from Massachusetts through the northern Gulf of Mexico and Brazil. The only significant US fishery occurs in south Florida waters. Landing trends reflect, in part, changes in the location of the fishery, which has moved somewhat from southeast Florida (Atlantic) to Monroe County in southwest Florida (Gulf) beginning in the early 1990s (McBride *et al.* 1996).

Ballyhoo US Landings by Year — Nominal Data Value in $US (000); Quantity in tonnes; (NMFS)					
	2004	**2005**	**2006**	**2007**	**2008**
Value	467	439	808	785	634
Quantity	295	304	468	443	347

Ballyhoo are targeted by lampara-net fishers and sold as bait for large pelagic (e.g., billfishes) fishing by recreational anglers. Based on stock assessment the fishery was deemed fully exploited and the Fish and the Wildlife Conservation Commission adopted several management regulations in 2003 limiting daily commercial catch, implementing seasonal closures and enacting a five-year moratorium on lampara-net practices. Commercial catch rates on the Atlantic Coast declined somewhat after 2003, but are still higher than during the 1992—2000 period. Standardized commercial catch rates are lower on the Gulf coast, reflecting differences in the number of trips in which fishers targeting other species caught ballyhoo as by-catch. In 2008, 347 tonnes, valued at $634,000 was landed in the US.

COMMERCIAL USES

Mainly used as bait for offshore game fishes such as sailfishes and marlins; utilized as a food fish in the West Indies (Ref. 3723). Minor commercial use in other fisheries; usually as bait.

LIFE CYCLE

Ballyhoo matures during their first year at about 6.9"–7.9". Spawning for younger females occurs seasonally, during spring and summer months however the spawning by older females occurs throughout the year. Reproduction peaks during late spring or early summer, and all mature females are able to spawn daily during the same time period.

Females produce an average of about 1,500 eggs. Ballyhoo produces large eggs that contain a sticky substance that allows the eggs to attach to floating debris and sea grasses, where the larvae also develop. The species grow rapidly, and females grow more quickly than males. Maximum age appears to be 2–3 years.

Ballyhoo form sizable schools and feed mostly on sea grass and small fishes, including copepods, siphonophores and decapods. Sea birds and coastal pelagic species are key predators.

BARRACUDA

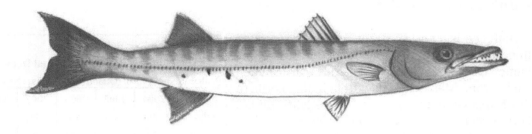

Great Barracuda, *Sphyraena barracuda*

GENERAL

Barracudas (family Sphyraenidae) take their name from the Latin, meaning "pike-like" fishes. Their bodies are elongated and slender, perfectly adapted to successful ocean predators. They often ambush prey and can attack with great speed and violence. There are about 26 species of barracuda (genus *Sphyraena*) worldwide, in all the major oceans. The **great barracuda** is distributed throughout the Atlantic Ocean, as well as the Indian and Pacific Oceans. The great barracuda specie is often considered potentially dangerous to humans because of its aggressive behavior and sharp teeth. Although occasional attacks on humans have been reported, none have been fatal. Unprovoked attacks are sometimes attributed to poor visibility or the fish's attraction to shiny objects and/or other indications of prey. Barracudas are both a game and a food fish. The largest catch of a great barracuda was 1.7 meters (5.5 ft.) weighing in at 46.8 kg (103 lb.) off the coast of the Bahamas.

Also Known As
Short Barracuda/ Picuda/ Becuna/ Seapike/ Pike

FishBase Name
Great barracuda

International Recognitions
Spain— Picúa

PHYSICAL DESCRIPTION

Max length: 200 cm TL male/unsexed; (Ref. 7251);
Common length: 140 cm TL male/unsexed; (Ref. 3692);
Max. published weight: 50.0 kg (Ref. 6949)

Barracudas have large mouths with a lower jaw that sticks out slightly and fang-like teeth. They are normally grey or silver on top fading into white on the belly with whitish tips on their dark violet caudal fins. They have 2 extensively separated dorsal fins and a forked tail fin which makes them fast swimmers. Size varies depending on species.

The great barracuda is distinguishable from other species as it has black spots on the lower sides of its body. Additionally there are usually about 18 to 25 dark bars present on the upper side of each fish. It is the largest in the genus; usually about 1.5 meters long, but may reach as much as 1.8 metres and weigh 50 kg. Great barracuda can be distinguished from Pacific barracuda (*Sphyraena argentea*), also known as the California or silver barracuda, by their much larger size, pale tipped tail fin and black blotches on the lower sides. The top of the head is concave and the mouth is large. They are more aggressive than their Pacific counterparts.

GREAT BARRACUDA

LANDINGS AND VALUES

Barracudas are residents of tropical and subtropical waters. They inhabit shallow waters with reefs, mangroves and sea grass, as well as the open sea. Great barracuda are reef associated instead of open water associated like the Pacific barracuda. Their depth range is from the surface to about 100m, but they generally stay in the top 30m. Juveniles are found in shallow waters, in estuaries, and among mangroves. Adults range from inner harbors to deep ocean waters. Pacific barracuda migrate south of California in the fall and remain along the Mexican coast for most of the year.

Barracudas US Landings by Year – Nominal Data Value in $US (000); Quantity in tonnes; (NMFS)					
	2004	2005	2006	2007	2008
Value	111	112	112	135	110
Quantity	68	71	62	68	60

Pacific Barracuda US Landings by Year – Nominal Data Value in $US (000); Quantity in tonnes; (NMFS)					
	2004	2005	2006	2007	2008
Value	45	56	39	61	16
Quantity	26	36	26	41	10

In 2008, 60 tonnes of great barracuda, valued at $110,000, was landed in the US. Most of the catches (53%) in 2008 were caught off the Florida East Coast. The gear used was mostly hand lines. An additional 10 tonnes of Pacific barracuda was also landed in 2008, valued at $16,000 (see table). This is not a Canadian fishery.

COMMERCIAL USES

Barracudas are popular both as food and game fish. They can be utilized fresh, dried, salted, smoked and frozen and are often broiled and baked as fillets or steaks. Larger species, like the great barracuda, have been implicated in cases of ciguatera food poisoning; however, this may be a localized phenomenon.

LIFE CYCLE

There is not a great deal of documented information about where and when spawning occurs. It is believed to be between April and September. During the breeding season, the females spawn a few times, releasing from 5,000 to 300,000 of eggs each time. Like most fish, barracudas leave fertilized eggs floating in the open waters until they hatch. Soon after hatching, the larvae settle in shallow estuaries where vegetation offers both protection and food for about one year, until they grow into juveniles. Upon entering adulthood, they move into deeper waters in areas with reefs and remain there for the rest of their lives.

Unlike males that mature sexually within the first 3 years of their lives, females take about 4 years. The age of a barracuda can be measured from the number of rings produced each year in its scales or in a tiny structure called an otolith found in its ear. Interestingly, it is not possible to visually differentiate between the genders of this fish. Barracudas can live up to 14 years. They are diurnal and solitary although occasionally congregate in small groups for feeding. Great barracuda feed on pelagic fish, cephalopods and shrimp.

BASS, SEA

Black Sea Bass, *Centropristis striata*

GENERAL

The black sea bass is found in the large family Serranidae (sea basses and groupers) mainly consisting of bottom-dwelling fishes, although a few are pelagic. There is a challenge in nomenclature here. *The Seafood List* identifies "bass," "sea bass," "seabass" (one word) and "bass, sea" as four different market names. The market name for black sea bass is "bass, sea." In North America, the commercial fishery for fishes marketed as "bass, sea" is generally restricted to the **black sea bass** and incidental landings of the rock sea bass (*C. philadelphica*), the bank sea bass (*C. ocyurus*), the Atlantic creolefish (*Paranthias furcifer*) and the wreckfish (*Polyprion americanus*).

Two Pacific species, the splittail bass (*Hemanthias peruanus*) and the white seabass [*FishBase* name: white weakfish] (*Atractoscion nobilis*) are properly marketed as **seabass** (one word). One species, Pacific creolefish (*Paranthias colonus*) is correctly marketed as **sea bass** (2 words, rather than "bass, sea").

Also Known As
Blackfish/ Rock Bass/ Black Bass/ Bluefish/ Tallywag

FishBase Name
Black Seabass

International Recognitions
Germany—Schwarzer Zackenbarsch
Italy—perchia striata

Typically, fishes marketed as *bass* are freshwater species. However, a Pacific marine species, the giant sea bass, *Stereolepis gigas* (Polyprionidae family of wreckfishes) is marketed correctly as *bass.* The striped bass, *Morone saxatilis,* an anadromous species of the family Moronidae (temperate basses), often caught in marine coastal waters (or freshwater when it spawns) is also marketed correctly as *"bass."* Striped bass is native to Atlantic waters; but, because of its excellent eating qualities, was introduced to the Pacific in the late 1800s. (See bass entry in this book.) Large groupers too are sometimes marketed (incorrectly) as sea bass (see grouper entry).

PHYSICAL DESCRIPTION

Max length: 66.0 cm TL male/unsexed; (Ref. 40637); Common length: 30.0 cm TL male/ unsexed; (Ref. 3708); Max. publ. weight: 4.3 kg (Ref. 4699); Max. reported age: 10 years (Ref. 6844)

The perch-like sea basses of the genus *Centropristis* are characterized by having a long, continuous dorsal fin and three heavy spines before the anal fin. The male black sea bass, as its name implies, has a body and head which is bluish-black to dark brown in color, with narrow horizontal stripes on its mottled sides. All fins are quite large in relation to the body. The upper lobe of its tail fin terminates in a threadlike projection. Unlike males, the females have a rounded tail fin. The rock sea bass and the bank sea bass have overall lighter coloring and more distinct vertical bars or stripes along their sides.

LANDINGS AND VALUES

The black sea bass is found in the more southerly waters of the east coast from Cape Cod to Florida and the Gulf of Mexico. (The rock sea bass, the bank sea bass, the creolefish and the wreckfish also overlap this range.) Its habitat includes both inshore and offshore, and on the bottom of the ocean floor near

Black Sea Bass US Landings by Year – Nominal Data Value in $US (000); Quantity in tonnes; (NMFS)					
	2004	2005	2006	2007	2008
Value	7,483	7,929	8,807	7,543	5,921
Quantity	1,754	1,525	1,521	1,174	975

rocks, reefs and man-made structures. It is fished by traps, longlines and bottom trawls. Sometimes a fish pot, similar to a lobster pot, is used. This device has a large enough opening for the sea bass, and is set without bait, simply enticing the fish through its need of satisfying curiosity or finding shelter. US landings of black sea bass in 1989 were approximately 1,725 million pounds, valued at almost $4.3 million (not shown) compared to the 2008 catch of 975 tonnes, valued at $5.9 million (see table). Commercial landings of other major sea basses were almost negligible (see table). **Recreational Fishery:** Approximately 1,000 tonnes of black sea bass was also landed recreationally in 2008 (not shown). In addition, the kelp bass, spotted sand bass and barred sand bass (*Paralabrax* spp. — all marketed as "bass, sea") although not found in the commercial fishery, contributed about 200 tonnes to recreational fishery in 2008 (not shown). **Aquaculture:** Sea bass is generally a valuable fish and a candidate for farming. European sea bass is being farmed in Canada, if not elsewhere. Sea bass is not a reported fishery in Canada.

COMMERCIAL USES

The black sea bass is considered a valuable commercial and game fish. It has fine, white flesh of excellent flavor, which does not deteriorate as rapidly as other fish in hot weather. It is especially esteemed by Chinese Americans and often offered in Oriental restaurants as sweet-and-sour sea bass. It can be baked, broiled or chowdered.

Sea Basses Rock, Bank, Creole Fish, Wreckfish Total US Landings by Year – Nominal Data Value in $US (000); Quantity in tonnes; (NMFS)					
	2004	2005	2006	2007	2008
Value	2	0	2	1	0
Quantity	2	0	1	1	0

LIFE CYCLE

Like the groupers, the sea basses are hermaphroditic. They usually start off as female, but change their sex to male at some point in their maturity. However, at least one sea bass, the belted sandfish, *Serranus subligarius,* (not on TSL; but in *ITIS* and *FishBase*) can self-fertilize, although cross-breeding is still normal. Spawning season for the black sea bass is the middle of May to the end of June, during which time the males develop a fleshy hump on the back of the neck in front of the dorsal fin. The eggs are about 0.04 inches in diameter and hatch in about 4 days at 60°F. Juveniles usually form small groups and feed on smaller fish (such as herring and anchovy) and crustaceans. In summer they can usually be found in shallow waters close to shore, but in winter they move to deeper waters far offshore. Predators include shark, skate and flounders.

BIGEYE

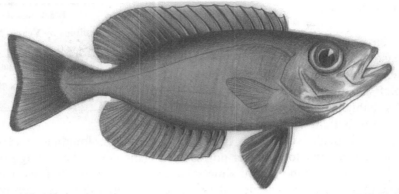

Bigeye, *Priacanthus arenatus*

GENERAL

Bigeye is the common name of 19 species (4 genera) of marine fishes in the Priacanthidae family. Two other species listed in *The Seafood List* are the red bigeye (*Priacanthus macracanthus*) and the short bigeye (*Pristigenys alta*). The *Priacanthus* genus is home to 13 of the species.

"Catalufa" is another name used for some members of the family. The common name of "bigeye" refers to the species' unusually large eyes, adapting to their carnivorous and nocturnal lifestyles. (Note that the term "bigeye" is commonly used to describe many other fish species in other families such as tuna, shark, snapper and grouper, etc.) The scientific name (from "prioo-," to bite and "akantha," thorn) refers to the family's very rough, spiny scales.

PHYSICAL DESCRIPTION

Max length: 50.0 cm TL male/unsexed; (Ref. 40637);
Common length: 35.0 cm TL male/unsexed; (Ref. 3661);
Max. published weight: 2,850 g (Ref. 40637)

Priacanthidae are most typically colored bright red, but other coloration patterns do exist for some species. Most species reach a maximum total length of about 30 centimeters (12 inches), although in a few species lengths of over 50 centimeters (20 inches) are known. The most striking characteristic of the bigeye is the very large eye, for which it is named, and the brilliant red to orange coloring. It is distinguishable from sea bass by rough scales over its entire head and a body with a longer anal fin than the soft ray portion of the dorsal fin. They have a sideways body, with short, wide dorsal fin and large ventral and small pectoral fins. Bigeye coloration is bright red with occasional black dots on fins and rays.

Also Known As
Common Bigeye/ Catalufa/ Blear-eye/ Glass-eye/ Atlantic bigeye

FishBase Name
Atlantic bigeye

International Recognitions
Spain— Catalufa toro
France— Beauclaire de roche
Italy— Catalufas
Japan— Beni—kintokidai
Germany— Großaugenbarsch

LANDINGS AND VALUES

The bigeye is a reef associated fish found on both sides of the Atlantic Ocean. In the western Atlantic they are found in tropical and subtropical waters from Nova Scotia to northern Argentina. The typical depth range is 15 – 100 meters, but they can go as deep as 200 meters (Fishbase).

Bigeye US Landings by Year — Nominal Data Value in $US (000); Quantity in tonnes; (NMFS)					
	2004	**2005**	**2006**	**2007**	**2008**
Value	2	1	4	5	4
Quantity	2	1	2	4	2

In 2008, 2 tonnes of bigeye valued at $4,000, was commercially landed in the US (see table). Almost of the catches in 2008 were caught on the Florida east coast. Hand lines are the common gear used in landing bigeye. It is not a reported Canadian catch.

COMMERCIAL USES

Bigeye is a minor commercial fishery; but it is also caught recreationally, and its bright color makes it useful in the aquarium trade. It is an excellent eating fish, but can cause ciguatera.

LIFE CYCLE

Bigeye is a somewhat solitary fish, but can form into small groups along coral or rocky bottom areas. They are nocturnal feeders and prey on small fishes and crustaceans as well as polychaetes, usually at the larval stages. They are prey to sharks, rays, jacks and other boney fishes. Little is reported on their reproductive and spawning behavior.

BLUEFISH

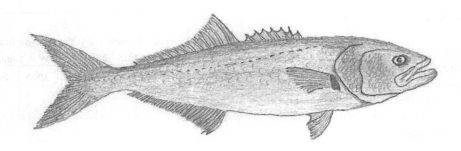

Bluefish, *Pomatomus saltatrix*

GENERAL

Also Known As
Tailor/ Snapper

FishBase Name
Bluefish

International Recognitions
Spain— Anjova
France— Tassergal
Italy— Pesce bianco
Japan— Okisuzuki
Germany— Blaubarsch

Beach bathers beware of this voracious feeder that, in its adult life, consumes a wide variety of fish and destroys countless more by slashing and mangling. Large schools of actively feeding bluefish do not make great beach companions. Several "accidental" attacks by **bluefish** on bathers enjoying warm Florida beaches have been reported.

With this fighting spirit, it should come as no surprise that bluefish are a leading recreational fishery on the US Gulf and Atlantic coasts, ranking fourth in 2004. This bluefish, incidentally, is not the same species as the pollock (*Pollachius virens*) of "Boston Bluefish" fame. Bluefish is one of only three species in the family Pomatomidae and the only member in North American waters. Two other different species called bluefish are also found in the Kyphosidae family (pilotfish and rudderfish).

Bluefish follow large schools of fish, eating twice their weight each day, often regurgitating so they can maintain their feast. Surprisingly, however, they have been known to disappear from areas for years at a time, even though there are plenty of mackerel, herring, or menhaden available for a bluefish feeding frenzy.

PHYSICAL DESCRIPTION

Max length: 130 cm TL male/unsexed; (Ref. 11441);
Common length: 60.0 cm TL male/unsexed; (Ref. 3482);
Max. published weight: 14.4 kg (Ref. 4699); max. reported age: 9 years (Ref. 6845)

The bluefish's body is oblong, stout and somewhat compressed; its head is blunt with a projecting heavy lower jaw and small eyes. Its mouth houses a single row of strong conical teeth in the upper and lower jaws. Moderately sized scales cover its head, body and the bases of its soft median fin. It is sea green in color above and silvery below. The median and pectoral fins are similarly tinted and there is a black blotch at the pectoral base.

LANDINGS AND VALUES

The bluefish is found in the tropical waters of all oceans except the eastern Pacific. The species has been noted in temperate waters as far north as the Bay of Fundy near Nova Scotia and New Brunswick. It prefers the open ocean but will follow schools of fish into tidal waters and estuaries and along beaches.

Bluefish US Landings by Year — Nominal Data Value in $US (000); Quantity in tonnes; (NMFS)					
	2004	**2005**	**2006**	**2007**	**2008**
Value	2,286	2,482	2,569	2,802	2,731
Quantity	3,692	3,260	3,223	3,473	2,791

The bluefish appears to migrate from north to south. In the winter it is common in North Carolina as well as Florida waters. In May, June and July it returns to the northern range. Commercially it is caught with gill nets (principally), but also hand lines, trawls and seines. Although not economically important to the Canadian fishery at present, the bluefish off the Atlantic coast of the United States not only supports a commercial fishery, but represents an important game species. US commercial landings in 2008 totaled about 2,800 tonnes, valued at approximately $2.7 million (see table). However, following striped bass, it was the largest recreational fishery in the US with 8,700 tonnes landed in 2008. The reader should note that the relative amounts of catch between the commercial and recreational fisheries are managed by quota.

COMMERCIAL USES

Bluefish is considered to be an excellent eating fish and is even compared with pompano and Spanish mackerel. It is usually marketed as fresh fillets, which is the preferred form when available, or smoked. For best results it should be quickly dressed after landing. In New England, it may be labelled "Cape Blue" to distinguish it from "Boston bluefish" (i.e., pollock).

LIFE CYCLE

It is believed that spawning probably takes place during spring south of Cape Hatteras, NC and then again offshore in the Mid-Atlantic during summer. Depending up size, females release 400,000 to 2 million eggs in open water and the larvae develop into juveniles near the surface, eventually moving to nearshore habitats. Juveniles prefer sandy bottoms, but also inhabit muddy or clay bottoms and vegetated areas. Juveniles travel in large schools near the coast feeding on crustaceans, molluscs and small fish including bluefish. Larger bluefish often follow schools of menhaden along the coast, feeding continuously—even regurgitating when full. Their stomachs have been found to contain up to 30 to 40 different kinds of prey, sometimes whole and sometimes in parts.

As a result of their voracious eating, they grow very quickly. Bluefish grow up to 10 inches in the first year depending on the spawning event (early spawned fish have a longer growing season and thus attain a larger size in the first year). Growth decreases significantly after maturity (age 2). They can live up to 14 years and reach sizes of up to 32 inches. Tunas, sharks, and billfishes are the only predators large and fast enough to prey on adult bluefish.

BONITO

Pacific Bonito, *Sarda chiliensis*

GENERAL

The bonito resembles a small tuna. In fact, the spotted (AKA "little") tunny, *Euthynnus alletteratus,* is sometimes marketed as bonito in Florida, while in Japan, a number of small tunas are commonly marketed as bonito. However, in the US, the market name "bonito" has been legally approved for use only with the following fishes: *Cybiosarda elegans*—leaping bonito, *Gymnosarda unicolor*—dogtooth tuna, *Orcynopsis unicolor*—plain bonito, *Sarda australis*—Australian bonito, *Sarda chiliensis*—**Pacific bonito** and *Sarda sarda*—Atlantic bonito.

The Pacific bonito belongs to the Scombridae family (mackerels, tunas and bonitos) whose members, with their forked tails and heavy muscles, are well-suited to a roving, predaceous existence near the ocean's surface. The Pacific bonito delights anglers from Alaska to California with its fighting spirit and splendid color. *FishBase* identifies two sub-species of bonito in the Eastern Pacific: *Sarda chiliensis lineolata* is the northern subspecies, while the Eastern Pacific Bonito *Sarda chiliensis chiliensis* is the southern subspecies. Various bonito species are landed on both the Pacific and Atlantic Coasts.

PHYSICAL DESCRIPTION

Max. Size: 102 cm TL (male/unsexed; Ref. 9015);
Max. Published Weight: 11.3 kg (Ref. 168)

The bonito's back is a brilliant greenish blue color on which there are oblique, dark, slanting stripes. The sides are silvery and its belly is white. The dorsal fins are set close together and the body is fully scaled. Small "finlets" behind the dorsal and anal fins are the trademark of mackerels, tunas and bonitos. The Pacific bonito has 7-9 dorsal finlets and 6-7 anal finlets.

Both the Pacific and the Atlantic bonito have a distinguishing "corselet," or sharp demarcation line, between the enlarged scales in the pectoral region and the scales on the rest of the body. The Atlantic bonito usually has a bluer back than its Pacific cousin and more oblique dorsal stripes.

Also Known As
California Bonito/ Skipjack

FishBase Name
Eastern Pacific bonito

International Recognitions
Spain— Bonito chileño
France— Bonite du Pacifique oriental
Italy— Bonito
Germany— Pelamide

LANDINGS AND VALUES

Pacific Bonito				
US Landings by Year — Nominal Data				
Value in $US (000); Quantity in tonnes; (NMFS)				
	2004	**2005**	**2006**	**2007**	**2008**
Value	196	6	1,530	159	643
Quantity	354	10	2,491	222	803

Atlantic Bonito				
US Landings by Year — Nominal Data				
Value in $US (000); Quantity in tonnes; (NMFS)				
	2004	**2005**	**2006**	**2007**	**2008**
Value	103	135	79	194	48
Quantity	31	46	26	52	14

Bonitos are found on both coasts of North America. In recent years catches on the Pacific coast have overtaken Atlantic Ocean catches. In the two populations (subspecies) of Pacific bonito; one is found from the Gulf of Alaska to southern Baja, California and off the coast of Mexico, while the other ranges the Pacific Ocean between Peru and Chile. The greatest concentration in North America is off the coast of Southern California. Like salmon, the bonito is caught by seines, gillnets and trolls.

US Pacific bonito landings in 1990 totaled about 4,350 tonnes valued at $1.9 million (not shown). In 1998, Pacific landings were 1,143 tonnes (not shown); however, since then landings have been down considerably with only 803 tonnes landed in 2008, valued at $643,000 (see table).

The Atlantic bonito reached the 800 tonne range in landings for several years in the early 1990s, but even these levels have fallen dramatically in more recent years (see table). Bonito species are not reported as a commercial fishery in Canada.

There is still a considerable recreational fishery in California and on the Atlantic coast for bonitos. As a game fish, it is known to jump 10 feet out of the water when hooked.

COMMERCIAL USES

During summer and fall, it is often found in large quantities off the Santa Barbara Islands where, in the company of barracuda, it is a major sport fishery. Bonito is a fine eating fish that is even compared to the taste and texture of salmon. They have a great quantity of blood which gives the meat a beef-look and will cause rapid decomposition unless the fish is cleaned and gutted immediately after landing. The Pacific bonito is a popular canned fish in some areas. It is also marketed fresh, frozen and smoked.

LIFE CYCLE

In California, the Pacific bonito is known to spawn between January and May. It is a pelagic, migratory species whose abundance varies from year to year. A rapid swimmer that feeds mainly at, or near, the surface, it is usually fished near shore where it can be found in large schools in pursuit of squid, shrimp, herring, anchovies and other small fishes.

BROTULA OR CUSKEEL

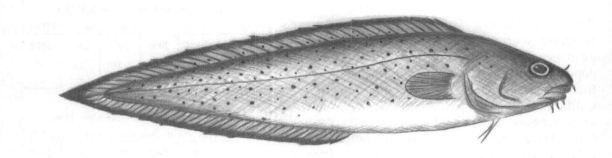

Bearded Brotula, *Brotula barbata*

GENERAL

Brotula look similar to cuskeels and are in the same family, but different sub-family. Worldwide, there are 5 species in the brotula genus (family – Ophidiidae, subfamily – Brotulinae), but none are a major commercial fishery. However, minor commercial fisheries are reported for two of them. The **bearded brotula** is the main species landed in North America. It is reef associated fish often regarded as a bottom feeder, but also at home near the ocean's surface.

PHYSICAL DESCRIPTION

Max length: 94.0 cm TL male/unsexed; (Ref. 40637);
Common length: 50.0 cm TL male/unsexed; (Ref. 5217);
Max. published weight: 8.5 kg (Ref. 40637)

Brotula have an elongated eel-like body (same family as cuskeels) that is completely covered with small, imbricate (i.e., overlapping) cycloid (i.e., curved) scales. The dorsal and anal fins are continuous around the body. There are barbels present on the snout and chin. Coloration is dark brownish with a red tint and the tips of the fins are a little darker. The ventral fins are dark and gradually become darker at the edges.

At first glance, the bearded brotula might be confused with one of the many cuskeels such as shortbeard cuskeel (*Lepophidium brevibarbe*) found in similar waters.

Also Known As
Cusk-eel

FishBase Name
Bearded brotula

International Recognitions
Spain— Brótula de barbas
France— Brotule barbée
Japan— Kusauo
Germany— Scheibenbauch

LANDINGS AND VALUES

Bearded Brotula US Landings by Year — Nominal Data Value in \$US (000); Quantity in tonnes; (NMFS)					
	2004	2005	2006	2007	2008
Value	15	8	11	13	12
Quantity	6	3	5	5	5

Brotula appear worldwide in both shallow and deep seas (15 meters to 120 meters). Adults are benthopelagic and can move through the open waters as well as along the bottom. They are most often found along the continental shelf over sandy or muddy bottoms. Juveniles are more common in reefs. In North America, bearded brotula range from northern Florida to the Gulf of Mexico, the Caribbean, and southward to northern South America.

In 2008, 5 tonnes of Breaded Brotula valued at \$12,000, were landed in the US. All of the catch in 2008 was caught on the Florida West Coast. The gear used was mostly long lines (reef fishing).

COMMERCIAL USES

Bearded Brotula are often inadvertently caught by snapper fishermen and, unfortunately, discarded. Similarly, they are an unfamiliar species to many consumers; yet to commercial fish houses they are often one of the most highly prized catches, reported to command 6 to 10 times the original purchase price once reaching market. In living fish, the flesh has a very soft texture, but it becomes firm when cooked. It is an excellent eating fish with flaky white flesh and a mild taste. It is reportedly sometimes referred to as the "poor man's grouper."

LIFE CYCLE

Very little is known of the biology of this fish. They are reported to be oviparous (open water/substratum egg scatterers). The eggs float in mats until fertilization and larvae development occurs.

BUTTERFISH

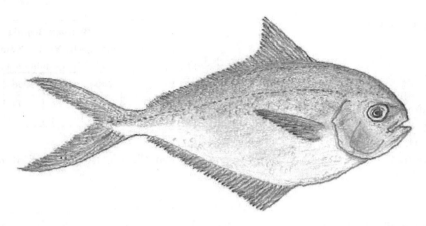

Butterfish, *Peprilus triacanthus*

GENERAL

Although many fish species are called butterfish, this butterfish is the well-known Atlantic Ocean member of the Stromateidae family (butterfishes, harvestfishes and rudderfishes) that includes about 67 species. In addition to the **butterfish** described here, there are three other similar species native to North American waters legally marketed as butterfish: the Gulf butterfish (*P. burti*), which inhabits the entire Gulf of Mexico from the Tampa region of Florida to the Yucatan; the harvestfish (*P. paru*), which inhabits Chesapeake Bay and north Gulf of Mexico to Argentina; and the Pacific Ocean species [common name: Pacific pompano (*P. simillimus*)], which ranges from the Queen Charlotte Sound, British Columbia, to central Baja, California and the Gulf Region. Butterfish derive their name from a slippery mucus coating that resembles soft butter.

PHYSICAL DESCRIPTION

Max length : 30.0 cm TL male/unsexed; (Ref. 7251);
Common length : 20.0 cm TL male/unsexed; (Ref. 2702)

The butterfish has an ovate body that is shallow to moderately deep and strongly laterally-compressed. The head is short and blunt with big eyes, a small mouth and a projecting lower jaw. There is a single row of weak teeth in each jaw. The butterfish has one dorsal fin, a long, deeply-forked caudal fin, an anal fin, long wing-like pectoral fins and a pelvic fin (although absent in adults). Small, cycloid, deciduous scales cover its body and dorsal, caudal and anal fins. It is bluish or greenish-silver on back (often mottled with large dark spots) and silvery on its belly.

Spots on the (Atlantic) butterfish distinguish it from the Gulf butterfish (except in areas where their habitat overlaps) and the harvestfish; the latter also grows larger and has much longer dorsal and anal fins. The Pacific Ocean butterfish resembles some jacks and pompanos and is marketed both as butterfish and Pacific pompano. However, most "true" pompanos are from a different family, Carangidae (jacks and pompanos).

Also Known As
Dollarfish/
Skipjack/
Harvesterfish/
Sheepshead

FishBase Name
Atlantic
butterfish

International Recognitions
Spain—
Palometa
pintada
France—
Stromaté
fossette

LANDINGS AND VALUES

The Atlantic butterfish is found in the western North Atlantic and ranges from the Gulf of St. Lawrence (sparingly), the Miramichi estuary, the south and east coasts of Newfoundland, the southwest Grand Bank, the outer coast of Nova Scotia, the Bay of Fundy and St. Mary Bay, Passamaquody Bay and Minas Basin and southward to Cape Hatteras. The Gulf butterfish is found off Florida and in the Gulf of Mexico.

Atlantic butterfish in both Canadian and US Atlantic ranges prefer warmer waters and seek sandy or sandy-silt bottoms from May to November. In the winter months butterfish are found offshore in depths of 600 feet (Canadian region), but return to shallow waters in late spring and summer. In the southern part of the range they migrate inshore in

Butterfish US Landings by Year — Nominal Data Value in $US (000); Quantity in tonnes; (NMFS)					
	2004	2005	2006	2007	2008
Value	980	940	1,039	1,242	1,199
Quantity	968	692	897	1,001	955

late spring and back to the continental shelf edge in late autumn. US landings for butterfish were 955 tonnes in 2008, valued at approximately $1.2 million (see table). These landings would seem to include Atlantic coast butterfish, as no landings are reported for Pacific butterfish. Separate landings are reported for harvest fish (see table below). There is no commercial fishery for butterfish in Canadian waters. Incidental catches would be processed for fishmeal or pet food.

COMMERCIAL USES

The Atlantic butterfish is more highly valued than the Gulf butterfish, both for its higher fat content and for having fewer parasites. As such, it has established a major market in Japan. Butterfishes make a delicious pan fish and are renowned for their fine flavor. In fact, the Pacific butterfish is sold as a gourmet product in many Southern California fish markets.

Harvestfish US Landings by Year — Nominal Data Value in $US (000); Quantity in tonnes; (NMFS)					
	2004	2005	2006	2007	2008
Value	97	136	152	269	175
Quantity	39	52	58	108	81

LIFE CYCLE

Little is known of the spawning behavior of the Atlantic butterfish in North Atlantic waters. Spawning is known to occur a few miles offshore in the Gulf of Maine from June to August, but mostly in July. Spawning in the more southern range occurs earlier. The spherical, transparent eggs are 0.027 to 0.032 inches in diameter and have one (occasionally more) small oil globule. Hatching occurs in two to three days at temperatures of approximately 65°F.

Once hatched, butterfishes grow rapidly during the first 24 hours—almost doubling size. They continue at a rapid growth rate for the first year and reach maturity at two years when they are approximately 6 to 8 inches in length. The young often take shelter under floating jellyfish where they are protected from predators and have an available food source in the copepods and other edible organisms that are caught in the jellyfish's tentacles. Their mucus coating protects them from jellyfish stings. Butterfish eat a variety of organisms, including small fishes, squid, amphipods, shrimp, marine worms and jellyfish. The butterfish is known to be a food fish for several commercially important species including haddock, silver hake, bluefish and weakfish.

CAPELIN

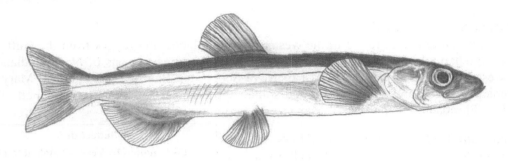

Capelin, *Mallotus villosus*

GENERAL

The **capelin** is a member of the smelt family Osmeridae, which also includes the rainbow smelt (see entry in this book). While it is circumpolar and is found on both coasts, the major commercial fishery in North America is centered in Newfoundland. Capelin is one of the world's largest fisheries, but it is also recognized as an important forage fish. In fact, in the Northwest Atlantic, where it is presently under strict quota to help revive groundfish stocks, some suggest it should not be fished at all.

Plankton forms the largest biomass in the ocean, but only a few, mostly small, fishes such as capelin, Arctic cod and sand lance (as well as most shellfish and some whales) feed on plankton directly. These fishes serve as the main food for other fishes such as cod, haddock and flounder; as well as food for whales, seals and sea birds. During the mid-1970s, it was estimated that upwards of 3 million tons of capelin were consumed annually by the Atlantic cod. There are several distinct stocks of capelin off Newfoundland and all but one spawn on beaches. The traditional "capelin scull" on Newfoundland beaches is an annual event for marine predators, but also for local residents who scoop them up in buckets and dip nets for a campfire treat.

Also Known As
Caplin/ Lodde/ Moiva

FishBase Name
Capelin

International Recognitions
Spain— Capelan
France— Capelan
Japan—
Karafuto—shishamo
Germany— Lodde

PHYSICAL DESCRIPTION

Max length: 20.0 cm TL male/unsexed; (Ref. 11626); 25.2 cm TL (female);
Common length: 15.0 cm TL male/unsexed; (Ref. 4645);
Max. published weight: 52.0 g (Ref. 56475); max. reported age: 10 years (Ref. 72498)

The capelin is a small, slender fish with an elongated body that seldom exceeds 8 inches in length. Its dorsal is translucent, olive to bottle green, supporting a centrally located, soft-rayed dorsal fin and (unlike small herring) has a small adipose fin (a marker for the salmonids, a family of fishes with similar life histories to many smelts). The anal fin is long and low (larger on the male) with fanned pelvic and pectoral fins and a deeply forked caudal or tail fin. Like most smelts, its sides below the lateral line are silvery. The capelin's underside has scale margins dotted with dusky specks. At spawning times, the slightly larger males undergo noticeable physical changes. They develop two sets of spawning ridges. A dorsal pair runs the length of the body and a ventral pair runs from the pectoral fin back to the pelvic fin just beneath the tail. These ridges are formed by outgrowths of scales that are soft and hairy. Due to the growth of soft spawning ridges on the male, both the Latin and Germanic names of capelin mean "hairy."

CAPELIN

LANDINGS AND VALUES

The smelt family is found only in the Northern Hemisphere and capelin fishing is pretty well restricted to colder waters in both the Atlantic and Pacific Oceans. The largest distribution in the northwestern Atlantic Ocean is off the coast of Newfoundland and Labrador, although Iceland

Capelin					
Canadian Landings by Year — Nominal Data					
Value in $Cdn (000); Quantity in tonnes; (DFO)					
	2004	**2005**	**2006**	**2007**	**2008**
Value	9,089	10,683	11,691	10,067	10,075
Quantity	33,682	36,952	42,180	37,599	39,175

has a large fishery as well. Capelin is also fished off the European coast by countries such as Norway, Denmark, Russia and Poland.

In the early 1970s offshore fishing for capelin began in earnest as markets were developing in Japan, particularly for roe, as well as in Europe. In 1989, capelin represented a $15.8-million fishery (landed value) to Newfoundland fishermen. Because of quota cuts to help revive the cod stocks, the capelin fishery in 2008 was only 39,000 tonnes and $10 million (see table). As capelin is believed to be a food fish for cod and other groundfish, some observers blame the capelin fishery for the loss of cod stocks on the Grand Banks.

COMMERCIAL USES

Traditionally, capelin fished off Labrador and Newfoundland was used for local consumption and for bait, dog food and fertilizer. Capelin caught just before spawning is often frozen whole and shipped to Japan, where the female roe is considered a delicacy. Capelin stocks are an important forage fish for the valuable cod, salmon, halibut and herring fisheries. As such, significantly increased quotas will likely only occur if and when the cod and other stocks revive.

LIFE CYCLE

Capelins swim in large offshore schools during most of the year, migrating inshore to sandy and gravelly beaches to spawn between April and September. The time of spawning depends on water temperature. On the east coast, it begins first in the warm waters of the Gulf of St. Lawrence and continues much later in the colder waters off Labrador. Spawning usually occurs at night, or on cloudy days. Before spawning the sexes are segregated, with males near the shore and females in deeper water. As the females ripen, both sexes move closer to shore and swim onto a beach to mate. (The exception to this is the capelin stock on the southeast shoal of the Grand Banks, which spawns in colder waters 100 to 200 feet deep.) After spawning, most capelin die and are washed out to sea. The eggs attach themselves to the gravel and sand and usually hatch in 15 to 20 days. Tidal action washes the larvae out to sea, where they mature and later join any surviving adults in large feeding schools. Capelin mature at three to four years of age when they return to shore to spawn often followed inshore by large numbers of cod.

Further understanding of their role in the ocean food chain and their wide fluctuations in abundance (possibly related to a short life span that could suffer from a poor year class) may shed further light on the health of groundfish stocks and other marine life.

COBIA

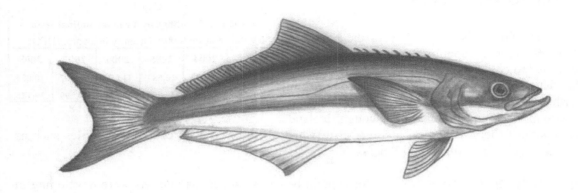

Cobia, *Rachycentron canadum*

GENERAL

Cobia is a uniquely-attractive and streamlined fish and the only species in the family Rachycentridae. This family is in the same large suborder (Percoidei) as the temperate basses family (Percichthyidae), and remoras family (Echeneidae). They are also known to feed in a manner similar to remoras. Cobia will follow other large fishes and turtles, sneaking in to scavenge whatever is left behind. The cobia name comes from the Greek words "rachis" (vertebral column) and "kentron" (sharp point).

PHYSICAL DESCRIPTION

Max Length: 200 cm TL male/unsexed; (Ref. 10790);
Common Length : 110 cm TL male/unsexed; (Ref. 3487);
Max. Published weight: 68.0 kg (Ref. 7251);
Max. Reported Age: 15 years (Ref. 9739)

The cobia is a torpedo-shaped fish with a long flat head and a lower jaw that projects past the upper jaw. The teeth are villiform (i.e., slender and crowded like the bristles of a brush). It has a dark brown dorsal coloration, going to silvery white on the bottom. Dark lateral lines run the length of the body. They have 7 to 9 sharp, retractable dorsal spines and the body is embedded with scales. Juveniles have a truncated tail and horizontal black and white stripes. In adults the caudal fin is lunate-shaped. Cobias lack a swim bladder and must constantly swim to survive (or sink — to the bottom).

Also Known As
Crabeater/
Sergeantfish/
Bonito/
Cabio/
Cubby Yew/
Black kingfish/
Black salmon/
Cabio/ Black
Kingfish/
Lemonfish/
Ling

FishBase Name
Cobia

International Recognitions
Spain—Cobia
France— Mafou
Japan— Sugi
Germany—
Offiziersfisch

LANDINGS AND VALUES

Cobia is found circum-globally in all tropical oceans, but somewhat strangely, does not inhabit the eastern Pacific Ocean coasts of North and South America. On the Atlantic coast it is found from Nova Scotia, to the Gulf of Mexico and the Caribbean, down to northern Argentina. Cobia is a pelagic fish that prefers habitats such as offshore reefs, but is drawn to

Cobia US Landings by Year — Nominal Data Value in $US (000); Quantity in tonnes; (NMFS)					
	2004	**2005**	**2006**	**2007**	**2008**
Value	459	355	388	439	416
Quantity	96	75	83	81	78

any structures in open water such as pilings, buoys, platforms and drifting flotsam. Cobia can also found inshore inhabiting bays, estuaries and mangroves. Cobia is not usually fished commercially because of its solitary nature; however, it is highly prized as a sport fish and also caught as bycatch in other fisheries. In 2008, 78 tonnes of cobia, valued at $416,000 was commercially landed (see table). Most of the catches in 2008 were caught on Florida West and East coast. The rest was mostly caught in North Carolina, Louisiana, and Virginia. The gear used was mostly long lines, reel and rod. The recreational catch is not recorded; however they are not overfished. Cobia biomass is considered significantly above maximum sustainable yield (MSY).

Aquaculture Status: Cobias grow very quickly and can reach 6-7 kg within one year of hatching (three times the growth rate of Atlantic salmon). Farmed cobia also has a favorable feed conversion ratio, another plus for an aquaculture species. These characteristics make cobia an appealing aquaculture species. Although commercial production of cobia has just recently begun in the west, it already has a successful history in Asia, most notably in Taiwan, where cobia is stocked in around 80% of ocean cages.

COMMERCIAL USES

It is a highly sought after food fish throughout its range for some markets. Traditionally in Mexico, for example, it is known as "esmedregal" and is the fish of choice for weddings and celebrations. In Belize, it is fished as "cabio," and a captured cobia may not make it to market as it is considered a family treat.

LIFE CYCLE

Cobia become sexually mature at around 2-3 years of age and their spawning season, depending on location, can last from April to September. They form large spawning aggregations and spawn once every 9-12 days and up to 15 to 20 times each season, usually in open water. In shallow bays, cobia larvae have been observed hatching approximately 24-36 hours after fertilization. The larvae are 2.5 mm long and lacked pigmentation. Five days after hatching, they are developed enough for active feeding. A pale yellow line is visible, extending the length of the body. By day 30, the juveniles take on the appearance of an adult with two color bands running from the snout to the tail. Cobia can grow quickly and have a moderately long life span.

Maximum ages observed for cobia in the Gulf of Mexico were 9 and 11 years for males and females, respectively; while off North Carolina maximum ages were 14 and 13 years, respectively. They prey on fish, squid, and crab, and like remoras, will also scavenge after sharks or rays. They are believed to be prey to larger pelagic fish, such as dolphinfish, especially when small.

COD

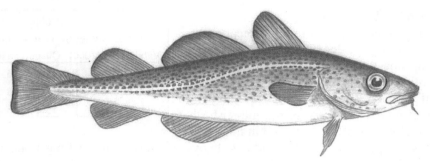

Atlantic Cod, *Gadus morhua*

GENERAL

The subfamily Gadinae (cods and haddocks) of the cod family Gadidae is comprised of 22 species (*ITIS*). Phycine hakes (subfamily Phycinae) and cuskfishes (subfamily Lotinae) comprise the other two subfamilies of Gadidae (*ITIS*). (Note that *FishBase* recognizes 24 species/subspecies in the family Gadidae, and views hakes and cuskfishes as separate families, rather than subfamilies.) The subfamily includes the Atlantic and Pacific tom cods (*Microgadus* spp.*)* and the Arctic and polar cods. [In *The Seafood List*, *Boreogadus saida* is "Arctic cod" and *Arctogadus glacialis* is "polar cod," but the opposite is true in *FishBase*.] However, the **Atlantic cod** is the largest cod species and traditionally the most plentiful. A closely related species, the Pacific cod, *G. macrocephalus*, is now the largest cod catch, by far. Some stocks of Atlantic cod are now on Canada's Species at Risk list.

PHYSICAL DESCRIPTION Max length: 200 cm TL male/unsexed; (Ref. 1371); Common length: 100.0 cm TL male/unsexed; (Ref. 1371); Max. published weight: 96.0 kg (Ref. 9988); Max. reported age: 25 years (Ref. 173)
The Atlantic cod has several distinguishing features. It has three soft-rayed dorsal fins and two anal fins. The tail is only slightly concave, nearly square. It is a large-mouthed fish with a projecting upper jaw and a chin projection called a barbel. The upper body of the cod is usually grey or green, but depending upon its surroundings, may shade to a reddish brown. The dorsal and sides are covered with rounded brownish to red spots. It has a whitish belly and a pale lateral line extending from the gills to the tail. The Pacific cod looks much like the Atlantic cod although it may be spotted with larger and fewer pale areas on its back and has white-edged fins. The Arctic cod and Atlantic and Pacific tomcods often appear to be smaller Atlantic codfish, but are separate species that only grow to 12 or 14 inches.

LANDINGS AND VALUES Common to both sides of the Atlantic Ocean, in North America, Atlantic cod is found from Greenland to Cape Hatteras. Until recent years, Atlantic cod was the target of fleets of large offshore draggers and factory trawlers. The inshore fishery is smaller and uses nets, traps and lines. The fishery has largely collapsed; apparently, mostly from over-fishing.

Also Known As
Rock Cod/
Codling/ Scrod
Cod

FishBase Name
Atlantic cod

International Recognitions
Spain— Bacalao
del Atlántico
France— Morue
de l'Atlantique
Italy— Merluzzo
bianco
Japan— Madara
Germany—
Dorsch

In 1989, the Canadian cod catch was about 450,000 tonnes, valued at about $200 million and the US catch was about 35,400 tonnes valued at about $48 million (not shown). By 2008, the Canadian catch was only 26,830 tonnes, valued at approximately $45 million (see table). In 2008, US Atlantic cod catch was 8,066 tonnes, valued at approximately $27 million (see table). Pacific cod is a small catch in Canada with about 360 tonnes landed in 2008, valued at about $500,000 (not shown). US Pacific cod landings in 1989 were 169,000 tonnes valued at $55 million (not shown). In 2008, the US Pacific cod catch was 224,055 tonnes, valued at almost $274 million (see table). Most of the Pacific cod catch is in Alaskan waters. In addition, the US game fished 1,900 tonnes of cod in 2008.

Atlantic Cod Canadian Landings by Year — Nominal Data Value in $Cdn (000); Quantity in tonnes; (DFO)					
	2004	**2005**	**2006**	**2007**	**2008**
Value	35,238	34,060	37,147	42,812	45,030
Quantity	24,732	26,191	27,402	26,733	26,830

Atlantic Cod US Landings by Year — Nominal Data Value in $US (000); Quantity in tonnes; (NMFS)					
	2004	**2005**	**2006**	**2007**	**2008**
Value	21,672	20,847	20,469	27,071	26,908
Quantity	7,284	6,311	5,723	7,657	8,066

Endangered Status: The Newfoundland and Labrador Atlantic cod is designated as endangered by COSEWIC and is under consideration for addition to the *Species at Risk Act* (*SARA*).

Aquaculture: Cod is farmed in Norway and Iceland, while there are other on-going initiatives elsewhere (e.g., Canada). Profitability is still an issue, among other, more technical problems.

COMMERCIAL USES

Cod is a multi-purpose fish available fresh/frozen, whole and as fillets and steaks. It is often frozen in blocks as well as salt cured or smoked for export. Atlantic cod is considered to salt better than any other groundfish. Cod has also been used extensively in generic fish products such as frozen fish sticks, canned fish and chicken haddie, and is popular for "fish 'n' chips." Cod tongues and cheeks are considered a special treat by some. Pacific cod is less valued due to its finer meat that "chunks" and renders it less valuable for portions. Cod liver oil is valuable as a source of omega-3 oils and vitamins A and D. Other cod species, particularly Arctic varieties, can be marketed in the US as cod; however, these fish are generally not plentiful.

LIFE CYCLE

Atlantic cod stocks migrate back and forth across various banks of the continental shelf. The different stocks spawn at different times depending on location, but generally between March and June. They usually spawn at depths of from 600 to 2,000 feet, where the water temperature is 36° to 40°F; but they also spawn in warmer and shallower coastal waters.

Pacific Cod US Landings by Year — Nominal Data Value in $US (000); Quantity in tonnes; (NMFS)					
	2004	**2005**	**2006**	**2007**	**2008**
Value	148,982	150,738	197,237	224,301	274,160
Quantity	267,917	248,910	235,290	221,159	224,055

A female can produce more than 2 million eggs, although few survive to reach maturity. The eggs initially rise to the surface, where the larvae live off a yolk sac for 1-2 weeks. When the young cod reach about 1.5 inches in length, they move to the bottom. Atlantic cod usually mature between 5-8 years of age, at lengths of 18 to 24 inches. The males mature slightly sooner and are generally smaller than females. Atlantic cod are often caught between 4-8 years of age; i.e., before maturity. They will eat nearly any kind of fish or shellfish. Capelin is considered a favorite prey, while seals a major predator. Pacific cod ranges throughout the North Pacific from California to Korea and seems to grow faster than Atlantic cod.

CROAKER

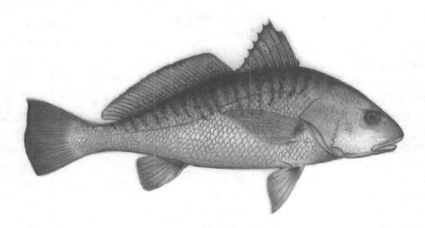

Atlantic Croaker, *Micropogonias undulatus*

GENERAL

The **Atlantic croaker** is a member of the Sciaenidae family (drums and croakers) that also includes seatrouts, weakfishes, spot and kingfishes. The name croaker originates from the croaking sound these fish make by vibrating the muscles of their swim bladders when spawning. They are one of the most abundant fish in the coastal waters of eastern North America. The white croaker, *Genyonemus lineatus,* is also a small commercial fishery on the Pacific coast, particularly California. Worldwide, there are about 70 genera and 270 species in the Sciaenidae family (*FishBase*). *The Seafood List* identifies 32 species with the market name croaker that fall within the family. Many species in the family can physically resemble each other closely.

Also Known As
Hardhead

FishBase Name
Atlantic croaker

International Recognitions
Spain—Corbina
France—Tambour brésilien
Italy—Scienidi
Japan—Ishimochi
Germany—Adlerfisch

PHYSICAL DESCRIPTION

Max length : 55.0 cm TL male/unsexed; (Ref. 40637);
Common length : 30.0 cm TL male/unsexed; (Ref. 3702);
Max. published weight: 2,580 g (Ref. 40637); max. reported age: 5 years (Ref. 12193)

Croakers are greenish or grayish silvery to brassy yellowish and highly iridescent above, silvery white below. The back and sides have many brassy or brownish short, irregular, oblique bars formed by the connection of spots on their scales. Bars may become less distinct in larger adults. They have an inferior mouth and a chin with several pores and a row of short, slender barbels on each ventral side of the mouth. They have a deeply notched dorsal fin with a double concave caudal fin. The Atlantic croaker is closely related to, and also resembles, spotted seatrout, weakfish and red drum (e.g., see entries on weakfish and drum in this book). Spot (*Leiostomus xanthurus*) is also a similar fish, but has no barbels and has a dark patch on its side.

LANDINGS AND VALUES

The Atlantic croaker inhabits mud and soft bottomed estuaries and bays along the Atlantic coast from the Gulf of Mexico to Massachusetts. In 2008, 8,162 tonnes of Atlantic croaker valued at $9.4 million, was landed (see table). Most of the commercial catch in 2008 was caught in Virginia (62%). The rest was mostly caught in North Carolina (32%) and Maryland (5%). The gear used was mostly gill nets, otter trawl bottoms and pound nets. On the west coast, 32 tonnes of white croaker was commercially landed in 2008, valued at $45,000. Spot croaker (or "spot") landings of 1,309 tonnes, valued at $1.8 million, were also recorded in 2008 (see table). Most of these landings were also in Virginia, North Carolina and Maryland.

Atlantic Croaker US Landings by Year – Nominal Data Value in $US (000); Quantity in tonnes; (NMFS)					
	2004	2005	2006	2007	2008
Value	8,589	9,046	9,717	8,860	9,424
Quantity	11,569	11,131	9,461	9,241	8,162

Pacific White Croaker US Landings by Year – Nominal Data Value in $US (000); Quantity in tonnes; (NMFS)					
	2004	2005	2006	2007	2008
Value	50	48	58	44	45
Quantity	30	29	37	29	32

In addition, 2,700 tonnes of Atlantic croaker (almost 11 million fish) were caught recreationally in 2008; almost as many individual fish as spotted seatrout, but less tonnage (8,000 tonnes of spotted seatrout were caught, as well as 2,000 tonnes of spot). This was also ahead of other drum, kingfish and seatrout individual fish totals (also see drum, kingfish and weakfish entries). **Endangered status of Atlantic croaker:** Currently being managed due to possible overfishing. **Aquaculture Status:** not cultured.

Spot (Croaker) US Landings by Year – Nominal Data Value in $US (000); Quantity in tonnes; (NMFS)					
	2004	2005	2006	2007	2008
Value	3,358	3,314	2,866	4,269	1,798
Quantity	3,059	2,326	1,453	2,569	1,309

COMMERCIAL USES

Croaker is an important commercial and game fish. Millions of pounds are landed each year and sold within the US as well as exported to other countries. The annual catch has declined in the past few years and is generally attributed to overfishing. The main season is from summer to fall. While large croakers are marketed for their meat, smaller croakers are used as baitfish in the crab and seatrout fishery. Croakers are not recommended for consumption raw because they can pass trematodes to humans.

LIFE CYCLE

Croakers mature quickly at 1-2 years of age. Depending on location, croakers migrate out from shore in the fall and winter to spawn. During spawning, males use muscles along the sides of their swim bladders to create a croaking noise and attract females. Females will release from 100,000 up to 2 million eggs; each egg is about 0.35 mm in diameter. After hatching, the pelagic larvae drift toward shore with the currents. Recruitment is highly variable.

Atlantic croaker can live up to 8 years. Their diet includes shrimp crabs, and various detritus (dead and decomposing plant and animal matter). They use barbels on their chins to detect food on the ocean floor and feed on shrimp, crabs and detritus. Their predators include striped bass, shark, spotted seatrout, other croakers and humans. Atlantic croakers that live in the northern part of their range mature later and live longer than those in the southern part of the range. Fishing and predation reduce more than 95% of the Atlantic croaker population every year.

CUNNER

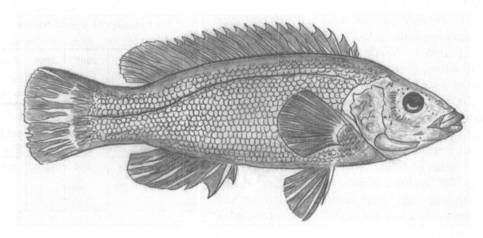

Cunner, *Tautogolabrus adspersus*

GENERAL

Cunner belongs to the wrasse family, Labridae. Wrasses are found worldwide in 60 genera and about 500 species, with 21 species in the Northwest Atlantic. Many of the species are small and colourful. Major commercial wrasse species in North America include the **cunner**, the hogfish (*Lachnolaimus maximus*), the California sheephead, (*Semicossyphus pulcher*) and the tautog (*Tautoga onitis*). In *FishBase*, cunner is the only species with the genus *Tautogolabrus*. However, *ITIS* lists *T. brandaonis* as another (unnamed) species. The tautog is perhaps the closest commercially-fished relative of the cunner.

Cunners seem to have the ability to go into short term hibernation in the winter under rocks or in shallow water which helps them survive, as they are vulnerable to low temperatures.

Also Known As
Biergall/ Perch/ Sea Perch/ Blue Perch/ Bergall/ Nipper

FishBase Name
Cunner

International Recognitions
France— Limbert achigan

PHYSICAL DESCRIPTION

Max. length: 38.0 cm TL male/unsexed; (Ref. 7251); Common length: 15 - 25 cm. TL
Max. published weight: 1 Kg (Ref. 7251); Common weight: 0.5 Kg
Max. reported age: 6 years (Ref. 1009)

Cunners have a pointed snout and are medium-deep bodied and moderately laterally compressed in shape. Their tail is truncated with a deep caudal peduncle and a dorsal fin that runs the length of the body that is two-thirds spined, followed by soft rays. Spots are variable and some have bright yellow lips and mouth lining. They have several rows of uneven teeth shaped liked cones. The ventrals stand under or a little behind the pectorals; both of moderate size, and the pectorals are rounded. Coloration can vary with environment, but often ranges from reddish brown (darker or paler) or bluish with brownish tinge on top, variously mottled with blue, brown, and reddish. The belly is usually a vivid bluish, sometimes whitish.

LANDINGS AND VALUES

Cunner US Landings by Year — Nominal Data Value in $US (000); Quantity in tonnes; (NMFS)					
	2004	2005	2006	2007	2008
Value	9	9	9	13	28
Quantity	2	3	2	2	4

Cunners inhabit shallow bottoms of inshore waters and are distributed from Newfoundland and the Gulf of Saint Lawrence to Chesapeake Bay. They apparently don't aggregate in large quantities in deeper waters, although the fish are larger. In 2008, 4 tonnes of cunner was landed in the US, valued at $28,000. All of the catch in 2008 was caught in New York and Rhode Island. The gear used was mostly hand lines, pots and traps. A small recreational fishery of 99 tonnes in 2008 was also reported (not shown). It is not a reported fishery in Canada; however, it is likely caught as a bycatch and presently discarded.

COMMERCIAL USES

Small commercial fishery. Not considered a game fish, but does provide recreation and is considered a good panfish.

LIFE CYCLE

They congregate in large groups around wharves, wrecks and submerged seaweed and eel grass beds. They spawn during the late spring through summer. Eggs are buoyant, transparent, 0.75 to 0.85 mm. in diameter and do not have an oil globule. Incubation takes about 40-72 hours, depending upon temperature. At hatching the larvae are about 2 to 2.2 mm long, and at 15 mm length, the young cunner is practically in adult form. They are variable in color and maturity is reached in 2-3 years. Females are generally larger than males.

Cunners tend to stay in the same area year-round. They are omnivorous and eat fish, shrimp, clams, sea urchins, small lobster, mussels and eel grass. Small cunner fry taken at Woods Hole were found to have fed chiefly on minute crustacea such as copepods, amphipods, and isopods.

CUSK

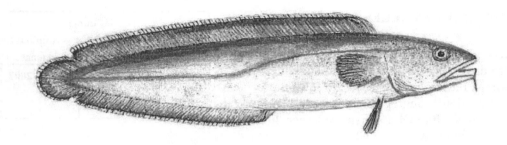

Cusk, *Brosme brosme*

GENERAL

The **cusk,** a member of the cod family Gadidae, subfamily Lotinae, (cuskfishes - *ITIS*) is the single species in its genus. It is a stout, but slow-moving fish that dwells on rough, rocky, or gravelly bottoms in the relatively cool to warm (43 to 50°F) waters of the Atlantic Ocean. Although most members of the cod family prefer colder waters and retreat to deep waters during the winter months, the cusk seems to prefer relatively warm waters and intermediate depths. Also, unlike many other groundfishes, it tends to travel alone, or in small groups.

PHYSICAL DESCRIPTION

Max length : 120 cm TL male/unsexed; (Ref. 9988); common length : 50.0 cm TL male/unsexed; (Ref. 1371);
Max. published weight: 30.0 kg (Ref. 9988);
Max. reported age: 20 years (Ref. 1371)

Also Known As
Tusk/ Torsk/
European Cusk/
Brosmius/
Moonfish

FishBase Name
Tusk

**International
Recognitions**
Spain— Brosmio
France—
Assiette
Italy— Brosmio
Germany—
Brosme

The cusk has a large head with a correspondingly large mouth and a slightly protruding upper jaw. Several rows of teeth are located on its jaws and the roof of its mouth. The color can vary from a dark reddish or greenish brown to lighter brown, which shades to a cream or white on the belly. All fins are white with black margins narrowly edged in white. The scales are small and cycloid. The lower jaw has a long chin barbel; a characteristic of the cod family. It has an elongated body with one dorsal fin, one anal fin and a rounded caudal that blends into its dorsal and anal fins. It closely resembles an ocean pout and somewhat resembles a hake (also once classified as a member of the Gadidae family), but neither the pout nor the hake have a continuous dorsal fin. The continuous dorsal and anal fin makes the cusk easy to distinguish from other fishes and other members of the cod family. The aging of cusk by examination of otoliths is under question; some scientists believe these have been misread and cusk actually live 40-50 years.

LANDINGS AND VALUES

The cusk is found on both sides of the North Atlantic. In the west, it has been sighted off southern Greenland and is found in the Strait of Belle Isle, the Grand Banks, occasionally in the Gulf of St. Lawrence and southward to Cape Cod and occasionally as far as New Jersey. However, populations appear to be centred in the Gulf of Maine and Scotia Shelf.

CUSK

The fishery was always a by-catch fishery and cusk is still caught this way, mainly by longlines directed at other groundfish such as cod and haddock. It usually inhabits depths of 300 to 1,200 feet, in waters with temperatures from 36° to 54°F and may prefer depths of 400 to 600 feet and temperatures of 43° to 50°F. Canada landed 613 tonnes of cusk valued at about $600,000 in 2008 (see table). As there is no longer a longline fishery, US 2008 landings of 33 tonnes are very low, declining from more than 2,363 tonnes in 1985.

Cusk Canadian Landings by Year — Nominal Data Value in $Cdn (000); Quantity in tonnes; (DFO)					
	2004	2005	2006	2007	2008
Value	614	812	787	982	591
Quantity	927	905	883	1,046	613

Endangered Status: Cusk landings in the Gulf of Maine and the southeastern Scotian Shelf have declined since 1970 and the fish is, or has been, a candidate for *Species of Concern* in the US and a candidate for the *Species at Risk Act* (SARA) in Canada under the Committee on the Status of Endangered Wildlife in Canada (COSEWIC); however, it is not presently considered threatened.

COMMERCIAL USES

The cusk is a lean, white-fleshed fish that has been appreciated in the past as a lower-price substitute for cod. It is marketed largely as fresh and frozen fillets, particularly by commercial fisheries north of Cape Cod, but it can also be smoked, cured and used in canned chicken haddie, sticks and portions.

Cusk US Landings by Year — Nominal Data Value in $US (000); Quantity in tonnes; (NMFS)					
	2004	2005	2006	2007	2008
Value	96	116	110	120	50
Quantity	78	97	66	87	33

LIFE CYCLE

The average age of spawning was thought to be 6 years, with males maturing earlier than females; however, this age is now under question. On the Nova Scotian shelf, cusk is believed to spawn from May to August, with most spawning occurring in the last two weeks of June and usually in depths less than 600 feet. In the Gulf of Maine, however, spawning is believed to occur from April to July.

A 22-inch cusk can lay 100,000 eggs, while one twice as large may lay 4 million. The buoyant, spherical, pelagic eggs are about 0.05 to 0.06 inches in diameter and have a coppery tint, a pinkish oil globule and a finely pitted surface. The eggs will hatch when they are about 0.15 inches in diameter. As it grows, the young cusk remains near the surface until about 2 inches in length, when it will seek the bottom. What it eats is somewhat unknown as cusk will regurgitate (or the stomach everts) upon capture; accordingly, the contents are unavailable for examination. It has, however, been reported that cusk inhabiting European waters prey on fish and crustaceans (especially crabs and molluscs) and the occasional starfish. It is assumed that the western cusk enjoys the same diet. The cusk is a sluggish fish and may be easy prey. Cod, halibut and seals are known predators; and it is believed that spiny dogfish, skate, white hake, goosefish and flounder are also. Except for seals, the numbers of many predators have decreased and predator impact is now lessened. However, predation and possible slow growth to maturity may help explain its presently poor recruitment in North America.

CUTLASSFISH

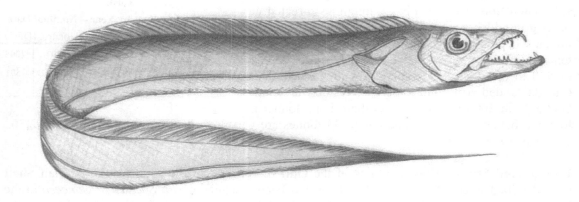

Atlantic Cutlassfish, *Trichiurus lepturus*

GENERAL

Cutlassfish belong the family Trichiuridae, subfamily Trichiurinae, (cutlassfishes and hairtails). Worldwide, there are 11 species in the genus (*ITIS*) and the **Atlantic cutlassfish** is found circumpolar in both temperate and tropical waters. There are four species listed under the market name "cutlassfish" in *The Seafood List;* all from the Trichiuridae family. The black scabbardfish, *Alphanopus carbo,* the silver scabbordfish, *Lepidopus caudatus* and the smallhead hairtail, *Lepturacanthus savala;* however, only the Atlantic cutlassfish and the black scabbordfish are found in North American waters. They are often called ribbonfish because of their shape and silvery coloration. Unlike most fish, cutlassfish have no scales and are instead covered with a metallic-like skin. They are known to steal bait and for their sharp, barbed teeth among unlucky anglers.

PHYSICAL DESCRIPTION

Max length : 234 cm TL male/unsexed; (Ref. 26340);
Common length : 100.0 cm TL male/unsexed; (Ref. 26999);
Max. published weight: 5,000 g; Max. reported age: 15 years (Ref. 7142)

Cutlassfish have a pointed tail and cutlass-tapered body. They have no scales and a dorsal fin that runs the entire length of the body. Their lower jaw extends past the upper jaw and they are covered in a shiny metallic-colored skin. They are a steel-blue color when alive and silver after death. The anal fin is almost nonexistent.

LANDINGS AND VALUES

In the western Atlantic, the Atlantic cutlassfish is found from Cape Cod, south to Florida, the Caribbean and Gulf of Mexico and further south to Argentina. In the Eastern Pacific, it is found from California to Chile. They are a coastal species and often found and in bays and channels. In 2008, 25 tonnes of Atlantic Cutlassfish valued at $39,000, was landed. Most of the catch in 2008 was landed in Texas and North Carolina. The rest was caught on the Florida East Coast. The gear used was mostly gill nets and combined gears.

Atlantic Cutlassfish					
US Landings by Year — Nominal Data					
Value in $US (000); Quantity in tonnes; (NMFS)					
	2004	2005	2006	2007	2008
Value	49	24	67	70	39
Quantity	22	11	24	24	25

COMMERCIAL USES

Cutlassfish are fished commercially in the US for export to other countries. They are marketed as sashimi, dried, salted, or frozen overseas. They are also used as a baitfish in the US. Cutlassfish are not sought-after by anglers, although they are often caught incidentally using small fish, shrimp, or artificial lures. Their principal use in the US is as bait for offshore species such as king mackerel, Spanish mackerel and wahoo.

LIFE CYCLE

Their life history is not well understood, but juveniles are found in late spring or early summer indicating a winter/early spring spawning. They are open water/substratum egg scatterers. Adults and juveniles have opposing complimentary vertical migration for feeding. Adults feed at the surface during the day, while juveniles migrate to the surface at night to form loose feeding aggregations. They feed in a tail down position, often suspended right below the surface, looking for smaller fish and shrimp. They feed on shrimp, squid, lobster, crab and smaller fish. They are prey to mackerel, tunas, bluefish, seatrout, rays, sharks, dolphins and whales.

DEALFISH

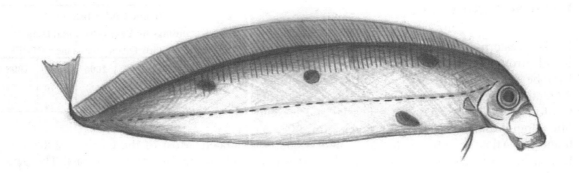

Dealfish, *Trachipterus arcticus*

GENERAL

The **dealfish** belongs to the family Trachipteridae (ribbonfishes), which has a worldwide presence in the oceans. There are 3 genera and 11 species in the family, with 7species in the genus *Trachipterus* (*ITIS*). None of the species are listed in *The Seafood List* and the dealfish is not considered a food fish at the present time. Dealfish are bathypelagic (deep ocean) fish, but not bottom feeders. It appears that not a lot is known of them.

PHYSICAL DESCRIPTION

Max length : 300 cm TL male/unsexed; (Ref. 35388)
Bathypelagic marine fish living at depths of 300—600m

Dealfish are characterized by a long, laterally-compressed body with a short head, somewhat bulbous eyes, narrow mouth and small dentition. The dorsal fin extends the length of the back with small pectoral fins and there is no anal fin.

Also Known As
Ribbonfish

FishBase Name
Dealfish

International Recognitions
Spain—
Cardenal
atlántico
France—
Trachyptère
atlantique
Germany—
Bandfisch
Iceland—
vogmær

LANDINGS AND VALUES

The dealfish is thought to be distributed throughout the North Atlantic from New York to Florida and from Iceland and Norway to the Madeira Islands. It is now considered that there may be two separate species, one on each side of the Atlantic Ocean. It is also generally believed to be a solitary species with some gathering for feeding or breeding.

Dealfish US Landings by Year — Nominal Data Value in $US (000); Quantity in tonnes; (NMFS)					
	2004	2005	2006	2007	2008
Value	2	0	0	0	11
Quantity	2	0	0	0	12

In 2008, 12 tonnes of dealfish valued at $11,000, was landed in the US (see table). All of the catches in 2008 were landed in Virginia. The gear used was mostly pound nets.

COMMERCIAL USES

Perhaps for bait, aquarium and/or research demand; otherwise none at present.

LIFE CYCLE

Dealfish reach sexual maturity at 200cm or and age of 14 years. All stages of development including eggs, larvae and young are pelagic. They prey on small fish and squid. They are thought to be solitary, but may aggregate for breeding or feeding purposes.

DORY

Buckler Dory, *Zenopsis conchifer*

GENERAL

The **buckler dory** belongs to the family Zeidae (dories). In various early surveys in the Gulf of Maine the species was identified as the American John Dory (*Zenopsis ocellata*); however, *ITIS* now recognizes this scientific name as a synonym for *Z. conchifer,* known as buckler dory in *The Seafood List.* The species appears to have wide distribution in the world's oceans, including both sides of the Atlantic Ocean; but is not found in the Pacific Ocean. In total, there are 5 dory species in 2 genera in the Zeidae family listed in *ITIS*; 3 of these are listed in *The Seafood List* including the mirror dory, *Zenopsis nebulosa.* Another species with the market name "dory" is found in the Cyttidae family (silver dory, *Cyttus novaezealandiae*).

The (European) John Dory, *Zeus faber,* is considered a poor swimmer, but a good predator that stalks prey and captures it by shooting out a tube located in its mouth.

PHYSICAL DESCRIPTION

Max length : 80.0 cm TL male/unsexed; (Ref. 4253);
Common length : 50.0 cm TL male/unsexed; (Ref. 5217);
Max. published weight: 3,200 g (Ref. 7251)

The buckler dory has a round and laterally-compressed deep body, concave head, large and obliquely-set mouth, slender caudal peduncle, two part dorsal fin (spiny and soft rayed) with long dorsal fin spines, brush-shaped caudal fin, and tiny round pectoral fins. The coloration is silver with dark spots that fade with age. Adults usually retain a vague "eyespot" behind the operculum, thought to frighten predators and/or confuse prey. Its silvery coloration, the presence of plates along the base of its dorsal and anal fins, and only three anal spines distinguishes the buckler dory from the European John Dory (*Z. faber*), which has four stout anal spines and lacks plates along the first dorsal fin.

Also Known As
American John Dory/
Silvery Dory

FishBase Name
Silvery John Dory

International Recognitions
Spain— Pez de San Pedro
France— Saint—Pierre doré
Italy— Pisci San Perdu
Japan— Matou—dai
Germany— Sankt Petersfisch

LANDINGS AND VALUES

In North America, the buckler dory inhabits the muddy bottomed, coastal waters of the western Atlantic from Sable Island, Canada, to northern North Carolina (*FishBase* Ref. 7251). It is a deepwater, benthopelagic species found from 50 to 600 meters, but most often between 150 and 300 meters.

Buckler Dory US Landings by Year — Nominal Data Value in $US (000); Quantity in tonnes; (NMFS)					
	2004	2005	2006	2007	2008
Value	61	10	41	57	48
Quantity	48	7	22	28	23

In 2008, 23 tonnes of buckler dory (reported as American John Dory), valued at $48,000, was landed in the US, likely as a bycatch. The landings in 2008 were reported from Rhode Island, New York and Connecticut.

COMMERCIAL USES

Other species of dories are commercially fished for food in other parts of the world and the flesh is considered excellent steamed, fried, broiled, boiled, microwaved and baked (*FishBase* Ref. 9988). There is also a demand in the aquarium trade.

LIFE CYCLE

Little is known about the lifecycle of these fish. Evidence to date would suggest they reach maturity at about 4 years, spawn in late winter or early spring and are are open water/substratum egg scatterers. They feed on smaller fish and squid and are prey for sharks and larger fish. They school in small groups.

DRIFTFISH

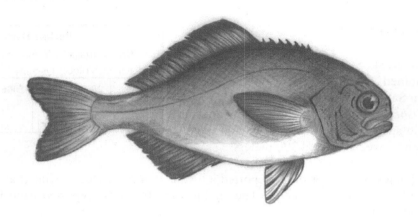

GENERAL

The American **barrelfish** has apparently never been spotted underwater. It is part of the family *Centrolophidae*, (same family as rudderfishes and medusafishes) and is believed to be a long–lived, deepwater species. They get their name from juveniles of the species that are often found floating within or below marine debris such as boxes, barrels, or driftwood. The family comprises about 32 species in 7 genera (*ITIS*); or 30 species in 8 genera (*FishBase*). Only two driftfish (market name) are listed in *The Seafood List* including the black driftfish, *Hyperoglyphe bythites*.

Also Known As
None Known

FishBase Name
Barrelfish

International Recognitions
Spain— Rufo derivante
France— Rouffe des épaves

PHYSICAL DESCRIPTION

Max length: 91.0 cm TL male/unsexed; (Ref. 7251);
Common length: 30.0 cm SL male/unsexed; (Ref. 4542);
Max. published weight: 12.3 kg (Ref. 7251)

The barrelfish has a stout body with a blunt, rounded nose, convex forehead and small mouth. They have rounded scales on their back and sides of the head. It may be mistaken for the black driftfish as their ranges in the western Atlantic Ocean overlap and not much is known about this species.

It is distinguished from the black ruff, *Centrolophus niger,* by the dorsal fin and spines. The caudal fin is slightly emarginated and not deeply forked with a thick caudal peduncle.

The barrelfish changes color throughout its life from blackish to green with a white or pale colored belly. It is able to change color to match its surroundings.

LANDINGS AND VALUES

In the Western Atlantic, the barrelfish is found from Nova Scotia to southern Florida and eastern Gulf of Mexico. (The black driftfish is believed to be confined to the more semi-tropical waters around Florida and the Caribbean.) Adults are a deepwater pelagic fish; juveniles may be found closer to shore.

Barrelfish US Landings by Year — Nominal Data Value in $US (000); Quantity in tonnes; (NMFS)					
	2004	2005	2006	2007	2008
Value	44	28	28	55	33
Quantity	10	6	7	11	7

In 2008, 7 tonnes of barrelfish valued at $33,000, was landed. All of the catches in 2008 were caught on the Florida west coast. The gear used was electric or hydraulic reel.

COMMERCIAL USES

Most barrelfish are caught on the Blake Plateau as bycatch from the wreckfish (sea bass) fishery. There is a strong likelihood that the species may become more popular as a fishery. They are harmless to humans.

LIFE CYCLE

Adults are deepwater fish, occurring over continental shelves, while juveniles are often seen at the surface in association with floating debris. Adults are thought to school near the bottom and prey on small fishes, crustaceans, squid and molluscs. They are thought to be spring spawners, but little else is known.

DRUM

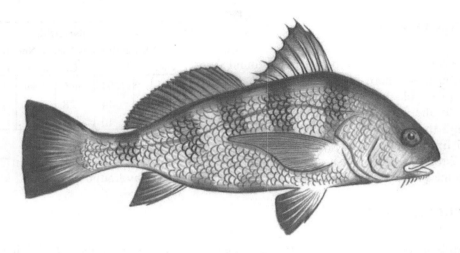

Black Drum, *Pogonias cromis*

GENERAL
The **black drum** is a member of the Sciaenidae family (drums and croakers) that also includes weakfishes/seatrouts and kingfishes (see entries in this book). As a whole, these fishes represent some of the best game fishing in the US. The ability to produce a croaking or drumming sound with their air bladders is the reason for the common names of drum and croakers. This ability is most developed in the black drum and anglers can sometimes hear the sounds from passing schools of fish. The red drum, *Sciaenops ocellatus*, (also known as channel bass and spottail) and the freshwater drum, *Aplodinotus grunniens* (also known as sheepshead and gaspergou) are 2 other drums in the family and all 3 drums are the single species in their genus.

PHYSICAL DESCRIPTION
Max length: 170 cm TL male/unsexed; (Ref. 7251); Common length: 50.0 cm TL male/unsexed; (Ref. 3702); Max. published weight: 51.3 kg (Ref. 4699); Max. reported age: 43 years (Ref. 7188)

Black drum is an oblong fish with a hump on its highly arched back. It has an inferior mouth with 12—13 barbels on the chin and small pharayngeal teeth set in broad bands used for grinding shells. The tail is truncated. Coloration ranges from silver to black with a coppery or brassy sheen fading to gray on the sides and belly. Fins are dusky to black in color. Juveniles may have 4—6 vertical black bars along the sides although coloration changes based on habitat or age. Fish living in bays or lagoons are generally darker in color with bronze dorsal sides fading to gray and white. The red drum can easily be distinguished from the black drum by a large black spot (s) at the base of its tail and by lack of barbels. Coloration of red drum is often coppery red on top, but this may vary. The freshwater drum looks similar to other drums, but has a more distinct shovel nose, rounded tail and no distinct markings or colorations.

Also Known As
Oyster Drum/
Sea Drum/ Gray
Drum

FishBase Name
Black drum

**International
Recognitions**
Spain—
Corvinón negro,
Corbina
France— Grand
tambour
Italy— Scienidi
Japan—
Ishimochi
Germany—
Adlerfisch

LANDINGS AND VALUES

In North America, both black drum and red drum are distributed from Nova Scotia and the Bay of Fundy to Florida and into the Gulf of Mexico. In 2008, there was 2,008 tonnes of black drum landed in the US, valued at $3.6 million. Most of the catch was caught in Louisiana (55%). The remainder was mostly caught in Texas, North Carolina and Alabama. The gear used was mostly trot lines with bait and combined gear.

Red drum commercial landings in 2008 were 119 tonnes, valued at $403,000, mostly in North Carolina (see table).

Black Drum US Landings by Year — Nominal Data Value in $US (000); Quantity in tonnes; (NMFS)					
	2004	2005	2006	2007	2008
Value	3,802	3,737	3,478	3,623	3,554
Quantity	2,600	2,133	2,004	2,028	2,008

Red Drum US Landings by Year — Nominal Data Value in $US (000); Quantity in tonnes; (NMFS)					
	2004	2005	2006	2007	2008
Value	96	212	265	397	403
Quantity	33	72	88	124	119

Freshwater drum (437 tonnes in 2008) is mostly landed in Louisiana, Ohio and Michigan (see table). **Recreational Fishery**: An additional 3,400 tonnes of black drum and 7,000 tonnes of red drum were landed recreationally in the US in 2008 (not shown). Recreational landings for freshwater drums are not recorded. **Aquaculture:** The red drum has been farmed in the US, China and elsewhere – it is no longer reported as a major farmed species in the US. **Endangered Status:** Black and red drum are managed recreational fisheries; limits on allowable size differs according to area.

COMMERCIAL USES

Black drum is an important commercial fishery as well as recreational fishery. Although it is considered a good eating fish; the red drum is usually preferred by anglers. Small fish are preferred for eating; larger black drum also may have many tapeworms (cestodes). These fishes can also both be found in the aquarium trade. Freshwater drum is also an appreciated food fish, but has offsetting odor and cleaning issues for some anglers. Drums (fresh or frozen) can be pan-fried, broiled or baked.

LIFE CYCLE

Black drum are sexually mature between 2 and 4 years of ages and males mature before females. Spawning occurs both near shore in estuaries and bays and further out in the Gulf (red drum all spawn further out) from February to July. They are multiple spawners, with activity occurring approximately every three days. Females produce up to 32 million eggs per year. Larval stage is spent in sea grasses and juveniles occur in muddy bottom waters migrating to bays as they mature. They feed on surf clams, molluscs, amphipods, vegetation, shrimp, crabs and small fishes.

Freshwater Drum US Landings by Year — Nominal Data Value in $US (000); Quantity in tonnes; (NMFS)					
	2004	2005	2006	2007	2008
Value	116	121	143	151	162
Quantity	373	401	440	456	437

Both red and black drums are fast growing and can grow to large sizes.

EEL, CONGER

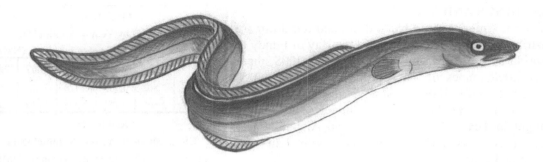

Conger Eel, *Conger oceanicus*

GENERAL
The family Congridae (conger eels) contains 3 subfamilies. The subfamily Congrinae includes 22 genera (including the *Conger* genus) and about 103 species (*ITIS*). The **conger eel** is one of 13 species in the *Conger* genus. The remaining 2 subfamilies are composed of 9 genera and approximately 76 species. These various species are found in all oceans. *The Seafood List* includes 12 species listed under the market name of "conger," as well as 11 species of "moray" eels, 3 species of "pike-conger" eels, and 1 species each of "snake" eel and "spiny" eel. There are also 5 species of freshwater eels listed (see entry in this book under "eel"). Conger eels are not considered harmful to humans. Although moray eels can give a nasty bite and have associated toxins, they too are not in the league of lethal venoms that can be received from the bites of poisonous water snakes.

PHYSICAL DESCRIPTION
Max length : 230 cm TL male/unsexed; (Ref. 7251);
Common length : 100.0 cm TL male/unsexed; (Ref. 3715);
Max. published weight: 40.0 kg (Ref. 7251)

Conger eels are much larger than the average eel. They have a pointy head and a compressed, tapered and snakelike body. The caudal fin is pointed and they have small round pectoral fin. Their skin lacks scales and coloration is gray brown and is paler on the sides going to a dirty white along the belly. An identifying characteristic is the upper jaw that protrudes beyond the lower jaw.

The most striking features of the giant snake eel, *Ophichthus rex,* (that can weigh up to 24 kg - Ref. 40637) are that its dorsal fin originates well behind the tips of the pectorals; 14-15 dark olive-brown, saddle-shaped markings along its back; its dorsal and anal fins are striped at the base and its pectoral fin is darker on dorsal side (Ref. 26938).

LANDINGS AND VALUES

Conger eels are distributed in the western Atlantic from Cape Cod, Massachusetts to north-eastern Florida and the Gulf of Mexico. They live along the coastline to the edge of the continental shelf and are often found around docks and jetties in inshore waters, but are a benthic species that have been found in depths of up to 500 meters (1,500 ft.). Near shore, they are commonly caught by anglers along piers, docks and jetties in the mid-Atlantic states.

Conger Eel US Landings by Year — Nominal Data Value in $US (000); Quantity in tonnes; (NMFS)					
	2004	2005	2006	2007	2008
Value	37	33	41	42	36
Quantity	37	32	37	36	28

In 2008, 28 tonnes of conger eel was commercially landed, valued at $36,000. Most of the catches in 2008 were caught in New Jersey (42%) and Rhode Island (32%). The rest was mostly caught in Virginia. The gear used was mostly pots and traps. About 6 tonnes of unidentified eels were landed in Florida, California and Hawaii in 2008, valued at $57,000.

Endangered Status: Susceptible to overfishing due to late sexual maturity.
Aquaculture Status: Not farmed.

The giant snake eel, *Ophichthus rex* and the eel-like wrymouth, *Cryptacanthodes maculates* (Family Cryptacanthodidae) are the only other species that show commercial landings in North America (including moray eels, *Gymnothorax* spp. and snake eels, subfamily Ophichthinae); however, these amount to a few pounds only, and in the odd year. About 38 kg of snake eel was landed in Texas in 2008, valued at $84. Similarly, 3 kg of wrymouth was landed in Canada in 2006, valued at $3.50.

Recreational Fishery: About 1,000 conger eels, 9,000 moray eels and 10,000 (3 tonnes) of unidentified eels were landed in 2008.

COMMERCIAL USES

Conger eek is commercially fished and highly prized for its firm, sweet taste. They are caught in bottom trawls, pots and by hook and line. A health alert has been issued because of the high levels of mercury contained in this fish.

LIFE CYCLE

Conger eel are nocturnal predators that prey on small molluscs, crustaceans and small fish. They breed only once in their lifetime, generally during the summer and then die. Spawning occurs offshore and females can produce between 3 and 6 million eggs. Eggs and larvae are pelagic. Feeds mainly on fishes, but also on shrimps and small shellfish.

ESCOLAR OR OILFISH

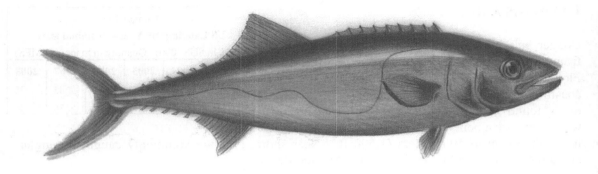

Escolar, *Lepidocybium flavobrunneum*

GENERAL

The **escolar** is a member of the family Gempylidae (snake mackerels) and is closely related to the various tuna and mackerel species (in the same order). There are 16 genera in the family; however, the escolar is the only species in its genus. Like many mackerels and tunas it is an oily fish and it is even approved to be marketed as "oilfish" by the FDA. Escolar are considered similar by some to Chilean sea bass and black cod with their jelly-like, oil-rich flavoured flesh. They range throughout most tropical to the temperate seas in deep water.

PHYSICAL DESCRIPTION

Max length: 200 cm SL male/unsexed; (Ref. 6181);
Common length: 150 cm SL male/unsexed; (Ref. 6181);
Max. published weight: 45.0 kg (Ref. 3403)

Escolar body coloration is a uniform dark brown becoming darker and closer to black with age. They have well developed pelvic fins with one spine and five soft rays. The fish has a prominent lateral keel and can grow up to 2 meters in length.

The escolar can be confused with the oilfish, *Ruvettus pretiosus,* (sometimes called the "castor oil" fish), because it is highly purgative. Both fish are uniformly dark-colored; however, the oilfish lacks the rounded tail of the escolar, with the tell-tale mackerel-like small finlets behind the dorsal and anal fins. Although both fish are oily and cater to similar markets, the flesh of the oilfish is dark and cooked fillets are reddish in color, versus white for the escolar.

Also Known As
Butterfish/
White Tuna

FishBase Name
Escolar

**International
Recognitions**
Spain— Escolar
negro
France— Escolier
noir
Japan—
Aburasokomutsu;
Barakuta

LANDINGS AND VALUES

Escolar are distributed tropically and temperately in most oceans and found on both coasts of North America. They are bathopelagic, open ocean fish found at depths between 200– 1,100meters. They live mainly on the continental slope, migrating vertically at night. It is almost always a bycatch of tuna longline fisheries. In the continental United States it is usually caught in the Gulf of Mexico from late winter through spring.

Escolar US Landings by Year — Nominal Data Value in $US (000); Quantity in tonnes; (NMFS)					
	2004	**2005**	**2006**	**2007**	**2008**
Value	116	71	79	113	119
Quantity	76	45	48	63	51

In 2008, 51 tonnes of escolar was landed in the US, valued at $119,000 (see table). Most of the catches (64%) in 2008 were caught in Louisiana. The rest was mostly caught on the Florida East Coast. The gear used was mostly long lines with hooks.

Endangered Status: Considered vulnerable due to late maturity, but not evaluated for IUCN status.

COMMERCIAL USES

Raw escolar is bright white to light creamish colour. When cooked it becomes a juicy snow white colour. Escolar is a rich fish popular in Hawaii, known as "walu." It is great for grilling and the distinctive taste holds up well to other strongly flavored fish such as Chilean seabass.

Escolar is consumed in European and Asian countries as well as the US; sometimes as sushi or sashimi. It is often mislabelled as white tuna or albacore, butterfish, oilfish or Hawaiian butter fish. It may also be sold as codfish, orange roughy or sea bass. Consumption of escolar can have adverse digestive effects known as keriorrhea, resulting in stomach cramps, diarrhea, headaches, nausea, and vomiting. However, it is the oilfish, *Ruvettus pretiosus* that is generally considered more threatening in this regard. Hence, although the FDA has issued a warning and fact sheets explaining potential adverse effects and a recommendation that escolar should not be marketed in interstate commerce, it is safe for consumption. A first time consumer may want to start with small fillets and/or tail flesh (where oil is less highly concentrated).

Wax components of escolar oil have some application in the medical and cosmetic fields.

LIFE CYCLE

Not much is known on the life cycle of escolar. They feed on squid, crustaceans, and a variety of fishes.

FLOUNDER, ARROWTOOTH

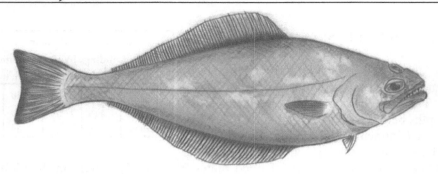

Arrowtooth Flounder, *Reinhardtius stomias*

GENERAL

Arrowtooth flounder (family Pleuronectidae) are one of the most abundant fishes in the Gulf of Alaska and are a significant food source for stellar sea lions. *FishBase* indentifies the species by the common name, "arrow-tooth flounder" and Latin name of *Atheresthes stomias,* the latter considered a synonym in *ITIS.*

PHYSICAL DESCRIPTION

Max length: 84.0 cm TL male/unsexed; (Ref. 2850);
Common length: 50.0 cm TL male/unsexed; (Ref. 56527);
Max. published weight: 8,600 g (Ref. 56527);
Max. reported age: 17 years (Ref. 56527)

Arrowtooth flounder are right eyed with an elongated diamond body shape and a crescent shaped caudal fin. The lateral line is nearly straight and curved over the pectoral fin. Eye side is a uniform dark gray brown to olive brown. The blind side is dirty white to light gray and scales are darker at the edges. The dorsal fin originates in the middle of the eye.

Although at first it may seem difficult to distinguish the various flatfishes, fishermen have found some "rules of thumb." For example, the mouth of the arrowtooth flounder is very large with two rows of arrow shaped teeth. The blackback has a black back; the gray sole is gray-brown on top and gray-white underneath with many small specks; the yellowtail is yellow near its tail and fins. The summer flounder has 5 distinctive colored spots always in the same place on its back.

Also Known As
Arrowtooth
Halibut/
Turbot/
Paltus

FishBase Name
Arrow-tooth
Flounder

International Recognitions
Spain—Halibut
del Pacífico
France—Faux flétan
du Pacifique
Denmark—Stillehav-
shellefisk

Common Flounders	Scientific Name	Range	US Landings		Canada Landings	
			1989 MT	2008 MT	1989 MT	2008 MT
Arrowtooth	*Reinhardtius stomias*	N. Pacific	4,435	39,173	123	11
Blackback	*Pseudopleuronectes americanus*	Atlantic	6,995	2,306	4,658	1,591
Witch (Gray Sole)	*Glyptocephalus cynoglossus*	N. Atlantic.	2,378	984	10,844	1,474
Southern	*Paralichthys lethostigma*	Mid-Atlantic	1,480	1,216	N/A	N/A
Summer	*Paralichthys dentatus*	Mid-Atlantic	8,182	4,131	N/A	N/A
Yellowtail	*Limanda ferruginea*	Atlantic	5,594	1,639	6,954	10,434
Total "flounder" (excludes plaice and sole, but includes other flounders not shown)			**34,145**	**49,790**	**23,704**	**13,801**

LANDINGS AND VALUES

Arrowtooth flounder is distributed along the outer continental shelf of the Pacific coast from Northern California to the Bering Sea. In the US, 39,173 tonnes of arrowtooth flounder, valued at $6.8 million, was landed in 2008 (see table). Note that the average catch for the 5-year period 2004-2008 was 24,000 tonnes, so 2008 catches were exceptionally high. In fact, arrowtooth accounted for almost 80% of US flounder landings in 2008 (i.e., excluding sole, plaice and larger flatfishes). Most of 2008 catch (93%) was in Alaska. The rest was mostly caught in Oregon, Washington and California.

Arrowtooth Flounder US Landings by Year — Nominal Data Value in $US (000); Quantity in tonnes; (NMFS)					
	2004	2005	2006	2007	2008
Value	2,089	3,680	3,924	3,263	6,789
Quantity	12,757	21,356	24,048	22,426	39,173

Arrowtooth Flounder Canadian Landings by Year — Nominal Data Value in $Cdn (000); Quantity in tonnes; (DFO)					
	2004	2005	2006	2007	2008
Value	3	11	23	11	12
Quantity	26	10	21	10	11

The gear used was bottom trawls, flatfish nets and other unspecified gear. In Canada, 11 tonnes, valued at $12,000 was landed in 2008, all in BC (see table). **Aquaculture Status:** Research stage (NOAA). **Endangered Status:** Arrowtooth are not overfished.

The total 2008 US landings for **all flounders** (Atlantic and Pacific, excluding plaice and sole) was 49,790 tonnes, valued at $55.3 million (see table); as compared to 1989 when 34,145 tonnes was landed, valued at approximately $82.3 million (not shown). In 2008, Canadian landings of **all flounders** (Atlantic and Pacific, except plaice and sole) totaled 13,801 tonnes, valued at approximately $10.4 million (see table); as compared to 1989 when 23,704 tonnes was landed.

COMMERCIAL USES

The arrowtooth has the same genus as turbot (see entry in this book); however, it tends to fall-apart and become very mushy when cooked. Recently, food additives have been successful in stopping this breakdown, increasing the marketability of arrowtooth flounder products as inexpensive flounder. However, the fresh catch is not well appreciated by many flounder lovers. It is often used as animal feed, but also in fish cakes and stews.

All Flounder (excludes Sole and Plaice) US Landings by Year — Nominal Data Value in $US (000); Quantity in tonnes; (NMFS)					
	2004	2005	2006	2007	2008
Value	67,926	68,032	65,487	57,507	55,329
Quantity	37,821	41,003	38,617	33,792	49,790

All Flounder (excludes Sole and Plaice) Canadian Landings by Year — Nominal Data Value in $Cdn (000); Quantity in tonnes; (DFO)					
	2004	2005	2006	2007	2008
Value	14,405	15,020	4,491	7,051	10,433
Quantity	16,867	17,443	3,942	7,451	13,801

LIFE CYCLE

Arrowtooth can be found from Alaska to California at depths between 160 and 1,600 feet. They are most commonly found over sand or sandy gravel bottoms and occasionally over low-relief rock-sponge bottoms. Spawning season varies by location, later in the season in the more northern latitudes. Males are sexually mature between 3 and 7 while females mature between 4 and 8. Eggs are fertilized externally and females often spawn multiple times per season. Eggs and larvae are pelagic, settling to the bottom after 4 weeks. They eat copepods and eggs in larval stages and smaller fish as juveniles and adults. They can live up to 27 years.

FLOUNDER OR SOLE

**Witch Flounder
(also called Gray Sole)**

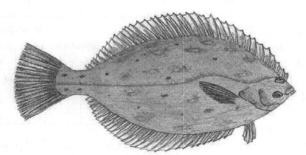

Blackback (Winter) Flounder
Pseudopleuronectes americanus

GENERAL

The **blackback flounder** (family Pleuronectidae) also known as "winter flounder" in Canada and *FishBase*, derives this latter name from its inshore winter migration in the mid-Northwest Atlantic range of its habitat. It is one of several small flatfishes usually marketed as flounder, but sometimes (correctly, in this case) as sole. Other common flounders include the arrowtooth, summer flounder (fluke), southern flounder, witch flounder (also known as gray "sole") windowpane and yellowtail flounder. The witch flounder overlaps the winter flounder habitat in North America, but is also found in the Eastern Atlantic. (Also see entries on other flounders, American plaice and sole in this book.)

PHYSICAL DESCRIPTION

Max length: 64.0 cm TL male/unsexed; (Ref. 7251);
Max. published weight: 3,600 g (Ref. 7251);
Max. reported age: 14 years (Ref. 52686)

Also Known As
Winter Flounder/
Lemon Sole/
Georges Bank Flounder

FishBase Name
Winter flounder

International Recognitions
Spain— Solla roja
France— Limande plie rouge
Italy— Sogliola limanda
Germany— Winterflunder

The blackback flounder has a small mouth just in front of the eyes, which usually lie on the right side of the fish. The body is completely covered with scales. The upper half has rough scales, even on the head, and is dark reddish-brown to almost black (hence, "blackback"). Depending on the local environment, this upper half can be spotted or mottled. It is one of the flatfishes that can alter pigmentation to match its surroundings. The underside, or blind side, is usually white with a yellowish tinge. This side is also scaled, though these scales are generally much smoother.

LANDINGS AND VALUES

The blackback flounder usually inhabits shallow waters from southern Labrador to Chesapeake Bay. Although often landed as a by-catch, fishing is most efficient with otter trawls and purse seines. Other methods include handlines, weirs, drag trawls, baited hooks and gillnets. US landings of blackback flounder totaled about 7,000 tonnes in 1989, valued at nearly $20 million (not shown). In 2008, US blackback flounder landings had declined to about 2,300 tonnes, valued at $10 million (see table). Canadian landings of blackback flounder in 2008 totaled 1,591 tonnes, valued at almost $2.2 million; as compared to the 1989 total of almost 4,452 tonnes valued at nearly $3.53 million (not shown).

Blackback (Winter) Flounder US Landings by Year — Nominal Data Value in $US (000); Quantity in tonnes; (NMFS)					
	2004	2005	2006	2007	2008
Value	11,791	10,690	12,138	12,356	9,683
Quantity	4,914	3,667	2,746	2,675	2,306

Blackback (Winter) Flounder Canadian Landings by Year — Nominal Data Value in $Cdn (000); Quantity in tonnes; (DFO)					
	2004	2005	2006	2007	2008
Value	2,235	1,742	1,771	2,259	2,171
Quantity	1,736	1,505	1,394	1,624	1,591

Endangered Status: Overfished/subject to overfishing in major habitats.
Aquaculture Status: Candidate for stock enhancement programs.

COMMERCIAL USES

All East Coast flatfish and some West Coast flatfish (e.g., arrowtooth, starry flounder and Pacific sanddab) are generally marketed as flounder and not sole, but there are exceptions. American plaice, a flatfish, is marketed as plaice; and some flounders can also be marketed as sole, fluke or dab. For example; East Coast blackback flounder and witch flounder/gray sole [*FishBase* name: witch flounder] can be marketed as either sole or flounder, according to *The Seafood List*. In North America, sole was traditionally a market name used for most West Coast flatfish; however, all sole can now be marketed as flounder, according to *The Seafood List*. Blackback flounder is available in all fresh and frozen forms, including whole, fillets, IQF and in blocks. Some is used in secondary products, such as canned chicken haddie. (Also see plaice and sole entries.)

LIFE CYCLE

The blackback's peak spawning season is from February to March in New England and later in Canadian waters. Depending on their size, females can produce up to 2.5 million eggs, but the average is about 500,000. The blackback differs from other demersal fish in that its eggs sink to the bottom in clusters. When larvae come out of the egg they swim upright, much like any other fish. As they mature, they roll onto their left side and the bottom eye moves around to the top, or right side. In northern waters the females mature at about 4 years of age and a bit earlier in more southerly locations. The males mature at around 2 or 3 years of age. The blackback's diet consists mainly of small invertebrates that live on the sea floor: worms, small crustaceans and fish eggs. Generally, the blackback is sedentary; movement is primarily motivated by food, currents and predators. They tolerate low levels of salinity and can be found in brackish water.

FLOUNDER OR FLUKE

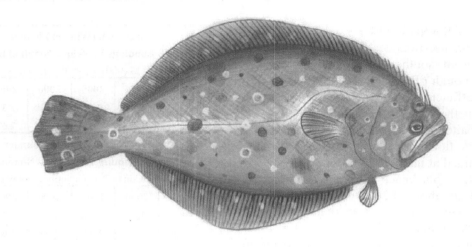

Summer Flounder, *Paralichthys dentatus*

GENERAL

The **summer flounder** and the southern flounder, *Paralichthys lethostigma*, are closely related species (same genus), with overlapping ranges and both are also known as, and marketed as, fluke. All commercially harvested flatfish in North America are right-eyed, except for fluke, which is a left-eyed flatfish (both eyes are on the left side of its body when viewed from above with the top fin facing up).

PHYSICAL DESCRIPTION

Max length: 94.0 cm TL male/unsexed; (Ref. 7251);
Max. published weight: 12.0 kg (Ref. 7251);
Max. reported age: 9 years (Ref. 52684)

Summer flounder bodies are laterally-compressed with both eyes on the left side. They are able to blend into their surroundings by changing the color and apparent texture of their skin.

Southern flounder and summer flounder, where their ranges overlap (North Carolina to North Florida), are difficult to easily distinguish from each other. Both fishes often have similar coloration, as well as a highly flattened body with eyes on the left side. In southern flounder, the caudle fin is separate and pectoral fins are small or absent. All other flatfish are right-eyed and so it is easy to distinguish fluke from these species.

Also Known As
Fluke/
Northern Fluke/
Plaice

FishBase Name
Summer
Flounder

**International
Recognitions**
Spain—Falso
halibut del
Canadá
France—Cardea
u d'été
Denmark—Som
merhvarre

LANDINGS AND VALUES

Summer flounder is benthic oceanic fish that lives at depths of 10–180 meters and is found in the North Atlantic from Maine to Northern Florida. Adults prefer sandy bottom areas where they can burrow but will also use a variety of mid and lower estuary environments including salt marshes and seagrass beds because of the sandy or muddy bottoms. In contrast, southern flounder are found from North Carolina to Texas, except for South Florida.

Summer Flounder US Landings by Year – Nominal Data Value in $US (000); Quantity in tonnes; (NMFS)					
	2004	**2005**	**2006**	**2007**	**2008**
Value	28,882	30,118	28,643	23,384	22,164
Quantity	8,140	7,749	6,332	4,344	4,130

Summer Flounder Canadian Landings by Year – Nominal Data Value in $Cdn (000); Quantity in tonnes; (DFO)					
	2004	**2005**	**2006**	**2007**	**2008**
Value	6	0	0	0	0
Quantity	5	0	0	0	0

In the US 4,130 tonnes of summer flounder, valued at $22.2 million, was comercially landed in 2008 (see table). In 2008, most of the catch (75%) was landed in North Carolina, Virginia, RI and New Jersey, with other landings in all states except Maine, NH and Gulf coast. The gear used was mostly gill nets and otter trawl. Summer flounder is occasionally landed in Canada, but is not a major fishery (see table). **Endangered Status:** Not overfished. **Aquaculture Status:** Studies show promise for farming.

Southern Flounder US Landings by Year – Nominal Data Value in $US (000); Quantity in tonnes; (NMFS)					
	2004	**2005**	**2006**	**2007**	**2008**
Value	3,971	3,492	4,962	5,081	5,762
Quantity	1,150	858	1,076	981	1,216

In addition, US commercial landings of southern flounder totaled 1,216 tonnes, valued at almost $5.8 million in 2008 (see table). Almost all was landed in North Carolina, with a little from the Gulf.

Recreational Fisheries: Approximately 3,600 tonnes of summer flounder and 700 tonnes of southern flounder were recreationally fished in 2008 in the US, accounting for about 85% of all flounder game fishing and almost 4% of all game fish landed.

COMMERCIAL USES

Summer flounder is highly valued commercially for its lean, white meat and delicate flavor in the US and is also exported to Japan as sashimi. Summer and southern flounder are also two of the most popular recreational fisheries on the US Atlantic/Gulf coast. Both are marketed fresh and frozen and are consumed baked, broiled, steamed and fried.

LIFE CYCLE

Summer flounder reach sexual maturity at about two years. Females range from 14.4–27 inches at maturity and can produce up to 4.19 million eggs. They release their eggs in several batches throughout the spawning season from September through February. Eggs are pelagic and will hatch in waters of the continental shelf. Larvae are transported by ocean currents towards the coast where they will eventually settle to the bottom. Larval flounder feed on zooplankton and small crustaceans. Juveniles eat more small fish and adults are opportunistic and will eat whatever they can find; for example, menhaden, bay anchovy, red and silver hake, bluefish, weakfish, rock crabs, squid, and small bivalves and crustaceans. Larval and juvenile flounder are preyed on by spiny dogfish, cod, hake and other larger fish. Adults are preyed on by sharks, rays and goosefish. Females live to about 14 years, and males 12.

FLOUNDER

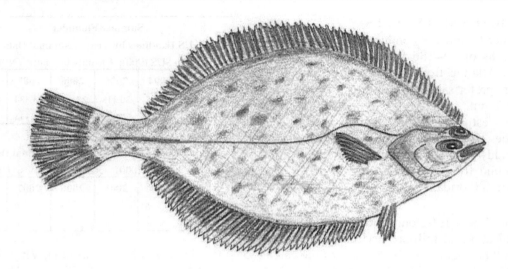

Yellowtail Flounder, *Limanda ferruginea*

GENERAL

Yellowtail flounder is from the family Pleuronectidae, of right-eyed flounders. They are distributed on bottom waters of the western Atlantic from southern Labrador, Canada to the Chesapeake Bay. There are believed to be 5 relatively distinct populations (3 within the US), which are highly non-migratory. The species became a valuable commercial species in the 1930s, with a decline in the winter flounder fishery and the increased use of new otter trawls; subsequently reaching average US catches of 14,000 tonnes in the late 1960s and early 1970s. The fishery declined considerably in following decades and has since become a benchmark species for fisheries management purposes. (Also see entries for sole, plaice, halibut, turbot and other flounders in this book.)

PHYSICAL DESCRIPTION

Max. length: 64cm TL;
Max. weight: 1,500g;
Max. age: 12 years;
Avg. age: 7 (NOAA)

The yellowtail flounder is a right eyed flounder with a highly arched lateral line. Coloration is mottled brown and tan with a white bottom to blend into their sandy bottom or gravel habitat. They are identifiable by their yellow colored tail and small mouths.

Also Known As
Rusty Dab/
Sand Dab

FishBase Name
Yellowtail
flounder

International Recognitions
Spain—Limanda
France—Limande à
queue jaune
Denmark—Gulhalet
ising
Finland—
Ruostekampela

LANDINGS AND VALUES

Yellowtail is found only in the western Atlantic from southern Labrador to Chesapeake Bay. Adults inhabit sandy to muddy bottoms in depths of 35 to 80 meters.

This species is a commercial fishery. They are caught using otter trawls, gillnets and dredges; usually in mixed species trawls.

The US fishery landed 1,639 tonnes in 2008, valued at approximately $5.4 million (see table). The Canadian fishery landed 10,434 million tonnes in 2008, valued at approximately $6.5 million tonnes.

Yellowtail Flounder US Landings by Year – Nominal Data Value in $US (000); Quantity in tonnes; (NMFS)					
	2004	2005	2006	2007	2008
Value	11,699	10,632	7,106	7,216	5,437
Quantity	7,235	4,117	1,939	1,754	1,639

Yellowtail Flounder Canadian Landings by Year – Nominal Data Value in $Cdn (000); Quantity in tonnes; (DFO)					
	2004	2005	2006	2007	2008
Value	9,780	10,677	587	2,707	6,531
Quantity	12,906	13,513	534	3,896	10,434

Endangered Status: Although there is ongoing research, the general consensus is that yellowtail is overfished, and subject to overfishing, in the US main catch areas. Hence they are under new management programs to facilitate rebuilding and maintenance of healthy stocks. **Aquaculture Status:** Yellowtail are not yet cultured, but are considered a good candidate for aquaculture because they grow quickly and have a high market value (NOAA).

COMMERCIAL USES

Yellowtail flounder is fished primarily for human consumption. It is a lean fish highly sought after in the restaurant trade in New England for its mild, sweet meat and firm texture. Yellowtail is marketed fresh and frozen as whole fish, fillets and blocks as well as fully prepared in various value-added formats.

LIFE CYCLE

Yellowtails are batch spawners during spring and summer months, peaking in May. Females grow faster than males and both mature between 2 and 3 years. After fertilization, eggs are deposited on the bottom but then float to the surface. They are pelagic drifters for about 2 months before changing form and settling to the bottom.

Yellowtail prey mainly on polychaete worms, amphipods, shrimps, isopods, other crustaceans and occasionally small fish such as sand lance and capelin; they are preyed on by spiny dogfish, and other larger fish species.

GREENLAND TURBOT

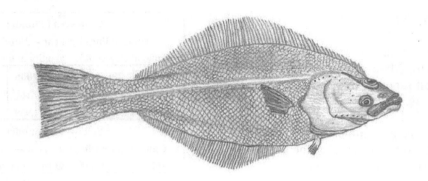

Greenland Turbot, *Reinhardtius hippoglossoides*

GENERAL

The **Greenland turbot** is one of the larger flatfish that lives near the sea bottom, at the deepwater edges of northern fishing banks. Although it is known as turbot, especially in Newfoundland, it is actually more closely related to the Atlantic halibut (but somewhat smaller) than it is to the true European turbot. In fact, it is often called Greenland "halibut" in Europe and in the Eastern US.

Like the Atlantic halibut, it is a member of the (right-eyed) flounder family Pleuronectidae, rather than the turbot family Scophthalmidae. As a flatfish, it is somewhat unusual in that it apparently spends much of its time swimming in the water column, behaving pelagically.

PHYSICAL DESCRIPTION

Max length: 80.0 cm TL male/unsexed; (Ref. 56370); 130 cm TL (female); Common length: 56.0 cm FL male/unsexed; (Ref. 55110); Max. published weight: 7,000 g (Ref. 173); Max. published weight: 45 kg; Max. reported age: 30 years (Ref. 3561)

Like other flatfish, the turbot swims on one side (the left) and has both eyes on the darker, top side (the right). Unlike other flatfishes, however, the Greenland turbot's eyes are not both fully on one side. The "left" eye only moves as far as the top edge of the forehead. Thus it actually has a better field of vision than most flatfish. Also, the underside is not the pale white color of most flatfish, but a dark grey — only a shade lighter than its dark blue to black top side. The turbot's lateral line is straight and doesn't arch around the pelvic fins as it does with the halibut. The turbot is not perfectly symmetrical and may swim with the dorsal fin upward.

Also Known As
Greenland Halibut/ Newfoundland Turbot/ Black Halibut/ Blue Halibut/ Little Halibut

FishBase Name
Greenland Halibut

International Recognitions
France—flétan noir
Germany— Schwarzer Heilbutt
Spain— hipogloso negro
Italy—halibut

LANDINGS AND VALUES

Greenland turbot is native to the icy waters on both sides of the Atlantic and Pacific oceans. In 2008, about 75% of the Canadian catch was landed on the East Coast, while 100% of the US catch was landed in Alaska. Often, it is fished using longlines, but Newfoundland fishermen also use gillnets. The small Gulf of St. Lawrence directed turbot fishery is relatively new. As recently as 1980, most landings were a by-catch of other fisheries. Catches off eastern Newfoundland and Labrador accounted for a little more than 70% of the east coast catch in 2008. Canadian landings approximated 17,000 tonnes in 1989, valued at approximately $7.5 million (not shown). In comparison, 2008 Canadian landings (Atlantic and Pacific) totaled 15,624 tonnes, valued at $25 million (see table). US landings in 2008 totaled 2,041 tonnes, value at $1.4 million (see table).

Endangered Status: Not overfished or subject to overfishing, although FAO cites declining sizes.

Turbot (Reported as Greenland Halibut) US Landings by Year — Nominal Data Value in $US (000); Quantity in tonnes; (NMFS)					
	2004	2005	2006	2007	2008
Value	684	778	550	342	1,405
Quantity	1,869	2,368	1,775	1,541	2,041

Turbot-Greenland Flounder Canadian Landings by Year — Nominal Data Value in $Cdn (000); Quantity in tonnes; (DFO)					
	2004	2005	2006	2007	2008
Value	38,431	43,530	38,131	33,487	25,042
Quantity	20,053	32,064	20,559	18,246	15,624

COMMERCIAL USES

Greenland turbot from Alaska and Canada was once shipped to the continental US as Greenland "halibut" [the present *FishBase* name]. However, due to the potential for name confusion with Pacific halibut, Greenland halibut landed in, or exported to, the US must now be labeled Greenland "turbot." The Greenland turbot is available fresh and frozen, as fillets, I.Q.F. and blocks. It is also cured and used in sticks and portions.

LIFE CYCLE

Greenland turbot generally spawn in deep, cold water. The Greenland and Labrador stocks migrate to the deep channels of Davis Strait in the winter and spawn in early spring at depths of 2,000 to 3,000 feet, where water temperatures are 32 to 39°F. Each fish lays up to 300,000 eggs, which drift for a few weeks in medium depths before rising to the surface as larvae. In the north, the shallow banks west of Disko Bay serve as important nursery grounds for the Greenland turbot. There, the larvae live at depths of about 800 feet. The Gulf of St. Lawrence stock spawns in the Laurentian Channel and the young develop in nursery areas north of Anticosti Island.

Like other flatfish, the larvae begin life as "normal" fish, swimming vertically with one eye on each side of the head. But after a number of weeks the left eye begins to migrate to the right. Soon the larvae begin swimming on one side and descend to the bottom. Male and female growth rates remain almost equal until they reach about 18 inches in length, after six or seven years. Then the males reach sexual maturity and their growth slows to almost a standstill as their body energy is redirected towards breeding. The females continue to grow and mature after about eight to nine years, when they are 28 to 30 inches in length. Most turbot feed on capelin or shrimp, though very large specimens may feed on cod, redfish, or squid. They are prey to cod and larger halibut as well as the Greenland shark, narwhales and white whales.

GREENLING

Kelp Greenling, *Hexagrammos decagrammus*

GENERAL

The **kelp greenling**, family Hexagrammidae (greenlings), includes 12 species in five genera — half of the species are in the genus *Hexagrammo* (greenlings), and 4 of these are listed under the market name greenling in *The Seafood List*. The family also includes the lingcod, *Ophiodon elongatus* and the atka mackerel, *Pleurogrammus monopterygius* (see lingcod entry in this book).

PHYSICAL DESCRIPTION

Max length: 61.0 cm TL male/unsexed;
Max. published weight: 2,100g
Max. reported age: 13 years

The body color of kelp greenlings differs between sexes. Males are gray to brownish-olive coloration, freckled with irregular blue/turquoise spots along the front of the body. Each spot is ringed by small reddish-brown spots. The interior mouth is yellowish. They may have an ocellus false eye at the end of their soft dorsal fin and the anal fin usually has one weak spine. Females have freckles all over; reddish-brown to golden spots with a gray to brownish background. Their fins are mostly yellowish-orange.

In contrast, its close relative, the atka mackerel, has a flat, narrow body, with a yellow belly and very noticeable alternating tan and dark vertical stripes. It has five lateral lines on each side and a long, gray or tan, uninterrupted dorsal fin. Also a relative, the ling cod's most noticeable feature is its large gaping mouth, with a projecting lower jaw and numerous sharp teeth, interspersed with fangs.

Also Known As
Rock Trout/ Sea Trout/ Boregat/ Bodieron

FishBase Name
Kelp Greenling

International Recognitions
Denmark— Tanggrønling

LANDINGS AND VALUES

The kelp greenling is a demersal marine fish found in the north Pacific Ocean from the Aleutian Islands west and south to southern California. It locates in rocky shore areas, kelp beds and sandy bottom areas down to about 40 meters depth. It is a small commercial fishery where 23 tonnes were landed in the US in 2008, values at $257,000 (see table). With only 2 tonnes landed in 2008, it is an even smaller commercial fishery in Canada (see table). It is usually caught as bycatch in hook and line fisheries.

Kelp Greenling US Landings by Year — Nominal Data Value in $US (000); Quantity in tonnes; (NMFS)					
	2004	2005	2006	2007	2008
Value	237	232	171	201	257
Quantity	25	23	16	20	23

Kelp Greenling Canadian Landings by Year — Nominal Data Value in $Cdn (000); Quantity in tonnes; (DFO)					
	2004	2005	2006	2007	2008
Value	0	0	1	0	5
Quantity	0	0	0	0	2

The atka mackerel is the largest fishery in the greenlings family; however, on a price per weight basis, the lingcod is still the more lucrative fishery. All three species overlap the same range in the North West Pacific.

There is a small recreational fishery for kelp greenling (15 tonnes in 2008), but a much larger one for lingcod. Atka mackerel are generally caught offshore in deep waters, and are not a significant recreational fishery.

Atka Mackerel US Landings by Year — Nominal Data Value in $US (000); Quantity in tonnes; (NMFS)					
	2004	2005	2006	2007	2008
Value	10,795	14,893	15,703	14,253	19,523
Quantity	49,180	58,733	59,337	57,589	57,620

COMMERCIAL USES

Kelp greenling has a market in the Asian communities in Vancouver, Seattle, San Francisco and Los Angeles. There is also a demand in the aquarium trade. Most of the atka mackerel catch is exported to Japan.

LIFE CYCLE

Kelp greenling courtship occurs in late fall with spawning from October to December. Males guard the nest at which females will be courted for egg deposition. Eggs hatch from January to February. Juveniles school together over rock faces before settling and going through metamorphosis into the benthic adult. Adults are sexually dimorphic. Males are brownish-orange and females white with orange spots. They feed on crustaceans, polychaete worms, brittle stars, molluscs and small fishes. Juveniles are prey for steelheads and salmon.

Atka mackerel habitate waters below 300 meters and can be found as deep as 500 meters. They begin reaching maturity at about 3 years of age and migrate to spawn, moving from the edge of the continental shelf to more shallow, nearshore waters. Here they form dense spawning aggregations. In the Aleutians, females batch spawn from July through September. Their eggs are deposited in crevices between rocks, and stick to this substrate due to the eggs' adhesive properties. Males guard the eggs for 40-45 days, until they hatch. Little is known about their juvenile life. Atka mackerel is considered an important forage fish for sea lions, flounders, cod and other marine fishes and mammals.

GRENADIER

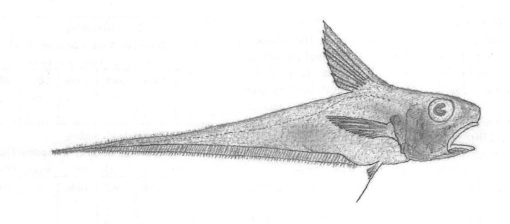

Rock Grenadier, *Coryphaenoides rupestris*

GENERAL

Rattail for lunch? North American research on grenadiers, or "rattails," is relatively recent and much is still unknown about these fishes here. However, the experience of various (mostly eastern) European countries that have fished them in the past indicates that grenadier meat is of high quality and handles and stores well. **Rock grenadier** fillets are white with a cod-like texture and have been described as being quite sweet tasting — perhaps worth trying for lunch, or dinner.

PHYSICAL DESCRIPTION

Maximum Size: 110 cm TL (male/unsexed; Ref. 35388);
Max. Published Weight: 1.7 kg (Ref. 40637); Max. Reported Age: 54 years

Grenadiers (family Macrouridae) of which there are many different species, have a large head and a long body that tapers to a point, hence the name "rattails." The rock grenadier is brown to grayish in color with black to brownish-gray fins. The head is broad and soft with a broad rounded snout that has a large blunt tubercular scute at its tip and a small barbel on the chin.

LANDINGS AND VALUES

Grenadiers are worldwide in distribution and can be found from the Arctic to the Antarctic. They live on, or near, the sea bottom. Some prefer the great depths of the middle ocean, while others are content with the shallower continental slopes. However, typically, they are a cold water and deep ocean fish, found in depths from 1,000 to 8,000 feet deep. The rock grenadier is one of about seven species of grenadier off the Atlantic Coast that has been available in commercial quantities in the past. However, its delayed maturity, slow growth, long lifespan and low fecundity means it is not resilient to heavy fishing pressure. It is believed that many grenadiers, including rock grenadier, have been over-exploited in many parts of their North Atlantic range.

Also Known As
Round Nose Grenadier

FishBase Name
Roundnose grenadier

International Recognitions
Spain—Granadero de roca
France—Grenadier de roche
Japan—Sokodaro
Germany—Grenadierfisch

Neither the United States nor Canada has established a directed fishery for grenadiers, although small catches are reported from year to year, usually as a by-catch. Several stocks have been identified off the Atlantic east coast, especially near Newfoundland and Labrador. In the past, fishing was usually done by large factory freezer trawlers from distant water fleets (DWF), in water depths from 2,300 to 6,500 feet. The method used was bottom or mid-water trawls and most of the fishing was done in the last half of the year, when ice posed the least problems to navigation and the fishing operation.

Grenadiers US Landings by Year — Nominal Data Value in $US (000); Quantity in tonnes; (NMFS)					
	2004	2005	2006	2007	2008
Value	62	59	39	47	51
Quantity	180	161	123	128	121

All Grenadiers Canadian Landings by Year — Nominal Data Value in $Cdn (000); Quantity in tonnes; (DFO)					
	2004	2005	2006	2007	2008
Value	45	44	41	21	12
Quantity	141	154	103	42	19

Since much is still unknown about these fishes off North America, and since fishing by Europeans in the North American EEZs has declined in past decades, it could be a viable fishery. The Total Allowable Catch (TAC) for EU vessels (mostly France) for Atlantic rock grenadier in 2003 was set at 5,106 tonnes, but catches were double that in 2001. According to *FishBase*, the commercial fishery of the blue grenadier (Called Hoki on *The Seafood List*), *Macruronus novaezelandiae,* has been certified by the New Zealand Marine Stewardship Council as sustainable; a species also believed to be of similarly late maturity to major Atlantic species. In 2008, US grenadier landings (all species) were 121 tonnes, valued at $51,000, while Canadian landings were 19 tonnes, valued at $12,000 (see tables).

Roughhead or "onion-eye" grenadier (*Macrourus berglax*) (not on *The Seafood List*, but listed as onion-eye on *ITIS* and *FishBase*) accounted for more than two-thirds of the catch in Canada in 2008.

COMMERCIAL USES

Past Canadian studies have shown that this fish has a high potential for human consumption. If the fish is gutted and iced immediately after being caught, the keeping time is more than 18 days, which is far better than most other whitefish species. These studies also showed the rock grenadier has an excellent shelf life: up to 15 months when stored at -41° F. Dehydration problems at this storage temperature can be alleviated through careful packaging.

LIFE CYCLE

It is believed that grenadiers grow slowly and spawn late, even into their teens. Past research has suggested that, in the Northwest Atlantic, spawning must occur at great depths, since very few sexually mature specimens have been found near the surface. However, the incidence of mature fish increases with depth. Studies have suggested there may be spring spawners, fall spawners, or perhaps both. They are prey for the Greenland turbot at certain times of the year. [*FishBase*: Rock grenadiers form large schools at 600 to 900 m depth (Ref. 9988). They feed on a variety of fish and invertebrates, but primarily on pelagic crustaceans such as shrimps, amphipods and cumaceans (i.e., hooded shrimp). Squid and lantern fishes constitute a lesser portion of the diet.]

GROUPER

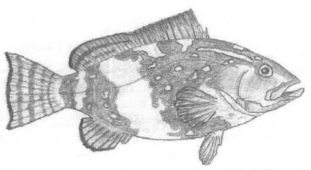

Red Grouper, *Epinephelus morio*

GENERAL

The **red grouper** is one of more than 30 grouper species found in North America belonging to the large and varied family Serranidae (sea basses* and groupers). This species is one of the most common groupers along with the gag grouper (*Mycteroperca microlepis*), the black grouper (*Mycteroperca bonaci*), the snowy grouper (*Epinephelus niveatus*) and the yellowedge grouper (*Epinephelus flavolimbatus*). Although termed "groupers," these fish are usually found alone and not in groups.[*also "seabasses" in *FishBase*]

Groupers are often known to be curious, intelligent animals that, after repeated contact with divers, will become so tame they will actually come out of their lairs to meet them. In fact, diving photographers have had difficulty keeping the Nassau grouper (*E. striatus*) far enough away to photograph it.

PHYSICAL DESCRIPTION

Maximum Size: 125 cm TL (male/unsexed; Ref. 26340);
Max. Published Weight: 23.0 kg (Ref. 9710); Max. Reported Age: 25 years.

The groupers are perch-like fishes characterized by a large mouth, projecting lower jaws with canine like teeth, a single-notched dorsal fin and eleven dorsal spines. Groupers may change color with maturation, as well as in different light intensity, becoming redder as the light dims. The red grouper has a reddish hue and often a blotchy body. It is distinguished from other *Epinephelus* groupers by a longer second dorsal spine, and an unnotched spinal membrane. Further, the pelvic fins of the red grouper are shorter than the pectorals and are inserted posterior to the pectoral fin base. The opposite is true for the Warsaw grouper, *E. nigritus*; the yellowedge grouper, *E. flavolimbatus*; and the misty grouper, *E. mystacinus*; all of which have a longer pelvic fin than pectoral fin, and the pelvic fins are inserted anterior to the pectoral fin base. Red groupers are distinguished from *Mycteroperca* spp. by having a shorter body, 11 dorsal spines, 9 soft anal fin rays and by thicker skin at the base of the dorsal and anal fins (Fischer 1978).

The size of groupers varies: *FishBase* reports the yellowfin grouper as the smallest of the common groupers with a maximum published weight of 18.5 kg, followed by the gag at 36.5 kg and the black grouper at 100 kg. By far, the two largest groupers are the Warsaw grouper (*E. nigritus*) that has been recorded as 198 kg and the goliath grouper (formerly known as the giant Atlantic Jewfish), *E. itajara*, which can reach 455 kg.

Also Known As
Cherna
Americana/
Negre

FishBase Name
Red grouper

International Recognitions
Spain—
Mero americano
France—
Mérou rouge
Japan—
Tsumagurohata
Germany—Roter Grouper

LANDINGS AND VALUES

The red grouper, like most groupers, is a tropical or warm temperate species. It is caught on the East Coast from as far north as Massachusetts, east to Bermuda, and south to the Gulf of Mexico, the Caribbean and Brazil. This non-schooling bottom fish prefers rocky habitats, coral reefs, shipwrecks, or manmade structures

All Groupers (excluding gag, graysby, hind and sand perch) US Landings by Year — Nominal Data Value in $US (000); Quantity in tonnes; (NMFS)					
	2004	**2005**	**2006**	**2007**	**2008**
Value	19,338	18,635	20,217	17,945	19,926
Quantity	4,230	3,845	3,731	3,024	3,513

such as piers. It is found as deep as 75 fathoms (450 feet). The large goliath (Jewfish) grouper found off the coasts of Florida and in the Gulf of Mexico was once prized by spear fishermen. While certain grouper species are valued as both sport fish and food fish, the red grouper is the most important species in the commercial fishery. The principal commercial fisheries for this species are in Florida, Cuba and Mexico. **Endangered Status:** The goliath, Warsaw and Nassau groupers are all now designated "species of concern" and the Jewfish and Warsaw groupers, in particular, are considered "critically endangered" on the IUCN Red List.

Red Grouper US Landings by Year — Nominal Data Value in $US (000); Quantity in tonnes; (NMFS)					
	2004	**2005**	**2006**	**2007**	**2008**
Value	13,808	13,753	15,265	12,698	15,241
Quantity	3,187	2,973	2,905	2,246	2,824

In 2008 the US catch of all groupers (excluding gag, graysby, hind and sand perch – see next entries) was 3,513 tonnes, valued at approximately $19.9 million (see table). In comparison, US landings of all groupers in 1989 were 5,990 tonnes, valued at approximately $21.4 million (not shown). The red grouper accounted for about 2/3rds of the catch at that time. Red grouper, which accounted for more than 76% of the US catch of all groupers in 2008, is reported in a separate table as 2,824 tonnes, valued at $15.2 million. Grouper is not a reported fishery in Canada.

COMMERCIAL USES

This is an important food fish that is especially popular in Mexico. It is available fresh and frozen as fillets or steaks. (For additional information, see other grouper and sea bass entries.)

LIFE CYCLE

Groupers generally spawn in aggregation in the winter and spring. After hatching, the fish undergo a larval period before moving close to the shore where the young groupers hide amid floating eel grass or seaweed. The red grouper, like other members of this family, feeds on small fishes and crustaceans. Some groupers can change the color of their skin as they move from one environment to another. This characteristic makes the grouper an effective predator of smaller fishes, rather than the prey of larger ones. However, the curious nature of the grouper means they are vulnerable to armed spear fishermen and fast-swimming sharks.

The majority of the groupers, like sea basses, are "hermaphroditic," (i.e., are male and female at the same time). Most red grouper females are "protogynous hermaphrodites" and will transform to males between the ages of 7 to 14 (*FishBase Ref. 55367*). Since older fish are larger, they are often the first target of human fishers and hunters. Hence, there is a possibility of creating an imbalance in the natural sex ratio of the population, since many female groupers may never reach the terminal male stage. This could be a factor limiting reproduction.

GROUPER OR GAG

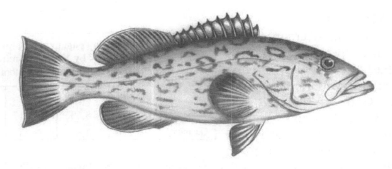

Gag, *Mycteroperca microlepis*

GENERAL

Gag grouper belongs to the family Serranidae of groupers and sea basses (subfamily Epinephelinae and tribe Epinephelini – *ITIS*). The genus name, *Mycteroperca*, includes about 15 species and about 10 of these are found in *The Seafood List.* The species name, *microlepis*, derived from the Greek, "micro" or small and "lepis" meaning scale, are references to the small scales covering the body of this fish. When stressed, the gag can produce a thumping sound by contracting the muscles surrounding the swim bladder, similar to the abilities of the croaker and drum. Sand perch (*Diplectrum formosum*) is another species in the family Serranidae properly marketed as grouper. (Also see other grouper entries in this book.)

Also Known As
Velvet Rockfish/
Small-scaled
Rockfish

FishBase Name
Gag

International Recognitions
Spain—Cuna
aguají
France—Badèche
baillou

PHYSICAL DESCRIPTION

Max length: 145 cm TL male/unsexed; (Ref. 40637);
Common length: 50.0 cm TL male/unsexed; (Ref. 3708); Max. published weight: 36.5 kg (Ref. 40637).

Gag grouper have a very large horizontal mouth with the lower jaw protruding beyond the upper jaw and two canine-like teeth. They have long, compressed bodies. The body is brownish-grey gray with dark worm-like markings along the side. Coloration is highly variable and changes with age. Large gag are darker than younger, which have numerous dark brown or charcoal kiss-like markings along the sides. They can be confused with black grouper but are distinguished by their deeply notched preopercles, curved caudal fin and white margins. Caudal fins and anal fins are dark with white margins and a slightly truncate caudal fin.

Sand perch have elongated, slender and slightly compressed body. The head, eyes and mouth are large and there are two clusters of spines projecting between the eyes and the gill covering. The dorsal fins are continuous and have many dark brown and orange alternating bars and blue horizontal lines that extend along the head as well. The upper lobe of the caudal fin is extended in adults. This sand perch (marketed as grouper) should not be mistaken for the following species marketed as sandperch or sand perch: *Pseudopercis semifasciata* (Argentinean sandperch) *Pseudopercis numida* (the Namorado sandperch – marketed as "sand perch") and sandperches in the genera *Mugiloides* spp. and *Parapercis* spp.

LANDINGS AND VALUES

Gags are found offshore along reefs and rocky bottoms in the western Atlantic from North Carolina through to the Gulf of Mexico and Yucatan Peninsula and into the Caribbean. They can be found in groups of 5-50 individuals, but are usually seen as solitary individuals. Gags are commercially and recreationally fished and are

Gag US Landings by Year — Nominal Data Value in $US (000); Quantity in tonnes; (NMFS)					
	2004	2005	2006	2007	2008
Value	9,390	9,079	6,134	6,981	7,026
Quantity	1,675	1,521	928	944	926

considered one of the more valuable species in the southeast. In 2008, 926 tonnes were landed in the US, valued at approximately $7 million (see table). In addition, an estimated 1,850 tonnes of *Mycteroperca* spp. were landed recreationally, including gags (not shown). **Endangered Status:** Vulnerable to overfishing; NMFS does not consider it overfished as yet.

Sand perch are found in grassy inshore bays and banks ranging from North Carolina to southern Florida and into the Gulf of Mexico. In 2008, less than 1/2 tonne was commercially landed, valued at approximately $1,000 (see table).

Sand Perch US Landings by Year — Nominal Data Value in $US (000); Quantity in tonnes; (NMFS)					
	2004	2005	2006	2007	2008
Value	0	1	3	3	1
Quantity	0	--	1	2	--

COMMERCIAL USES

Grouper has a mild flavor described as a cross between bass and halibut. Gag and black grouper are considered firmer in texture, but less sweet than red grouper. Grouper is grilled, fried, poached, steamed, baked, broiled, sautéed, and used in soups or chowders. Cases of ciguatera poisoning have been reported. Sand perch are used commercially as a food fish, a recreational fishery, and as bait fish.

LIFE CYCLE

Gag males mature later than females at 8 years while females mature between 5-6 years. Similar to other serranids, gags are protogynous hermaphrodites; i.e., they begin life as female, however after a few years of spawning as a female, some change sex, becoming functional males. They spawn from January to May in water temperatures of about 70 degrees. Eggs are pelagic and once they hatch, larvae migrate to sea grass beds and estuaries, oyster reefs, marshes, and mangroves. They feed on crustaceans, small fishes, cephalopods, and shrimp. Their predators include sharks and other large fishes.

The sand perch is primarily a warm-water, inshore fish. Offshore it is usually associated with wrecks and reefs and occasionally deep channels. It prefers to live in holes that are either built or pre-existing and can be very territorial. The size of the territory increases with the size of the fish. Sand perch are synchronous hermaphrodites - individual fish possess both male and female organs, producing sperm and eggs at the same time. Spawning at 2-3 years peaks in spring and early summer, usually offshore in deep water. It is believed that mating pairs form and result in cross-fertilization. Eggs are released into the water column and fertilized externally. They feed on benthic crustaceans and fish. Maximum size is about 12 inches and life span is about 6-7 years.

GROUPER OR HIND

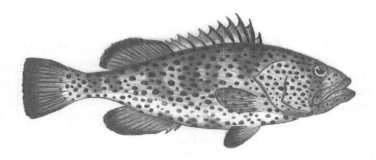

Red Hind, *Epinephelus guttatus*

GENERAL

Red hind is a member of the family Serranidae, which includes seabasses and groupers. The genus *Epinephelus* includes about 100 species and about 33 are listed in *The Seafood List;* most *Epinephelus* are listed under the market name grouper, but two are listed only as "hind" and one only as "cabrilla." **Red hind** can be marketed as either grouper or hind. Red hind are known to ambush their prey from hiding spots catching them unaware and engulfing them whole, but are easily approached by divers.

Graysby (*Cephalopholis cruentata*), marketed as grouper and scamp (*Mycteroperca phenax*), marketed as scamp, are two other commercial and recreational species in the Serranidae family. Both are distributed throughout the western central Atlantic from North Carolina through southern Florida and the Gulf of Mexico including the Bahamas and the Caribbean (see scamp entry in this book).

Also Known As
Spotted Jewfish/ Strawberry Grouper/ Black Grouper

FishBase Name
Red Hind

International Recognitions
Spain—Mero colorado
France—Mérou couronné

PHYSICAL DESCRIPTION

Max length: 76.0 cm TL male/unsexed; (Ref. 5222); Common length: 40.0 cm TL male/unsexed; (Ref. 5217); Max. published weight: 25.0 kg (Ref. 5217); Max. reported age: 17 years (Ref. 3095)

Both the red hind and the rock hind (*Epinephelus adscensionis*) have numerous dark spots on a lighter background. This distinguishes them from the speckled hind (*Epinephelus drummondhayi*) now on the US "species of concern" list. Red hind have pale pink bodies with red spots that are uniformly distributed. Their back and sides lack large black blotches or saddles that are present on the rock hind. The soft portions of both the dorsal and anal fins are margined in black on the red hind. They also have five faint diagonal bars made up of connected darker spots along their sides.

Similar looking to red hind, grasby have a flat body with a rounded caudal fin and superior, horizontal mouth. They have three flat spines in the opercle and the bases of their soft dorsal and anal fins are covered with scales and thick skin. Their body is mostly white with small orange spots closely spaced and used for camouflage. They have four contrasting spots, either white or black, along the body, below the dorsal fin. These spots can be used to differentiate the graysby from the red hind.

LANDINGS AND VALUES

Red Hind					
US Landings by Year — Nominal Data					
Value in $US (000); Quantity in tonnes; (NMFS)					
	2004	2005	2006	2007	2008
Value	47	123	45	50	51
Quantity	11	22	8	8	8

The red hind is distributed throughout the Atlantic from North Carolina into the Gulf of Mexico and the Caribbean. It is most abundant off Bermuda and in the West Indies at depths that reach 120 meters (400ft.). It prefers reefs, rocky areas and wrecks and use the crevices as habitat over which they are very territorial. Red hind are generally fished by hook and line or spear and managed commercially and recreationally. There are limits on fishing gear and size and amount caught. In 2008, eight tonnes of red hind was landed commercially in the US, valued at $51,000 (see table). In addition, an estimated 954 tonnes of *Epinephelus* spp. were landed recreationally, including red hind (not shown).

Less than 1/2 tonne of grasby was landed in 2008, valued at approximately $2,000 (see table).

Endangerment Status: Neither the red hind nor the graysby is highly sought after and are not considered threatened (Least concern – IUCN).

COMMERCIAL USES

Graysby					
US Landings by Year — Nominal Data					
Value in $US (000); Quantity in tonnes; (NMFS)					
	2004	2005	2006	2007	2008
Value	0	0	0	1	2
Quantity	0	0	0	--	--

Red hind is fished for food. This fishery is particularly important in the Caribbean. It can be grilled, fried, poached, steamed, baked, broiled, sautéed, and used in soups or chowders. There have been reports of ciguatera poisoning (Ref. 31172). Grasyby is not considered a good food fish, but there is an aquarium trade for both species.

LIFE CYCLE

Red hind spawn from March to July and are protogynous hermaphrodites (females become males when they have reach about 40cm in length). Females produce up to 3 million eggs per spawning. They feed on small fishes, crabs, shrimps and squid. Prey is captured by ambush from hidden holes and crevices.

Graysbys inhabit rocky roofs and ledges at depths greater than 30 meters. They are considered a solitary species and usually very secretive. They stay within a home range and can be found hiding in and around wrecks. Like other groupers, they are a hermaphroditic species that start as females and later become fully functional males. Little is known about their spawning, but eggs and larvae are thought to be planktonic. They are nocturnal predators and prefer smaller fishes and shrimp. They feed using a powerful suction and use their tongue and jaws to hold the prey until they can swallow them whole.

GRUNT

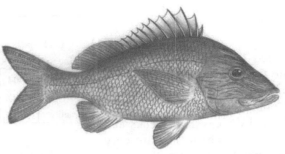

White Grunt, *Haemulon plumierii*

GENERAL

There are about 150 species and 19 genera in the grunt family
Haemulidae (formerly, family Pomadasyidae). About 31 species with
the market name **grunt** are listed in *The Seafood List*, although a few,
such as the margate, *Haemulon album*, have two approved market
names (e.g., grunt or margate). They are named for the pig-like grunts
they make (with pharyngeal [throat] teeth). Some species in the genus
Haemulon are also characterized by bright, reddish mouth linings and a
behavior trait where two individuals approach and "kiss." The purpose
of this, whether sexual or aggressive, is not known. Margate (*FishBase*
name "white margate") is a large member of the grunt family. Its
species name, *album,* relates to its coloration, which is the lightest of
any species in the grunt family. The pigfish, *Orthopristis chrysoptera,*
is another member of the family that, unlike margate, is correctly
marketed only as grunt. The name pigfish probably originates from the
noises it makes when caught or harassed.

Also Known As
Black Grunt/
Common Grunt/
Ronco Ronco/
Boar Grunt

FishBase Name
White grunt

**International
Recognitions**
Spain—Ronco
margariteño
France—Gorette
blanche
Japan—Aosuji-
isaki

PHYSICAL DESCRIPTION

Max length: 53.0 cm TL male/unsexed; (Ref. 40637); Common length: 30.0 cm TL
male/unsexed; (Ref. 3798); Max. published weight: 4,380 g (Ref. 4699)

Grunts are snapper-like, but lack canine teeth. The white grunt has narrow blue stripes along
the side of its head and body coloration is variable, but tending toward light yellow. They can
be identified by differing scale sizes with larger scales above the lateral line and smaller
below. In contrast, pigfish have an elevated back and long tapered snout. The mouth is
oblique and the jaw extends vertically from the first nostril. Oblique rows of scales are
present along the lateral line and extend onto the base of the caudal, pelvic and pectoral fins
and sheath the base of the anal and dorsal finds. They are often characterized by irregular
barring on the cheeks, mottled coloration, or indistinct, irregular vertical bars. Pigfish can
sometimes be confused with pinfish however the dorsal spines and eyes are smaller; and the
distance between the mouth and the eye is larger. Margate has a typical grunt shape including
the large mouth and prominent lips, but has a more elevated arched back and is more
compressed. Teeth are in narrow bands and are smaller than in other grunts. Coloration is
usually silvery white with grey fins. The inside of the mouth is orange with yellowish lips and
snout. There is a broad but indistinct band along the sides and faint spots on the scales of the
back and sides. Margate can be confused with the yellow and white grunt.

LANDINGS AND VALUES

Grunts are found along shores in warm and tropical waters of the major oceans. The white grunt is a reef associated fish distributed sub tropically in the western Atlantic from the Chesapeake Bay through the Gulf of Mexico and the Caribbean. It is found at depths from the surface to 40 meters. Margate and pigfish (other grunts) also overlap the white grunt range in these waters. The tables show the landings of various grunts; however, most landings are for unspecified species. In total, US commercial landings of all grunts were 188 tonnes in 2008, valued at $460,000 (see table above). In addition, an estimated 1,000 tonnes of grunts were landed recreationally; more than 75% of this was white grunt in 2008.

All Grunts (incl: White, Pigfish and Margate) US Landings by Year — Nominal Data Value in $US (000); Quantity in tonnes; (NMFS)					
	2004	2005	2006	2007	2008
Value	471	406	334	388	460
Quantity	297	238	163	148	188

COMMERCIAL USES

Grunts are edible and valued as food, although most species are small. Important as it is as a food fish, particularly in Florida, it is a good game fish as well. It is usually marketed fresh. There have been some reports of ciguatera poisoning.

White Grunt US Landings by Year — Nominal Data Value in $US (000); Quantity in tonnes; (NMFS)					
	2004	2005	2006	2007	2008
Value	35	18	40	41	51
Quantity	11	9	16	17	19

LIFE CYCLE

White grunts are generally found in dense schools along patchy reefs, with coral or sandy bottoms. Juveniles are found along seagrass beds of thalassia testudinum. They can be very territorial and often use a "kissing" display pushing each other on the lips with mouths open during territorial disputes. Padgett (1997) reports that 50% of females reach maturity at 16.7 cm TL, and 50% of males at 18.0 mm TL. Off western Florida white grunts appear to spawn once per year, but other analysis suggests they are batch spawners with peak activity occurring in May (Murie and Parkyn 1999). Spawning appears to occur almost year-round in the southernmost portions of the distributional range (Munro et al. 1973). They prey on crustaceans, small molluscs and small fishes.

Margate US Landings by Year — Nominal Data Value in $US (000); Quantity in tonnes; (NMFS)					
	2004	2005	2006	2007	2008
Value	18	15	22	14	15
Quantity	14	11	16	9	10

Pigfish US Landings by Year — Nominal Data Value in $US (000); Quantity in tonnes; (NMFS)					
	2004	2005	2006	2007	2008
Value	8	9	56	134	138
Quantity	14	14	23	23	22

Pigfish: This species schools and seasonally/nocturnally-diurnally migrates for forage. It feeds on crustaceans and small fish, which it crushes with pharyngeal plates before swallowing. Juveniles inhabit shoals or grassy areas of bays.

Margates are found in the western Atlantic and Florida Keys, south through Brazil. They are reef associated, preferring depths of 20—60 meters, but are also found in seagrass beds and along wrecks and sand flats. They often school with other margates or are found in pairs. They use their snout to forage in the sand for invertebrates and prey on crustaceans, worms and urchins.

HADDOCK

Haddock, *Melanogrammus aeglefinus*

GENERAL

Crash, crash and crash again! In the past 60-odd years **haddock** (cod family, Gadidae) became one of the principal fisheries on the east coast of North Atlantic, only to be overfished and depleted time and again. It was a major fishery in Newfoundland, Nova Scotia and New England in the 1950s when catches of 50,000 tonnes were average to each region. Catches dropped in the 1960s and 1970s, never to return again in Newfoundland; but the resource started coming back by the early 1980s elsewhere, until it crashed again in the early 1990s. Populations have recently increased in Nova Scotia and New England, but faster growth to maturity and slower overall growth rates have confounded catches, with hints that the genetic make-up of at least some stocks may have been impacted by size-selective fishing that has caused evolutionary changes.

Also Known As
Scrod Haddock

FishBase Name
Haddock

International Recognitions
Spain—Eglefino
France—Églefin
Germany—Schellfisch

PHYSICAL DESCRIPTION

Max length : 112 cm TL male/unsexed; (Ref. 5951);
Common length : 35.0 cm TL male/unsexed; (Ref. 4645);
Max. published weight: 16.8 kg (Ref. 9988); Max. reported age: 20 years (Ref. 4645)

Haddock resemble cod in most respects, although haddock are generally smaller and live in deeper waters. Haddock can foremost be identified by a distinctive large, black, thumbprint-shaped spot located below the lateral line, just behind the head. This distinguishing feature is often called "Satan's mark" or "St. Peter's mark." Differing also is the foremost of its three dorsal fins, which is higher, rising to a point. Like other family members, the pelvic fins are situated either under, or in front of, the pectoral fins. Black lateral lines (unlike white in the cod) separate the fish's purplish grey head and back from its silver grey underside. Although specimens of 30 pounds or more are known, it is unusual to find a haddock of more than 10 pounds today.

LANDINGS AND VALUES

Haddock range on both sides of the Atlantic from the Barent Sea and Iceland to the Bay of Biscay on the European side; and from the Grand Banks to southern New England on the North American side. Haddock, like cod, inhabit well-defined areas as separate "stocks," or "populations," with little intermixing. Haddock is caught by various methods: trawls, traps, baited hooks, gillnet, and longlines. It is usually found in waters of 150 to 450 feet deep.

The haddock fishery in Newfoundland was all but destroyed in the 1960s and the major fishery is now off Nova Scotia and New England. This event was a prelude to the collapse of the total groundfish fishery (including Newfoundland and other Atlantic Region cod) that was to come only 20 years later in the north-western Atlantic waters. Both species have so far proved difficult to regenerate on the Grand Banks. The Canadian haddock catch in 2008 was 20,542 tonnes valued at $26.5 million (see table). This compares to a 1989 catch of 26,044 tonnes valued at $25.4 million (not shown). The US catch was 6,205 tonnes in 2008, valued at almost $16.1 million (see table). This compares to a 1989 catch of 1,746 tonnes, valued at $4.6 million (not shown). **Aquaculture:** Haddock have been grown commercially in New Brunswick, Canada and in a demonstration project in Scotland. There are also broodstock in Norway.

Haddock US Landings by Year — Nominal Data Value in $US (000); Quantity in tonnes; (NMFS)					
	2004	**2005**	**2006**	**2007**	**2008**
Value	18,520	19,045	11,425	12,296	16,097
Quantity	8,237	7,542	3,265	3,625	6,205

Haddock Canadian Landings by Year — Nominal Data Value in $Cdn (000); Quantity in tonnes; (DFO)					
	2004	**2005**	**2006**	**2007**	**2008**
Value	20,391	26,904	26,848	27,656	26,494
Quantity	16,489	20,466	16,960	19,238	20,542

COMMERCIAL USES

Before 1900, haddock was only sold fresh because of its inferior salting properties. The storage problem and a limited market made the haddock a minor commercial fish during this period. This all changed with the advent of new filleting and freezing technologies in the 1920s. Haddock is now available in all forms: fresh, frozen, IQF, whole, fillets, in blocks and cured. It is found in canned chicken haddie and in fish sticks and portions. It is a popular choice for fish'n'chips. Smoked haddock, often known as "finnan haddie," (after Findon, Scotland, where it was first smoked) is also available. The term "scrod," often seen on restaurant menus, is a trade name for small (1.5 to 2.5 pounds) haddock, cod and pollock.

LIFE CYCLE

Major haddock stocks exist on Georges Bank and on the southern Scotia Shelf and Bay of Fundy area. On the Scotian Shelf, peak spawning occurs on Browns Bank in the spring between April and June and perhaps a little earlier on Georges Bank. These fish grow quickly and approximately 50% of female haddock are mature by age 3. The number of eggs produced by young females is low, but increases dramatically with age. A large female can lay more than 2 million eggs. The eggs float to the surface where they hatch and sometime during the fall, in September or October, the young haddock descend to the bottom. Here they live out the remainder of their lives. Because of their feeding habits they prefer sand or gravel bottoms.

Haddock prey on invertebrates, with bivalves and brittle stars making up the bulk of the diet, which also includes shrimp, hermit crabs and echinoderms such as sea urchins and sand dollars. Small fish, such as sand lance, young herring and young argentines provide about one-third of the larger haddock's diet. Haddock is preyed upon by cod, pollock, silver hake and older, larger halibut. Haddock grow rapidly until they reach sexual maturity at about 17 in. (43 cm), after which growth slows. At 10 years of age a haddock will average about 26 in. (66 cm).

HAGFISH

Atlantic Hagfish, *Myxine glutinosa*

GENERAL

The class Myxini (hagfishes), order Myxiniformes includes only one family, Myxinidae, but has 4 subfamilies, 6 genera and about 80 species. The **Atlantic hagfish** is one of these species and the only hagfish in the Northwest Atlantic. The class Myxini belongs to the superclass Agnatha (jawless fishes) and the Atlantic hagfish is a relative of the lamprey eel. With an evolutionary history of 300 million years, these fishes are considered to be the most primitive vertebrate species, living or extinct. In North America, the main commercial hagfish species appear to be the Pacific hagfish, *Eptatretus stoutii* and the black hagfish, *Eptatretus deani,* on the Pacific Coast and the **Atlantic hagfish** on the Atlantic Coast. Hagfish are not listed in *The Seafood List.* There is also a Gulf hagfish, *Eptatretus springeri*, found in very deep water (400–730 meters) in the northern Gulf of Mexico.

Also Known As
Slime Eel

FishBase Name
Hagfish

International Recognitions
Spain—Pez moco
France—Myxine
Italy—Missine
Germany—Blindinger

PHYSICAL DESCRIPTION

Max length : 80.0 cm TL male/unsexed; (Ref. 35388); Common length : 30.0 cm TL male/unsexed; (Ref. 35388); Common length :40 cm TL (female)

Hagfishes lack a true jaw and paired fins. Hagfish skeletons are composed of cartilage and the dorsal fin is a skin fold while the jaw is a rasping plate with horn-like teeth. The Atlantic hagfish have one pair of gill openings attached to 6-7 internal gill pouches per opening. The species has paired barbels on the tip of the snout and four barbels around the mouth. They are almost blind, but possess a good sense of smell. The skin is smooth and scale-less with a series of slime glands that produce protective mucus.

The black hagfish is a bottom dwelling oceanic species found at depths ranging from 100–2700 meters in the eastern pacific ocean from south-eastern Alaska to central California. The caudal fin is fairly broad and round with ray like markings. They are prune to blackish colored and can have large unpigmented spots on their sides and at the edges of the caudal and ventral finfolds.

The Pacific hagfish is found in slightly more shallow water than the black hagfish, from depths of 16–633 meters, but they have the same distribution from Alaska to California. Coloration varies between dark brown, tan, grey and brownish red. They are often lightly tinted blue or purple along the sides, although never black and rarely with white, which can help distinguish them from the black hagfish. They are a parasitic for larger fish, entering via the mouth or anus and feeding on viscera and muscle tissue.

LANDINGS AND VALUES

Hagfishes US Landings by Year — Nominal Data Value in $US (000); Quantity in tonnes; (NMFS)					
	2004	**2005**	**2006**	**2007**	**2008**
Value	191	706	606	1,713	2,940
Quantity	238	672	512	1,291	1,904

Hagfish Canadian Landings by Year — Nominal Data Value in $Cdn (000); Quantity in tonnes; (DFO)					
	2004	**2005**	**2006**	**2007**	**2008**
Value	1,993	2,179	1,915	1,735	1,584
Quantity	1,866	1,908	1,696	1,548	1,461

The Atlantic hagfish is found in deep, cold waters to depths of 1,100 meters or more. In the western north Atlantic, hagfish are distributed from Davis Straits, Greenland to the continental slope waters off of Florida. They inhabit soft clay or muddy sediments and maintain temporary burrows in the sea floor.

Hagfish are often considered a nuisance by fishermen because they can feed on targeted species. A fishery developed for the various species on both North American coasts in the early 1990s. US landings in 2008 totaled 1,904 tonnes, valued at almost $3 million (see table). In Canada, 2008 landings were 1,461 tonnes, valued at approximately $1.6 million. Atlantic hagfish are caught using baited hagfish pots (usually 55-gallon plastic barrels with funneled holes) attached to sinking line and buoys. Rows of smaller holes in the pots allow smaller fish to escape. Although a hagfish fishery exists in the Gulf of Maine, the resource is not actively managed at present.

COMMERCIAL USES

All hagfish are exported whole to Korea where they are utilized as food and their skins are manufactured in leather products.

LIFE CYCLE

Age at maturity and life expectancy are unknown in the Gulf of Maine, as are spawning locations. Atlantic hagfish are hermaphroditic, but it is unknown if both sexes are functional at the same time. Spawning may occur at any time of year. Females produce batches containing an average of 20 -30 eggs. Development from egg to hatchling may be several months, based on egg yolk volume. They prey primarily on shrimp, worms and small crabs. They also scavenge dead and dying fish, mammals and shellfish.

HAKE

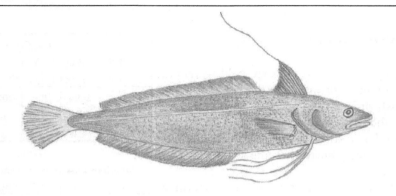

White Hake, *Urophycis tenuis*

GENERAL

Traditionally, hake was processed and used in the preparation of fishmeal, a common poultry feed. However, due to an increasing demand for white fish, it has been successfully introduced to the North America market. **White hake** is classified as a member of the cod family Gadidae (subfamily, Phycinae) by *ITIS,* but is ranked as belonging to a separate family, Phycidae (Phycid hakes) by *FishBase.* (Note: The classification of the Gadiformes remains a matter of contention, and although some authors treat Phycidae as a valid family, ITIS is following Cohen et al. [1990] in retaining it as a subfamily until a new understanding emerges). Red hake (*U. chuss*), or "squirrel hake," is often confused with the larger "white hake," which it closely resembles. For this reason, they are often marketed as the same fish. The white and red hakes are quite different from the "whiting" hakes of the family Merlucciidae (Merluccid hakes), such as the Atlantic silver hake (*Merluccius bilinearis*), but are often marketed in the same channels. The silver hake or Atlantic "whiting," is a cousin of the Pacific whiting (*M. productus*) – also called incorrectly, Pacific hake – and the European hake (*M. Merluccius)* – (see entry on whiting in this book). The silver hake is often viewed as one of the few remaining under-utilized species, as well. The blue antimora (*Antimora rostrata*) is a deep water fish that, on first glance, resembles the white hake, but is a different species.

Also Known As
Codling/ Squirrel Hake/ Ling/ Steakfish

FishBase Name
White hake

International Recognitions
Spain—Locha blanca
France—Merluche blanche
Italy—Musdea americana
Germany—Gabeldorsch

PHYSICAL DESCRIPTION

Maximum Size: 133 cm TL (male/unsexed; Ref. 40637);
Maximum Published weight: 21.0 kg (Ref. 4699); Maximum Reported Age: 10 years.

Red and white hake have an elongated body, are somewhat rotund around the belly and laterally compressed behind the head. The head is small with a pointed snout and relatively large eyes and mouth. The first of the two dorsal fins is rectangular in shape, supporting a long filament that may extend twice the height of the fin itself in the red hake, but not quite so long in the white. The second dorsal fin is long and narrow, stretching the length of the body. Both species have elongated, thread-like pelvic fins, but again, they are shorter in the white hake than in the red. Both hake have a reddish-brown back and dusty, white sides with pale lateral lines. Their underside is yellowish, peppered with small black spots. Red hake have three or more gill rakers, while the white hake only have two. The mature white hake will grow twice as large as the red hake that normally does not grow beyond 20 inches.

LANDINGS AND VALUES

White hake have been known to range from Cape Hatteras, North Carolina, to the southern coast of Newfoundland, with the larger concentrations centered off Nova Scotia, in the Gulf of St. Lawrence and the south slope of the Grand Banks. Red hake have a similar range, but it appears that commercial quantities may not be present in the Gulf of St. Lawrence. US landings in 1989 of white hake were approximately 4,600 tonnes, valued at $4.0 million (not shown). In 2008, US landings had decreased to 1,266 tonnes, valued at $3.3 million (see table). In Canada, all hake (red, white and silver) landings in 1990 approximated 15,200 tonnes, valued at about $7.6 million (not shown). In 2008 the Canadian Atlantic white, red and silver hake catch was almost 15,700 tonnes, valued at almost $12.7 million (see tables). (Also, see whiting entry.)

White Hake US Landings by Year — Nominal Data Value in $US (000); Quantity in tonnes; (NMFS)					
	2004	2005	2006	2007	2008
Value	4,554	4,975	4,266	3,878	3,339
Quantity	3,507	2,671	1,701	1,514	1,266

White Hake Canadian Landings by Year — Nominal Data Value in $Cdn (000); Quantity in tonnes; (DFO)					
	2004	2005	2006	2007	2008
Value	2,003	3,268	3,080	2,594	2,640
Quantity	3,726	4,489	3,909	3,072	2,930

COMMERCIAL USES

Hake is available fresh, frozen, smoked, and cured. It is sometimes used in fish sticks and portions. The white flesh has a soft texture and an excellent mild flavor. Fresh fillets from large fish are usually marketed as hake or white hake. Fresh hake will deteriorate quickly, developing a rubbery texture even at normal storage temperatures, and must be moved quickly to market.

Red Hake US Landings by Year — Nominal Data Value in $US (000); Quantity in tonnes; (NMFS)					
	2004	2005	2006	2007	2008
Value	355	480	394	430	295
Quantity	483	429	453	510	258

Red Hake Canadian Landings by Year — Nominal Data Value in $Cdn (000); Quantity in tonnes; (DFO)					
	2004	2005	2006	2007	2008
Value	90	74	65	206	234
Quantity	171	164	147	231	263

LIFE CYCLE

The hake are a demersal (bottom-dwelling), continental shelf species. They live over a sand or mud ocean floor at depths of 100 to 3,000 feet, preferring water temperatures from 40° to 68°F.

Spawning occurs offshore in summer or early fall for red hake, and almost year-round for white hake, depending on the habitat. In less than a week, larvae barely 1/10 of an inch long emerge from transparent eggs. They will spend the next two to three months feeding on plankton and other organisms near the ocean surface. When they reach 10 to 12 inches, they swim to deeper waters to join the adult population. Partly due to their size, young hake are prone to predators. To avoid detection, juveniles will hide in the shells of live or dead scallops during the day, emerging at night in search of food.

Silver Hake (Atlantic Whiting) US Landings by Year — Nominal Data Value in $US (000); Quantity in tonnes; (NMFS)					
	2004	2005	2006	2007	2008
Value	9,983	8,527	6,710	7,878	7,420
Quantity	8,622	7,595	5,559	6,354	5,753

Silver Hake (Atlantic whiting) Canadian Landings by Year — Nominal Data Value in $Cdn (000); Quantity in tonnes; (DFO)					
	2004	2005	2006	2007	2008
Value	9,505	7,709	8,773	9,249	9,722
Quantity	13,388	11,337	12,358	12,059	12,464

HALIBUT

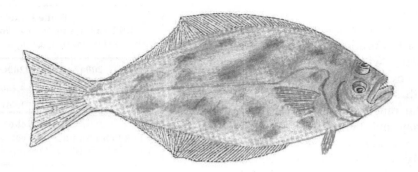

Pacific Halibut, *Hippoglossus stenolepis*

GENERAL

Halibut are not only the largest flatfish but also one of the largest species in the sea. There are reports of halibuts (both Pacific and Atlantic) reaching more than 8 feet in length and weighing more than 700 pounds, although these specimens are rare. The **Pacific halibut** belongs to the family Pleuronectidae (right-eyed flounders) (*ITIS*) as it has both eyes on the right side of the body. In many respects it is similar to the Atlantic halibut *(H. hippoglossus)* and some scientists suggest they may even be the same species. Another large flatfish that somewhat resembles the Pacific halibut is the California or "bastard" halibut *(Paralichthys californicus)*. Turbot, or Greenland "halibut," is another large flatfish that is caught on both coasts (also see turbot, plaice and flounder entries in this book).

PHYSICAL DESCRIPTION

Maximum Size: 258 cm TL (male/unsexed; Ref. 40637); 267 cm TL (female); Maximum Published Weight: 363.0 kg (Ref.); Max. Reported Age: 52 years (DFO)

The halibut can be distinguished from other flatfish by its size and slightly concave tail. It has a large gaping mouth and several sharp teeth. The lateral line loops around the pectoral fin and then continues straight onto the tail. The Pacific halibut is colored only on the right, or top, side. Depending on camouflage requirements, it is a mottled greenish brown or dark brown. The underside is white but may become a mottled grey in older fish. The California halibut can be distinguished from the Pacific halibut by its caudal fin which is convex and somewhat indented on the lobes, its larger mouth and by the fact that it is usually (but not always) left-eyed.

LANDINGS AND VALUES

Pacific halibut are found on the continental shelf of the Pacific coast from Santa Barbara, California, to Nome, Alaska, with the major concentrations off British Columbia and Alaska. Atlantic halibut are found on both sides of the Atlantic Ocean and from Greenland south to Virginia on the North American side. Pacific halibut is caught primarily on longlines, but also as a by-catch (illegal to retain) in otter trawls. Both longline and nets take some proportion of immature fish and, together with late maturity, can threaten sustainability. However, managed by the Pacific Halibut Commission, the species is currently at historic high levels of abundance.

US halibut landings are almost totally a Pacific fishery (95% Alaska) with only 10 to 30 tonnes of the total halibut catch per year coming from the Atlantic (not shown). At 30,362 tonnes and a market value of $217.4 million, the 2008 US Pacific halibut catch is a major fishery (see table). The total Canadian halibut catch was 6,849 tonnes, valued at almost $46 million in 2008 (see table). The Canadian Atlantic (coast) halibut catch represented approximately 30% and 40% of this total, by volume and value, respectively (not shown separately). US landings of California halibut (a separate species) totaled almost 2,100 tonnes in 1987;

Pacific Halibut US Landings by Year — Nominal Data Value in $US (000); Quantity in tonnes; (NMFS)					
	2004	2005	2006	2007	2008
Value	176,797	177,483	201,974	227,090	217,413
Quantity	35,905	34,576	32,594	31,713	30,362

Pacific and Atlantic Halibut Canadian Landings by Year — Nominal Data Value in $Cdn (000); Quantity in tonnes; (DFO)					
	2004	2005	2006	2007	2008
Value	72,686	63,040	71,181	53,908	46,139
Quantity	8,445	8,378	9,109	7,991	6,849

but only 216 tonnes, valued at $2.3 million, in 2008 (not shown). **Endangered Status:** Atlantic Halibut are Species of Concern (US). **Aquaculture:** halibut is now the focus of farming efforts in many places; including Norway, Scotland, Nova Scotia, Maine and Washington.

COMMERCIAL USES
Very large halibut (over 80 pounds) are known as "whales;" however, smaller (5 to 10 pounds) "chicken halibut" account for most of the catch. It is marketed as steaks, fillets, smoked halibut, cheeks and fletches (boneless, skinless fillets). Much is sold to the hotel and restaurant trade where it is often served as "poached halibut," a snow-white, gourmet dish that is often made more appealing when garnished with colourful vegetables, herbs and spices. Halibut is very low in calories, so it is a superb diet food if you can afford it. It is also a good source of omega-3 oils and vitamins A and D. Occasionally, products such as bait, liver, viscera and canned halibut are also marketed.

LIFE CYCLE
Halibut move from deep water along the edge of the continental shelf to shallower banks and coastal waters during the summer and return to deep water in the winter to spawn. This migration may involve distances of hundreds of miles. A number of spawning sites have been found off the coasts of Alaska and BC, and to a lesser extent, in the Bering Sea. However, since fish are caught in many areas, it is believed that spawning is widespread, although it is more prolific in specific spawning areas. Males mature sexually at about seven to eight years, while the average age of maturity for females is 12 years. A female can produce several million eggs, which float freely, usually at depths of 900 to 1,200 feet. The eggs hatch after approximately 16 days. The hatched larvae are dependant on yolk sacs for food for another 4 to 5 weeks while their mouths develop. Until they are about 3/4 inches long, halibut larvae are similar to those of other fish. Then, the left eye begins to travel to the right side of the head and pigmentation increases on the right side. By the time they are 2 inches long, they have become bottom-dwellers, swimming on their sides rather than upright. Mature halibut feed almost entirely on other fish and shellfish. An average specimen weighs 3 pounds at 4 years, 40 pounds at 10 years and as much as 100 pounds at 20 years. Females grow larger than males.

HERRING OR SEA HERRING OR SILD

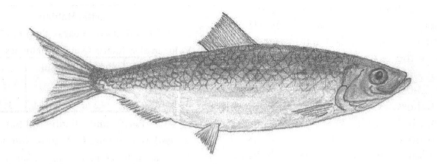

Pacific Herring, *Clupea pallasii*

GENERAL

Although for many years viewed as differing only at the subspecies level, scientists now consider the **Pacific herring** as a different species than Atlantic herring (*Clupea harengus*). Obviously the market has noticed too, as the value of Pacific herring has always been considerably greater than the Atlantic species. In fact, the two stocks differ markedly in their spawning behavior, and particularly, in the market quality of the roe they produce. Both species belong to the family Clupeidae (also see entries on alewife, shad and menhaden). Due to overexploitation, the Pacific herring fishery collapsed in the late 1960s. At that time, the fishery switched from supplying low-value reduction plants (for fishmeal and oil), as it had since the 1930s, to supplying roe to the Japanese.

Small Atlantic herring are often canned as sardines. However, although they belong to the same family (Clupeidae) and are closely related, they are not a true sardine like the west coast Pacific sardine (*Sardinops sagax*).

PHYSICAL DESCRIPTION

Maximum Size: 46.0 cm TL (male/unsexed; Ref. 27436);
Maximum Reported Age: 19 years

The Pacific herring has a smooth, streamlined body, much deeper than it is thick. Its back is iridescent steel blue to greenish blue. Its silvery sides and belly provide excellent camouflage in the open ocean. The tail is deeply forked and it has a single dorsal fin on its back, a large mouth and a slightly jutting lower jaw. The scales are loosely attached. Although similar to the Atlantic herring, the Pacific herring matures more quickly, spawns differently and is slightly smaller. The round herring, *Etrumeus teres*, also found on both coasts, resembles the Pacific and Atlantic *Clupea* spp.; however, the round herring is more cylindrical and has a strikingly blue back.

LANDINGS AND VALUES

Pacific herring is caught primarily for its roe, a delicacy prized in Japan, where it is almost exclusively exported. Spawning is in the spring. Timing is critical in the roe industry. If fish are taken too early, the roe is immature; too late and the fish are spawned out. The fishery is conducted from larger vessels with purse seines and from smaller vessels with gillnets.

Also Known As
California Herring
Easter Herring
Seld

FishBase Name
Pacific Herring

International Recognitions
France—hareng du Pacifique
Germany—Pazifischer Hering
Spain—arenque del Pacifico
Italy—aringa del Pacifico
Japan—nishin

Pacific herring roe is also harvested by artificial means from kelp. Atlantic herring is fished all year-round, but the largest catches are made in the spring and fall during the two spawning periods. However, the weir fisheries in the Bay of Fundy concentrate on juveniles (sardines) in the summer months. US Pacific herring landings accounted for approximately 35% of the total (marine) catch of 115,232 tonnes and about 53% of the value of all marine herring of almost $45 million in 2008 (see table). The US Atlantic herring represented almost 65% of the catch and 46% of the value, as other herring catches were incidental. The Canadian fishery parallels the US, as the Atlantic catch,

All Herrings - Atlantic and Pacific (including blueback, Atlantic thread and kelp roe) US Landings by Year — Nominal Data Value in $US (000); Quantity in tonnes; (NMFS)					
	2004	**2005**	**2006**	**2007**	**2008**
Value	30,687	34,902	30,307	34,977	44,713
Quantity	121,486	138,278	133,070	105,728	115,232

All Herrings - Atlantic and Pacific Canadian Landings by Year — Nominal Data Value in $Cdn (000); Quantity in tonnes; (DFO)					
	2004	**2005**	**2006**	**2007**	**2008**
Value	72,266	71,844	53,547	56,703	46,688
Quantity	208,704	193,140	183,470	179,448	150,362

which was 93% of the total catch in 2008 was only 73% of the total value - indicating the higher value of herring roe on the west coast (see table). (Notes: The Canadian table only reflects BC roe herring and does not reflect the BC roe-on-kelp harvest (138 tonnes) and other BC food/bait herring products, valued at $4.2 million and $1.2 million, respectively in 2008 (see table). The US table of landings includes herring roe-on-kelp, but the value is very small and only reported for 2007 and 2008; e.g., in 2008 it was 15 tonnes, valued at almost $13,000.)

Endangered Status: Certain Alaska populations are "Candidate for Species of Concern" (US).

COMMERCIAL USES

Only about five percent of Pacific herring goes for food. The major product is salted roe "caviar" or "kazunoko" (in Japan). Excess or lower quality herring is sold as bait or made into fishmeal and oil.

BC Roe-on Kelp - Canada Value in $Cdn (000); Quantity in tonnes; (DFO)					
	2004	**2005**	**2006**	**2007**	**2008**
Value	7,882	3,921	5,376	7,315	4,178
Quantity	421	286	305	214	138

Pacific herring roe is known for its firmness, while Atlantic herring roe is considered softer and serves a different market in Japan. Atlantic herring is a bait fish and a food fish available in a variety of forms including sardines, smoked "kippers" and marinated "Solomon Gundy." Herring is also sold whole, as fillets and pickled or cured. Herring is also a source of omega-3 fatty acids (oils) used in health supplements.

LIFE CYCLE

Pacific herring become sexually active when they are 3 or 4 years old. They then migrate from offshore feeding grounds to coastal waters where spawning takes place. The spawning season is between February and June, with peak activity from late March to early April. Pacific herring spawn in shallow waters, many of them returning to the beaches where they themselves were spawned. The average female will lay between 20,000 and 40,000 sticky, transparent eggs, which cling to eelgrass, kelp and other marine plants. (In fact, herring are even impounded and kelp is hung in the enclosure until roe is deposited on it for processing.) During fertilization, the sperm, or milt, released by the males can turn the ocean opaque and milky white for miles. This helps protect the spawning fish from predatory seagulls. Depending on water temperature, the eggs hatch 10 to 21 days after fertilization and coastal waters are filled with tiny herring larvae measuring about 0.35 inches. At 1.5 inches the young larvae, now juveniles, form schools.

HOGFISH

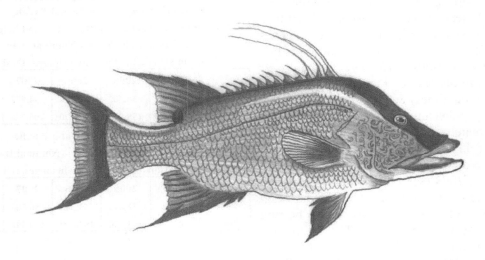

Hogfish, *Lachnolaimus maximus*

GENERAL

The hogfish is member of the wrasse family (Labridae) and is the single species of its genus. It is named after the head of the male which resembles a hog's snout. The hogfish is one of the few species that change from female to male (protogynous hermaphroditic) once it has reached sexual maturity. The color pattern also changes dramatically between juveniles and adults. A number of other wrasse species, particularly in the *Bodianus* genus, have "hogfish" as part of their common name; including two listed in *The Seafood List*; the spotfin hogfish, *Bodianus pulchellus* and the Spanish hogfish, *Bodianus rufus*. Hogfish is also vernacular for the pigfish, *Orthopristis chrysoptera,* but this is a very different species (grunt).

PHYSICAL DESCRIPTION

Max length: 91.0 cm TL male/unsexed; (Ref. 7251);
Common length: 35.0 cm TL male/unsexed; (Ref. 3726);
Max. published weight: 11.0 kg (Ref. 36052);
Max. reported age: 11 years (Ref. 8550)

Also Known As
Common Hogfish/
Hogsnapper/
Capitan/
Perro Perro

FishBase Name
Hogfish

International Recognitions
Spain—Doncella de
pluma
France—Labre
capitaine
Denmark—Ornefisk

Hogfish is a deep bodied species with a distinctly arched dorsal profile. The laterally compressed body is high and round in contrast to other wrasses, which tend to be smaller and cigar-shaped. It is the only wrasse with elongated dorsal spines. It has thick lips and a protruding jaw and snout used for rooting out food. The caudal fin is slightly lunate and the tips of the dorsal and anal fins are pointed. Color is variable, but generally pearly white to a mottled brownish red with a black spot at the rear base of the dorsal fin. There is also a dark stripe that runs from the snout to the dorsal fin and back to the caudal fin. Color changes with age. Scales on the back are often edged in yellow and juveniles are usually pink or grey.

HOGFISH

LANDINGS AND VALUES

In the western Atlantic Ocean, the hogfish ranges from Bermuda and North Carolina, south to the Caribbean Sea and northern Gulf of Mexico, as well as the northern coast of South America. It is very common off Florida and the islands of the Caribbean in shallow waters. Juveniles are often found in

Hogfish US Landings by Year — Nominal Data Value in $US (000); Quantity in tonnes; (NMFS)					
	2004	2005	2006	2007	2008
Value	157	125	129	146	213
Quantity	31	23	23	24	33

seagrass beds in Florida Bay. They prefer open bottom or coral reef habitats and aggregate loosely around reefs, wrecks or other hard bottom areas. In 2008, 33 tonnes of hogfish were landed by commercial fisheries, valued at $213,000 (see table). The recreational fishery does not record specific hogfish catches, but they are considered small.

Aquaculture Status: Several successful attempts to raise hogfish in captivity have shown promise for the aquaculture industry.

Endangered Status: There is no formal stock assessment for this species and commercial catch of hogfish has decreased within the past decade. Recreational catch has fluctuated and fishing pressure has reduced populations in some areas considerably. The IUCN currently lists them as vulnerable.

COMMERCIAL USES

Hogfish is valued as a high quality and tasty food fish. It is marketed fresh and frozen and has been raised in captivity. It is a prized game fish although reports of ciguatera poisoning have occurred.

LIFE CYCLE

Hogfish spawn between September and April and are considered protogynous hermaphrodites. After a female reaches about 8 inches and exerts social dominance, she can become a male. Hogfish schools consist of a group of females called a harem and one male who guards the females and spawns with them exclusively. Eggs are released into the surrounding waters and hatch approximately 24 hours after fertilization. After the larval state, juveniles settle out of the water column, commonly around sea grass beds.

Hogfish prey mostly on molluscs, sea snails, clams, crabs and sea urchins. They use their snout to turn over the substrate to find food. Hogfish have pharyngeal jaws and use their teeth to crush prey. Hogfish are prey to larger fish, sharks and humans.

JACK

Lookdown, *Selene vomer*

GENERAL

Lookdowns belong to the family Carangidae (jacks and pompanos) that includes 30 genera and about 150 species. The genus *selene* in the family, is known as the moonfish genus and includes the Pacific moonfish, *Selene peruviana* and Atlantic moonfish, *Selene setapinnis*. The **lookdown** also looks very similar to the Mexican lookdown (also called the hairfin lookdown in *FishBase*), *Selene brevoortii*, found on the Pacific coast and, at first sight, it would be difficult to tell them apart.

PHYSICAL DESCRIPTION

Max length: 48.3 cm TL male/unsexed; (Ref. 9626);
Common length: 35.0 cm TL male/unsexed; (Ref. 5217);
Max. published weight: 2,100 g (Ref. 40637)

Similar to the Atlantic moonfish, *S. setapinnis* (same genus), but can be distinguished by its more rhombus-shaped very deep body, longer and steeper head, and different anal and dorsal fins. The second rays on both fins are significantly longer, giving the fins a rounded shape. The head of the lookdown is steeply concave giving it a "lookdown" appearance. Lookdowns have silvery coloration on both sides and are tinted darker on top. The caudle fin is forked.

Atlantic moonfish are a short, deep-bodied fish, but more rounded than rhombus-shaped, strongly laterally compressed with an almost completely vertical facial profile and concave shape. Their dorsal fin has 9 spines and they have very short, small pelvic fins.

Also Known As
Atlantic Lookdown/
Moonfish/
Horsehead/
Dollarfish

FishBase Name
Lookdown

International Recognitions
Spain—Lookdown
France—Musso panache
Denmark—Almindelig hestehoved
Japan—Shiroganeaji

LANDINGS AND VALUES

Lookdown US Landings by Year — Nominal Data Value in $US (000); Quantity in tonnes; (NMFS)					
	2004	2005	2006	2007	2008
Value	4	17	25	14	36
Quantity	2	9	13	8	19

Lookdowns can be found along the Western Atlantic coast from Maine to Florida including the Gulf of Mexico and along the coast of Central and South America. They are marine fish that live from the surface to approximately 50 meters depth. They can be found in shallow coastal waters over hard or sandy bottom areas sometimes in estuaries or sandy beaches. Lookdowns generally travel in schools or small groups. They are not a major commercial fishery, but 19 tonnes, valued at $36,000, was landed in the US in 2008 (see table).

Atlantic moonfish range from Nova Scotia, Canada, to the Gulf of Mexico and to more tropical waters. They are a benthic marine fish found in brackish to salt waters. Moonfish are generally found in deep inshore waters to about 55 meters in depth. They may form small surface schools, but are generally a bottom dwelling fish. In 2008, 24 tonnes of Atlantic moonfish were landed in the US, values at $52,000 (see table).

Recreational fishery: Various jacks accounted for more than 3,000 tonnes of gamefish landings in 2008; as inshore fishes, it is expected that lookdowns and moonfish would represent at least a small part of that total.

COMMERCIAL USES

Atlantic Moonfish US Landings by Year — Nominal Data Value in $US (000); Quantity in tonnes; (NMFS)					
	2004	2005	2006	2007	2008
Value	46	53	50	61	52
Quantity	24	26	24	29	24

Lookdown and moonfish have an excellent flavor and are marketed fresh or frozen. They are also a gamefish and have a demand in the aquarium trade. There have been reports of ciguatera poisoning (Ref. 30911).

LIFE CYCLE

Little is reported on the life cycle and reproduction of these fish. They feed on small crab, shrimp, fishes and worms.

KILLIFISH

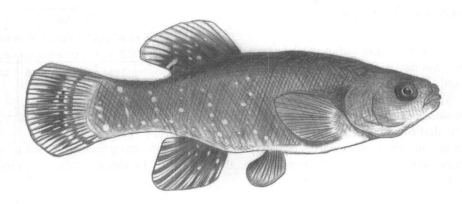

GENERAL

Mummichog is a relatively small fish that belongs to the family Fundulidae (killifishes and topminnows). The family includes 4 genera and about 37 species, but most are found in the *Fundulus* genus. *The Seafood List* records 3 species with the market name killifish including the marsh killifish (*Fundulus confluentus*) and the striped killifish (*Fundulus majalis*); however, there are also other related families of killifish species (e.g., Cyprinodontidae). It is also believed that there may be 2 subspecies of mummichog: *Fundulus heteroclitus macrolepidotus* is considered to be the northern form of the species that is distinguished from *F. heteroclitius heteroclitius* by egg structure and spawning behavior. The specie is not a highly sought food fish, but has some research interest for embryological, physiological, and toxicological studies and other utilization value.

Also Known As
Mudminnow/ Pike Minnow/ Mudfish/ Killy

FishBase Name
Mummichog

International Recognitions
Spain—Fúndulo
Denmark— Zebrastribet tandkarpe
Germany— Killifisch

PHYSICAL DESCRIPTION

Max length : 15.0 cm TL male/unsexed; (Ref. 27139);
Common length : 8.9 cm TL male/unsexed; (Ref. 12193)

The mummichog is sexually dimorphic. Breeding males can be distinguished from females by their more brilliant and intense pigmentation. Males also have vertical stripes along the sides, not found in females. Females, in general, tend to be paler than males. Very small fish of both sexes have dark transverse line on their sides, which disappear as they mature. Species color can vary by environment.

LANDINGS AND VALUES

Mummichogs are benthopelagic and can be found in both fresh and marine environments along the western Atlantic Ocean from Canada to north-eastern Florida, including the lower Chesapeake and Delaware bays. They are a shallow living fish, found mostly in saltwater marshes and tidal creeks. They are a hardy species and can survive in most habitats. They travel in large schools that may contain hundreds of individuals. They are able to breathe air when out of water. They are often caught in seines and traps and sold as live bait. Commercial landings for mummichogs are modest, usually 1 to 2 tonnes per year, if at all (see table). Most have been caught in the Long Island Sound area.

Mummichog US Landings by Year — Nominal Data Value in $US (000); Quantity in tonnes; (NMFS)					
	2004	2005	2006	2007	2008
Value	13	15	21	12	0
Quantity	2	2	2	1	0

The species is commonly found in many locations and is not presumed to be endangered.

COMMERCIAL USES

Mummichogs are used as bait and as a food fish. They are considered an underutilized species and have been tested cooked in cans as a sardine-liked product (Univ. of Delaware). They might qualify as pet food as well. The mummichog can also be used as an environmental marker as it sometimes the only species that can survive in polluted and/or oxygen-deprived waters. Its unique biology has made it valuable for classroom teaching and scientific experiments.

LIFE CYCLE

Mummichogs become sexually mature at two years and typically live for three. Mummichog are oviparous; they spawn on new and full moons in the spring and summer, laying eggs near the high tide line in empty shells or dead vegetation. They are omnivores, feeding on plant matter and preying on benthic invertebrates, worms, fish eggs and small fish and are preyed on by bluefish, striped bass, sharks, and rays.

KINGFISH (& CORBINA)

Northern Kingfish, *Menticirrhus saxatilis*

GENERAL

The **northern kingfish** (also known as "king whiting" and "northern whiting") is a member of the Sciaenidae family (drums and croakers) that also includes seatrouts and weakfishes (see entries in this book). There are 9 species in the genus *Menticirrhus,* and, including northern kingfish, 4 of these are listed in *The Seafood List* under the kingfish market name; the Gulf kingfish (*M. littoralis*), the southern kingfish (*M. americanus*) and the California corbina (*M. undulates*). [The latter, *M. undulates,* can also be marketed under the "corbina" market name, as well as the kingfish name.] Northern kingfish do not make typical "drumming" noises like other members of the drum and croaker family, but they do make sounds by grinding their pharyngeal (throat) teeth. The northern, southern and Gulf kingfishes (the latter two have the *FishBase* names of "southern kingcroaker" and "Gulf kingcroaker," respectively) are commonly called "king whiting" or just "whiting" by US fishers. This use of the name "whiting" is technically "slang" and should not be confused with species more appropriately designated as whiting in *The Seafood List* (for additional information, see the whiting entry in this book).

PHYSICAL DESCRIPTION

Max length : 46.0 cm TL male/unsexed; (Ref. 7251);
Common length : 30.0 cm TL male/unsexed; (Ref. 3702);
Max. published weight: 1,110 g (Ref. 40637)

Northern kingfish have a long spine on the first dorsal fin and a barbel on the chin. Dark, irregular bars are present along the body of the fish. The first two bars form a distinct V-shape. The markings on southern kingfish and Gulf kingfish are not nearly as prominent and do not form the V-shaped pattern; otherwise they look the same.

Also Known As
Northern Whiting/
King Whiting/
Sea Mullet/
Hake/ Barba

FishBase Name
Northern kingfish

International Recognitions
Spain—Lambe
zorro
France—Bourrugue
renard
Denmark—Nordlig
kongetrommefisk

LANDINGS AND VALUES

Northern kingfish, southern kingfish and Gulf kingfish are found in oceanic to brackish waters in the Western Atlantic. Their range in North America extends from the Gulf of Mexico to southern Florida and up to Massachusetts. They are usually found in shallow waters along the coast, preferring sandy or muddy bottom areas. Juveniles may spend more time in tidal rivers and low salinity creek environments while adults are found in the surf zone and estuaries.

Commercial fishing is usually as a bycatch. In 2008, 624 tonnes of kingfishes (includes northern, southern and Gulf) valued at $1.27 million dollars, were landed commercially. Most of the catches were landed in North Carolina (67%) and Florida (25%). The gear used was mostly gill nets. It is not a reported fishery in Canada.

Kingfishes (Northern/Southern/Gulf) also known as King Whiting US Landings by Year – Nominal Data Value in $US (000); Quantity in tonnes; (NMFS)					
	2004	2005	2006	2007	2008
Value	1,374	1,081	1,135	1,266	1,268
Quantity	695	577	530	583	624

Northern Kingfish US Landings by Year – Nominal Data Value in $US (000); Quantity in tonnes; (NMFS)					
	2004	2005	2006	2007	2008
Value	0	0	0	1	0
Quantity	0	0	0	0	0

Recreational Fishery: 1,300 tonnes of kingfishes were landed recreationally in 2008 in the US. A small amount (4 tonnes) of Pacific corbina was also landed recreationally on the west coast.

COMMERCIAL USES

Primarily a gamefish and an excellent food fish. Small for fillets and are usually pan fried whole.

LIFE CYCLE

Northern kingfish become sexually mature at 2-3 years of age; males usually before females. Spawning typically occurs inshore, but may also occur offshore in open water. Spawning duration ranges from April until August, depending on the region. The eggs float in the water column and usually hatch in 2-3 days, depending on water temperature.

Northern kingfish grow quickly and can reach 28 cm in 6 months. Most growth is from mid-summer to late fall, with little or no growth occurring in the winter. The average life expectancy of northern kingfish is 2-3 years, although they can live as long as 4 years.

Northern kingfish are bottom feeders that eat shrimp, small molluscs, worms, young fish, crabs, and other crustaceans; primarily by using their senses of smell and touch.

LADYFISH

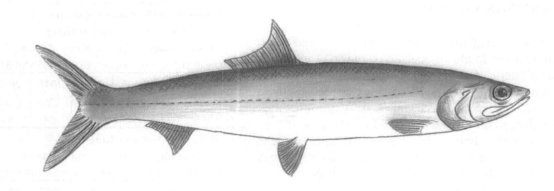

Ladyfish, *Elops saurus*

GENERAL

Ladyfish is from the family Elopidae (ladyfishes). This family is closely related to the tarpon family, Megalopidae, the only other family in the order Elopiformes. *The Seafood List* records 3 species listed under the market name ladyfish, including the (Hawaiian) ladyfish, *Elops hawaiensis,* and the machete *Elops affinis.*

Hogfish are sometimes (incorrectly) called ladyfish.

PHYSICAL DESCRIPTION

Max length: 100cm TL;
Max weight: 10.1 kg

Ladyfish have a slender, torpedo shaped body; a tiny pointed head with terminal mouth; small, sharp teeth; deeply forked tail; and small scales. Dorsal coloration is silver blue to green fading to silver, laterally and ventrally. Dorsal and caudal fins are dusky yellow and pectoral and pelvic fins are pale and speckled. The species is similar looking to a juvenile tarpon.

Also Known As
Tenpounder/ Bony Fish/ Bigeye Herring/ Bonefish/ Chiro

FishBase Name
Ladyfish

International Recognitions
Spain—Malacho
France—Guinée-machète
Denmark—Ladyfisk
Japan—Karaiwashi
Germany—Frauenfisch

LANDINGS AND VALUES

In North America, ladyfish is found from Cape Cod to the Gulf of Mexico and the Caribbean. It inhabits a wide range of salinities and can also be found in bays, estuaries and mangroves; as well as tidal pools and canals. In 2008, US landings were 674 tonnes, valued at almost $1.2 million (see table). Most commercial catches were made off Florida (west coast) and Alabama.

Ladyfish US Landings by Year — Nominal Data Value in $US (000); Quantity in tonnes; (NMFS)					
	2004	2005	2006	2007	2008
Value	714	1,023	1,056	946	1,153
Quantity	670	875	804	550	674

Endangered Status

This species is impacted by destruction of estuaries and mangrove forests through development as larvae and juveniles use these estuaries. It is, however, not listed as endangered. Further, net prohibitions in Florida may have resulted in decreased commercial landings; the 5-year average was down by one-third in 2009 (not shown).

COMMERCIAL USES

They are a minor commercial fishery but are a good sport fish for light tackle anglers and are used for bait. They are known for leaping above the water surface when hooked. It is marketed fresh, salted and frozen; but like tarpon, is not considered highly valuable as a food species.

LIFE CYCLE

Ladyfish spawn offshore in the fall. Larvae are long and ribbon like and age of maturity is not known. They feed on smaller fish (especially menhaden) and small crustaceans and are preyed on by larger fish, alligators, birds, sharks and porpoises.

LINGCOD

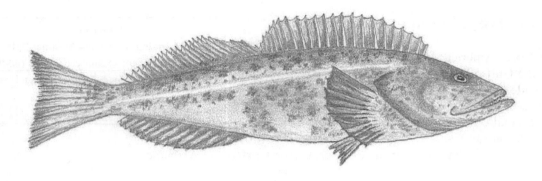

Lingcod, *Ophiodon elongatus*

GENERAL

The **lingcod** is the largest member of the family Hexagrammidae (greenlings) and is the most commercially and recreationally significant fish of this family. Classed as a west coast groundfish, it is neither a true cod, nor is it related to the lings. Its closest relatives are other greenlings, although it has characteristics in common with rockfishes and sculpins. The lingcod is valued by both commercial and sport fishermen for its great size and firm-textured, mild-tasting, white flesh. The scientific name is derived from the Greek "ophis" and "odons" for snake and tooth respectively, and the Latin for "elongate." The Atka mackerel (*Pleurogrammus monopterygius*) and the kelp greenling (*Hexagrammos decagrammus*) are two other significant commercial species in the greenling family found in similar ranges in the North Pacific (see entries in this book).

PHYSICAL DESCRIPTION

Max. Size: 152 cm TL (male/unsexed; Ref. 2850);
Max. Publ. Weight: 59.1 kg (Ref. 40637)
The most noticeable feature of the lingcod is its large gaping mouth, with a projecting lower jaw and numerous sharp teeth, interspersed with fangs. The high dorsal fin is notched into two sections, the tail is truncated and the anal fin runs from the tail to about the middle of the belly. It has large, fan-like, pectoral fins, complemented by a second smaller pair of pelvic fins just below. Small, smooth scales cover the entire body and head. Its color depends upon environmental conditions, but is usually a bold, mottled color in some shade of brown, grey, or—especially for smaller fish—green on the back and sides. The color fades to paler, occasionally blue or turquoise, shades on the belly.

LANDINGS AND VALUES

The lingcod can be found all along the western coast of North America, from California to Alaska. Landing records suggest that the greatest numbers are found in the waters off British Columbia. Although caught in areas with smooth, sandy bottoms, it prefers shallow waters (less than 600 feet) with a rocky bottom. Lingcod is a sport fishery, including scuba divers, as well as a commercial fishery. The commercial fishery uses trawls, handlines, troll gear and longlines. It is often a by-catch of other fisheries.

Also Known As
Blue Cod/
Buffalo Cod/
Green Cod/
Leopard Cod/
Cultus Cod/
Ling

FishBase Name
Lingcod

International Recognitions
France—Morue-
lingue
Japan—Ainame
Mexico- Molva

The early fishery, however, depended on handlining with live bait, from small to medium-sized vessels. These vessels were fitted with "live wells" where the fish could be kept alive in circulating water until they could be transferred to floating wooden storage boxes. In the last few decades, lingcod stocks have declined drastically, forcing fishery officials to stop lingcod fishing in some areas. The decrease in the lingcod population is suspected to be mostly due to over-fishing. The US catch of lingcod was reported as 284 tonnes in 2008, valued at approximately $736,000 (see table). The Canadian catch in 2008 is reported as 2,321 tonnes, valued at approximately $4.5 million (see table). The US catch is down from 4,195 tonnes and $3.3 million in 1989 and the Canadian catch is down from 3,870 tonnes, valued at approximately $2.8 million, in 1989 (not shown). US landings of close relatives, the atka mackerel and the kelp greenling, are also shown below.

Lingcod US Landings by Year – Nominal Data Value in $US (000); Quantity in tonnes; (NMFS)					
	2004	2005	2006	2007	2008
Value	434	465	580	666	736
Quantity	179	205	259	270	284

Lingcod Canadian Landings by Year – Nominal Data Value in $Cdn (000); Quantity in tonnes; (DFO)					
	2004	2005	2006	2007	2008
Value	6,138	5,082	5,138	4,818	4518
Quantity	2,933	2,798	2,422	2,483	2,321

COMMERCIAL USES

Lingcod is available whole dressed and as frozen fillets. However, it is primarily esteemed as a fresh fish and should be cleaned and packed on ice immediately upon landing. The flesh is lean and turns white when cooked.

Atka Mackerel US Landings by Year – Nominal Data Value in $US (000); Quantity in tonnes; (NMFS)					
	2004	2005	2006	2007	2008
Value	10,795	14,893	15,703	14,253	19,523
Quantity	49,180	58,733	59,337	57,589	57,620

LIFE CYCLE

Most lingcod are mature sexually at four to five years of age. Lingcod males generally begin to appear on shallow spawning grounds in October and November to select a site. In January, the females arrive and spawning takes place during the night, sometime during January or February. DNA evidence indicates that more than one female may contribute to an egg mass; each laying 100,000 to 500,000 eggs each. The

Kelp Greenling US Landings by Year – Nominal Data Value in $US (000); Quantity in tonnes; (NMFS)					
	2004	2005	2006	2007	2008
Value	237	232	171	201	257
Quantity	25	23	16	20	23

females immediately depart the spawning grounds, leaving the males behind to guard the eggs. The eggs are laid in rocky crevices where there is a good tidal flow, or swift current, to ensure an ample supply of oxygen. They are deposited in large sticky masses weighing as much as 30 pounds and hatch after about seven weeks. The small, blue-eyed larvae swim to the surface, where they stay for two to three months feeding on plankton and growing very quickly. They move to shallow inshore areas in late May. By early June, they are about 3 inches long. Then they swim down towards the seabed, where they begin to feed exclusively on small fish. After a year, when they are about 11 inches long, the larvae move offshore to reefs and rocky areas before joining the adult population. Lingcod prey on a variety of fishes: herring, cod, pollock and even octopus. Predators of juvenile lingcod include greenling, perch and larger lingcod. Large lingcod have few natural enemies among fish; however, mammals, such as sea lions, will feed on them.

LUMPFISH

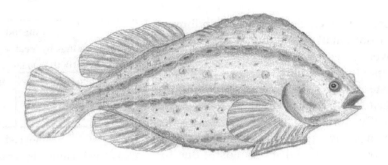

Lumpfish, *Cyclopterus lumpus*

GENERAL

The **lumpfish** (family Cyclopteridae, superfamily Cyclopteroidea) has been long sought in the European marketplace for its roe and is now receiving more attention in North America. The flesh is fat, rich and oily and has been used to some extent as a food in both Europe and North America. However, it is the roe that is most valuable. In Newfoundland, the home of the lumpfish fishery, only the smaller reddish males are preferred for eating. The lumpfish gets its peculiar name from the fashion in which it holds onto the sea bottom, or to objects floating by in the water, looking much like a lump—or just like more of the surroundings.

PHYSICAL DESCRIPTION

Maximum Size: 60.0 cm TL (male/unsexed; Ref. 7251);
Maximum Published Weight: 9.5 kg (Ref. 4701);

The lumpfish has a short, stout body, and like its relative the sculpins, is covered by hard, wart-like protrusions called tubercles. Its color ranges from blue or bluish- grey to greenish-brown. Its belly is pale yellow, though breeding males have red bellies. Females may reach 11 pounds in weight and up to 22 inches in length. The average male is smaller. Its pelvic fin has a circular flap of skin that can become a circular sucking disc, enabling the fish to grab and perch on objects. Its shape and structure suggest a sluggish, lazy fish.

LANDINGS AND VALUES

The North American lumpfish fishery, primarily located in Newfoundland, started in the late 1960s, and is based almost exclusively on roe production. A commercial lumpfish fishery has been active in Iceland for decades and a European fishery has been in existence for centuries. Lumpfish live in the coastal waters on both sides of the North Atlantic Ocean.

Also Known As
Lumpsucker/
Henfish/
Sea Hen/
Lump/
Sea Owl/
Paddle

FishBase Name
Lumpsucker

International Recognitions
France—lompe
Germany—
Seehase
Spain—liebre de
mar
Italy—ciclottero
Japan—dango-
uo

On the North American side, they are found from Hudson Bay and the Labrador coastline, south to New Jersey. There are major concentrations offshore on the St. Pierre Bank, off the south shore of Newfoundland, and due east of Cape Breton. There is a smaller concentration northeast of the Strait of Belle Isle. Although initially most lumpfish landed in Canada came from the northwest of Newfoundland, today most are from the southern shores.

Lumpfish Roe Canadian Landings by Year — Nominal Data Value in $Cdn (000); Quantity in tonnes; (DFO)					
	2004	2005	2006	2007	2008
Value	9,926	4,209	2,250	1,949	2,363
Quantity	1,865	1,334	1,134	454	294

Lumpfish are caught in gillnets of different sizes, depending on the size of the fish required. The principal season is from early May to the end of June, while the fish are on their shoreward spawning migration. Although small numbers of males are taken for human consumption, the larger female is the desired catch. Her eggs, or roe, supply a lucrative caviar market. Lumpfish landings occur in the US, but are almost non-existent, and not reported here. In Canada, lumpfish roe is the main catch, and almost entirely a Newfoundland fishery, with about 5% of landings coming from Quebec. The Canadian roe value in 2008 was almost $2.4 million (see table). In addition, about 57 tonnes of meat was landed in 2008, valued at $14,500 (not shown).

COMMERCIAL USES

Commercial popularity of the fish itself has been growing in North America and some smoked products have been sold in Europe. However, lumpfish are caught primarily for their roe as a caviar alternative. The mature, but not overripe, purple or red eggs may also be artificially colored. West Germany is traditionally the largest market, but lumpfish roe is a common product throughout Northern Europe.

LIFE CYCLE

Adult lumpfish inhabit rocky bottom areas. They favor deep, cold, offshore waters, but some have been found hiding under large beds of floating seaweed. They perform two seasonal migrations: shoreward, to spawn, in the early to middle spring; and seaward, on the return journey, in the autumn. The spawners are at least five years old. They spawn immediately after reaching their coastal spawning grounds, preferring rocky shores with abundant supplies of seaweed growth. They appear to have some homing ability, returning to areas where they have previously spawned. During the harvesting period, the eggs make up about 20 to 30 percent of the female's total body weight. An average-size female can produce up to 140,000 eggs, equivalent to about two pounds of roe.

After the eggs have been laid in a sponge-like arrangement, the females return to the offshore. The reddish males stay to guard the eggs and to assist in their development by aerating them with movements of their snouts and fins. Once the eggs hatch in early summer, the males return to sea and the normal yellow coloring of their bellies reappears. Growth rates and age are difficult to determine, but evidence suggests that females, at least, grow quickly up to the age of five. After this age, the growth rate is thought to slow almost to a standstill. At five years, the average length is about 12 inches. The lumpfish has a small mouth with feeble teeth, suggesting a diet of small, docile organisms such as small jellyfishes, fishes, crustaceans and worms. Some feeding probably occurs in seaweed near the surface where these small animals are plentiful.

MACKEREL

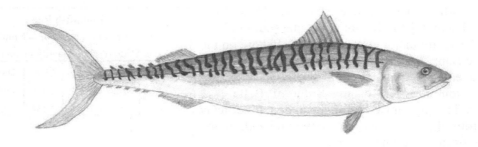

Atlantic Mackerel, *Scomber scombrus*

GENERAL

The **Atlantic mackerel** belongs to the tribe Scombrini, subfamily Scombrinae of the family Scombridae (mackerels, tunas, bonitos). There are many different mackerel species, widely distributed and often difficult to distinguish. Species similar to the Atlantic mackerel are the (Pacific) chub mackerel (*Scomber japonicus*), the Atlantic chub mackerel (*S. colias*) and Spanish mackerels (*Scomberomorus* spp.); the latter is sometimes thought to include the king mackerel (*S. cavalla*) and the cero (*S. regalis*); however, these are major fisheries in their own right. There are more than 20 species with the market name mackerel in *The Seafood List*, including the atka mackerel (greenlings family) and the jack mackerel (jacks and pompanos family). The Atlantic mackerel has no swim bladder (commonly known as an "air bladder"), which forces the fish to be in constant motion to prevent sinking. (Also see bonito, jack mackerel and tuna entries in this book.)

Also Known As
Boston Mackerel/ Caballa

FishBase Name
Atlantic mackerel

International Recognitions
Germany— Makrele
Spain—caballa
Italy—sgombro
Japan—hirasaba

PHYSICAL DESCRIPTION

Maximum Size: 60.0 cm FL (male/unsexed; Ref. 35388);
Max. Published Weight: 3.4 kg (Ref. 9988); Max. Reported Age: 17 years
Mackerel, like tuna, can be identified by the small "finlets" behind the dorsal and anal fins, tight caudal peduncle and rounded tail. The mackerel's great speed is enhanced by a torpedo-shaped body, tapering at tail and snout. The Atlantic mackerel is steely blue above with silvery, iridescent sides and 20 to 23 dark wavy bars down to the lateral line. Its belly is silvery white. The chub mackerel is similar to the Atlantic mackerel except the chub has spotted sides (under the bars) and a black spot in front of its pectoral fins. The Spanish mackerels are often yellow-spotted and have deeply-notched dorsal fins and a downward sloping lateral line.

LANDINGS AND VALUES

Atlantic mackerel are found on both sides of the Atlantic. In North America there are two distinct populations. Both populations over-winter on the edge of the continental shelf, mainly south of Georges Bank. In the spring, the southern mackerel stock moves inshore and spawns along the US coast, primarily off the coast of New Jersey, in April and May. The northern stock migrates through Nova Scotia waters and spawns primarily in the southern Gulf of St. Lawrence in June and July. These fish, as well as late spawners and immature fish, are found dispersed throughout east coast waters in the summer months. Some of the northern stock can migrate as far north as Labrador, while the southern stock will move as far south as North Carolina. In the fall, both stocks migrate back to their winter habitat.

Mackerel are caught by purse seines, gillnets, bar seines, handlines, traps and weirs. The Atlantic mackerel is the only major species of mackerel landed in Canada, totaling 29,110 tonnes in 2008 valued at $11.6 million (see table). US landings were 16,172 tonnes valued at $4.4 million in 2008 (see table). The US also lands chub and Spanish/king/ cero, mackerels. In 2008, total US mackerel landings were 24,547 tonnes, valued at $19.3 million (see table). Chub mackerel (almost all Pacific, particularly California) accounted for 14% of total landings and Spanish, king and cero for another 18%, by volume; the rest (66%) was Atlantic mackerel. King and Spanish mackerels are also major sport fisheries, accounting for about 5,000 tonnes of landings in 2008 (not shown). Atlantic and chub mackerels accounted for almost 1,000 tonnes of gamefish, while unspecified mackerels/tuna accounted for another almost 2,600 tonnes (not shown).

Atlantic Mackerel US Landings by Year — Nominal Data Value in $US (000); Quantity in tonnes; (NMFS)					
	2004	2005	2006	2007	2008
Value	13,911	6,952	17,305	6,738	4,373
Quantity	56,446	18,507	56,640	25,532	16,172

Atlantic Mackerel Canadian Landings by Year — Nominal Data Value in $Cdn (000); Quantity in tonnes; (DFO)					
	2004	2005	2006	2007	2008
Value	17,360	25,263	20,469	17,728	11,628
Quantity	53,800	55,956	53,951	53,355	29,110

COMMERCIAL USES

The Atlantic mackerel is used primarily as a food fish. It is available fresh and frozen, in fillets or whole, and is also available canned. It is delicious when freshly grilled or barbecued and even the finest restaurants serve the smoked product. It has fatty flesh with a wonderful flavor and is considered a favorite in some European countries, especially Portugal, where it has been fished for centuries. A perhaps under-utilized food fish, being inexpensive, it is sometimes used as bait.

All Mackerels (Atlantic, chub, king, cero, Spanish) US Landings by Year — Nominal Data Value in $US (000); Quantity in tonnes; (NMFS)					
	2004	2005	2006	2007	2008
Value	25,481	19,805	31,218	21,497	19,308
Quantity	64,884	26,992	68,169	35,934	24,547

LIFE CYCLE

The southern population moves inshore along the American coast to spawn in the spring. The northern population spawns primarily in the south western Gulf of St. Lawrence. Spawning usually takes place in late June and early July in a mean water temperature of 53°F. The female mackerel releases between 200,000 and 500,000 eggs. Eggs and sperm, released at the surface of the water, rely on water movement and turbulence to bring them together for fertilization. The fertilized eggs take approximately seven days to develop and hatch. However, mortality is high and only a small percentage of eggs reach the larval stage and larval mortality is also very high. This is believed due to the many groundfish and pelagic fish that feed on mackerel eggs and larvae. However, the eggs and larvae are also very sensitive to water temperatures and may die-off in a sudden change. Also, there is a possibility of cannibalization of small larvae by larger larvae, especially at high larval densities. The average length after the first year is 9 to 12 inches. Mackerel have been known to live up to 17 years, although adult mortality may be as high as 20% per year. Mackerels are the prey of many large fish, mammals and birds including, seals, tuna, whales, sharks and gannets. Mackerel can filter feed on zooplankton and also prey on smaller fish such as capelin and herring smelts.

MACKEREL, JACK

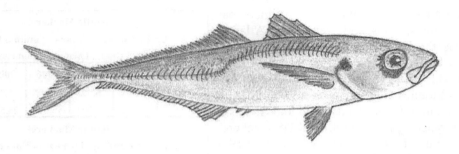

Jack Mackerel, *Trachurus symmetricus*

GENERAL

In appearance, and as a schooling fish, the **jack mackerel** is reminiscent of the Pacific mackerel, with a torpedo-shaped body, tight caudal peduncle, deeply forked tail and the vestiges of finlets in some adults. It is also a pelagic fish, but it is not of the mackerel family.

The jack mackerel belongs to the Carangidae (jacks and pompanos) family and is a fleet-finned, silvery fish that often ranges the oceans in predatory packs. The adult jack mackerel does most of its roving in the offshore as opposed to the inshore roaming of its relatives, the amberjacks (*Seriola* spp.), pompanos (*Trachinotus* spp.) and permits. In appearance it is similar to the Mexican scad (*Decapterus scombrinus*), and other scads in the genus *Decapterus* spp. (see scad entry in this book). There are a number of different Carangidae family species landed in the US including the yellowtail, blue runner and leatherjackets (see table next page).

PHYSICAL DESCRIPTION

Maximum Size: 81.0 cm TL (male/unsexed; Ref. 2850);
Maximum Reported Age: 30 years.

The jack mackerel is characterized by its slender cigar-shaped body, which is metallic blue to olive-green above and silvery below. It has long dorsal and pectoral fins. The spiny dorsal fin is a bit higher than the soft dorsal fin. There are scutes (bony scales) along its entire lateral line. Its eyes are large and there is a distinct black spot at the top rear of the gill cover.

The Mexican scad is very similarly shaped, but may be distinguished from the jack mackerel by its well-defined finlet behind each of the dorsal and anal fins and the scutes on the rear of the lateral line only. The scad is yellowish underneath, often with an orange or reddish side stripe. The jack mackerel lacks the wavy lines and the numerous finlets of the Pacific mackerel and so is easily distinguished.

Also Known As
Saurel
Rough Scad
Pacific Jack
Mackerel
California Horse
Mackerel
Spanish Mackerel

FishBase Name
Pacific Jack
Mackerel

**International
Recognitions**
Spain—Chicharro
ojotón
France—Chinchard
gros yeux

JACK MACKEREL

LANDINGS AND VALUES

The range of the jack mackerel is from southeast Alaska to southern Baja California, the Gulf of California and the Galapagos Islands. The adult fish run in large schools up to several hundred miles offshore. The juvenile fish tend to school nearshore in kelp beds and near piers and breakwaters.

Jack Mackerel US Landings by Year — Nominal Data Value in $US (000); Quantity in tonnes; (NMFS)					
	2004	2005	2006	2007	2008
Value	275	218	200	144	54
Quantity	1,212	297	1,169	631	261

As a commercial fishery, schooling younger fish are often taken nearshore by purse seiners. Older, larger fish are usually taken further offshore by bottom trawlers or albacore trollers, especially in Northern California. US landings of jack mackerel in 1989 totaled 10,745 tonnes, valued at almost $1.6 million (not shown). In 2008, catches were down to 261 tonnes, valued at $54,000 (see table). Off southern California, jack and Pacific (chub) mackerel, *Scomber japonicus,* school and are caught together. Both command the same ex-vessel price and serve pretty much the same markets. Although it is often fished recreationally from piers and boats, it does not readily take bait. However, various jacks accounted for more than 3,000 tonnes of gamefish landings in the US in 2008 (not shown). Commercial landings of other jack species are also reported here. None are a reported fishery in Canada.

Other Jacks or Carangidae Species (Excludes Lookdown, Pompanos, some Amberjacks, etc.) US Landings by Year — Nominal Data Value in $US (000); Quantity in tonnes; (NMFS)						
Species		2004	2005	2006	2007	2008
Almaco Jack,	Value	128	87	107	171	188
Seriola rivoliana	Quantity	75	50	58	85	91
Yellowtail Jack	Value	53	28	53	36	18
Seriola lalandi	Quantity	22	10	18	11	6
Bar Jack,	Value	37	28	28	42	79
Carangoides ruber	Quantity	23	16	15	23	42
Blue Runner,	Value	295	213	200	267	259
Caranx crysos	Quantity	260	159	123	166	150
Crevalle Jack,	Value	349	320	421	359	425
Caranx spp.	Quantity	223	195	259	218	241
Leatherjackets	Value	440	435	362	538	552
Oligoplites spp.	Quantity	176	170	134	181	168
Other Jacks (nei)	Value	138	120	109	114	133
	Quantity	48	46	49	52	60

COMMERCIAL USES

The jack mackerel, along with the chub mackerel, is commercially important as a cannery fish. Both of these fish have been used for pet food and fish meal. Other members of the jack family are excellent market fish, particularly the pompanos, which sell at a premium price. However, the jack mackerel is treated more as a mackerel, than a jack, in the marketplace.

LIFE CYCLE

The jack mackerel, like all jacks, spawns at sea. Females become sexually mature at a young age and some will reproduce at 2 years, while all are spawning when they are 3 years old. Jack mackerel can live 20-30 years so for fish with a long life span, they become sexually mature at a very young age.

Spawning takes place from March through June and occurs over an extensive area from 80 to over 240 miles offshore. Young fish may associate with floating objects and shallow waters; however, the adult fish usually school offshore, at the surface to a depth of 600 feet or more. In the summer, these larger fish tend to migrate inshore and northward. The jack mackerel feeds on krill, squid, sardines, anchovies and lantern fish. They fall prey to larger predators including the yellowtail, sea bass, sea lion, porpoises, swordfish and pelican.

MAHI—MAHI

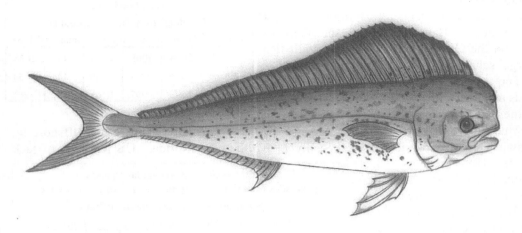

Dolphin, *Coryphaena hippurus*

GENERAL

The **dolphin** belongs to the family Coryphaenidae (dolphinfishes or dolphins). There is only 1 genus and 2 species in the family, the other species being the pompano dolphin, *Coryphaena equiselis* (also pompano dolphinfish-*FishBase*). Both are listed in *The Seafood List* under the market name mahi—mahi (meaning strong—strong in Polynesian). These unique and pretty fishes can be found worldwide in tropical and subtropical waters.

PHYSICAL DESCRIPTION

Max length : 210 cm TL male/unsexed; (Ref. 9846);
Common length : 100.0 cm TL male/unsexed; (Ref. 3390);
Max. published weight: 40.0 kg (Ref. 30874);
Max. reported age: 4 years (Ref. 2885)

Physically defined by striking golden coloration on sides and metallic blues and greens on back and sides with white and yellow on the underside. Also, mature males have a bony crest on the front of the head. The dorsal fin extends from above the eye to just before the caudal fin (58—66 rays). Smaller individuals may have vertical bars on their sides. They can be distinguished from the pompano dolphin by their much larger size in adulthood (almost double), their concave anal fin (versus straight anal fin on the pompano dolphin), less dorsally-compressed (body depth in adults less than 25% of standard length, whereas it is normally more than 25% for the pompano dolphin) longer pectorals (more than ½ head length versus less than ½ in the pompano) and generally larger ray counts in the fins. The tongue tooth patch is small and oval-shaped in the dolphin, but large (50%-60% of the surface) and rectangular in the pompano dolphin. Small specimens can be difficult to tell apart. Neither fish is related to mammal dolphins.

Also Known As
Dorado/ Common Dolphinfish

FishBase Name
Common Dolphinfish

International Recognitions
Spain—Lampuga
France—Coryphène commune
Italy—Capuni
Japan—Toohyaku
Germany—Goldmakrele

LANDINGS AND VALUES

Dolphins of both species are distributed around the world in the same tropical and subtropical waters and are found in both open waters and near the coast (pelagic-neritic). Both species can travel together in mixed schools and are highly migratory. However, it appears the larger common dolphins are more likely to be found near the shore in the southern eastern US, in depths averaging 5–10 meters although they can be found down to 85 meters. US landings totaled 1,037 tonnes in 2008, valued at $5.1 million (see table). Florida and North Carolina accounted for most of the Atlantic landings; about 60% were caught in Hawaii

Dolphins - *Coryphaena* spp. US Landings by Year — Nominal Data Value in $US (000); Quantity in tonnes; (NMFS)					
	2004	2005	2006	2007	2008
Value	6,532	4,684	4,865	5,743	5,127
Quantity	1,466	937	929	1,183	1,037

Dolphins - *Coryphaena* spp. Canadian Landings by Year — Nominal Data Value in $Cdn (000); Quantity in tonnes; (DFO)					
	2004	2005	2006	2007	2008
Value	36	40	68	151	46
Quantity	22	24	40	90	27

in 2008. Some evidently follow the Gulf Stream as far north as Canada as a small amount is landed here also (see table). Approximately 6,400 tonnes were also landed in the US recreational fishery (not shown). As a schooling fish they can be caught by nets, as well as handlines. The use of surface floats, flotsam and drifting weeds can be used to attract dolphins. **Endangered Status:** Listed as "least concern" by IUCN (they are prolific spawners that grow rapidly). **Aquaculture:** There is currently no reported commercial aquaculture of mahi-mahi in North America.

COMMERCIAL USES

Dolphins are a major gamefish as well as commercial fishery. They are sold fresh and frozen. They are often grilled or baked or filleted for sushi or sashimi. The meat is tender, but firm with creamy-white to pink color and large moist flakes. It is sweet tasting with a slightly strong flavour. There are reports of ciguatera poisoning (Ref. 30911).

LIFE CYCLE

Dolphins reach sexual maturity at 4–5 months and spawn in the open sea and possibly closer to the coast in warmer waters. Eggs and larvae are also pelagic. They can spawn repeatedly, as much as once every 2–3 days for the spawning season with 33,000– 60,000 eggs per spawning event. Spawning occurs year round, but peaks with latitude in waters above 75 degree. Spawning seasons are from November to July in the Florida current and from June through July in the Gulf Stream off North Carolina and from August to September in the Pacific Ocean off California. Spawning in the Pacific occurs in open water away from islands or along the continental shelf; in the Atlantic, it occurs under sargassum (floating algae) patches. Dolphins, both juveniles and adults, often hide, feed and spawn in sargussum. Lifespan is generally short – around 5 years.

Dolphins will form schools and prey on most fish and zooplankton as well as crustaceans and squid (i.e., non-selective, opportunistic feeders). Predators include large tuna, rough toothed dolphin, marlin, sailfish and swordfish. Juveniles are particularly vulnerable to predation.

MARLIN

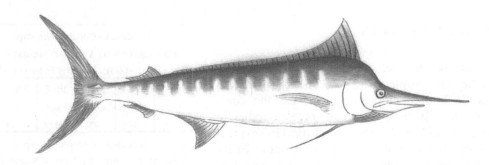

Blue Marlin, *Makaira nigricans*

GENERAL

The term billfish is applied to a number of different predatory fish characterised by their large size (swordfish can be over 4 metres long) and their long, sword–like bill. **Blue marlin** is a member of the family Istiophoridae that includes 5 genera of billfishes (*ITIS*), composed of 4 marlin species, 4 spearfish species and 1 sailfish species. The 3 other marlin species include the black marlin, *Istiompax indica* white marlin *Kajikia albida,* and striped marlin, *Kajikia audax*. (Note: *FishBase* recognises the **blue marlin** as a separate species in the Pacific Ocean; i.e., the Indo-Pacific blue marlin, *Makaira mazara,* while *ITIS* does not. *FishBase* and *The Seafood List* recognize the genus for white and striped marlin as *Tetrapturus* and the genus for black marlin as *Makaira,* while *ITIS* does not.) The swordfish, *Xiphias gladius*, belongs to another family, Xiphiidae, in the same billfish suborder.

PHYSICAL DESCRIPTION

Maximum Size: 500 cm TL male/unsexed (Ref. 11441); 500 cm TL (female)
Max. Reported Age: Males may live for 18 years, and females up to 27
Max. Publ. Weight: 636.0 kg (Ref. 40637); max published weight: 820 kg

The blue marlin is blue-black above and silvery white below, with about 15 rows of light blue vertical stripes. The pronounced first dorsal fin is black to dark blue and other fins are brownish black with a tinge of dark blue in some individuals. The anal fin bases are tinged silvery white. The bill is the result of a long, spear-shaped upper jaw. May differ from the Pacific species and/or populations by differences in the pattern of the lateral line system. The white marlin is a relatively much smaller species growing to a maximum of about 82 kg that is dark above, but silvery white splattered with brown on the sides and silvery white below. The striped marlin (same genus as white) grows mid-size between the white and blue marlins and is dark above and silvery white below, with about 15 rows of cobalt-colored stripes. The black marlin is dark blue above, silvery white below; sometimes with light blue vertical stripes. It is similar to the blue marlin, but has a shorter beak when at same age and the flanks and membrane of first dorsal fin are blue black are without spots.

Also Known As
Sailfish/
Spikefish/
Boohoo/ Agika
Prieta/
Kurokajiki

FishBase Name
Atlantic Blue
Marlin

**International
Recognitions**
Spain—Aguja
azul
France—Makaire
bleu
Italy—Marlin
azzurro
Japan—Nishikuro
Germany—Blauer
Marlin

LANDINGS AND VALUES

Billfishes are important apex predators feeding on a wide variety of smaller fish and cephalopods. While billfish are most common in tropical and subtropical waters, they are highly migratory and swordfish; in particular, but also marlins, are occasionally found in temperate waters. Atlantic blue marlins can be found in the western Atlantic from Brazil to Cape Cod but some ride the Gulf Stream to Newfoundland and others have been tagged in the South Pacific. In contrast, white marlin only ranges in the Atlantic Ocean, while the black and striped marlins are only found in the Indo-Pacific Ocean.

Blue Marlin US (Hawaii) Landings by Year — Nominal Data Value in $US (000); Quantity in tonnes; (NMFS)					
	2004	2005	2006	2007	2008
Value	1,113	972	969	913	1,019
Quantity	406	440	443	339	418

Striped Marlin US (Hawaii) Landings by Year — Nominal Data Value in $US (000); Quantity in tonnes; (NMFS)					
	2004	2005	2006	2007	2008
Value	1,353	1,537	1,602	1,109	1,048
Quantity	425	553	676	283	464

Blue marlins are normally caught as bycatch in tuna and swordfish longline fisheries. In the Atlantic Ocean the blue marlin is not a commercial fishery in the US, but has been under intense pressure in past years. Fishing vessels are required to release all billfish caught within 200 miles (320 km) of the US coastline. However, the survival rate for the fish is low because of death or damage during capture. **Endangered Status:** Neither the Atlantic blue or white marlins are currently listed as endangered under the UN IUCN or the US NMFS; however, both are clearly severely threatened and pressure is on to stop longlining in areas where the marlins concentrate. The threat to Pacific marlins is thought to be similar. Commercial and recreational fishing is mixed in Hawaii, allowing some catch to be landed – 418 tonnes of blue marlin in 2008, valued at $1 million and an almost identical amount of striped marlin (see table). About 3 tonnes ($5,000) of black marlin was also landed in Hawaii and about 3 tonnes ($4,000) of white marlin was landed in Canada in 2008 (not shown).

COMMERCIAL USES

Blue marlins from the Atlantic and Indo-Pacific have commercial value throughout the world. Like bluefin tuna, the meat has a high fat content and is particularly valued in Japan for sashimi. The blue marlin is also one of the most highly sought after gamefish due to their relative size, rarity, beauty and great fighting qualities. The recreational sport fishing pursuit of blue marlin and other billfish has generated a multi–million dollar industry that includes hundreds of companies and thousands of jobs in boat building, marinas and dealerships, tackle manufacturing and sales. The most established sport fisheries for blue marlin in the Atlantic are found in the US eastern seaboard and Gulf Coast, as well as the Bahamas and several Caribbean islands. The IGFA (International Game Fish Association) all–tackle world record is 1,402 pounds and 2 ounces (636 kg). Marlin is marketed as fresh or frozen.

LIFE CYCLE

Blue marlins are open water/substratum egg scatterers and non-guarders. In the Atlantic, mature fish have been observed spawning July to September. Eggs are transparent and 1 mm diameter when ripe and buoyant (pelagic). The fish show preference for blue water and rarely gather in schools. Older ones are usually found scattered as single individuals (same in Pacific). They feed mainly on fishes but also prey on octopods and squids. In the Pacific, they are not usually seen close to land masses or islands, unless there is a deep drop-off of the shelf. They feed on squids, tuna/mackerel-like fishes, crustaceans and cephalopods.

MENHADEN

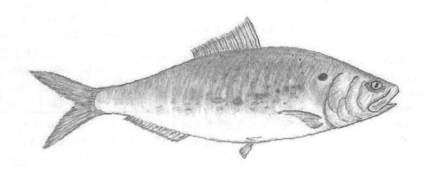

Atlantic Menhaden, *Brevoortia tyrannus*

GENERAL

The various species of menhaden are members of the herring (Clupeidae) family and are close relatives of the alewife and shad. Like other herrings, they are plankton eaters, gulping gallons of water a minute and filtering out as much as a pint of microscopic food an hour. (For additional information, see alewife, herring and shad entries in this book.)

The two most important species are the Gulf menhaden (*Brevoortia patronus*) and the **Atlantic menhaden**. The yellowfin (*B. smithi*) and finescale (*B. gunteri*), two other menhaden species, are found in and around the Gulf of Mexico area; however, they are not as prevalent as the first two species.

Large schools swimming close to the surface are identified by the gulls feeding on them. Just about every fish in the ocean feeds on menhaden as well—fortunately, they are one of the most populous fish in their range.

Also Known As
American Menhaden/ Mossbunker/ Skipjack/ Shad/ Pogy/ Bunker

FishBase Name
Atlantic menhaden

International Recognitions
Spain—Lacha tirana
France—Menhaden tyran
Italy—Alaccia americana
Germany—Menhaden

PHYSICAL DESCRIPTION

Maximum Size: 50.0 cm TL (male/unsexed; Ref. 188)

Menhaden are silvery fishes characterized by a strongly compressed body with a fatty ridge that extends from the back of the head to the dorsal fin. Distinguishing features are the large head and the row of scales behind it, a large terminal mouth (toothless), one angular dorsal fin, a forked tail and a distinct shoulder spot. Unlike the alewife, adults and mature young menhaden have about six lines of other spots on the side behind this shoulder spot. The Atlantic menhaden is usually bluish green with a silvery or brassy belly and sides and pale yellow fins. The Gulf menhaden has a larger head and its dorsal fin is closer to its head than that of the Atlantic menhaden.

LANDINGS AND VALUES

The Atlantic menhaden can be found on the East Coast as far north as Maine and New Brunswick and as far south as southern Florida, whereas the Gulf menhaden is located in the northern Gulf of Mexico to southern Florida and Texas. In a marine environment (versus brackish and

Menhaden US Landings by Year — Nominal Data Value in $US (000); Quantity in tonnes; (NMFS)					
	2004	2005	2006	2007	2008
Value	75,045	62,520	69,683	92,725	88,767
Quantity	678,236	564,187	591,604	673,040	594,284

freshwater), these fishes are found in shallow waters at, or near, the surface of the continental shelf, or close to large estuaries and bays. They occur in large schools that can weigh many hundreds of tons. They are generally fished in the fall when the schools are moving southward. Generally, most are caught by purse seines; boats circle the school with a net, and menhaden are pumped out of the net into a refrigerated hold. Because of the compactness of the schools, bycatches (non-menhaden species) are estimated to be less than 1%.

Landings of both the Atlantic and Gulf menhaden have decreased over the years, but the decrease has been more significant for the Gulf menhaden. In 1988 menhaden landings were the most important of American commercial fish landings in terms of quantity, but were low in terms of value. In 1989 they were replaced as the largest US catch by the Alaska pollock. US landings (both Atlantic and Gulf menhaden) in 1989 totaled almost 907,440 tonnes, valued at approximately $85 million (not shown). By comparison, 2008 landings were 594,284 tonnes valued at almost $89 million (see table). Menhaden is not a commercially reported catch in Canada, but some may be included as a bycatch of other fisheries.

COMMERCIAL USES

Menhaden is generally too boney and oily for human consumption. Currently, about 15% to 20% of menhaden is harvested by the bait fishery and the balance is primarily used to make industrial products. Menhaden is manufactured into oil for use in chemical industries (for example, cosmetics, soaps, paints and lubricants) and menhaden meal is an ingredient in many animal feeds and fertilizers. The meal provides a unique, high-protein blend of nutrients and is a component of many cattle, swine, poultry and aquaculture feeds, where it improves growth rates. Like other herrings, menhaden oil is rich in heart healthy omega-3 fatty acids and is a FDA approved health food additive. The oil is also an ingredient in many food products including pasta sauces, salad dressings and soups and cooking oils.

LIFE CYCLE

Although menhaden are anadromous, they appear to spawn mainly at sea and so are unlike shad and alewife in this respect. However, ripe menhaden have been found in rivers, and some appear to stay in fresh water year-round, suggesting freshwater spawning. The eggs are 0.05 to 0.08 inches in diameter, have an oil globule, and are buoyant. One-year-old fish are about 5 inches long; two-year-olds, about 8.5 inches; and three-year-olds, about 10 inches. They rarely exceed 18 inches or 4 pounds. They consume primary foods such as plankton, zooplankton and small crustaceans and are preyed on by most large fishes—e.g., cod, pollock, bluefish, tuna and shark.

MOJARRA

Striped Mojarra, *Eugerres plumieri*

GENERAL

Mojarras belong to the family Gerreidae (mojarras) that includes 6 genera and about 50 species; about one-half of species are found in the genius *Gerres* spp. (*ITIS*). The **striped mojarra** is one of two species listed in *The Seafood List*; the other being the Irish mojarra, *Diapterus auratus*.

PHYSICAL DESCRIPTION

Max length : 40.0 cm TL male/unsexed; (Ref. 3722);
Common length : 30.0 cm TL male/unsexed; (Ref. 3722);
Max. published weight: 1,020 g (Ref. 4699)

The striped mojarra has a somewhat oblong, laterally-compressed body; small head with pointed snout and a slender caudal peduncle. The dorsal area is more cone-shaped than rounded, with the cone culminating in the start of a dorsal fin about 1/3 body length back from the head; the dorsal fin peaks at the front, falling in size towards the middle portion and continuing at about ½ peak size almost to the caudle. Pelvic and anal fins are both salient with the anal fin uniquely contoured for depth at front and diminishing in size towards the caudle, with the outside edge forming an almost perpendicular angle to the caudle area. The pelvic fin is low on the body and extends from the gill area to more than ½ body length. The caudel fin is deeply V-shaped. The fish has a silvery coloring, sometimes with yellow tinges, interrupted by black stripes running from head to tail (reminiscent of a striped bass) that become smaller and vaguer towards the belly area.

Also Known As
Mojarra

FishBase Name
Striped mojarra

International Recognitions
Spain—Mojarra rayada
France—Blanche rayée

LANDINGS AND VALUES

Mojarras					
US Landings by Year — Nominal Data					
Value in $US (000); Quantity in tonnes; (NMFS)					
	2004	2005	2006	2007	2008
Value	521	463	608	604	816
Quantity	243	196	252	239	298

The striped mojarra is a marine water species found in subtropical waters in the western Atlantic from South Carolina to Western Florida and the Gulf of Mexico and Caribbean to Brazil. The species prefers shallow coastal waters and is found mostly over muddy bottoms and in mangroves and will travel significant distances into brackish and freshwater environments. US commercial landings totaled 298 tonnes in 2008, valued at $816,000 (see table). The only landings in 2008 were in Florida (both east and west coast).

Irish mojarras (*Diapterus auratus*) are distributed tropically from North Carolina through to Brazil. They can often be found in shallow coastal waters, particularly mangrove-lined areas, or around vegetated sand flats. Juveniles are often more widely dispersed than adults, and both feed on benthic invertebrates.

COMMERCIAL USES

The mojarra is usually marketed fresh or processed into fishmeal. It is also considered a gamefish and a baitfish.

LIFE CYCLE

Little is reported on the lifecycle and reproduction of the striped mojarra. It is believed to be a bottom feeder close to shore (to avoid predators) and preys on insects, worms, crustaceans, small bivalves and detritus.

MONKFISH

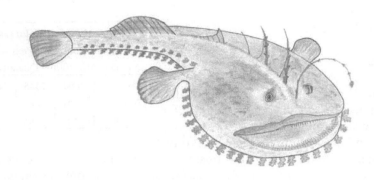

Goosefish, *Lophius americanus*

GENERAL

One would scarcely believe that monktails, served in fine dining rooms in many parts of the world, are the product of such a hideous-looking fish. The **goosefish** (often called "angler") is one of several members of the family Lophiidae (4 genera, about 25 species) native to North American waters and one of two main food species. The goosefish has been described as a mouth with an attached tail, and reports of goosefish eating prey almost as big as themselves are common. In areas where their habitats overlap it may be confused with the blackfin goosefish, *Lophius gastrophysus* (common name "monkfish") which it resembles; however, the *L. americanus* is the primary catch in North America. Two other monkfish that are specified on *The Seafood List* are the *Lophius piscatorius* (common name "monkfish") and the *Lophius litulon* (common name "angler"), but neither of these species are common to North America. The *L. gastrophysus* is not listed on *The Seafood List*.

PHYSICAL DESCRIPTION

Max length : 120 cm TL male/unsexed; (Ref. 7251);
Common length : 90.0 cm TL male/unsexed; (Ref. 3787);
Max. published weight: 22.6 kg (Ref. 40637); Max. reported age: 30 years (Ref. 796)

A cartilaginous fish, the body of the goosefish is greatly depressed and very soft; so soft, in fact, it will collapse when out of water. The head is very large, wider than the trunk, and is also depressed. The front contours are rounded with several low, conical tubercles (lumps) on top of the head, near the inner edge of, and behind, the eyes. The mouth is extremely large, almost as wide as the head. The lower jaw extends considerably beyond the upper jaw. Both jaws have a row of large, irregular, canine-like teeth. The skin is scaleless, smooth and slippery.

Goosefish have a brownish dorsal with fine, dark matting. The belly is dirty white. The backs of the dorsal, caudal and pectoral fins are dark, and the tips are almost black. The pelvic fins have a reddish tint. By way of contrast, the blackfin goosefish grows to about one-half the size (60 cm) of the goosefish, has a pectoral fin with a black inner edge and a black band toward the rear on the underside of the fin. Also, the third dorsal spine on the head is longer on the blackfin than on the goosefish.

Also Known As
American Goosefish/
Angler/
Monktail/
Fishing Frog/
Allmouth/
Molligut/
Sea-devil/
Lotte

FishBase Name
American angler

International Recognitions
France—
baudroie
d'Amérique

LANDINGS AND VALUES

The goosefish occurs in the western Atlantic from Newfoundland southward along the continental shelf to northern Florida. The blackfin goosefish replaces the *L. americanus* in waters south of Florida. The goosefish occupies a great range of depths, from the surface to as deep as 2,200 feet. It can tolerate temperatures from 32 to 70°F, although there are indications that it will move into deeper, cooler water when the surface layers become too warm. Although it is a directed fishery in some areas, many landings occur as a by-catch, taken by trawls, gillnets, longlines, dredges, traps and seines. The US catch was 11,340 tonnes in 1989, valued at $12.7 million (not shown). It has since dropped to 9,956 tonnes in 2008, valued at almost $24.6 million (see table). It is a smaller catch in Canada with 2008 landings of 499 tonnes, valued at $619,000 (see table). The Canadian catch in 1989 was approximately 1,770 tonnes, valued at $1.4 million (not shown).

Goosefish US Landings by Year — Nominal Data Value in $US (000); Quantity in tonnes; (NMFS)					
	2004	2005	2006	2007	2008
Value	33,393	42,252	33,459	28,820	24,564
Quantity	21,151	19,013	14,578	12,146	9,956

Monkfish Canadian Landings by Year — Nominal Data Value in $Cdn (000); Quantity in tonnes; (DFO)					
	2004	2005	2006	2007	2008
Value	2,524	3,729	2,693	586	619
Quantity	2,271	2,387	1,896	501	499

COMMERCIAL USES

When marketed as food fish, it is the caudal or tail section that is processed and sold as monktail. The product has a lean, light-textured white flesh that has been compared to the taste of lobster. Up until relatively recently, goosefish was discarded or was used in the manufacture of fishmeal. It is now considered a great delicacy and North American demand has steadily increased, taking most of the catch. Goosefish livers are also prized product in Europe and Japan.

LIFE CYCLE

In northern Atlantic waters, goosefish spawn from June to September. One female can produce up to 1 million eggs. The eggs are about 0.02 inches in diameter, with one or more pink to straw-colored oil globules. They are laid on a mucous sheet, or veil, that floats at or near the surface. The sheet is a slight purple color. This veil may be 30 to 40 feet long and more than 12 feet wide. Veils containing over 3 million eggs have been found. Eggs hatch in one to two weeks and larvae are able to develop in a wide range of water temperatures. Soon after hatching, curiously elongated dorsal head spines and pelvic fins develop and pigmentation occurs.

Goosefish may reach a length of 2.5 inches before their first winter and 5 inches by their first year. Mature fish average from 5.5 to 11 pounds; however, much larger specimens measuring up to 4 feet in length have been reported. Monkfish have been known to partially bury themselves in the ocean bottom, using their "head lure" to attract unsuspecting prey. It is a voracious predator and fishermen need to be careful as they can inflict serious wound with their sharp teeth. Mature monkfish have few enemies, but swordfish is one. Juveniles may fall prey to larger groundfish.

MULLET

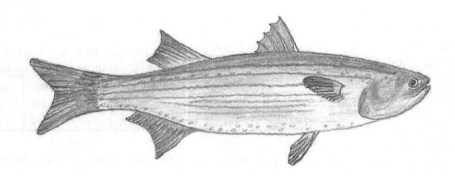

Striped Mullet, *Mugil cephalus*

GENERAL

There are approximately 80 species of mullets in the Mugilidae family, whose members inhabit the coastal areas of all tropical and temperate seas, although some species will enter and even inhabit, freshwater. The **striped mullet** is a catadromous species of mullet, spawning in saltwater and spending much of its life in fresh or brackish water.

The **striped mullet** is sometimes known as the "jumping mullet" for its unique habit of jumping out of the water. It may do this to avoid predators or to increase oxygen intake in oxygen deprived environments, but it is a frisky fish in any case. Mullet have thick-walled gizzard-like organs and a long gastrointestinal tract that enables them to feed on decaying organic matter.

The sea mullets are not related to the freshwater or common suckers *Catostomus* spp., which in North America are sometimes marketed (incorrectly) as mullet.

PHYSICAL DESCRIPTION

Max length: 100.0 cm SL male/unsexed; (Ref. 2804);
Common length: 50.0 cm SL male/unsexed; (Ref. 7399);
Max. reported age: 16 years (Ref. 28725)

Mullets are torpedo-shaped fish with a dark brown, green, or blue back and silvery sides. All members of the family bear a common resemblance. In the striped mullet all scales (except those on its lower body) have a dark spot at their base. These series of dark spots form rather conspicuous stripes on its sides. It has a blunt nose with a small mouth and thin lips with a bump at the tip of the lower lip. The pectoral fins are short and do not reach the first dorsal fin. The second dorsal fin begins almost directly above the point where the anal fin begins. There is no visible lateral line.

Unlike the white mullet, *M. curema,* (for which it is often mistaken) and the redeye mullet, *M. gaimardianus,* both the dorsal and anal fins of the striped mullet are <u>not</u> scaled.

Also Known As
Sea Mullet
Gray Mullet
Common Gray
Mullet
Black Mullet
River Mullet

FishBase Name
Flathead grey
mullet

International Recognitions
Germany—
Meeräsche
Spain—mujol
Italy—cefalo
mazzone
Cantonese— wu
tau

LANDINGS AND VALUES

The striped mullet can be found nearly worldwide in both tropical and temperate waters. On the east coast of North America the striped mullet ranges from Nova Scotia to Brazil, including the Gulf of Mexico (although it is notably absent from the Bahamas and most of the West Indies and the Caribbean). On the West Coast, it is found from San Francisco to Chile.

Striped Mullet US Landings by Year — Nominal Data Value in $US (000); Quantity in tonnes; (NMFS)					
	2004	2005	2006	2007	2008
Value	9,917	7,669	10,960	6,759	7,271
Quantity	7,180	5,054	6,971	5,295	6,121

The mullet lives in coastal waters and estuaries and usually travels in enormous schools. In the Gulf of Mexico, it is commonly harvested by gillnets and haul seines at river mouths, in bays and off beaches from October to January. In Florida and Louisiana, large numbers of roe mullet are taken during the annual migration to offshore spawning grounds. Due to over-fishing, Florida imposed a ban on net fishing in the mid-1990s that has, at least, significantly curtailed inland fisheries and marks a come-back of the fishery. Although the various US species are often not differentiated, the striped mullet accounted for about 97% of the commercial catch in 2008. US landings of **all mullets** in 1989 totaled about 14,337 tonnes, valued at $15 million (not shown). The 2008 catch is much lower at a 6,300 tonnes, valued at $7.6 million (see tables). In addition, almost 1,500 tonnes were landed recreationally in the US in 2008 (not shown). The Canadian fishery does not report any mullet landings.

COMMERCIAL USES

Where found in abundance, mullet are fished commercially as food fish and are marketed fresh, dried, salted and frozen. Prepared fresh, mullet can be boiled, stewed, baked, or fried. Mullet gizzard is prepared similarly to chicken gizzard. Mullet is also economically important as a bait fish. Mullet roe is marketed fresh or smoked and is exported to Asia

White Mullet and Unspecified Mullets US Landings by Year — Nominal Data Value in $US (000); Quantity in tonnes; (NMFS)					
	2004	2005	2006	2007	2008
Value	553	489	483	361	333
Quantity	150	133	176	188	186

where striped mullet is often cultivated in freshwater ponds. Mullet is also an ingredient in Chinese medicine.

LIFE CYCLE

During the autumn and winter months, adult mullet migrate far offshore in large aggregations to spawn. Fecundity is usually high with up to 5 million eggs produced. The eggs are a transparent pale yellow with an average diameter of 0.72 mm. Each egg contains an oil globule and floats to the surface where hatching occurs about 48 hours after fertilization. The larvae are approximately 2.5 mm in length. After a few weeks, the larvae reach 16-20 mm in length and move inshore. Juveniles spend the remainder of their first year in coastal waters, salt marshes and estuaries. In autumn, they often move to deeper water while the adults migrate even further offshore to spawn. After this first year of life, the mullet can tolerate great variations of salinity and can be found in a variety of saltwater and freshwater habitats including the ocean, salt marshes, estuaries and fresh water rivers and lakes.

Mullets are not fish eaters. They swim along the bottom sucking in mouthfuls of mud from which they extract microscopic particles of animal and vegetable matter, expelling the refuse. In rich feeding spots, schools of mullets are known to create pandemonium reminiscent of barnyard fowls at the feeding tray. Their feeding behavior often leaves "trails" in the sediment. The mullet is preyed on by nearly every other mammal, bird and fish larger than itself. This includes sharks, dolphins, pelicans and seatrout.

OCEAN POUT

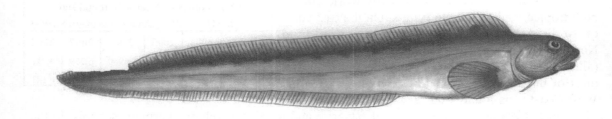

Ocean Pout, *Zoarces americanus*

GENERAL

Ocean pout belong to the family Zoarcidae, of eelpouts. There are about 50 genera and close to 300 species in the family. **Ocean pout** is the only species of genus *Zoarces* found in the northwest Atlantic, and it is the only species listed with the market name "ocean pout" in *The Seafood List*.

These fish look similar to wolffishes, members of a closely related family and somewhat similar to cusk (see wolffish and cusk entries in this book). Freshwater burbot are sometimes also called pout.

Also Known As
Mutton Fish/
Conger Eel/
Mother-of-eels/
Ling

FishBase Name
Ocean pout

International Recognitions
France—Loquette d'Amérique

PHYSICAL DESCRIPTION

Max length : 110 cm TL male/unsexed; (Ref. 7251);
Max. published weight: 5,436 g (Ref. 4926);
Max. reported age: 18 years (Ref. 796)

Ocean pout are eel-like in shape with a continuous dorsal fin that runs from the nape of the neck to the base of the caudal peduncle, but does not connect to the caudle fin. The anal fin is connected to the caudal fin and runs to the middle of the ventral side of the fish. They have a wide gaping mouth and thick fleshy lips. Jaws are lined with thick conical teeth. The body is 8 times as long as it is deep. They can have blackish mottling on dorsal fins and base with red coloration on the dorsal, fading to dirty white or yellowish on the belly.

In contrast, the wolffish has a much higher dorsal fin and a distinctly separate caudal fin on both dorsal and anal sides. The cusk has a continuous dorsal, caudle and anal fin – all white in color, with black margins narrowly edged in white – and the lower jaw has a long chin barbel.

LANDINGS AND VALUES

Ocean Pout US Landings by Year — Nominal Data Value in $US (000); Quantity in tonnes; (NMFS)					
	2004	**2005**	**2006**	**2007**	**2008**
Value	6	4	6	3	3
Quantity	5	3	4	3	1

Ocean pout are only found in the northwest Atlantic from Labrador, Canada to Delaware, USA. They are a non-migratory demersal fish, usually found alone on the bottom and often caught by fishers seeking other groundfish. Commercial interest in this species peaked during the second World War when US landings approximated 2,000 tonnes. Then the species became infected with a protozoan parasite that caused lesions and consumer demand subsided. US landings in the 1950s and 1960s were generally small, but began to increase in the late 1970s and peaked at almost 2,200 tonnes in 1987. The fishery slowly declined from this level and fell off almost completely again since the mid-1990s. Some of the reasons for this are believed to be a change in management practices and changes in locations fished and gear used. It should be noted too that international fleets began landing ocean pout in very large quantities off North America in the mid-1960s; however, this effort ended in the early 1970s.

In 2008, 1 tonne of ocean pout valued at $3,000 was commercially landed in the US (see table). All of the catches in 2008 were caught in Maryland using pots and traps for fish. Past directed fishing efforts used trawl net gear. Peak fishing season was from late winter to early spring. The present occassional Canadian landings in this fishery are not worth reporting.

Endangered Status: Presently, the stock is believed to be in an overfished condition, but not presently overfished.

COMMERCIAL USES

The ocean pout is considered to be an excellent eating fish with a sweet tasting meat.

LIFE CYCLE

In the southern part of their range, ocean pout are found in benthic habitats in the Gulf of Maine, Georges Bank and the mid-Atlantic to Delaware. They have low fecundity and eggs are laid in hard bottom sheltered nests guarded by the females. It is believed that these fish are solitary but come together for spawning. They are found at depths between 10-100m. They feed on a variety of molluscs, crustaceans, echinoderms as well as other invertebrates. They can eat other fish but are not great predators.

PERCH, OCEAN

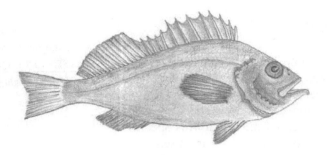

Deepwater Redfish, *Sebastes mentella*

GENERAL

Atlantic **redfish** belong to the family Scorpaenidae (*ITIS*) or Sebastidae *(FishBase)* of the order Scorpaeniformes (scorpion fish). Hence, although marketed as ocean perch, they are not "true" perches at all. Although there are generally thought to be three species of redfish present in western Atlantic waters, there is considerable confusion in the nomenclature. *ITIS* and *The Seafood List* agree with *FishBase* on two Latin names of species (*S. mentella* and *S. fasciatus*), but with different common names. Moreover, there appears to be a mixed-up in a third species (*S. marinus*) and perhaps fourth species (*S. norvegicus*)*. Except for size, the various redfish species are so similar to each other they are usually all marketed as ocean perch. The Pacific ocean perch (*Sebastes alutus*), sometimes known (incorrectly) as the "longjaw rockfish," is similar to the Atlantic redfish and is also marketed as "ocean perch." However, in the Pacific Region, the Pacific ocean perch is just one species of more than 100 species of the genus *Sebastes* ("rockfish") — a market name specific to the west coast. Pacific ocean perch generally account for more than half the total *Sebastes* spp. catch in the US (see rockfish entry in this book). [*Note: some fishes are not included as North American species as they generally occur beyond a 200-metre depth limit off the coast; also see below.]

Also Known As
Atlantic Redfish
Deepwater Rosefish

FishBase Name
Beaked redfish

International Recognitions
Spain—Sébaste du Nord
France—Sébaste du Nord
Germany—Seeaal

PHYSICAL DESCRIPTION
Max length: 58.0 cm NG male/unsexed; (Ref. 58426); Max. reported age: 75 years (Ref. 45673)

Redfishes are immediately recognizable by their orange to flame-red color (for which they are named), spiny fins (hence, scorpion) and extremely large eyes. They are a laterally compressed fish, with one dorsal fin running from behind the gills almost to the tail. Other distinguishing features include a prominent beak formed by the lower jaw and a bony fan of spines around the gill cover. The **deepwater redfish** (*S. mentella*) [*FishBase* name: "beaked redfish"] is distinguished by its more orange than red color. It is more common than the other Atlantic species and is generally found in deep waters. The Labrador redfish (*S. fasciatus*) [*FishBase* name: "Acadian redfish"] and the redfish (*S. marinus*) [*FishBase* name: "golden redfish"] are two other redfish species, but *S. marinus* is identified as invalid and a synonym for *Serranus scriba* in *ITIS*. (Authors note: this appears to be a mix-up as *S. scriba* is a subtropical species in the Eastern Atlantic in *FishBase*.)

Meanwhile, the species *Sebastes norvegicus* is designated as the "golden redfish" in *ITIS* and *The Seafood List* and is recognized as a valid species in *FishBase* with no common name. *S. marinus*, in past Canadian literature, has been viewed as the largest western Atlantic Ocean redfish species; while *S. mentella* is mid-size and *S. fasciatus* is smaller. The Atlantic and Pacific ocean perches look very similar, although the Pacific species usually has a dark saddle along the back near the dorsal fin.

(Atlantic Ocean) Redfish (Acadian) US Landings by Year — Nominal Data Value in $US (000); Quantity in tonnes; (NMFS)					
	2004	**2005**	**2006**	**2007**	**2008**
Value	458	713	795	998	1,286
Quantity	398	561	499	781	1,075

(Atlantic Ocean) Redfish (*S.* spp.) Canadian Landings by Year — Nominal Data Value in $Cdn (000); Quantity in tonnes; (DFO)					
	2004	**2005**	**2006**	**2007**	**2008**
Value	7,611	9,323	9,504	6,169	5,164
Quantity	12,930	16,043	14,316	9,215	7,829

LANDINGS AND VALUES

The western Atlantic redfish fishery began around 1935 in the Gulf of Maine, and with the discovery of other stocks, expanded to most areas of the northern Atlantic fishery. During the day, redfish are caught by bottom trawls. The night fishery uses mid-water trawls to catch redfish as they rise for night feeding. US landings of ocean perch are primarily in the Pacific region with 28,981 tonnes landed in 2008, valued at $12.7 million (see table). Canadian catches of ocean perch are greater in the Atlantic region; in 2008 landings were 7,829 tonnes, valued at almost $5.2 million (see table). On the Pacific coast, the ocean perch is technically a rockfish and may sometimes be reported as such. However, this book has separated the redfish from other rockfish landings (see rockfish entry). **Endangered Status:** The Labrador redfish is listed as endangered; while the deepwater redfish is listed as "least concern" and the redfish (or golden redfish) is not evaluated.

COMMERCIAL USES

Most redfish are processed into frozen fillets, with or without the skin, and sold throughout North America as ocean perch. It is a medium-fat fish, with a bright red, firm skin when scaled.

Pacific Ocean Perch (*Sebastes Alutus*) US Landings by Year — Nominal Data Value in $US (000); Quantity in tonnes; (NMFS)					
	2004	**2005**	**2006**	**2007**	**2008**
Value	4,885	5,755	10,538	14,768	12,716
Quantity	20,602	19,475	23,192	28,118	28,981

LIFE CYCLE

Most Atlantic redfishes are deep-swimming, living at depths between 300 and 2,000 feet. (The larger the fish, the deeper the water in which they live.) During the day, redfish stay very close to the bottom, moving up at night, usually to feed.

Pacific Ocean Perch (*Sebastes Alutus*) Canadian Landings by Year — Nominal Data Value in $Cdn (000); Quantity in tonnes; (DFO)					
	2004	**2005**	**2006**	**2007**	**2008**
Value	6,799	6,387	6,720	5,891	5,418
Quantity	5,971	5,152	5,347	4,688	4,311

Evidence suggests that these stocks migrate very little. The species are ovoviviparous, giving birth to live offspring. Spawning occurs during the spring and early summer. The eggs are fertilized and incubated within the female and are retained there after they hatch until the yolk sacs have been absorbed. The female gives birth to about 20,000 to 40,000 young fish the next spring. Redfishes tend to mature slowly and live long lives, factors that are important in stock management. They generally reach sexual maturity and a market size of 10 inches by age 10. They can attain a length of 16 to 20 inches by age 40. Females are usually larger than males. They feed on small fishes and are preyed upon by halibut, cod, swordfish and seals.

PLAICE

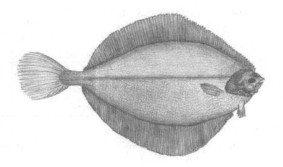

American Plaice, *Hippoglossoides platessoides*

GENERAL

American plaice (family Pleuronectidae) is one of several species of right-eyed flounders found in the western Atlantic. It is in the same family as the Atlantic and Pacific halibuts; the Greenland turbot; the yellowtail, winter/blackback, witch and arrowtooth flounders and the rock, petrale and Dover soles, amongst many other highly commercial species. Like its brethern, newly hatched plaice swim upright and are symmetrical. However, within days, the left eye begins to move across the skull, and eventually, both eyes become situated on the right side.

Fish lovers might well ask, "What ever happened to the American plaice?" With landings often in the 75,000 to 100,000 tonne range in the 1970s, it was the largest Canadian groundfish catch next to cod. The US also landed upwards of 15,000 tonnes of plaice in the early 1980s. Alas, with stock collapse (presumed due to overfishing) the name is seldom heard these days. However, the cod stocks are coming back... and so might the mighty American plaice. It is a relatively coldwater species and, ironically, might have been better named Canadian plaice, or even Newfoundland plaice, as most of the formerly large catches were from the Grand Banks. Two other species, European plaice, *Pleuronectes platessa*, and Alaska plaice, *Pleuronectes quadrituberculatus,* also carry the market name "plaice" in *The Seafood List*.

Also Known As
Canadian Plaice/
Dab/
American Dab/
Sand Dab/
Sea Dab/
Black Dab/
Sole
Plie Canadienne

FishBase Name
American Plaice

International Recognitions
Spain—Platija americana
France—Balai
Italy—Passera canadese
Germany—Scharbenzunge

PHYSICAL DESCRIPTION

Max length: 82.6 cm NG male/unsexed; (Ref. 58426);
Max. published weight: 6,400 g (Ref. 7251); Max. reported age: 30 years (Ref. 6263)

A typical flatfish, the American plaice is strongly compressed laterally, with both eyes situated on the upper side. The head is relatively small, usually less than one-fifth the body length. The large mouth, with small teeth in both jaws, and the color (in northern waters, usually a rusty brown) distinguish it from other flounders. The plaice has a soft-rayed dorsal fin extending from just above the eye to the base of the caudal peduncle. The anal fin stretches almost the entire length of the abdomen. Pelvic and pectoral paired fins are present and are relatively small. The prominent lateral line extends from the rounded tail fin, arching over the pectoral fin. The pigmented upper side of the plaice is generally reddish to greyish-brown in color, while the underside is white. The tips of the dorsal and anal fins may also be white.

LANDINGS AND VALUES

Plaice is found on both sides of the North Atlantic, as well as Alaska, and is a primary flatfish landed in Europe. In North America, it prefers cold temperatures and is often found in deeper waters from the far north to Rhode Island. Offshore fishing vessels using otter trawls, gill nets and Danish seines account for the majority of the catch.

American Plaice Canadian Landings by Year — Nominal Data Value in $Cdn (000); Quantity in tonnes; (DFO)					
	2004	**2005**	**2006**	**2007**	**2008**
Value	2,324	2,089	1,551	1,374	1,188
Quantity	2,752	2,934	1,459	1,660	1,713

American Plaice US Landings by Year — Nominal Data Value in $US (000); Quantity in tonnes; (NMFS)					
	2004	**2005**	**2006**	**2007**	**2008**
Value	4,445	3,999	4,162	3,552	4,101
Quantity	1,709	1,352	1,107	989	1,079

Excluding halibut and turbot, in 2008 approximately 18,932 tonnes of small flatfishes (flounder, sole and plaice) was landed in Canada, valued at $17.6 million (not shown). Of this total, 1,713 tonnes, valued at $1.2 million, was American plaice (see table). This catch is significantly lower than landings in the 1970s and 1980s. For example, almost 47,000 tonnes of American plaice was landed in Canada 1989, but the fishery collapsed shortly afterwards and has not returned. In the US, 298,557 tonnes of small flatfishes were landed in 2008, valued at almost $180 million (not shown) of which 1,079 tonnes was plaice, valued at $4.1 million (see table). Recent US landings of plaice are down from 1989 levels of 3,500 tonnes (not shown). The price differentials between Canadian and American products may be explained somewhat by frozen versus fresh product prices, lower demand for the species in Canada and the distance to export markets, requiring greater middleman involvement and lower ex-vessel prices to be competitive. (Also see flounder and sole entries.)

COMMERCIAL USES

American plaice is a lean, white fish with a fine flavor. It is marketed as plaice and often (incorrectly) as sole and is available fresh or frozen - normally in fillet form.

LIFE CYCLE

Spawning occurs during the spring or early summer. The most active spawning grounds appear to be along the Grand Bank. The average, mature female produces from 250,000 to 500,000 eggs. The eggs are spherical and buoyant, floating near the surface. Hatching usually occurs within 10 to 15 days, depending upon the water temperature. Generally speaking, American plaice is a slow-growing but relatively long-lived species. The age can be determined by counting the number of growth rings on the otoliths (ear bones). Males mature at age four or five, measuring 8 to 10 inches; females at age eight to nine and measure 12 to 14 inches. The commercial fishery usually harvests fish that range in age from 5 to 20 years, although American plaice up to 30 years of age have been reported. American plaice feed upon smaller fishes such as capelin and sand lance. Their predators include cod, halibut and other larger fishes. Migration appears to be limited to offshore movement into deeper waters during the winter, with a return to shallower waters in spring.

POLLOCK

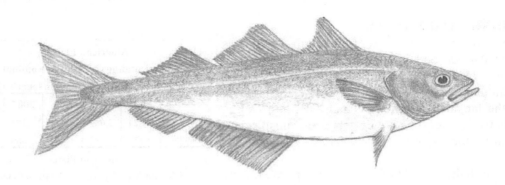

Pollock, *Pollachius virens*

GENERAL

A member of the cod family Gadidae, the pollock is a groundfish (similar to the European "pollack," *Pollachius pollachius*) that can be found throughout the North Atlantic. A schooling fish by nature, it has supported both an inshore and offshore fisheries for many years. The pollock is also a good sport fish and many have been taken by anglers using flies, lures or live bait.

Although often marketed as "bluefish," the pollock should not be confused with the true Atlantic bluefish (*Pomatomus saltatrix*) which is a very different species, although it is also prized as both a commercial and sport fishery. Similarly, this pollock is a different species than the Alaska (walleye) pollock (*Theragra chalcogramma*) found on the Pacific Coast of North America.

PHYSICAL DESCRIPTION

Max length: 130 cm TL male/unsexed; (Ref. 1371);
Common length : 60.0 cm TL male/unsexed; (Ref. 4645);
Max. published weight: 32.0 kg (Ref. 7251); Max. reported age: 25 years (Ref. 1371)

The pollock closely resembles its relatives, the cod and haddock. It has three dorsal fins and two anal fins. It is generally green, from deep olive to brownish green on its back, blending to pale yellow or grey sides below the lateral line. The belly can be either silver-grey or white. The lateral line stretches the length of the body and is white or pale grey. Young pollock often have a red or orange line on the sides and fins, but this is only temporary and a result of living in shallow coastal areas.

The pollock can be easily distinguished from the cod or haddock by its distinctive forked tail, green color, pointed snout and projecting lower jaw with a much smaller chin barbel. Other differences are that the haddock has a dark lateral line, while the cod has spots or blotches.

Also Known As
Saithe/
Coalfish/ Coley/
Green Cod/
Boston Bluefish

FishBase Name
Saithe

International Recognitions
Spain—Carbonero
France—Lieu noir
Italy—Merluzzo nero
Germany—Blaufisch

LANDINGS AND VALUES

Pollock can be found from southern Newfoundland to New Jersey on the North American side of the North Atlantic, and from Greenland to northwest Europe to the Bay of Biscay on the European side. Though they can be caught year- round, the peak harvest period for pollock is during the mid-winter and summer months. Pollock is fished both in the inshore and offshore fisheries, using gillnets, handlines and longlines. Occasionally, seines are used when schools are near the surface. Otter trawls account for only a small fraction of the total catch. Offshore vessels now supply most of the pollock landed, taking about 70 percent of the catch in recent years. The US catch in 1989 was approximately 10,435 tonnes, valued at about $10 million (not shown). The 2008 catch was approximately 7,000 tonnes, valued at $7.9 million (see table). The Canadian catch in 1989 was 44,872 tonnes valued at $20 million; but it too had dropped significantly by 2008, with catches down to 5,798 tonnes, valued at $4.8 million (see table).

(Atlantic Ocean) Pollock US Landings by Year — Nominal Data Value in $US (000); Quantity in tonnes; (NMFS)					
	2004	2005	2006	2007	2008
Value	5,610	7,795	7,547	8,519	7,870
Quantity	5,069	6,505	6,059	8,335	6,986

(Atlantic Ocean) Pollock Canadian Landings by Year — Nominal Data Value in $Cdn (000); Quantity in tonnes; (DFO)					
	2004	2005	2006	2007	2008
Value	4,221	4,560	3,509	5,352	4,789
Quantity	8,777	8,082	4,895	6,944	5,798

COMMERCIAL USES

Pollock is often marketed fresh (slightly lower-priced than cod), but it can also be found salted and dried. Fresh or frozen fillets, known as Boston bluefish or deep sea fillets are also popular ways to prepare pollock. Scrod pollock, sometimes advertised on restaurant menus, refers to small (1.5 to 2.5 pounds) pollock.

LIFE CYCLE

The pollock are late fall to early winter spawners, with breeding beginning around October, generally when water temperatures begin to drop to between 46 and 50°F. Peak spawning takes place from November to February, when the water is a chilly 41 to 43°F. They prefer a water depth between 90 and 300 feet. The average female produces about 200,000 eggs, though records show that large females have produced over 4 million eggs. These eggs are buoyant and drift near the surface. Depending on the ambient water temperature, incubation takes from seven to nine days. When they hatch, the larvae feed off a yolk sac for the first five days. At this time, they are 1 to 1 1/4 inches long and exhibit most of their adult traits. The larvae begin to migrate inshore to nursery areas almost immediately. Harbor pollock, as they are known in the first three years of life, can be found all along the coast. Subsequently, they move back out to deeper waters where they mature at age five or older. Then the cycle begins again. The evidence that pollock possess strong homing tendencies is convincing, as they can be traced back to the same inshore locations in subsequent years. The growth rate is rapid during the early stages of development: from 5 to 6 inches per year for the first three years, from 2 to 4 inches per year for the next three years, and slowing to 1 to 2 inches per year as the fish reaches sexual maturity at five years onward. They are voracious predators of small fish including herring, cod, whiting, porgy and butterfish.

POMPANO

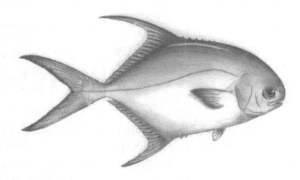

Florida Pompano, *Trachinotus carolinus*

GENERAL
The **Florida pompano** belongs to the family Carangidae, of jacks and pompanos. There are about 20 species of pompano in the genus *Trachinotus,* and they all look very much alike, with an oblong body and similar fin structure. *The Seafood List* identifies 9 species marketed under the name pompano, all with the same pompano genus except one. The African pompano, *Alectis ciliaris*, which is really a threadfish, is also found in the western Atlantic and looks much like a pompano except that with a steeply inclined head, it is more pentagon-shaped and has a less deeply forked tail. Together with the the **permit**, *Trachinotus falcatus*, these 3 species compose the major commercial catches of fishes marketed as permit landed in the US.

Also Known As
Common Pompano/
Atlantic Pompano/
Sunfish/
Butterfish

FishBase Name
Florida pompano

International Recognitions
Spain—Pámpano amarillo
France—Pompaneau sole
Italy—Leccia stella

PHYSICAL DESCRIPTION
Max length: 64.0 cm TL male/unsexed; (Ref. 7251); Common length: 40.0 cm TL male/unsexed; (Ref. 5217); Max. published weight: 3,760 g (Ref. 40637)

Florida pompano are deep bodied fish with a small mouth, and no scutes. They have a green to gray-blue coloration on dorsal side fading to silver along the sides. There is often a gold highlight on throat, pelvic and anal fins. There us also a blue tint above and in front of the eye. They can be confused with the jack crevalle; however, the pompano has a smooth tail and caudal peduncle. Likewise, with the African pompano and the permit, the pompano is not as strongly angled and rarely grows to more than 6 pounds, whereas the permit and African pompano can grow to 40 pounds.

Permit: Max length: 122 cm FL male/unsexed; (Ref. 40637); Common length: 94.0 cm FL male/unsexed; (Ref. 3277); Max. published weight: 36.0 kg (Ref. 5217)

The permit is characterized by the deeply forked tail and elongated dorsal fin. It is also identifiable by its highly laterally compressed body making the fish appear tall and thin. They have bright silver sides and are bluish-green or brown coloration on the dorsal side. Bellies will occasionally show yellow or black blotches, where fins are dark gray or black. They have no teeth beside granular ones that are on the tongue and used for crushing molluscs and crustaceans. They are similar to the pompano but are deeper bodied and larger.

LANDINGS AND VALUES

The Florida pompano is found in the western Atlantic from Massachusetts to the Gulf of Mexico. The African pompano and the permit are also found in the same range in the western Atlantic, often distributed among reefs and sandy or muddy bottom areas from the surface to 36 to 60 meters. Pompano are often found in channels and holes as adults, while juveniles can be found in the surf zone in summer months.

Florida Pompano US Landings by Year — Nominal Data Value in $US (000); Quantity in tonnes; (NMFS)					
	2004	2005	2006	2007	2008
Value	1,481	1,326	1,721	1,570	1,590
Quantity	178	157	223	211	221

In 2008, 221 tonnes of Florida pompano, valued at $1.6 million, was landed (see table). Commercial landings of African pompano and permit were much smaller (see tables).

African Pompano US Landings by Year — Nominal Data Value in $US (000); Quantity in tonnes; (NMFS)					
	2004	2005	2006	2007	2008
Value	16	8	10	14	16
Quantity	4	2	3	4	4

Endangered Status: Unevaluated – Florida pompano and permit; Least concern – African pompano (IUCN)

Aquaculture Status: Pompano have been reared in captivity. Although original interest focused on the Florida pompano, fish farmers have recently begun to experiment with the mariculture of permit, raising them in large near-shore pens for commercial sale (FMNHI).

COMMERCIAL USES

All pompano are highly valued as food fish and game fish. Florida pompano alone recorded 290 tonnes of recreational catches in 2008 and is one of the most highly priced marine food fish. Permits are caught as a food fish and as a sport fish. There have been reports of ciguatera poisoning in African pompano. There is also an aquarium trade for pompanos.

Permit US Landings by Year — Nominal Data Value in $US (000); Quantity in tonnes; (NMFS)					
	2004	2005	2006	2007	2008
Value	20	28	26	22	22
Quantity	7	10	7	7	7

LIFE CYCLE

Pompano inhabit oyster reefs and seagrass beds and prefer turbid water. They can be found in large schools particularly during spawning. Spawning occurs offshore between March and September. Eggs are pelagic and juveniles can be found in the surf zone, moving offshore in the winter. Pompano eat molluscs, small fishes, crustaceans and other invertebrates. Local movements are not influenced by the tides, but seasonal movements are based on changes in water temperature.

Permits are often found in the surf of sandy beach areas sometimes in 2 feet of water or less. They often congregate around reefs, jetties, and wrecks. They feed in pairs or alone on molluscs, copepods, amphipods, crustaceans and other fish and insets. They use their snout to forage in the substrate. They are preyed on by sharks and barracudas. Permit spawn year round but primarily from May through June, decreasing during the winter months.

PORGY OR SCUP

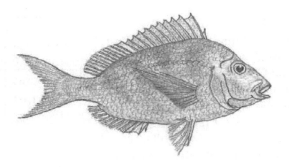

Scup, *Stenotomus chrysops*

GENERAL

The **scup**, an important food and sport fish, is a member of the Sparidae family, commonly known as porgies (about 35 genera and 130 species – *FishBase*). Porgies of the genera *Dentex* spp*., Calamus* spp. and *Diplodus* spp.; as well as the pinfish, *Lagodon rhomboids,* and spotted pinfish, *Diplodus holbrookii* (also known as "spottail seabream" in *FishBase*), are all commonly, and correctly, marketed as porgy in North America. Many porgies around the world have "bream" or "seabream" in their common name in *FishBase.* In the US, commercial landings in the porgy family are reported under porgy (4 species), but also separately as scup, pinfish and sheepshead. However, the "sheepshead" (*Archosargus probatocephalus*) is correctly marketed as sheepshead — not as porgy or "convict fish," (as it is sometimes called because of its bar coloration); while the other 3 groupings are correctly marketed as porgy. "Sea bream" is another market name and common name in *The Seafood List* (*TSL*) for several species in the porgy family including *A. rhomboidalis* [*FishBase name:* "Western Atlantic seabream"], and *Pagellus* spp., all marketed correctly as sea bream and incorrectly as sheepshead or porgy. (Note: The squirefish, *Chrysophrys auratus*, is recognized as a synonym of "silver seabream*," Pagrus auratus*, in *FishBase*; while *P. auratus* is recognized as a synonym of *C. auratus* in *ITIS.*)

Also Known As
Maiden/ Fair Maid/ Ironsides/ Northern Porgy

FishBase Name
Scup

International Recognitions
Spain—Sargo de América del Norte
France—Spare doré

PHYSICAL DESCRIPTION

Max length: 46.0 cm TL male/unsexed; (Ref. 7251); Common length: 25.0 cm TL male/unsexed; (Ref. 9988); Max. published weight: 2,060 g (Ref. 40637)

Porgies are a deep-bodied, laterally-compressed fish with a short deep head, continuous dorsal fin and a deeply-forked caudal fin. They can change body pattern quickly. The scup is usually a dull silvery color with faint, irregular, dark bars on its body with the bar closest to its mid-body being the most prominent. There are generally light blue specks on the body and a light blue strip along the base of its dorsal fin. Large eyes are located up and back from a small mouth, which houses incisor or canine-like front teeth and molar rear teeth that are used to crush and grind shellfish. It has large pointed pectorals and a deeply-rounded, large tail fin. The sheepshead can be quickly distinguished from the scup by its five to six very dark diagonal bars and larger size (up to 3 feet). The sea bream is a similar size, but can be distinguished by the eye-sized dark blotch on the shoulder just below the lateral line, many narrow bronze stripes and orange pelvic fins.

LANDINGS AND VALUES

The scup can be found in the western North Atlantic from Nova Scotia to as far south as Florida, although it is infrequently found north of Cape Cod or south of North Carolina. Two separate stocks are suspected, one centered off southern New England and the other off New Jersey and south. The scup prefers the warm/temperate and tropical waters and is most commonly found in coastal bays or around coral reefs where shellfish are common. The scup is an inshore fish in the warm weather, but moves to the deeper offshore water in the winter. Close to shore, it is often caught commercially in fish traps or pound nets from April until late October. Most, however, is caught by otter trawls. US landings in 2008 totaled 2,143 tonnes, valued at almost $5.3 million (see table). Additional porgy landings of 156 tonnes (comprised of 90% red porgy, *Pagrus pagrus*) in 2008 were valued at $447,000 (see table). Scup represent about 90% of all porgy landings.

Scup US Landings by Year — Nominal Data Value in $US (000); Quantity in tonnes; (NMFS)					
	2004	2005	2006	2007	2008
Value	332	157	97	8,063	5,284
Quantity	238	160	64	4,200	2,143

Other Porgies (red, knobbed, jolthead, whitebone) US Landings by Year — Nominal Data Value in $US (000); Quantity in tonnes; (NMFS)					
	2004	2005	2006	2007	2008
Value	228	166	263	412	447
Quantity	98	69	96	148	156

Pinfish landings were 67 tonnes in 2008 and valued at $356,000; while sheepshead landings were 783 tonnes, valued at almost $800,000 (see tables). In addition, approximately 7,045 tonnes of porgies were landed recreationally; comprised of about 45% sheepshead and 25% scup and 25% pinfishes, in 2008. In fact, porgies are estimated to represent approximately 10% of the total recreational fishery on the US Atlantic coast. Porgy is not a significant fishery in Canada.

COMMERCIAL USES

The scup is valuable as both a food and sports fish, especially in the mid and north Atlantic areas of the US. Scup is the primary catch off New England and New Jersey, while other porgies (landed further south and in the Gulf of Mexico) are usually marketed as bream, pinfish or sheepshead. Porgy is generally marketed whole fresh locally, when it is available.

Pinfish US Landings by Year — Nominal Data Value in $US (000); Quantity in tonnes; (NMFS)					
	2004	2005	2006	2007	2008
Value	294	287	323	357	356
Quantity	31	43	57	76	67

Sheepshead US Landings by Year — Nominal Data Value in $US (000); Quantity in tonnes; (NMFS)					
	2004	2005	2006	2007	2008
Value	787	732	672	736	784
Quantity	1,007	786	545	751	783

LIFE CYCLE

Sexual maturity is usually complete by age 3 when the fish are about 8 inches in length. Spawning occurs in the spring and early summer (principally May and June). The transparent, spherical eggs, which are about 0.035 inches in diameter, hatch in about 40 hours at water temperatures of approximately 70°F. The eggs are free-floating and given no parental care. The juvenile fish stay near shore, sometimes entering fresh water. Their strong teeth assist them in feeding on various molluscs and crustaceans. Their diet also includes many soft-bodied invertebrates including shrimps and marine worms. In the winter months, some schools will migrate as far south as Virginia and North Carolina, while others just move to warmer waters offshore. Small porgies are considered a valuable forage fish for other species including, cod, shark and anglerfish.

ROCKFISH

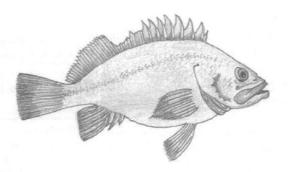

Yelloweye Rockfish, *Sebastes ruberrimus*

GENERAL

Rockfish belong to the family Scorpaenidae [*FishBase* family: Sebastidae] of the order Scorpaeniformes, or "scorpion fish," so-called because the spines of these fish are often somewhat venomous, but usually not dangerous, to humans. The rockfish genus *Sebastes* includes approximately 110 species of which about thirty are fished commercially in west coast waters and three in east coast waters. The three East Coast *Sebates* species are usually marketed as "ocean perch," but sometimes under the generic common name of "redfish," while the West Coast species *S. alutus* is alone marketed as Pacific "ocean perch." Historically, the Pacific ocean perch was the most popular and valuable "rockfish" species for both domestic and foreign fleets. However, as ocean perch demand increased in the late 1980s, all *Sebates* species have experienced increased exploitation. (Also see ocean perch entry in this book.)

The **yelloweye rockfish** and many other rockfishes are also commonly, and legitimately, marketed as "red snapper" on the US West Coast; but these are not the true red snappers of the family Lutjanidae. In Canada, the species *S. ruberrimus* is also approved to be called "snapper," "red snapper" or "Pacific red snapper," while other rockfish can be called "Pacific snapper." The traditional red snapper, *Lutjanus campechanus*, and the Caribbean red snapper, *L. purpureus* are found in Atlantic tropical waters. (See red snapper entry in this book.) Some rockfish species are also referred to as rockcod; however, this is misleading as rockcod usually (and correctly) refer to fish in the Nototheniidae (ice cod) family.

Also Known As
Pacific Red Snapper
Rasphead Rockfish

FishBase Name
Yelloweye Rockfish

International Recognitions (rockfish)
Spain—Rascacio;
Cabracho
France—Scorpène
Italy—Scorfano
Germany—Drachenkopf

PHYSICAL DESCRIPTION

Max length: 104 cm TL male/unsexed; (Ref. 40637); Max. published weight: 17.8 kg (Ref. 40637); Max. reported age: 118 years (Ref. 39247)

Rockfish are easily recognized by their bass-like build. Distinctive features include a large, broad head, usually bearing spines and strong ridges, and heavily-spined fins. The dorsal fin is continuous; the anal fin has three spines. Their color depends on the species, ranging from black to drab green to brilliant orange and crimson. Some rockfish are accented with wide, red or black vertical stripes. The yelloweye rockfish is distinguished from other rockfish by its coloring: orange-yellow with pink on the back and sides and a paler underside.

LANDINGS AND VALUES

The geographic range for the various rockfish species varies considerably. In general, they can be found throughout the North Pacific Ocean from southern California to Kyuss Island. Most of the various species inhabit the continental shelf and upper slope regions. They are located at a wide range of depths, from the inter-tidal zone down to 3,000 feet. They are primarily a bottom species, although a few, such as the yellowtail and widow rockfish, spend some time at mid-water depths. High opening otter trawls are the most common gear-type used.

All Rockfishes –excl: P. Ocean Perch and Thornyheads US Landings by Year — Nominal Data Value in $US (000); Quantity in tonnes; (NMFS)					
	2004	2005	2006	2007	2008
Value	11,602	10,303	11,920	12,022	13,515
Quantity	13,427	12,969	12,863	13,413	14,511

All Rockfishes –excl: P. Ocean Perch and Thornyheads Canadian Landings by Year — Nominal Data Value in $Cdn (000); Quantity in tonnes; (DFO)					
	2004	2005	2006	2007	2008
Value	18,580	17,346	16,989	19,467	17,635
Quantity	13,267	13,037	12,220	13,361	12,925

They are also caught by anglers by jig or troll. The US landed value of rockfishes (excluding ocean perch and thornyheads) was 14,511 tonnes in 2008, valued at approximately $13.5 million (see table). Canadian catches of rockfishes (excluding ocean perch and thornyheads) in 2008 were 12,925 tonnes, valued at $17.6 million (see table). Approximately 1,600 tonnes of rockfish was also landed recreationally in the US in 2008, led by the black rockfish at almost 600 tonnes (not shown). **Endangered Status:** This species is listed as "Threatened" in the Puget Sound/Georgia Basin (US) and of "Special Concern" (*SARA*) in Canada. **Aquaculture:** Rockfish (*S. schlegeli*) has been farmed in pens in Korea.

COMMERCIAL USES

There is a large domestic market for yelloweye fresh fillets on the US West Coast where it is often served as "red snapper." (The red snapper name is legal in some states but not recognized for interstate commerce.) This is a lean fish with white, flaky flesh that is excellent steamed or baked and served in sauce, or deep-fried for secondary products such as fish sticks. Rockfish fillets are marketed as "red" or "brown," with red having less oil content, a longer shelf life and a premium price. Some is filleted for export to Japan and Europe. More than 60 species of rockfishes are listed in *The Seafood List*.

LIFE CYCLE

The *Sebastes* genera (rockfishes) bear live young, which may contribute to the diversity of species. There are three phases in the *Sebastes* reproductive cycle: insemination, fertilization and parturition. The female is inseminated during the autumn months, though actual fertilization takes place in the winter or early spring. The larvae are approximately 0.25 inches long when released. The time of parturition varies greatly, but for most species between January and May. Depending on species and size, a female may release 200,000 to 800,000 larvae. During the first stage of development, young larvae are pelagic before settling to the bottom. Although larvae species are not easy to differentiate, identities become more apparent as they grow into juveniles and develop adult characteristics. They are slow growing and long lived; growing slow to maturity leaves them vulnerable to over-fishing. Males mature earlier than females, but adult females are usually larger than males of the same age. Rockfish are considered a non-migratory fish with only localized movement. There are indications, however, that some species undergo seasonal depth migration. Some swim in schools, while others are solitary and hide in rocks and crevices. Rockfish eat a variety of food: herring, sand lance, crabs, shrimp and euphausiids.

ROSEFISH (& THORNYHEADS)

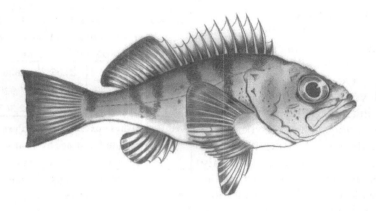

Blackbelly Rosefish, *Helicolenus dactylopterus*

GENERAL

The **blackbelly rosefish** belongs to the family of rockfishes, scorpionfishes and thornyheads – Scorpaenidae [*FishBase* family: Sebastidae] so-called because of spiny dorsal fins that are often somewhat venomous, but usually not dangerous, to humans. As such, it is a close relative of the scorpionfishes, such as rockfishes and ocean perch. Also true to many of its family characteristics, the blackbelly rosefish has venom glands.

The shortspine thornyhead (*Sebastolobus alascanus*), also known as the "idiot" fish, and the longspine thornyhead (*S. altivelis*) are two other closely related species in a family that includes upwards of 70 genera. The preferred market name for these species is "thornyhead," as differentiated from rosefish, rockfishes and ocean perch (see other entries in this book).

PHYSICAL DESCRIPTION

Max length: 47.0 cm TL male/unsexed; (Ref. 41333);
Common length: 25.0 cm TL male/unsexed; (Ref. 4510);
Max. published weight: 1,550 g (Ref. 40637);
Max. reported age: 43 years (Ref. 41452)

The rosefish has dorsal spines with soft rays in back, typical of rockfishes and scorpionfishes. It also has large, fan-like pectoral fins and large eyes. The dorsal body is rose-colored, often with mottled V-shaped vertical bars extending onto the dorsal fin area. The tail is rose-colored and the ventral area is an iridescent white. There is often a darkish spot in the cheek area.

The Shortspine thornyhead is red or red orange, has large eyes and often has white patches when seen underwater. It has a shorter third dorsal spine than the longspine thornyhead. It is distinguished from other rockfishes by the spiny ridge across its cheek and 16 dorsal spines, while rockfishes normally have 13.

Also Known As
Redfish/ Serran Imperial/ Fanegal/ Cardonniera

FishBase Name
Blackbelly rosefish

International Recognitions
Spain—Gallineta
France—Sébaste chèvre
Italy—Capa arze
Germany— Blaumaul

LANDINGS AND VALUES

Common to both sides of the Atlantic, in North America the blackbelly rosefish can be found in benthic areas of the continental shelf between Nova Scotia and South America, between 50 meters and 1100 meters.

Blackbelly Rosefish US Landings by Year — Nominal Data Value in $US (000); Quantity in tonnes; (NMFS)					
	2004	2005	2006	2007	2008
Value	71	2	57	6	0
Quantity	29	1	21	2	0

It is not a highly commercial species, but landings are reported for most years. In 2007, 2 tonnes were reported landed in the US, valued at $6,000. It is also possible that some landings of these fish could be mixed in with ocean perch (or redfishes) landings.

The shortspine thornyhead is a larger catch on the West Coast, with Oregon leading California and Washington States in US landings. In total, almost 1,400 tonnes were landed in the US in 2008, valued at $3.5 million (see table). The British Columbia total was 461 tonnes, valued at $934,000 in 2008.

Shortspine Thornyhead US Landings by Year — Nominal Data Value in $US (000); Quantity in tonnes; (NMFS)					
	2004	2005	2006	2007	2008
Value	1,713	1,866	2,108	2,509	3,518
Quantity	651	631	663	957	1,379

Endangered Status: This is is a deepwater species listed as Endangered on the IUCN Red List. The longspine thornyhead is listed as "Special Concern" under *SARA* (Canada).

Shortspine Thornyhead (Idiot) Canadian Landings by Year — Nominal Data Value in $Cdn (000); Quantity in tonnes; (DFO)					
	2004	2005	2006	2007	2008
Value	1,506	640	1,662	1,314	934
Quantity	888	359	827	667	461

COMMERCIAL USES

Prices would suggest the rosefish is highly valued commercially, or perhaps reflects the marketing as a fresh product.

Thornyheads are highly prized in Japan where the fish is known as "kinki"; and China, where it is called "red dragon fish." They are venomous.

LIFE CYCLE

In the western Atlantic, it appears that the rosefish reproduction cycle begins in the fall with spermatozoa deposited within the female and carried until eggs are fertilized internally in winter in a zygoparous form of oviparity.

Larvae and juveniles are pelagic. The rosefish feeds on smaller fish, crustaceans, cephalopods and echinoderms (Ref. 4570).

SABLEFISH

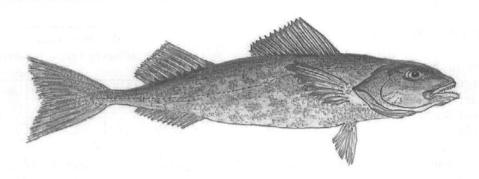

Sablefish, *Anoplopoma fimbria*

GENERAL

The **sablefish** is a member of the exclusive Anoplopomatidae family, whose only other member is the skilfish (*Erilepis zonifer*). Although the skilfish has sometimes been categorized in a family of its own (Erilepididae), this family is no longer recognized.

Sablefish are a sleek, black-skinned fish found in cold, deep waters of the North Pacific. The valuable sablefish is often harvested live in traps to ensure a top quality product.

Although sometimes marketed as "black cod" or "butterfish," it is a species entirely different from these fishes (see entries for these species in this book).

PHYSICAL DESCRIPTION

Max length: 120 cm TL male/unsexed; (Ref. 9988);
Common length : 80.0 cm TL male/unsexed; (Ref. 9988);
Max. reported age: 114 years (Ref. 39324)

The adult sablefish has an elongated body that is a blackish or greenish gray above with slightly paler blotches, forming a chainlike pattern on its upper back. Its belly is a paler color. Solid yellow, albino and other unusually colored sablefish have been sighted. Young sablefish (under 6 inches) are a blue-black above with a white belly.

It has two very separate dorsal fins. The anal fin, almost identical to the second dorsal fin, is located directly below it. Small scales are weakly toothed on their exposed edge making the sablefish rough to touch. It is very different from the true cods, which have three dorsal fins and two anal fins.

The skilfish has a deeper body with dorsal fins closer together and 12 to 14 spines in the first dorsal fin, versus 17 to 30 in the sablefish. However, it is easily mistaken for the sablefish and may be included in some catches.

Also Known As
Black Cod/
Butterfish/
Bluefish/
Candlefish/
Coal Cod/
Coalfish/
Skilfish/
Skil

FishBase Name
Sablefish

International Recognitions
France—morue charbonnière
Japan—gindara

LANDINGS AND VALUES

The sablefish ranges from Japan and the Bering Sea to central Baja. The North American fishery is centered in Washington State, BC and Alaska. The adult members of this species prefer the muddy bottom in waters of depths of 1,000 to 6,000 feet (or even deeper). Younger sablefish are usually found in shallower, more coastal waters. They are typically caught in specially designed traps in BC and on longlines in Alaska, and to some extent, by trawls. Skilfish share a similar habitat but they are not a major catch.

Sablefish US Landings by Year — Nominal Data Value in $US (000); Quantity in tonnes; (NMFS)					
	2004	2005	2006	2007	2008
Value	135,316	136,240	132,156	115,610	124,590
Quantity	23,972	23,176	21,422	19,902	19,634

Sablefish Canadian Landings by Year — Nominal Data Value in $Cdn (000); Quantity in tonnes; (DFO)					
	2004	2005	2006	2007	2008
Value	22,016	30,686	32,903	23,669	20,431
Quantity	3,006	4,719	4,536	3,564	3,095

US landings of sablefish in 1989 totaled approximately 44,806 tonnes, valued at $73.5 million (not shown). Landings in 2008 show a significant decline in catch, while price has increased, creating revenues of more than $124 million (see table). Canadian landings in 1989 were approximately 5,000 tonnes, valued at approximately $13.5 million. These landings have also decreased, but value increased to $20 million in 2008 (see table).

Endangered status: Stocks are judged to be fished at sustainable levels. **Aquaculture:** There is currently no aquaculture of this species in the US; however, Canadian initiatives have developed hatchery technology to produce juvenile sablefish with the goal of large-scale, ocean or offshore farms. Opponents have reacted, citing potential damage to wild stocks and also the prospect that increased production will just drive prices down and costs up, benefiting export consumers, but neither North American producers or consumers.

COMMERCIAL USES

Traditionally, sablefish has been exported to Japan and Hong Kong but it is becoming increasingly available in North America. It is a premium product that chefs prize for flaked pearly white flesh and sweet, rich flavor. Sablefish is a fatty fish that is ideal for smoking but may lose its flavor when frozen for long periods. It is processed frozen-at-sea (FAS), fresh and smoked (whole and as fillets) and sometimes salted and pickled. Most of the quick-frozen sablefish is marketed in the Orient. Smoked sablefish is sometimes labelled as "smoked Alaska cod" and sablefish fillets may be labelled as butterfish.

LIFE CYCLE

Sablefish spawn at sea during the winter months. The fertilized eggs are about 0.082 to 0.084 inches in diameter without an oil globule and float in mid-water. At four months, they are about 1 inch long. By the second or third year, they are 1.5 to 2 pounds in weight. As the juvenile fish develop, they gradually move to deeper, bottom waters. Sablefish are voracious predators of rockfish, pollock, shrimp, herring, flatfish and small sablefish. They are long-lived, with ages over 40 years regularly recorded, but most fish caught are 4 to 10 years old.

SALMON, ATLANTIC

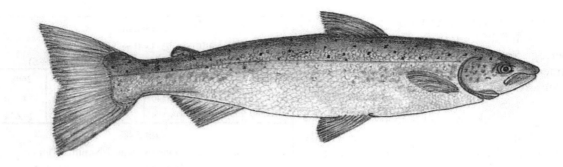

GENERAL

Atlantic salmon are native to rivers of North America from New England to Ungava Bay; and in Europe, from northern Spain to Russia and Iceland. However, they are now most abundant in river systems in Newfoundland and Labrador, the Gulf of St. Lawrence and northern Europe. The commercial salmon fishery is presently closed in North America, following closures in Labrador in 1998 and in New Brunswick, Nova Scotia and Newfoundland proper in 1972. Atlantic salmon was declared endangered in the US in 2000 and in 2003 in Canada (Bay of Fundy). Since its decline, it has become a major aquaculture industry that is, somewhat surprisingly, much larger on the West Coast. Apart from those that are naturally landlocked (sebago or ouananiche salmon), the Atlantic salmon is a classic anadromous fish, migrating from the sea to its native stream to spawn. For many years, it was not known where the salmon went at sea; however, a common feeding ground was found off the west coast of Greenland in the 1950s. Some salmon stocks from both Europe and North America migrate to this area to feed, primarily on shrimp. The Atlantic salmon is a member of the Salmonidae family.

Also Known As
Sea Salmon
Kennebec
Sebago Salmon
Ouananiche
Black Salmon

FishBase Name
Atlantic salmon

International Recognitions
France—saumon de l'Atlantique
Germany—Echter Lachs
Spain—salmón
Italy—salmone del reno

PHYSICAL DESCRIPTION

Max. length: 150 cm TL male/unsexed; (Ref. 7251); 120 cm TL (female); Common length: 38 cm TL male/unsexed; (Ref. 3561); Max. pub weight: 46.8 kg (Ref. 41037); Max. rep age: 13 years (Ref. 274)

The Atlantic salmon is an elongated fish, slightly compressed laterally. The head is relatively small, with a pointed mouth and well-developed teeth. Like other salmon, it has a fleshy adipose fin just behind the dorsal fin. The color depends upon age or life stage. Young salmon or parr have from 8 to 11 dark vertical bars or parr marks along both sides with a single red spot between each. The dorsal is typically spotted-grey or sometimes brown, paling to a whitish underbelly. Mature salmon at sea have silver sides shading to a white belly, and a darker back ranging from blue-green to blue-grey. Upon returning to freshwater, adults lose much of the silvery shade and become much darker, taking on a pink hue with reddish blotches along the sides. The males develop an enlarged lower jaw with a hook or "kype" at the tip. The Atlantic salmon can be distinguished from its Pacific cousins by the numerous "X-shaped" black spots scattered along its sides above the lateral line, and by the lack of spots on its tail fin. Atlantic salmon also have less than 10 rays on the anal fin, while Pacific salmons have 13 to 19.

AQUACULTURE

Early accounts of settlers indicate that Atlantic salmon at one time were plentiful; however, the pressures of over-fishing, pollution and obstruction of river systems resulted in serious loss of stocks. By 1850, the Atlantic salmon were all but wiped out in New England, except for a small fishery on the Penobscot River in Maine. Closures in Canada came much later, but particularly after the open sea fishery off Greenland began in earnest in the 1950s. Fortunately for the consumers of this gourmet fish, salmon aquaculture has been fairly successful.

All Salmon Aquaculture Canadian Production by Year — Nominal Data Value in $Cdn (000); Quantity in tonnes; (DFO)					
	2004	2005	2006	2007	2008
Value	400,180	543,343	748,246	604,917	624,582
Quantity	90,646	98,370	118,061	102,509	104,075

All Salmon Aquaculture US Production by Year — Nominal Data Value in $US (000); Quantity in tonnes; (NMFS)					
	2004	2005	2006	2007	2008
Value	56,679	37,439	42,569	40,814	45,128
Quantity	15,157	9,401	10,485	11,001	16,714

Yearly Canadian production reached 104,000 tonnes in 2008, valued at $625 million (see table), with about 70% of that total grown in BC and 30% in Atlantic Canada. (About 80% of salmon aquaculture in BC is Atlantic salmon and 20% is chinook and coho.) Salmon aquaculture in the US and Atlantic Canada is almost 100% Atlantic salmon. New Brunswick accounts for 90% of production within Atlantic Canada. US production in 2008 was 16,714 tonnes, valued at $45 million (see table). Maine and Washington State were the two largest US producers.

COMMERCIAL USES

Many consider "lox" or smoked salmon to be salmon at its finest. It is also available fresh or frozen as steak, sides, or whole. Although in worldwide demand, the great supply of farm-raised Atlantic salmon has kept prices relatively low. Norway alone produced about 900,000 tonnes in 2009 (~65% of world production) and Scotland and Chile are other large producers. Consumer concerns about disease and sea lice damage to wild species as well as often high antibiotic, mercury and PCBs levels combined with the need for wild feed continues to impact market acceptance of farmed salmon. Wild Atlantic salmon is still a prized sports fish in New Brunswick and Nova Scotia. However, outside of Labrador, sport fishing is usually limited to "hook and release," although grilse (one sea-winter salmon) can often be retained.

LIFE CYCLE

General: Spawning occurs in the fall. The female digs a nest (redd) and will lay several thousand eggs, which the male will immediately fertilize. Most Atlantic salmon will survive spawning (survivors are known as "slinks," "kelts" or "black salmon,") and will rest for several weeks, or remain in fresh water over the winter before migrating back to sea. The eggs remain buried in the sand or gravel of the riverbed to develop over the winter period. In the spring, the newly hatched fish (alevins) eventually emerge from the gravel as fingerlings (fry). In a few months, they reach a length of about 2.5 inches and develop parr marks, becoming salmon parr. When parr reach a length of 5 to 6 inches, which can take one or two years depending upon location, they become silvery smolts and migrate to the sea where they grow rapidly.

Exceptions: Some salmon return early (one year or less) to their native rivers to spawn. Others may spend two or more years at sea. Some spawning may also occur in winter. In warmer southern waters, parr may migrate after only one year. Evidence seems to indicate that some populations stay close to their home rivers, while others may travel to feeding grounds off western Greenland. Upon returning a "one sea winter" (1SW) grilse would weigh about 5 pounds. Larger salmon are usually "multiple sea winter" (MSW) fish.

SALMON, CHINOOK OR KING OR SPRING

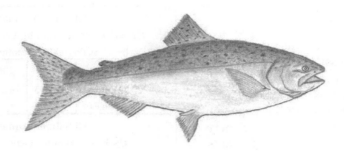

Chinook Salmon, *Oncorhynchus tshawytscha*

GENERAL
The **Chinook salmon**, also known as king or spring salmon is the largest of the *Oncorhynchus* branch (Pacific coast salmons) of the Salmonidae family. In fact, the largest Chinook is even larger than the record Atlantic salmon that lives longer and can experience multiple spawnings.

PHYSICAL DESCRIPTION (Also see Salmonidae Table.)
Pacific salmons generally: Like all members of the salmon family, the Pacific salmons have a single dorsal fin located at mid-body and a small, fleshy adipose fin located in front of the tail fin. Pacific and Atlantic salmons, as well as many trouts, are difficult to distinguish. Pacific salmons generally have a deeper, less-streamlined body than Atlantic salmon. Pacific salmons either have spots, speckles, or no speckles at all, while Atlantic salmon has irregular, cross or X-shaped spots (and only above the lateral line). Pacific salmons have 13 to 19 rays on their anal fins, while the Atlantic salmon has less than 10.
Chinook salmon:
Max length: 150 cm TL male/unsexed; (Ref. 40637); Common length: 70.0 cm TL male/unsexed; (Ref. 9258); Max. published weight: 61.4 kg (Ref. 27547); Max. reported age: 9 years (Ref. 12193)

The upper body of the chinook is dark green to black, with **small round black spots** extending from the top of the head to **both lobes** of the tail fin and to the dorsal fin. The sides and belly are silver with a faint yellow tint. The gums and mouth are both black. In a spawning fish, the color may be bright red, but is most often a dull, blotchy yellowish-red and males develop a hooked upper jaw. The flesh is almost always red, not pink, but there are some stocks of white-fleshed chinooks.

LANDINGS AND VALUES
Chinook range from southern California to Alaska, with some small populations in the Arctic and along the Asian coast. The species has also been successfully introduced into the Great Lakes (where it supports a recreational fishery) and is found in over 150 streams and rivers along the west coast. The principal landing season is June to September, but "spring" chinooks can spawn in April in some rivers. Some rivers also have more than one stock of chinook. These stocks migrate at different times so there is the possibility of a summer run in June and July, and another run in August and September.

Also Known As
Tee Salmon/
Winter Salmon/
Quinnat
Salmon/ King
Salmon/ Spring
Salmon

FishBase Name
Chinook salmon

**International
Recognitions**
Spain—Salmón
real
France—Saumon
royal
Italy—Salmone
reale
Germany—
Quinnat

They are caught primarily by trolling, but also by gillnet, seine and as by-catch in other fisheries. US landings in 1989 totaled about 25,000 tonnes, valued at $53 million (not shown). By comparison, 2008 US landings were 4,475 tonnes, valued at $32.3 million (see table). The 1989 Canadian landings totaled about 5,100 tonnes, valued at nearly $19 million (not shown), but declined to 945 tonnes in 2008, valued at $8.8 million (see table). In the US, traditionally about 17% of all chinook landings were in the recreational fishery, but Pacific catches declined by nearly 90% in 2008 over the previous 10-year average (not shown). The sports fishery in BC, mostly for salmon

Chinook Salmon US Landings by Year — Nominal Data Value in $US (000); Quantity in tonnes; (NMFS)					
	2004	**2005**	**2006**	**2007**	**2008**
Value	58,163	48,699	43,746	43,316	32,277
Quantity	12,974	10,794	7,662	6,619	4,475

Chinook Salmon Canadian Landings by Year — Nominal Data Value in $Cdn (000); Quantity in tonnes; (DFO)					
	2004	**2005**	**2006**	**2007**	**2008**
Value	14,628	12,441	14,971	10,530	8,771
Quantity	2,465	2,020	2,051	1,416	945

like Chinook and coho, has been estimated to be worth 70 times the commercial fishery, pound for pound. **Endangered Status:** Chinook are threatened or endangered in many of their native waters, streams and rivers including the Columbia River (upper and lower), Sacramento River and other coastal areas. **Aquaculture:** Chinook is farmed in North America, but traditionally account for less than 20% of salmon production. Alaska efforts are focused on enhancement.

COMMERCIAL USES

When available, it is usually purchased fresh, frozen or smoked. The chinook is the fattest of the Pacific salmons with a flaky flesh that is rich in oil. Hence, it is the most popular choice of smoked salmon producers. The red-fleshed product competes highly with Atlantic salmon. White-fleshed chinook has the same texture and flavor but does not appeal to typical salmon markets. The US is the major market, but Japan is an export market for the frozen wild product.

LIFE CYCLE

Pacific salmons generally: Spawning occurs in the fall. The female digs one or more nests (redds) with her tail and will lay several thousand eggs. The male immediately fertilizes the eggs. After spawning, adults live for as little as a few days, up to a few months. (Death is caused by rapid aging brought on by excessive glandular activity during reproduction.) The eggs remain buried in the sand or gravel of the riverbed to develop over the winter period. In the spring, the newly hatched fish (alevins) eventually emerge from the gravel as fingerlings (fry). Those staying in fresh water reach a length of about 2.5 inches and develop parr marks in a few months, becoming salmon parr. When parr reach a length of 5 to 6 inches, which may take one to five years, depending upon location, they become silvery smolts and are ready to migrate to sea. The salmon grow rapidly at sea and most will spend two or more years there before returning to their native rivers to spawn. Some males, called "jacks," return prematurely.

Chinook salmon: Chinook demonstrate a wide variety of life history types. Spawning occurs earlier than other salmons, usually in spring and summer, but also into the early fall. Most parr will run to the ocean after only a few months, but more northerly or upstream populations may overwinter. Chinook are known to migrate great distances and return to spawn at varying ages, from 2 to 8 years. In southern regions, spawning age is between 2 and 5 years. In northern areas, spawning age is later. Unlike other Pacific salmons, a very small number of males survive to return to the sea, which may explain some of the larger catches of this species on record.

SALMON, CHUM OR KETA

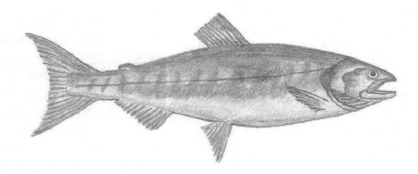

Chum Salmon, *Oncorhynchus keta*

GENERAL

Go west young man—and become a "chum rancher." Ocean ranching is the practice of increasing fish stocks by artificially raising and releasing huge numbers of juvenile fish that feed and grow in the natural marine environment. Subsequently, when these fish are recaptured, total landings are increased. **Chum salmon** ranching has become one of the larger fish enhancement projects in the world, but not without its problems or critics. Chum, like pink and sockeye salmons, has traditionally been more of a commercial, than a sports fishery.

PHYSICAL DESCRIPTION

Pacific salmons generally: Like all members of the salmon family (Salmonidae), the Pacific salmons have a single dorsal fin located at mid-body and a small, fleshy adipose fin located in front of the tail fin. Pacific and Atlantic salmons, as well as many trouts, are difficult to distinguish. Pacific salmons generally have a deeper, less-streamlined body than Atlantic salmon. Pacific salmons either have spots, speckles, or no speckles at all, while Atlantic salmon has irregular, cross or X-shaped spots (and only above the lateral line). Pacific salmons have 13 to 19 rays on their anal fins, while the Atlantic salmon has less than 10.

Chum Salmon:
Max length: 100.0 cm FL male/unsexed; (Ref. 559); Common length: 58 cm TL male/unsexed; (Ref. 3561); Max. pub weight: 15.9 kg (Ref. 40637); Max. reported age: 7 years (Ref. 1998)

The chum salmon is an attractive metallic blue and silver fish splattered with occasional black specks on its back, and faint purple stripes on its sides. In the sea, it is similar in appearance to the sockeye salmon but can be distinguished by its **white-tipped anal and pelvic fins**, narrower wrist (the area just in front of the tail fin) and larger size. Other salmons have black spots, but both chum and sockeye have **small specks or no specks at all**. When spawning, adult chum have greenish to dusky mottling on the sides, with males exhibiting distinctive reddish-purple vertical barring and the characteristic hooked snout with large, canine ("dog-like") teeth.

Also Known As
Dog Salmon/
Calico Salmon/
Chub/
Keta Salmon

FishBase Name
Chum salmon

International Recognitions
Spain—Keta
France—Saumon chien
Italy—Salmone keta
Germany—Chumlachs

LANDINGS AND VALUES

Chum are located along the Pacific coast, from northern California north to the Aleutian Islands, and across the Bering Sea to Japan (traditionally the world's largest producer and consumer) and China. Some have been known to migrate up larger rivers, such as the Yukon, where they travel over 2,000 miles to Teslin Lake. The spawning season for chum salmon is from July to November. Of all the Pacific salmon species, it is generally the latest to spawn. It usually returns to its spawning area in late autumn, occasionally into late winter. In northern rivers, however, "summer" chum may arrive as early as July. Most

Chum Salmon US Landings by Year — Nominal Data Value in $US (000); Quantity in tonnes; (NMFS)					
	2004	2005	2006	2007	2008
Value	24,255	19,895	45,126	37,139	67,430
Quantity	50,985	36,716	68,601	49,974	57,443

Chum Salmon Canadian Landings by Year — Nominal Data Value in $Cdn (000); Quantity in tonnes; (DFO)					
	2004	2005	2006	2007	2008
Value	11,195	10,907	10,268	6,620	3,000
Quantity	14,302	11,323	9,896	4,861	1,735

chum are caught by seine or gillnet and, infrequently by troll or sport fishers. US landings in 1989 were 30,852 tonnes, valued at $30.5 million (not shown). By comparison, 2008 US landings were 57,443 tonnes, valued at $67 million (see table). Canadian landings in 1989 were approximately 9,200 tonnes, valued at $11.8 million (not shown). In 2008, Canadian chum landings were 1,735 tonnes, valued at $3 million (see table). **Endangered Status:** Chums are threatened in some of their native streams and rivers including the Columbia River.

COMMERCIAL USES

Chum is a fatty fish, but since it is less fatty than pink and sockeye, less is canned. The flesh has a fine texture, ranging from pale to dark pink. Chum is available fresh, frozen, canned ("keta" brand) and smoked. Most is sold frozen, round or dressed. The US is a major market. Roe is also exported to Japan as "ikura." Chum is usually not farmed as its value is relatively low; however, it is ranched in Alaska, BC, Japan and elsewhere (and harvested when the fish return to spawn).

LIFE CYCLE

Pacific salmons generally: Spawning occurs in the fall. The female digs one or more nests (redds) with her tail and will lay several thousand eggs. The male immediately fertilizes the eggs. After spawning, adults live for as little as a few days, up to a few months. (Death is caused by rapid aging brought on by excessive glandular activity during reproduction.) The eggs remain buried in the sand or gravel of the riverbed to develop over the winter period. In the spring, the newly hatched fish (alevins) eventually emerge from the gravel as fingerlings (fry). Those staying in fresh water reach a length of about 2.5 inches and develop parr marks in a few months, becoming salmon parr. When parr reach a length of 5 to 6 inches, which, depending upon location, may take one to five years, they become silvery smolts and are ready to migrate to sea. The salmon grow rapidly at sea and most will spend two or more years there before returning to their native rivers to spawn. Some males, called "jacks," return prematurely.

Chum Salmon: Chum spawn in late autumn and, in some cases, early winter. ("Summers" spawn in August and September.) When they return to freshwater, their appearance and flesh quality deteriorate rapidly with males showing reddish or black bars across the sides and the females more greenish. The male develops a hooked nose and large doglike teeth that are used for display and to protect spawning territory. The fry migrate directly to the sea, but some from larger river systems may spend several months in fresh water. They usually spend between three and five years at sea before returning.

SALMON, COHO OR SILVER OR MEDIUM RED

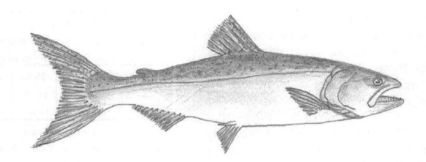

Coho Salmon, *Oncorhynchus kisutch*

GENERAL
Coho salmon is a favorite of sport fishers, who take them by spoon, fly, spinner or bait. Coho's high fat content makes it perfect for grilling or broiling, and cooking does not diminish its attractive color.

PHYSICAL DESCRIPTION
Pacific salmons generally: Like all members of the salmon family (Salmonidae), the Pacific salmons have a single dorsal fin located at mid-body and a small, fleshy adipose fin located in front of the tail fin. Pacific and Atlantic salmons, as well as many trouts, are difficult to distinguish. Pacific salmons generally have a deeper, less-streamlined body than Atlantic salmon. Pacific salmons either have spots, speckles, or no speckles at all, while Atlantic salmon has irregular, cross or X-shaped spots (and only above the lateral line). Pacific salmons have 13 to 19 rays on their anal fins, while the Atlantic salmon has less than 10.

Coho Salmon:
Max length: 108 cm TL male/unsexed; (Ref. 40637); 65.5 cm (female); Common length: 71.0 cm TL male/unsexed; (Ref. 593); Common length: 59.5 cm (female); Max. published weight: 15.2 kg (Ref. 40637); Max. reported age: 5 years (Ref. 36794)

Coho parr have a white leading edge on the anal fin, and an orange tint on all but the dorsal fin. As they become smolts, coho gradually lose their parr marks and their backs become green with dark spots. Adult coho are predominantly silver in color, with silver sides and underbelly, and metallic blue-green backs. Unlike other Pacific salmons, they have spots or specks on the upper lobe of the tail fin, but not on the lower lobe; and unlike Chinooks, their gums are white. They are most similar to Atlantic salmon in appearance and life cycle. During spawning, the males become bright red on their sides and develop a hooked snout with large teeth, while females are bronze to pinkish at that time.

LANDINGS AND VALUES
Coho can be found from southern California to Alaska. Their major range lies between Cook Inlet, halfway up the Alaska coast, to Oregon, with populations in Asia as well. The principal landing season, July through October, corresponds with their spawning runs.

Also Known As
Hoopid Salmon/
White Salmon/
Silver Salmon/
Medium Red
Salmon

FishBase Name
Coho salmon

**International
Recognitions**
France—
saumon argenté
Germany—
Silberlachs
Italy—salmonè
argentato

Cohos are predominantly caught by trolling commercial and sport fishers, but also in gillnets as a by-catch. The fishery has been subject to bans as stocks rebuild and commercial fishing is just returning in some areas. Cohos, like chinooks, have been successfully introduced into the Great Lakes, particularly Lake Michigan and Lake Superior, where they have flourished. There is no commercial fishery; however, they support an important recreational fishery there. US Pacific landings in 1989 totaled about 20,675 tonnes, valued at $39.6 million (not shown). By comparison, 2008 catches were 16,948 tonnes, valued at $45.2 million (see table). Canadian landings in 1989 approximated 8,600 tonnes,

Coho Salmon US Landings by Year — Nominal Data Value in $US (000); Quantity in tonnes; (NMFS)					
	2004	2005	2006	2007	2008
Value	32,615	25,967	34,766	25,363	45,200
Quantity	21,016	16,406	15,894	12,332	16,948

Coho Salmon Canadian Landings by Year — Nominal Data Value in $Cdn (000); Quantity in tonnes; (DFO)					
	2004	2005	2006	2007	2008
Value	3,824	3,462	2,388	2,621	1,906
Quantity	1,187	1,137	557	814	379

valued at about $17.6 million (not shown); declining to 379 tonnes in 2008, valued at $1.9 million (see table). **Endangered Status:** Cohos are threatened or endangered in many of their native waters, streams and rivers including the Columbia River and various coastal areas. **Aquaculture:** Some in North America; most in Chile for Japanese markets where it is often sold as lightly salted (tei-en).

COMMERCIAL USES

When stocks were more plentiful, coho was canned as "medium red salmon," a reference to the flesh color that is second only to the sockeye in intensity. Coho is now mostly available as fresh, frozen and smoked. Its high fat content and bright color make it popular choice for smoking. Frozen coho is also exported to Japan. The price is generally lower than other farmed salmons. Coho, like Chinook, has developed as a major sport, as well as a commercial fishery.

LIFE CYCLE

Pacific salmons generally: Spawning occurs in the fall. The female digs one or more nests (redds) with her tail and will lay several thousand eggs. The male immediately fertilizes the eggs. After spawning, adults live for as little as a few days, up to a few months. (Death is caused by rapid aging brought on by excessive glandular activity during reproduction.) The eggs remain buried in the sand or gravel of the riverbed to develop over the winter period. In the spring, the newly hatched fish (alevins) eventually emerge from the gravel as fingerlings (fry). Those staying in fresh water reach a length of about 2.5 inches and develop parr marks in a few months, becoming salmon parr. When parr reach a length of 5 to 6 inches, which, depending upon location, may take one to five years, they become silvery smolts and are ready to migrate to sea. The salmon grow rapidly at sea and most will spend two or more years there before returning to their native rivers to spawn. Some males, called "jacks," return prematurely.

Coho salmon: In spawning, even for salmon, males develop a strongly hooked upper jaw and kype (lower jaw). Spawning females go through similar changes, though the alteration is less noticeable. After spawning, adult cohos tend to survive longer than other species and may live in freshwater for a few months. Most coho parr stay from 1 to 2 years in coastal streams and lakes before migrating seaward as smolts. Although coho generally stay close to shore, they have been found as far as 2,500 miles out to sea. During their first year, they feed mostly on small herring, sand lance, larvae and small crustaceans. In their second year at sea, they feed on squid, larger herring and sand lance, increasing in weight from about 3 to 10 pounds.

SALMON, PINK OR HUMPBACK

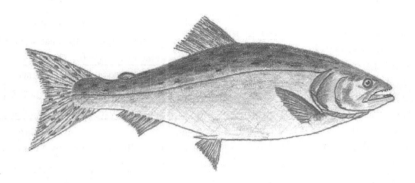

Pink Salmon, *Oncorhynchus gorbuscha*

GENERAL
The **pink salmon** is generally the smallest, but also most abundant, of the West Coast salmon. Like chum and sockeye, it is more of a commercial fishery than a sports fishery and much of the product is canned for worldwide markets. Like the chum salmon, it tends to spawn in the early reaches of rivers and the fry migrate directly to the ocean. This life cycle strategy is believed to have decreased the mortality that other salmons experience in their freshwater habitats. Pink salmon mature in 2 years, meaning that odd-year and even-year populations are unrelated and reflect yearly abundance.

PHYSICAL DESCRIPTION
Pacific salmons generally: Like all members of the salmon family (Salmonidae), the Pacific salmons have a single dorsal fin located at mid-body and a small, fleshy adipose fin located in front of the tail fin. Pacific and Atlantic salmons, as well as many trouts, are difficult to distinguish. Pacific salmons generally have a deeper, less-streamlined body than Atlantic salmon. Pacific salmons either have spots, speckles, or no speckles at all, while Atlantic salmon has irregular, cross or X-shaped spots (and only above the lateral line). Pacific salmons have 13 to 19 rays on their anal fins, while the Atlantic salmon has less than 10.

Pink Salmon:
Max length: 76.0 cm TL male/unsexed; (Ref. 9015); Common length: 50.5 cm TL male/unsexed; (Ref. 12193); Max. published weight: 6,800 g (Ref. 27436); Max. reported age: 3 years (Ref. 27547)

Pink salmon are commonly known as humpbacks, or "humpies," because of the extremely humped back developed by the males as they return to spawn. Young humpbacks have silver sides, but no parr markings like other salmon. As they mature, they develop blue backs and can be identified by the **large oval spots** on their backs and on **both lobes** of the tail fin. At spawning the coloring in males is reddish-yellow on the sides, while the female is more greenish. The males also develop a hooked upper jaw and large teeth.

Also Known As
Dog Salmon/
Gorbusch/
Haddo/ Holia

FishBase Name
Pink salmon

International Recognitions
France—
saumon rose
Germany—
Buckellachs
Italy—salmone
rosa

LANDINGS AND VALUES

This salmon is very abundant in Asia as well as North America. Pink salmon are fished along the coast of British Columbia and Alaska as they return home to spawn. The principal landing season is July through September. Pink salmon are fished with gill nets, purse seines, and trolling gear. They are also sought by sport fishermen using artificial lures. US landings in 1989 were about 135,768 tonnes, valued at $123.2 million (not shown). In 2008, catches were 118,173 tonnes (making it, by far, the largest salmon catch of all salmon species), valued

Pink Salmon US Landings by Year — Nominal Data Value in $US (000); Quantity in tonnes; (NMFS)					
	2004	2005	2006	2007	2008
Value	30,772	49,041	27,751	70,305	74,432
Quantity	135,155	224,356	100,590	207,504	118,173

Pink Salmon Canadian Landings by Year — Nominal Data Value in $Cdn (000); Quantity in tonnes; (DFO)					
	2004	2005	2006	2007	2008
Value	1,070	4,167	508	5,124	203
Quantity	3,578	12,638	1,431	11,198	353

at $74.4 million (see table). Canadian catches were about 30,850 tonnes in 1989, valued at approximately $30 million (not shown); declining to 353 tonnes in 2008, valued at $203,000 (see table).

COMMERCIAL USES

The pink salmon is a fatty fish with pink, rather than red, flesh of fine texture and a small flake. Pink salmon is available fresh, frozen and smoked, but most is canned for domestic consumption and exports to the United Kingdom, Australia and New Zealand. Canned "wild" salmon has gained new recognition in recent years for its heart-healthy omega-3 oil that has been shown to have less contaminants, such as mercury and PCBs, than many farmed salmon products.

LIFE CYCLE

Pacific salmons generally: Spawning occurs in the fall. The female digs one or more nests (redds) with her tail and will lay several thousand eggs. The male immediately fertilizes the eggs. After spawning, adults live for as little as a few days, up to a few months. (Death is caused by rapid aging brought on by excessive glandular activity during reproduction.) The eggs remain buried in the sand or gravel of the riverbed to develop over the winter period. In the spring, the newly hatched fish (alevins) eventually emerge from the gravel as fingerlings (fry). Those that stay in fresh water reach a length of about 2.5 inches and develop parr marks in a few months, becoming salmon parr. When parr reach a length of 5 to 6 inches, which, depending upon location, may take one to five years, they become silvery smolts and are ready to migrate to sea. The salmon grow rapidly at sea and most will spend two or more years there before returning to their native rivers to spawn. Some males, called "jacks," return prematurely.

Pink Salmon: Like other salmon, humpbacks are anadromous and migrate to their home stream between July and October. While some go a considerable distance upstream, most spawn in fresh water close to the sea and will die soon after spawning. The following spring, the small fry emerge from gravel spawning beds and travel directly downstream to the sea. During their first summer in saltwater, they remain close to shore. Then they move offshore, maturing rapidly while feeding first on plankton and gradually on more active prey. They usually return to spawn during their second summer at sea. Because of their fixed two-year lifespan, even- and odd-year stocks are effectively isolated from each other and do not interbreed.

SALMON, SOCKEYE OR RED OR BLUEBACK

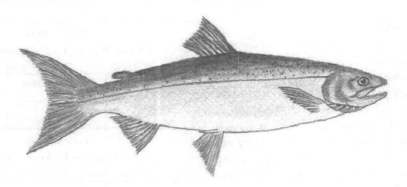

Sockeye Salmon, *Oncorhynchus nerka*

GENERAL

The **sockeye salmon** (or "blueback") is the best known of the 5 salmon species found on the Pacific coast (although rainbows or "steelheads" might be included here as well). It is highly valued for its famous red flesh, high oil content, and overall superior quality.

PHYSICAL DESCRIPTION

Pacific salmons generally: Like all members of the salmon family (Salmonidae), the Pacific salmons have a single dorsal fin located at mid-body and a small, fleshy adipose fin located in front of the tail fin. Pacific and Atlantic salmons, as well as many trouts, are difficult to distinguish. Pacific salmons generally have a deeper, less-streamlined body than Atlantic salmon. Pacific salmons either have spots, speckles, or no speckles at all, while Atlantic salmon has irregular, cross or X-shaped spots (and only above the lateral line). Pacific salmons have 13 to 19 rays on their anal fins, while the Atlantic salmon has less than 10.

Sockeye salmon:

Max length: 84.0 cm TL male/unsexed; (Ref. 5723); 71 cm (female); Common length: 45.0 cm TL male/unsexed; (Ref. 9988); Common length: 58 cm (female); Max. published weight: 7,710 g (Ref. 40637); Max. reported age: 8 years (Ref. 72462)

As its name implies, the blueback does indeed have a greenish blue back. Like the chum, the back and dorsal fin are usually **peppered with fine black specks** that are much smaller than those found on Chinook, coho, and pink. However, sometimes, there are no specks at all. It has silver sides and a pale belly. Sockeye meat is generally redder than chum and the lower fins are not white-tipped; otherwise, without scientific analysis, it is difficult to tell them apart. In spawning, the sockeye changes color: it is a dull brownish-red as it approaches home stream, but turns brilliant red with a green head, yellowish-green tail fin and white lower jaw as it moves upstream. The male also develops a humped back, long canine-like teeth and hooked jaws.

LANDINGS AND VALUES

The sockeye is present in many medium-to-large lakes, rivers, and streams on the west coast, from California to Alaska, and is also found in the Arctic and Asia, as far south as Hokkaido, Japan. In North America, populations south of the Columbia River in Oregon are small.

Also Known As
Redfish/ Spring-run Salmon/ Summer Sockeye

FishBase Name
Sockeye salmon

International Recognitions
France—saumon rouge
Germany—Rotlachs
Italy—salmon rosso

The principal landing season is from June to September, with a high concentration in July and August. Sockeye are usually caught by gillnet or seine, though trolls are sometimes used. In 1989 US landings totaled 123,539 tonnes, valued at $393.8 million (not shown). By comparison, 2008 catches were 101,970 tonnes, valued at nearly $176 million (see table). In 1989, Canadian landings approximated 34,000 tonnes, valued at close to $135 million (not shown); declining to 1,959 tonnes in 2008, valued at $7.7 million (see table). **Endangered Status:** Endangered in Cultus and Sakinaw Lakes, Canada (COSEWIC); Threatened in Ozette Lake and Endangered in Snake River (US).

Sockeye Salmon US Landings by Year — Nominal Data Value in $US (000); Quantity in tonnes; (NMFS)					
	2004	**2005**	**2006**	**2007**	**2008**
Value	156,970	187,211	159,475	205,363	175,915
Quantity	114,962	119,856	108,245	125,458	101,970

Sockeye Salmon Canadian Landings by Year — Nominal Data Value in $Cdn (000); Quantity in tonnes; (DFO)					
	2004	**2005**	**2006**	**2007**	**2008**
Value	22,681	4,045	33,373	6,674	7,707
Quantity	4,461	996	10,343	1,924	1,959

COMMERCIAL USES

A fatty fish, sockeye has a firm flesh of small flake and a deep orange or red color. About one-third of this highly prized "red" salmon was traditionally canned for the US and UK markets and most of the remainder frozen (often frozen-at-sea [FAS]), some for domestic consumption, but most for export to Japan. Canned "wild" salmon has gained new recognition in recent years for its heart-healthy omega-3 oil that has been shown to have less contaminants, such as mercury and PCBs, than many farmed salmon products. Sockeye is also available as smoked and salted roe ("sujiko" in Japan).

LIFE CYCLE

Pacific salmons generally: Spawning occurs in the fall. The female digs one or more nests (redds) with her tail and will lay several thousand eggs. The male immediately fertilizes the eggs. After spawning, adults live for as little as a few days, up to a few months. (Death is caused by rapid aging brought on by excessive glandular activity during reproduction.) The eggs remain buried in the sand or gravel of the riverbed to develop over the winter period. In the spring, the newly hatched fish (alevins) eventually emerge from the gravel as fingerlings (fry). Those that stay in fresh water reach a length of about 2.5 inches and develop parr marks in a few months, becoming salmon parr. When parr reach a length of 5 to 6 inches, which, depending upon location, may take one to five years, they become silvery smolts and are ready to migrate to sea. The salmon grow rapidly at sea and most will spend two or more years there before returning to their native rivers to spawn. Some males, called "jacks," return prematurely.

Sockeye salmon: Sockeye spawn primarily in lake systems: in rivers that feed into or are fed by lakes, in the outlets of lakes and on their spring-fed beaches. Spawning age depends a great deal on location. In southern rivers, sockeye spawn at 4 years. In northern waters, 5 years is the more common spawning age. And in northern Alaska and the Yukon, the age is usually 6. The young emerge from the gravel and spend up to 3 years in lakes usually located downstream from the spawning area. In May or June of their third year, the young salmon smolts begin their downstream migration to the ocean. They travel to the open ocean, south of the Aleutian Islands, to feed and grow. The fish average about 6 pounds on return.

SAND LANCE

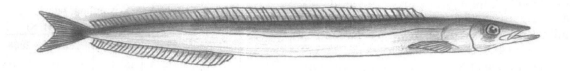

Northern Sand Lance, *Ammodytes dubius*

GENERAL

Sand lances (sand eels) have long been considered a major under-utilized fish resource of the western Atlantic Ocean. In Europe, 364,000 tonnes of sand lance (probably mostly *Hyperoplus lanceolatus*) was landed in 2008, compared to 9 tonnes of native sand lance in Canada and the US. Sand lances are not related to common eels, but belong to the family Ammodytidae (sand lances). The family includes about 7 genera and 26 species. The **northern sand lance** is listed in *The Seafood List* along with 3 other sand lance species, all of the genus *Ammodytes*.

The name is associated with their habit of burrowing into the bottom (*Ammodytes* is Greek for sand burrower). Sometimes this burying behavior takes place in the intertidal zone so that the fish remains in exposed beaches when the tide falls. Digging for sand lances is a popular pastime in some areas, where they are generally used as bait. It is not known how the fish can survive for hours in the sand, with little water for respiration.

PHYSICAL DESCRIPTION

Max length : 25.0 cm TL male/unsexed; (Ref. 7251)
Max age: 9 years (DFO)

The sand lance has a slender body, pointed snout and long dorsal and anal fins, but no pelvic fins. As they are bottom dwelling, they do not develop a swim bladder. Maximum length is about 37 cm - southeast Scotian Shelf. Size decreases to the north and south where maximum length of 20-25 cm. Colour is from deep blue-green to bronze on the back, with white belly when live, but the back darkens and dulls soon after death. The species appears to have chameleon-like independent eye movements. It is often confused with a capelin, which has similar fins and cylindrical body.

Also Known As
Sand eel

FishBase Name
Northern sand lance

International Recognitions
France—Lancon du Nord
Italy—cicerello

LANDINGS AND VALUES

Sand lance species are found in all the world's oceans, in coastal areas as well as deep waters. The northern sand lance is found in deep water on both sides of the North Atlantic and, in the western Atlantic, from Greenland to North Carolina. Its range overlaps the range of the slightly smaller American sand lance, *Ammodytes americanus,* which considered a more inshore species. There is no directed fishery and sand lance is reportedly often used as bait. The lack of a fishery does not indicate the lack of a large resource, which seems likely, but presently unproven. Commercial feasibility is unknown as knowledge of fish distribution and behaviour is still lacking. Further, as primarily an industrial fish product, demand and distance from markets are commercialization factors. Special gear, nets and techniques have also been developed for landing these fish in European waters, which would need to be adapted in North America. Moreover, as a forage fish, it would be necessary to manage these stocks closely to prevent endangerment to the sustainability of other benthic species such as cod and flounder.

American Sand Lance US Landings by Year — Nominal Data Value in $US (000); Quantity in tonnes; (NMFS)					
	2004	2005	2006	2007	2008
Value	0	0	0	50	42
Quantity	0	0	0	5	4

Sandeels-Sand Lance Canadian Landings by Year — Nominal Data Value in $Cdn (000); Quantity in tonnes; (DFO)					
	2004	2005	2006	2007	2008
Value	2	9	6	1	4
Quantity	2	8	6	3	5

In the US, 4 tonnes of sand lance were landed in 2008, valued at $42,000 (see table). In Canada the same numbers were 5 tonnes, worth $4,000 (see table).

COMMERCIAL USES

This is primarily an industrial fish that is usually reduced to oil and fertilizer, although European sand eels are also sometimes eaten.

LIFE CYCLE

Northern sand lances mature towards the end of their second year of life. Spawning occurs over sandy bottoms in shallow water during winter months. Eggs are laid on, or fall to the bottom, where they stick to grains of sand. Females lay many thousands of eggs and the larvae are reported as the most abundant and widespread fish larvae in the northwest Atlantic in the early months of the year. The larvae at first rise to surface where they stay for a couple weeks, but after they grow a few centimetres, they develop into juveniles and descend to the bottom for the remainder of their lives. Sand lances in the northwest Atlantic grow quickly for the first few years and then slowly after that. They primarily feed on small organisms, especially copepods. They are an important forage species for many predators, especially cod and other groundfish.

SAURY

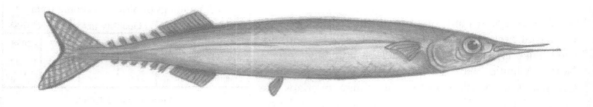

GENERAL

The **Atlantic saury** belongs to the family Scomberesocidae (sauries). There are 2 genera and 4 species in the family, although both *FishBase* and *ITIS* recognize two subspecies for Atlantic saury: *S. saurus saurus* and *S. saurus scombroides. The Seafood List* also includes the Pacific saury, *Cololabis saira.*

Often referred to as "skippers," sauries get this name by leaping out of water, sometimes in great numbers - especially when chased by predators.

PHYSICAL DESCRIPTION
Max length : 50.0 cm TL male/unsexed; (Ref. 7251);
Common length : 32.0 cm TL male/unsexed; (Ref. 3397)

Atlantic saury is similar to the needlefish with a narrow body and a long, beak-like snout lined with tiny teeth. The fish is olive green dorsally with bright, lighter-colored sides. The single dorsal and anal fins are each followed by a series of small finlets. It can also have a dark green spot above its pectoral fins and the pectoral fins are greenish.

The saury looks much like a freshwater gar (see entry in this book); however, that species has no finlets and also lacks a forked tail. Moreover, the gar is in a different family and found only in freshwater environments.

Also Known As
Skipper/
Needlefish/
Ocean Piper/
Skipjack/

FishBase Name
Atlantic saury

International Recognitions
Spain—Paparda del Atlántico
France—Balaou atlantique
Italy—Castaudiellu
Germany—Seehecht

LANDINGS AND VALUES

The saury is a pelagic oceanic fish preferring depths from the surface to 30 meters. Distributed in the western Atlantic from the Gulf of St. Lawrence to North Carolina, it is covered by the Law of The Sea as a highly migratory species. The species can travel in large schools. It can be caught at night using lights to attract schools, but is generally unexploited. They sometimes become stranded on beaches in great numbers. Although these fish can be found traveling in great numbers, their appearance is often sporadic, making them difficult to fish.

Atlantic Saury (Skippers) US Landings by Year — Nominal Data Value in $US (000); Quantity in tonnes; (NMFS)					
	2004	2005	2006	2007	2008
Value	2	3	3	3	3
Quantity	4	6	6	6	6

Commercial landings in the US totaled 6 tonnes in 2008, valued at $3,000 (see table). All of the reported catch in the last few years was in North Carolina. The fish can be found in eastern Canadian waters as well; however, there are no reported landings in recent years.

COMMERCIAL USES

The saury is often used as bait for longline fisheries, but is suitable for eating, canning and other inexpensive processing.

LIFE CYCLE

The saury is oceanic, but often found in large coastal schools. They appear to spawn in warm subtropical waters. Their eggs are covered with filaments like silver gars; however, these are not as adhesive as the gars and drift near the surface. The jaws develop slowly after the fry stage (40 mm.); the lower jaw grows first, so that a fry of 4 to 6 inches looks more like a little halfbeak.

They prey on zooplankton and fish larvae, as well as fish eggs and small fishes. As a surface fish, they are often preyed on by porpoises and larger predaceous fishes such as tuna and marlin; but are also prey to cod, pollock and bluefish.

SCAD

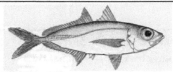

Bigeye Scad

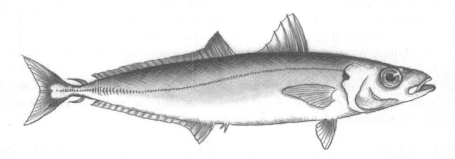

Mackerel Scad, *Decapterus macarellus*

GENERAL

The **mackerel scad** is a member of the Carangidae family (jacks and pompanos) as is the bigeye scad, *Selar crumenophthalmus,* and the European horse mackerel, *Trachurus trachurus*, also known as the "rough scad." All 3 species are marketed as scad, along with 8 other species on *The Seafood List* (*TSL*). The genus *Decapterus* accounts for 7 of the 11 species found under the scad market name in the *TSL* and the landing statistics confirm it is often difficult for fishers to easily tell many of these scad species apart.

Also Known As
Antonino/ Ocean Robin

FishBase Name
Mackerel scad

International Recognitions
Spain—Jurel; Chicharro
France—Chinchard; Faux Maquereau

PHYSICAL DESCRIPTION
Max length : 30.0 cm TL male/unsexed; (Ref. 26999)

The mackerel scad is an elongated, slender, and somewhat circular fish. There is a tell-tale (common to *Decapterus* spp.) separate, curved finlet between the dorsal and anal fins and the caudal fin. Another distinguishing characteristic is a small black mark on the dorsal edge of the gill cover (operculum). The color is iridescent black to bluish-green dorsally, fading to silvery white ventrally. The caudal fin is yellow-green or red, less forked than other jacks and there are no dark dots on lateral line (*FishBase*).

Bigeye scad [(Max length: 30.0 cm TL male/unsexed; Ref. 26999) *FishBase*] have an elongated and somewhat laterally-compressed body. The first 2 anal spines are separated from the anal fin. The transparent outer covering of the eye (adipose eyelid) covers almost the entire eye and there is a black spot on the operculum. The lateral line has 29 to 42 scutes. Coloration is metallic blue or bluish-green dorsally, shading to white ventrally, sometimes with a lateral yellow stripe present.

LANDINGS AND VALUES

Mackerel scad is found circum-globally. In the western Atlantic mackerel scad ranges from Nova Scotia to South America, and in the Pacific from the Gulf of California to South America and across to Hawaii and beyond. It is mostly present in schools around islands or deep reefs and prefers clear water and average depths of 30 – 35 meters (100 ft.).

Bigeye scad are found circum-tropically and in North America from Nova Scotia to Brazil in the western Atlantic and from Mexico to Peru in the eastern Pacific. They have the same distribution as mackerel scad, but are also present in the Gulf of Mexico and Caribbean. They are mostly nocturnal and sometimes found in turbid waters.

All of the mackerel scad reported catches, and about half of the bigeye scad reported catches, are in Hawaii. All of the remaining scad catches (i.e., bigeye and other scad nei) were landed in Florida (mostly west coast). In 2008, landings for mackerel scad were 74 tonnes, valued at $441,000 (see table). In the same period, landings for bigeye scad totaled 150 tonnes, valued at $591,000 (see table). Landings for unidentified scads [e.g., bigeye, round (*D. punctatus*) and redtail (*D. tabl*) etc.] totaled 236 tonnes, valued at $408,000 in 2008 (see table). Gear used is handlines and small mesh nets. About 15 tonnes of scad was also landed recreationally in the US in 2008. **Endangered Status:** Neither bigeye scad nor mackerel scad are endangered in Hawaii; not evaluated elsewhere (IUCN).

Mackerel Scad US Landings by Year – Nominal Data Value in $US (000); Quantity in tonnes; (NMFS)					
	2004	2005	2006	2007	2008
Value	350	342	449	457	441
Quantity	78	70	89	87	74

Bigeye Scad US Landings by Year – Nominal Data Value in $US (000); Quantity in tonnes; (NMFS)					
	2004	2005	2006	2007	2008
Value	752	738	822	899	591
Quantity	238	253	184	212	150

Scads Not Otherwise Identified (nei) US Landings by Year – Nominal Data Value in $US (000); Quantity in tonnes; (NMFS)					
	2004	2005	2006	2007	2008
Value	795	1,057	461	559	408
Quantity	387	474	325	395	236

COMMERCIAL USES

Scad is a food fish, gamefish, and is also used as a baitfish. It can be marketed fresh, salted or dried. Scad is important food fish in Hawaiian culture. There have been reports of ciguatera poisoning in both mackerel scad and bigeye scad.

LIFE CYCLE

Mackerel scad spawn in the summer months. Fertilization is external and the eggs are pelagic. After hatching, larvae remain in the pelagic environment forming large schools. Juveniles enter the coastal fishery in late fall and winter and grow quickly once they move inshore. They are sexually mature by the end of the first year. They are zooplankton feeders. Mackerel scad have a healthy and abundant population around Hawaii due to early sexually maturity (1 year) and high reproduction rates (lay many eggs). Predators include jacks, snappers and groupers.

Bigeye scad are mostly nocturnal and sometimes found in turbid waters. Fertilization is external and eggs are scattered in open water. They are known travel in schools of hundreds of thousands of fish. They feed on small shrimp and benthic invertebrates while inshore and fish and zooplankton when they move offshore.

SCAMP

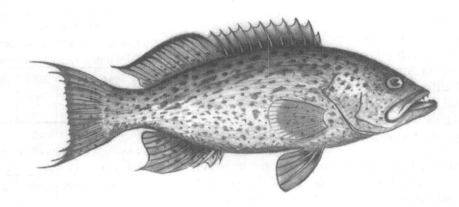

Scamp, *Mycteroperca phenax*

GENERAL

The **scamp** is a species in the family Serranidae (groupers and sea basses). In the grouper genus *Mycteroperca*, the scamp is one of the few fishes not marketed as grouper, but goes by its common name. (Also see grouper and sea bass entries in this book.)

Scamp can be very aggressive predators and often swallow their prey whole.

PHYSICAL DESCRIPTION

Max. length: 107 cm TL male/unsexed; (Ref. 40637);
Common length: 30.0 cm TL male/unsexed; (Ref. 3708);
Max. published weight: 14.2 kg (Ref. 40637);
Max. reported age: 21 years (Ref. 6846)

Scamp is a light gray to dark brown color and as they mature, their caudal fin rays elongates and red-brown spots develop along the body that combine to form lines along their side. They also have yellow around corners of mouth. It is similar looking to the yellowmouth grouper, *Mycteroperca interstitialis*.

Also Known As
Bacalao

FishBase Name
Scamp

International Recognitions
Spain—Cuna garopa
France—Badèche galopin

LANDINGS AND VALUES

Scamp				
US Landings by Year — Nominal Data				
Value in $US (000); Quantity in tonnes; (NMFS)				

	2004	2005	2006	2007	2008
Value	1,690	1,834	1,894	2,360	2,118
Quantity	292	295	272	314	274

Scamp is distributed in the western Atlantic from North Carolina to southern Florida into the Gulf of Mexico and Caribbean. Habitat is latitude dependent, preferring inshore reefs further north and offshore reefs in the tropical range. Scamp is both a commercial and recreational fish. In the US, 274 tonnes was landed commercially in 2008, valued at approximately $2.1 million (see table). Most of the commercial fish were landed off the Florida West Coast and the Carolinas. In addition, 1850 tonnes of *Mycteroperca* spp. (groupers) were landed recreationally in 2008; probably including scamp.

COMMERCIAL USES

Scamp, like all grouper, is an excellent eating fish. The skin is tough and strongly flavored and should be removed before cooking. The lean white meat is firm and moist with large flakes and a sweet, mild flavor. It can be grilled, fried, baked, broiled and steamed.

LIFE CYCLE

Scamps are distributed in the western Atlantic and generally found over ledges and high-relief rocky bottoms in the eastern Gulf of Mexico and over low-profile bottoms at depths of 30 to 100 m in North Carolina. They migrate onshore when water temperatures decline. Juveniles are often found in the shallow waters along the coast by jetties and in mangroves. They feed on squid, crustaceans, and smaller fish in reef areas. Scamp spawns during the late spring months, beginning life as a female and becoming male after 3 years or four spawning seasons.

Scamps are managed by SAFMC through gear restrictions and catch limits (10), 20" size limit. They are the second most important species in the US southeast and are considered seriously depleted.

SCULPIN

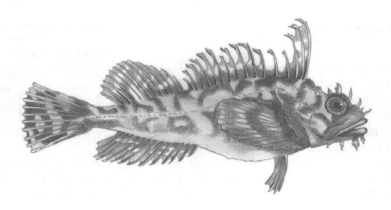

Atlantic Sea Raven, *Hemitripterus americanus*

GENERAL

Also Known As
Raven/ Yellow Sculpin/ Red Sculpin/ Sea Sculpin

FishBase Name
Sea Raven

International Recognitions
France—Hémitriptère atlantique

The **Atlantic sea raven** belongs to the family Hemitripteridae (sea ravens), which in both *ITIS* and *FishBase,* falls under the order Scorpaeniformes, although subject to different taxonomic views in-between. The family includes 3 genera and 8 species with 3 species in the *Hemitripterus* genus, including the bigmouth sculpin, *H. bolini*, a North Pacific species. *The Seafood List* includes 2 other species of fishes found under the market name sculpin in the separate, but related family, Cottidae the main home for "sculpins" (approximately 300 species in 70 genera). Sculpins by and large are relatively inactive, bottom-dwelling fishes found mostly in colder marine waters. One way the sea raven differs from other sculpins is that it can bite quite sharply, having large teeth.

PHYSICAL DESCRIPTION
Max length: 64.0 cm TL male/unsexed; (Ref. 7251);
Max. published weight: 3,200 g (Ref. 7251)

The sea raven can be a colourful brilliant red to reddish purple or even light brown or yellowish to darkish brown, paler on the sides than dorsally and usually with a yellow belly. Some are variously mottled with a paler or darker background colors, or plain white. The fins are barred in light and dark and the pectoral and anal fins can be yellow-rayed. It has a wide mouth with several rows of long sharp teeth as distinguished from long-horned sculpin or short-horned sculpin.

Its most distinctive features are the flabby growths on its head, the ragged profile of its first dorsal fin and prickly skin. When taken out of the water, the belly becomes inflated with water and it is unable to submerge.

LANDINGS AND VALUES

The sea raven inhabits rocky or hard bottomed coasts of the northwest Atlantic from Labrador to the Chesapeake Bay. It is not a highly commercial species and is used primarily for bait. Last reported US landings were 2 tonnes in 2007, valued at $3,000 (see table). Landings of other sculpins totaled 714 tonnes, valued at $471,000 in 2008 (see table). Almost all sculpin landings were in Alaska and, quite likely, were of the great sculpin, *Myoxocephalus polyacanthocephalus*. Sculpins are a minor gamefish as well, with 37 tonnes (mostly cabezon) landed on the West Coast.

Sea Raven US Landings by Year – Nominal Data Value in $US (000); Quantity in tonnes; (NMFS)					
	2004	**2005**	**2006**	**2007**	**2008**
Value	2	0	1	3	0
Quantity	1	0	1	2	0

Sculpins (excludes sea raven) US Landings by Year – Nominal Data Value in $US (000); Quantity in tonnes; (NMFS)					
	2004	**2005**	**2006**	**2007**	**2008**
Value	17	33	26	38	471
Quantity	146	201	262	584	714

The sea raven is not a large landing in Canada either; however, 154 tonnes of sculpin were commercially landed in 2008, valued at $48,000. All of this catch was on the East Coast.

COMMERCIAL USES

The sea raven is a good food fish, but not sought after commercially. In the northwest Atlantic, it is often used as bait for lobster pots. Some sculpins have venomous spines and/or poisonous eggs, but this is not a concern with the sea raven.

LIFE CYCLE

It is believed the sea raven spawns in autumn and early winter throughout its range. Warfel and Merriman reported that it deposits eggs at the bases of finger-like branches of the finger sponge and

Sea Raven Canadian Landings by Year – Nominal Data Value in $Cdn (000); Quantity in tonnes; (DFO)					
	2004	**2005**	**2006**	**2007**	**2008**
Value	0	0	0	8	0
Quantity	0	0	0	24	0

Sculpins (excludes sea raven) Canadian Landings by Year – Nominal Data Value in $Cdn (000); Quantity in tonnes; (DFO)					
	2004	**2005**	**2006**	**2007**	**2008**
Value	55	264	228	230	48
Quantity	110	186	207	187	154

sometimes on the smaller Halichondria sponge, where they stick together in clusters. It appears the female does not lay all her eggs at one time, but deposits several times at different places over the spawning season. The eggs are large, averaging 3.9 to 4 mm. in diameter with a tough egg membrane. The eggs are yellow at first, but soon change to an amber color and, at that point, are heavy enough to sink. They appear to reach 2-4 inches in about 6-8 months and about 6 inches by 1.5 years.

The sea raven is voracious eater and feeds on molluscs, sea urchins, crustaceans, smaller fish, and other benthic invertebrates. It is reported they are preyed on by goosefish (*FishBase*).

Searobin

Northern Searobin, *Prionotus carolinus*

General

Searobins belong to the order of Scorpaeniformes that includes scorpion fishes and sculpins and are found in the family Triglidae, related to the rockfishes, and more distantly greenlings (see entries in this book). There are 15 genera and more than 120 species in the family, many with a red or reddish coloration. This, in combination with their long pectoral fins, which resemble flapping wings as they swim, explains their name. *The Seafood List* notes 7 species found under this market name in 4 different genera.

Physical Description

Max length: 38.0 cm TL male/unsexed; (Ref. 7251);
Common length: 30.0 cm TL male/unsexed; (Ref. 3822)

Searobins have six spines, three along each side that resemble legs. These are thought to have originally been part of the pectoral fins. They are now used in part for sensory reception. They have a mottled coloration of reddish-brown to grey and an underbelly that is white. In addition to the long pectoral rays (wings), they can be identified by their flat bony head, blue eyes and tapered tail. Their skull is unusually strong and some species possess armored plates on their body.

The northern searobin is identifiable by the croaking sound produced as a result of vibrating its swim bladder with drumming muscles when caught.

Also Known As
Gurnard/ Robin/
Flying Fish/
Green Eye/
Carolina Robin

FishBase Name
Northern
Searobin

**International
Recognitions**
Spain—Rubio
carolino

LANDINGS AND VALUES

The northern searobin ranges from Nova Scotia to central Florida and the coastal Gulf of Mexico. It is a bottom dwelling fish living from depths of 15-170 meters (50-550 ft.) and preferring sandy bottoms. In 2007, the US commercial fishery landed 32 tonnes, valued at $10,000 (see table). They are a gamefish as well, with 42 tonnes landed in the US in 2008 (not shown). They are not a reported fishery in Canada.

Searobins US Landings by Year — Nominal Data Value in $US (000); Quantity in tonnes; (NMFS)					
	2004	2005	2006	2007	2008
Value	10	3	8	10	0
Quantity	36	18	17	32	0

COMMERCIAL USES

Searobins are used for food and fish meal as well as bait for hand-lines and traps. They are marketed fresh, frozen or as caviar. Their meat is firm and tender when cooked and often substituted for scorpionfish, among others.

LIFE CYCLE

Their life cycle is not well known; however, they spawn from late spring to summer and lay their eggs over sandy bottom areas. They are not nesting parents and do not care for their young after fertilizing the eggs. Searobins prey on crustaceans, squid, bivalves, shrimp and other fishes and are known to be preyed on by sharks and rays.

SHAD

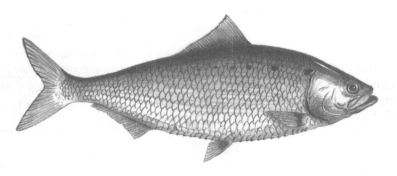

American Shad, *Alosa sapidissima*

GENERAL

The **American shad** is a member of the family Clupeidae (herrings, river herrings, menhadens, sardines). The genus *Alosa*, subfamily Alosinae, includes many of the shads and other river herrings (about 23 species in *ITIS* and 24 in *FishBase,* not including subspecies). *The Seafood List* identifies 9 species of shad, several of which are common on the Atlantic East Coast. These include the American shad, the hickory shad (*A. mediocris*), the Alabama shad (*A. alabamae*), the gizzard shad (*Dorosoma cepedianum*), and the threadfin shad (*D. petenense*). The alewife and blueback herring also share the *Alosa* genus. (Also see alewife and menhaden entries in this book.)

Like the river herrings, at one time shad swarmed the rivers of eastern North America and approximately 23,000 tonnes of American shad was landed in the US and Canada in 1896. However, as in the case of other anadromous species (e.g., salmon, alewife), dams, pollution and perhaps overfishing have long since curtailed catches of that magnitude.

Also Known As
Atlantic Shad/
Potomac Shad/
Northern Silver
Shad

FishBase Name
American shad

International Recognitions
Spain—Sábalo
americano
France—Alose
savoureuse
Italy—
Allaccia
americana
Germany—
Amerikanische
Finte

PHYSICAL DESCRIPTION

Max length: 76.0 cm TL male/unsexed; (Ref. 6885); 61.7 cm SL (female); Common length: 50.0 cm SL male/unsexed; (Ref. 188);
Max. published weight: 5,500 g (Ref. 7251);
Max. reported age: 13 years (Ref. 72462)
Length at first maturity: 305 - 485 cm

American shad is moderately compressed with a distinct keel. The coloration is silver with either blue or green-metallic luster on dorsal side. The shoulder has a dark spot often followed by several more and occasionally by a second row. Teeth are small and weak and the adipose eyelid is well developed. It can be confused with the blueback herring, *A. aestivalis,* and the alewife, *A. pseudoharengus* (which has a steeply rising jaw not present in American shad), as well as the hickory shad, *A. mediocris* (where coloration is more green to black than silver).

LANDINGS AND VALUES

American shad is multi-faceted traveller and can be found in oceanic to brackish and fresh water environments at various depths up to 250 meters (825 ft.) deep. It is distributed throughout the Atlantic from Newfoundland and the St. Lawrence River basin to central Florida. It was introduced to the Pacific in the 1870s and is now found from Alaska to Baja, California. The US American shad catch was 275 tonnes, valued at $616,000 in 2008 (see table). The Canadian marine catch in 2008 was only 5 tonnes, valued at $5,000 (see table). The Canadian catch was increased by freshwater landings of 15 tonnes, valued at $12,000 in 2008 (see table). The US gizzard shad accounted for almost 70% of total US shad landings, while the American shad accounted for about 30% of the landings, but 60% of the value (see table). American shad are caught commercially in weirs, traps and gillnets while spawning and occasionally at sea. They are also a gamefish in many areas. **Endangered Status:** Alabama shad is a Species of Concern (US).

American Shad US Landings by Year — Nominal Data Value in $US (000); Quantity in tonnes; (NMFS)					
	2004	2005	2006	2007	2008
Value	846	780	658	790	616
Quantity	678	575	340	426	275

American Shad Canada Marine Landings by Year — Nominal Value in $Cdn (000); Quantity in tonnes; (DFO)					
	2004	2005	2006	2007	2008
Value	27	27	18	7	5
Quantity	41	45	27	19	5

COMMERCIAL USES

Marketed fresh, frozen, salted or smoked. The flesh is white and flaky and the fish is also known for its excellent roe.

American Shad Canada Freshwater Landings — Nominal Value in $Cdn (000); Quantity in tonnes; (DFO)					
	2004	2005	2006	2007	2008
Value	2	2	2	12	12
Quantity	2	32	2	14	15

LIFE CYCLE

The American shad is mostly oceanic, but returns to freshwater streams in the spring. Males arrive in the river first, and after females arrive, spawning timing is temperature dependent (12°C –18.3°C). Spawning occurs at night with each female accompanied by several males. Eggs are released in open water where they are fertilized by the males. Approximately 20,000 to 150,000 eggs or more can be released (numbers are independent of female size). Individual fertilized eggs (2.5mm – 3.5mm diameter; transparent pink or amber color) slowly sink to the bottom and are carried along in the current. The larvae hatch after 8-12 days and the spent fish return to sea where they travel in schools. Juveniles are found in rivers during the summer and as they mature form schools and stay in groups to move downstream. After entering the ocean in the fall, they remain there until they return to spawn. They feed on plankton, small copepods and mysids and occasionally on smaller fish. They are preyed upon by seals, but adults have few predators.

Gizzard Shad US Landings by Year — Nominal Data Value in $US (000); Quantity in tonnes; (NMFS)					
	2004	2005	2006	2007	2008
Value	788	561	693	200	407
Quantity	1,870	1,081	731	656	1,187

Hickory Shad US Landings by Year — Nominal Data Value in $US (000); Quantity in tonnes; (NMFS)					
	2004	2005	2006	2007	2008
Value	49	57	21	13	15
Quantity	114	103	38	24	35

SHARK, DOGFISH OR CAPE

GENERAL

What is a dogfish? Fishers usually describe dogfish as small sharks. Marine biologists have designated a family of sharks, Squalidae, as dogfish sharks. *The Seafood List* identifies nine species (generally small and from more than one family) as acceptable to market under the name dogfish. The **spiny dogfish** is believed to be the most abundant species of dogfish that includes the smooth dogfish (*Mustelus canis*) and the black dogfish (*Centroscyllium fabricii*) found in North American waters. Of all the various species of sharks commercially landed in the US and Canada (about 25), dogfish sharks alone accounted for approximately 80% of the total weight and 60% of the value in 2008.

The Pacific Ocean spiny dogfish, once considered a separate species (*Squalus suckleyi*), is now viewed as the same species as the Atlantic spiny dogfish. Once described as a nuisance by fishers because it would damage gear and catches, the spiny dogfish is now in demand worldwide.

PHYSICAL DESCRIPTION

Max length: 160 cm TL male/unsexed; (Ref. 247); 120 cm TL (female);
Common length: 100.0 cm TL male/unsexed;
Max. published weight: 9,100 g (Ref. 11389);
Max. reported age: 75 years (Ref. 39247)

Like all true sharks, the dogfish skeleton is cartilaginous rather than bony. But unlike most other sharks, dogfish have well-developed "spiracles" (remnants of the first gill slit behind the eye), no anal fin and no "nictitating" (closing) eye membrane. The spiny dogfish is slate grey over the back and sides, fading to a white belly. Rows of small white spots, especially noticeable in younger fish, mark its sides. It is a slender, streamlined species with the family trademark (unlike the smooth dogfish) of a single sharp spine in front of both dorsal fins.

Also Known As
Spring Dogfish/
Spiked Dogfish/
Grayfish/
Spur Dog/
Picked Dogfish/
Rock
Salmon (UK)

FishBase Name
Piked Dogfish

International Recognitions
France—aiguillat commun
Germany—Dornhai
Spain—galludo; mielga

LANDINGS AND VALUES

Spiny dogfish can be found on both sides of the North Atlantic and along North America's Pacific coast. They prefer temperate to sub-arctic water temperatures, from 43 to 52°F, and depths of less than 360 meters (1,200 feet). On the east coast, dogfish range from Greenland, south to North Carolina. They winter off the Carolinas and Virginia and migrate north in the summer months to the nutrient-rich waters off Nova Scotia and Newfoundland. By late autumn, most will have left Canadian waters to return south. In the Pacific, the species is common in shallow waters from Alaska to central California. In Canada, dogfish is primarily a

All Dogfish US Landings by Year — Nominal Data Value in $US (000); Quantity in tonnes; (NMFS)					
	2004	2005	2006	2007	2008
Value	1,409	1,255	1,866	2,195	3,323
Quantity	2,344	2,267	3,437	4,288	5,757

All Dogfish Canadian Landings by Year — Nominal Data Value in $Cdn (000); Quantity in tonnes; (DFO)					
	2004	2005	2006	2007	2008
Value	3,088	3,900	4,631	2,126	1,152
Quantity	7,859	7,701	4,857	6,476	3,727

west coast fishery with east coast landings accounting for only about 40% of the catch in 2008. Total 2008 Canadian landings were 3,700 tonnes, valued at more than $1.1 million (see table). In Canada, dogfish are usually caught by trawl and baited longlines. In the US fishery, draggers are often used. The US dogfish catch (including spiny, smooth and unclassified) increased in recent years to 5,757 tonnes in 2008, valued at $3.3 million (see table). Most of the catch in landed in Virginia and Massachusetts in the east and Washington State in the west. Spiny dogfish makes up most of the catch of dogfish species in both the US and Canada. Because of slow growth, many sharks are subject to quotas.

COMMERCIAL USES

Unlike many other fish, dogfish are not filleted. Although they may be sold frozen, headed and gutted (H/G), usually, the belly flaps are cut out, the fins and tails removed, and the body skinned, leaving a white carcass or "back." This process is necessitated because dogfish secrete urea (an ammonia compound) through their skin, which imparts an unpleasant flavor. The body meat and belly flaps are exported to Europe, especially Germany, where they are smoked and sold as a delicacy. The tails and fins are also frozen and exported to Asian markets. The backs are wrapped and frozen, either individually or in blocks, for export to England, where dogfish is a mainstay of the fish 'n' chip industry. Oil from the fish, formerly important for vitamin A, makes a fine of grade machine oil. Shortfin mako shark is considered the world's best quality shark meat; it is marketed fresh in the US and in Europe. Other largely appreciated species are thresher (*Alopias* spp.), porbeagle and requiem. However, the FDA has issued an advisory to pregnant women and children concerning mercury contamination in (especially) large sharks. (Also see mako shark entry.)

LIFE CYCLE

Off the east coast of the US, mating and breeding occur in the winter months. Sexually mature dogfish gather in large schools. The embryos (up to 14, but averaging about 5) have a gestation period of 1.5 to 2 years, one of the longest of any vertebrate. Birth is given to live "pups" about 10 inches (25 cm) in length. These immediately form large schools near the surface. After their yolk sac is gone, they feed almost exclusively on plankton and jellyfish. As they grow older, the pups descend to deeper waters. Adult dogfish prey mostly on fishes, mainly herring and capelin, but will feed on krill (euphausiid) and small crustaceans (copepods).

Shark, Mako

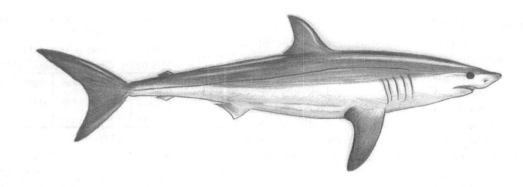

Shortfin Mako Shark, *Isurus oxyrinchus*

General

About 25 species of shark are landed commercially in the US, although for most species, catches are minimal. The **shortfin mako** is an apex predator and one of the fastest of all sharks. It can also leap out of the water when hooked. The size of its fins gives one clue to its name, while its Latin name refers to its pointed nose. It is a member of the family Lamnidae, order Lamniformes (mackerel sharks) that has 3 genera and 5 species and is closely related to the longfin mako, *I. paucus*, the great white shark, *Carcharodon carcharias,* the salmon shark, *Lamna ditropis* and the porbeagle, *Lamna nasus*. It is a potentially dangerous fish and has attacked people and boats, although rarely.

Physical Description

Max length: 400 cm TL male/unsexed; (Ref. 13574);
Common length: 270 cm TL male/unsexed; (Ref. 5217);
Max. published weight: 505.8 kg (Ref. 4699);
Max. reported age: 32 years (Ref. 86588)

Also Known As
Blue Pointer/
Bonito Shark/
Atlantic Mako
Shark/ Pacific
Mako Shark

FishBase Name
Shortfin Mako

**International
Recognitions**
Spain—Marrajo
dientuso
France—Taupe
bleue
Italy—Muanto
Germany—
Blauhai

All mackerel sharks commonly have a sharply-pointed, conical snout and large, dark eyes; a large mouth filled with relatively few, but large sharp teeth; large gill slits; relatively small second dorsal and anal fins; a narrow caudal peduncle supported by strong keels; and a crescent-shaped caudal fin. In contrast, makos are large spindle-shaped sharks with sharp snout, small black eyes and hooked teeth. The caudal fin is crescent-shaped with a strongly developed lower lobe. It is bi-colored with blue dorsally and white underbelly. It has small anal and pectoral fins.

Commonly Fished Sharks	Scientific Name	Range	All US Shark Landings		All Canada Shark Landings	
			1989 MT	2008 MT	1989 MT	2008 MT
Porbeagle	*Lamna nasus*	Most Oceans	4	N/A	N/A	125
Mako	*Isurus oxyrinchus*	Worldwide	304	126	N/A	46
Sandbar	*Carcharhinus plumbeus*	Worldwide	1	48	N/A	N/A
Blacktip	*Carcharhinus limbatus*	Worldwide	55	177	N/A	N/A
Thresher	*Alopias vulpinus*	Worldwide	559	215	N/A	1
Sharks (nei)	--	--	--	734	--	6
Total (includes dogfish and others not shown)			12,964	7,575	2,941	3,907

LANDINGS AND VALUES

Makos are wide-ranging oceanic offshore pelagic species to depths of 740 meters, although preferring depths to100 -150 meters. The shortfin mako is found throughout tropical and temperate regions: in the western Atlantic from Maine to Brazil including the Gulf of Mexico and in the Pacific from the Aleutian Islands along the coast of California to Chile. The two species of makos overlap in their ranges. They are caught in gillnets as well as on pelagic longlines and with sports fishing gear.

As a sports fish, it is appreciated for its powerful, torpedo-like runs and spectacular leaps. As a commercial species 246 tonnes were landed in the US

Mako Sharks US Landings by Year – Nominal Data Value in $US (000); Quantity in tonnes; (NMFS)					
	2004	2005	2006	2007	2008
Value	452	355	345	430	365
Quantity	270	244	207	258	246

All Sharks (excluding Dogfish) US Landings by Year – Nominal Data Value in $US (000); Quantity in tonnes; (NMFS)					
	2004	2005	2006	2007	2008
Value	5,436	5,631	6,113	4,146	2,995
Quantity	3,224	3,215	3,513	2,503	1,818

in 2008, valued at $365,000; while Canada landed 47 tonnes, valued at $42,000 (see tables). Note that this data includes both longfin and shortfin makos. Most US catches are landed in Hawaii; most Canadian catches are from the western Atlantic. In total, approximately 1,800 tonnes of sharks (excluding dogfish) were landed in the US in 2008, valued at almost $3 million (see table). Canadian landings (excluding dogfish) were about 10% of the US total (see table). **Endangered Status:** Like many top predators, the mako is under concern from several quarters (e.g., Greenpeace) and is rated "threatened" (COSEWIC) and "vulnerable" (IUCN Red List). The porbeagle, basking, and other less prominent sharks, are also Species of Concern.

COMMERCIAL USES

The high quality meat is utilized fresh, frozen, smoked, dried and salted; liver oil is extracted for vitamins, the fins are used for soup, the hides are used for leather and the jaws and teeth are sold as ornaments and trophies

Mako Sharks Canadian Landings by Year – Nominal Data Value in $Cdn (000); Quantity in tonnes; (DFO)					
	2004	2005	2006	2007	2008
Value	85	104	77	87	42
Quantity	81	96	71	72	47

LIFE CYCLE

Tagged sharks indicate a wide seasonal migration, and breeding and nursing areas are not well understood. Reproduction is ovoviviparous with litters of 4-25 pups with larger females giving birth to more and larger pups; they are born during spring in both

All Sharks (excluding Dogfish) Canadian Landings by Year – Nominal Data Value in $Cdn (000); Quantity in tonnes; (DFO)					
	2004	2005	2006	2007	2008
Value	413	395	247	180	171
Quantity	330	329	273	177	180

hemispheres. Gestation is 15-19 months and reproduction occurs every 2-3 years. Makos prey on a wide range of bony fishes, especially bluefish in the western Atlantic, mackerels, tunas, bonitos and other sharks and cephalopods. Larger adults may also prey on billfishes. Mammals have been conspicuously absent in examined stomachs, but can be expected.

Mackerel sharks have an inherent circulatory ability to retain body heat, providing them with the endurance, speed and strength benefits of warm bloodedness, without the accompanying high metabolic cost. The result of a streamlined-body profile in a type of high-performance "engine" helps make the mackerel shark similar to a "predatory machine," capable of sustained activity in even the coldest oceans.

SHEEPHEAD

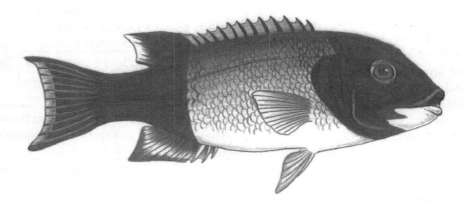

California Sheephead, *Semicossyphus pulcher*

GENERAL

California sheephead belong to the family Labridae (wrasses) and are therefore related to the cunner, hogfish and tautog (see entries in this book). There are 2 other species in the genus; the Galápagos sheephead wrasse (*S. darwini*) found off Ecuador and Peru and the currently unnamed *S. reticulates* found in the western Pacific.

This sheephead might easily be confused with the sheepshead (porgy), *Archosargus probatocephalus* (Family: Sparidae) found on the Atlantic East Coast — a totally different species.

PHYSICAL DESCRIPTION

Max length: 91.0 cm TL male/unsexed; (Ref. 2850);
Max. published weight: 16.0 kg (Ref. 2850);
Max. reported age: 53 years (Ref. 56049)

The California sheephead is elongate, robust, and compressed. They have unusually long sharp teeth similar to canines. As juveniles, they are a uniform pink to red with a white lower jaw. As they age, the midsection of the body becomes a darker red, the jaw remains white and the posterior becomes black. Adult males and (the previously younger) females have different color patterns and body shapes. Females are a uniform pinkish red with white lower jaw and undersides. As the females change to the male sex, they become larger, with black tail and head sections, a wide, reddish-orange mid-section, red eyes and fleshy bumps on the forehead.

Also Known As
Sheepie/
Goat/ Fathead

FishBase Name
California
sheephead

**International
Recognitions**
Spain—Vieja de
California
France—Labre
californien

LANDINGS AND VALUES

The sheephead is only found off the coast of California from Monterrey Bay to Baja and in the Gulf of California. They prefer rocky bottom areas, particularly with kelp beds and are reef associated. Sheephead usually live at depths from about 7-33 meters (20-100 ft.), but are occasionally found at 60

California Sheephead US Landings by Year — Nominal Data Value in $US (000); Quantity in tonnes; (NMFS)					
	2004	2005	2006	2007	2008
Value	328	358	367	301	401
Quantity	39	40	39	31	37

meters (180 ft.). In 2008, 37 tonnes of landings were recorded in the US, valued at $401,000 (see table). They were at one time a common species, but numbers have been greatly reduced by overfishing, especially spearfishing (listed as "vulnerable" by IUCN Grouper and Wrasse Specialist Group). They are currently occasional to uncommon in Central California.

COMMERCIAL USES

Sheephead is a popular sport fish and puts up a good fight when hooked or speared. It is also recognized as a good food fish. Originally, the commercial fishery was conducted by Chinese fishers in the 1800s who salted and dried it. In the late 1980s, commercial fisheries once again began supplying sheephead (live) to the Asian market. To manage the fishery and prevent overfishing, the California Department of Fish and Game in 2001 established regulations that restrict the catch size of sheephead and the areas where these fish may be caught.

LIFE CYCLE

Sheephead are protandric hermaphrodites, beginning life as females and changing to males at about 7 years of age. Spawning occurs between July and September. Males become territorial and heard females while eggs and sperm are broadcast. Females can spawn up to 300,000 eggs per season.

They feed on sea snails, urchins, molluscs, crustaceans, sea cucumbers and squid. They use their large canine teeth to pry food from rocks and a pharyngeal plate for crushing their prey. They are active daytime hunters and at night hide in crevices and construct a cocoon, which masks their scent from predators. They are capable of breaking open shells with their powerful jaws and can inflict serious flesh wounds with their sharp incisors.

SILVERSIDE

Atlantic Silverside, *Menidia menidia*

GENERAL

The **Atlantic silverside** is believed to be one of the most common fishes along the Atlantic Coast of North America. Silversides are found in subfamily Menidiinae of the family Atherinopsidae (New World silversides). The subfamily is comprised of 7 genera and approximately 80 species. There are seven species in the genus *Menidia* (Atlantic silversides (Ref: *ITIS*). These 7 species are all found along the Atlantic Coast of North America; most are quite small, many are centred on the Gulf of Mexico and southern states, two appear in freshwater and can reproduce there. The Atlantic silverside appears the species with the most northern range.

FishBase indicates 109 species in the total Atherinopsidae family. *The Seafood List* (*TSL*) records 5 species under the market name silverside. However, the Atlantic silverside is the only species listed under the genus *Menidia* in *TSL*.

Also Known As
Northern Silverside/ Dotted Silverside/ Spearling

FishBase Name
Atlantic Silverside

International Recognitions
Spain—Pejerrey del Atlántico
France—Capucette
Germany—Mondährenfisch

PHYSICAL DESCRIPTION

Max length: 15.0 cm TL male/unsexed; (Ref. 7251); Common length: 11.5 cm TL male/unsexed; (Ref. 12193); Max. reported age: 2 years (Ref. 12193)

Silversides are elongated, slender, and thin-bodied. The head is short and triangular with an oblique mouth and large eyes. They have two dorsal fins. Coloration is translucent gray-green to greenish-yellow dorsally with silver sides and a white belly with large scales and smooth margins. There is a distinct lateral, metallically-lustered silver stripe, edged above by dark line that originates at the pectoral fin and ends at the caudal fin. The caudal fin is concave and may be yellowish tinged, and the top of the head is grey. The silvery coloration is believed to confuse predators when swimming in schools. They can be confused with the anchovy, but are distinguished by a smaller mouth. They can easily be distinguished from smelts, as smelts have an adipose fin (also see smelt and anchovy entries in this book).

LANDINGS AND VALUES

Atlantic silversides are distributed from Newfoundland and the Gulf of St Lawrence to north-eastern Florida. They prefer inshore coastal areas and stillwaters particularly around river mouths over grassy sea beds. They will swim offshore in the winter to avoid the colder water temperatures. The main commercial fishery is in PEI, Canada – a large island of many sandy beaches, pockmarked with small harbours and estuaries and surrounded by eel grass. Gear used is primarily trap nets, but dip nets are also legal. The season is Oct.–Dec. (inclusive). Canadian landings were 444 tonnes in 2008, valued at $407,000 (see table). In 2008, US landings were 16 tonnes, valued at $33,000 (see table). Most of the US catch was in the Mid-Atlantic States.

Silversides Canadian Landings by Year – Nominal Data Value in $Cdn (000); Quantity in tonnes; (DFO)					
	2004	2005	2006	2007	2008
Value	284	291	615	427	407
Quantity	295	273	551	494	444

Silversides US Landings by Year – Nominal Data Value in $US (000); Quantity in tonnes; (NMFS)					
	2004	2005	2006	2007	2008
Value	5	0	0	4	33
Quantity	2	0	0	2	16

COMMERCIAL USES

In PEI, original markets were for animal feed. Later, a food market in Japan developed. More recently still, US zoo markets for exotic bird feed and other bait markets have developed. They are also used for scientific research because of their sensitivity to changes in the environment and also because they are a major forage fish for other species. In US regions, they are often sold as bait.

LIFE CYCLE

This is a short-lived species that is believed to mature at about 1 year of age, spawn and die shortly after. Although 2+ year old fish have been reported, the population dynamics of a short life span means that this is a resource that is hard to manage.

The spawning season occurs in Spring to early Summer, later in northern latitudes. Observations of spawning activity suggest it occurs during daylight hours in large schools and may coincide with high tides and/or lunar cycles and is followed by other spawning activity at 2-week intervals. There is some suggestion that northern and southern stocks may represent 2 subspecies. Reproduction is oviparous and eggs are deposited on the bottom substrate during spawning events that occur very close to the shoreline.

Adults prey on smaller organisms like copepods, mysids (i.e., small, shrimp-like crustaceans), shrimp, small squid, marine worms, algae, diatoms and detritus. They will also eat their own eggs. They are prey to striped bass, bluefish and mackerel, as well as many other fishes and seabirds.

SKATE

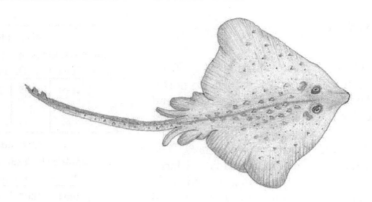

Thorny Skate, *Amblyraja radiata*

GENERAL

Skates are in the same class, Chondrichthyes (cartilaginous fishes), as sharks and the same family, Rajidae, as rays (e.g., sting ray, manta ray). Unlike some rays, however, the **thorny skate** is neither electrical nor poisonous, though the males have very sharp mating claspers called knives. Of the 200 species of skates worldwide, the thorny skate, the smooth skate (*Malacoraja senta*) and the winter skate (*Leucoraja ocellata*) are three of the more commercially important species in North Atlantic waters. The big skate (*Raja binoculata*) the California skate (*R. inornata*) and the longnose skate (*R. rhina*) are some of the more important skates on the Pacific coast. Skates, like sharks, are primitive fishes; however, it is believed they evolved after jawless fish like lampreys, and perhaps at the same time as some bony fish.

PHYSICAL DESCRIPTION
Max length: 105 cm TL male/unsexed; (Ref. 53748);
Max. published weight: 11.4 kg (Ref. 53748)

The skate is immediately recognizable by its flattened body and long, thin tail. Unlike flounder that are laterally compressed and swim on one side, the skate is compressed dorso-ventrally, i.e., top to bottom like a pancake. The flattened sides merge with the pectoral fins to form the wide wings it uses to propel itself. The long, well-developed tail is used primarily as a rudder. It has two small dorsal fins close together near the end of the tail. Behind the pelvic fins at the base of the tail, the male has a set of large claspers used for mating. On top of the head are two spiracles, or breathing holes, through which water is inhaled. Water is expelled through the gill slits on the underside. The mouth is also located on the underside, forcing the skate to land on top of its victim to feed. Skates range in color from pale to dark brown, with darker splotches on the dorsal side. On the bottom, they are white with sooty patches. The plentiful thorny skate can be differentiated from the smooth skate by its size (nearly twice as large) and by its large number of thorny spines. There is a row of thorns down the spine, a few on the shoulders, and one in front of, and behind, each eye. The base of the thorns is a distinctive star shape, sometimes giving it the name "starry" skate.

Also Known As
Arctic Thorny Skate
Starry Skate
Atlantic Prickly Skate

FishBase Name
Starry ray

International Recognitions
Spain—Raya radiante
France—Raie radiée
Germany—Sternroche

242

LANDINGS AND VALUES

The thorny skate is common throughout the Atlantic from Baffin Island, northern Canada, to South Carolina. This species appears to be most plentiful off the coast of southern New England in depths of 90-450 meters (about 300-1,500 ft.). In Canada, the greatest numbers are found around the southern tip of the Grand Banks in deeper waters. Although they support directed fisheries in some regions (caught with trawls and longlines), skate landings are often the result of by-catches incidental to the fish sought. The tables reflect landings of all skate species.

All Skates US Landings by Year — Nominal Data Value in $US (000); Quantity in tonnes; (NMFS)					
	2004	**2005**	**2006**	**2007**	**2008**
Value	7,380	7,050	9,211	10,731	10,575
Quantity	25,109	24,467	24,751	27,177	29,311

All Skates Canadian Landings by Year — Nominal Data Value in $Cdn (000); Quantity in tonnes; (DFO)					
	2004	**2005**	**2006**	**2007**	**2008**
Value	1,898	1,885	757	969	744
Quantity	3,943	3,590	2,703	2,729	1,996

The thorny skate on the East Coast and the big skate on the West Coast make up the majority of the landings in Canada; while a larger variety of skate species are landed in the US. US landings, about 29,300 tonnes in 2008, valued at $10.6 million, are considerably higher than Canadian catches of almost 2,000 tonnes, valued at $744,000 (see tables). Massachusetts, Rhode Island and Alaska were major US landing sites in 2008, while BC landed almost one-half of the Canadian catch.

Endangered Status: US Species of Concern. Because of over-fishing, slow growth to maturity and relatively low fecundity, several other skates and rays (basically larger skates) are listed on the World Conservation Union (IUCN) Red List as an "Endangered Species."

COMMERCIAL USES

Skate wings are very much in demand in many parts of Europe where they are considered a delicacy. The wings, which are cut into strips before they are cooked, have a rich flavor similar to scallops.

LIFE CYCLE

Thorny skates usually reach sexual maturity at 22 inches. Although it appears they may reproduce year-round, spawning season is thought to be concentrated between March and September. The eggs are fertilized within the female by the male inserting its claspers and injecting sperm. The eggs remain in the uterus until an egg sac has formed around each egg. These sacs, about 3 to 4 inches long depending upon the size of the female, are laid two at a time over a week. Each female will lay between 6 and 40 eggs. The incubation time in the egg sacs is at least six months.

Skates are the source of those dark-colored pouches, known as sailor's or mermaid's "purses," that wash up on beaches. They are actually the discarded egg cases from skate hatchings. Before hatching, the egg cases are often preyed upon by halibut, goosefish, Greenland sharks and various predatory gastropods (snails). The gray seal is a major predator of adult thorny skates. The thorny skate is a bottom feeder often targeting crustaceans (e.g., crabs, shrimp), fish (eel, finfish, cod, smaller haddock, redfish and herring) and worms.

SNAPPER

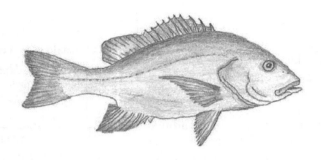

Red Snapper, *Lutjanus campechanus*

GENERAL

Snappers are mainly tropical fish, but some live in warmer temperate waters. The name "snapper" arose because of the violent jaw movements exhibited after they were caught, often resulting in injury to an unwary fishers. There are more than 100 snapper species worldwide and at least 29 species are found in North American waters. Many of these are members of the *Lutjanus* (common snappers) genus of the family Lutjanidae (snappers). On the East and Gulf coasts, these include the schoolmaster (*Lutjanus apodus*), gray snapper (*L. griseus*), Caribbean **red snapper** (*L. purpureus*) and the **red snapper** (*L. campechanus*). A Pacific snapper (*L. peru*) [also called Pacific **red snapper** in *FishBase*] is found on the West Coast, but is not reported as a commercial landing. Other major snappers include the vermilion snapper (*Rhomboplites aurorubens*) and the yellowtail snapper (*Ocyurus chrysurus*).

PHYSICAL DESCRIPTION

Max length: 100.0 cm TL male/unsexed; (Ref. 26938);
Common length : 60.0 cm TL male/unsexed; (Ref. 55);
Max. published weight: 22.8 kg (Ref. 40637); Max. reported age: 57 years (Ref. 48779)

The body and head of the red snapper are entirely red, fading to rose-white on the underbelly. The eyes are small with a red iris. It closely resembles the Caribbean red snapper except this fish has dorsal spots and larger eyes. Snappers are commonly named for their colors. The yellowtail snapper is, as its name would imply, tan-yellow. The cubera and dog snappers found off Florida can reach sizes of 100 pounds or more. The snapper is often a reef fish and shares the same habitat as sea basses and groupers, similar looking fishes from a different family. Snappers, sea basses and groupers are perch-like fishes with sloping heads that are often armed with sharp, canine teeth. These fish all have similar dorsal and anal fin configurations. However, snappers usually have a distinct shovel-nosed snout and different colors from sea basses and groupers.

True snappers should also be distinguished from several Pacific rockfish species – as well as bluefish, bream, porgies and other species that are popularly (but incorrectly) marketed as "snapper." Up to a dozen rockfish species (e.g., yelloweye rockfish) can legally be marketed as snapper on the US West Coast, but only *L. campechanus* can legally be shipped interstate as "red snapper." Canada has similar codes related to labeling various rockfishes as "snapper."

Also Known As
Mexican Snapper
Caribbean Red
Snapper
Northern Red
Snapper

FishBase Name
Northern red
snapper

**International
Recognitions**
Spain–Pargo del
Golfo
France–Vivaneau
campèche

LANDINGS AND VALUES

Snappers can be found throughout the Gulf and Atlantic coasts and in the Pacific, off the coast of California and Hawaii. Almost all of US commercial landings are in the Gulf and Atlantic, with a small catch in Hawaii (110 tonnes in 2008). Florida, Texas and Louisiana are major landing states. The red snapper and the Caribbean red snapper are found mostly in the Gulf of

All Snappers (including red snappers) US Landings by Year – Nominal Data Value in $US (000); Quantity in tonnes; (NMFS)					
	2004	2005	2006	2007	2008
Value	25,254	23,954	25,649	23,459	24,595
Quantity	4,846	4,267	4,281	3,795	3,942

Mexico and Caribbean, but also as far north as Long Island. The Pacific (red) snapper is the only true snapper found on the West Coast and not a significant commercial fishery at present.

Adult snappers and groupers are often found around offshore reefs and are fished together. Most commercial fishing in the Gulf Region is done with baited hooks and lines on electric and hydraulic reels, using squid or fish as bait. From 2 to 40 hooks may be used with one reel. The longline fishery for yellowedge grouper is also used in the

Red Snappers US Landings by Year – Nominal Data Value in $US (000); Quantity in tonnes; (NMFS)					
	2004	2005	2006	2007	2008
Value	12,119	11,683	13,428	9,964	8,755
Quantity	2,191	1,916	2,139	1,411	1,172

snapper fishery, as is the occasional otter trawl. The fishery is monitored under strict quotas, closures and other management tools. The Gulf shrimp fishery, once a major source of juvenile snapper by-catch and mortality, has undergone gear by-catch reduction modifications since 1998.

In 1989 there was approximately 4,800 tonnes of snappers (1,800 tonnes of red snapper) landed in the US, valued at approximately $22.6 million ($10.3 million of red snapper). In 2008, all snapper landings totaled 3,942 tonnes, valued at approximately $24.6 million (see table). In 2008, 1,172 tonnes of red snapper was landed, valued at $8.8 million (see table); as well as 1,780 tonnes of vermillion snapper, valued at almost $10 million (not shown). In addition, more than 9,200 tonnes of snapper were landed in the US recreational fishery in 2008; about 70% of this total was red snapper and gray snapper. It is not a fishery in Canada.

COMMERCIAL USES

Many of the snappers—the yellowtail snapper and the gray snapper, for example, are excellent food fish. An exception is the dog snapper, which has been implicated in ciguatera poisoning (a poison resulting from toxic algae eaten by fish). The snappers are important commercially both as a food fish and as sport fish. Of the various species, the red snapper is the principal food fish. It is often sold whole (gutted, head on) to avoid substitution by other species posing as snapper.

LIFE CYCLE

Snappers spawn primarily away from reefs and over a firm sandy bottom at depths of 18-36 m (60-120 ft.). Anywhere from 200,000 to more than 9 million eggs can be laid, depending on the age and size of the fish. The eggs hatch within 24-48 hours after fertilization and soon begin feeding on algae and zooplankton. After about six weeks, the larval snappers move inshore where they undergo a transformation into the juvenile form. Some species have been known to enter brackish and fresh water. The young in particular are often found near shore tide pools and estuaries. Larger fish may be found on shallow reefs and especially around oil rigs in the Gulf of Mexico. The adult is also a deepwater fish that can gather in large schools in deep underwater canyons and depressions. Snappers are voracious predators feeding on such smaller prey as grunts, croakers and crustaceans. Their major natural enemies are sharks and large sea bass.

SOLE OR FLOUNDER

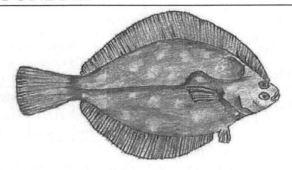

Rock Sole, *Lepidopsetta bilineata*

GENERAL

The **rock sole** is a member of the Pleuronectidae family (right-eyed flounders). The name "sole" originates from a family of flatfishes called Soleidae. However, the name is commonly applied to other flatfish families. The name "sole" seems to be particularly popular on the Pacific Coast, while flounder is most common on the Atlantic Coast, and some flatfish are now "approved" for the use of both market names (see flounder entry in this book) in *The Seafood List (TSL)*. There is another rock sole, *Paraplaqusia bilineata* (family *Cynoglossidae*) reported in *TSL* and *ITIS*. (Two species with the same common name is generally unacceptable and may be corrected in the future.)

PHYSICAL DESCRIPTION

Max length: 58.0 cm TL male/unsexed; (Ref. 6885); 60 cm TL (female); Max. Publ. weight: 1,800 g (Ref. 56370); max. reported age: 22 years (Ref. 6885)

Also Known As
Rock Flounder/
Twolined
Flounder/
Whitebellied
Flounder

FishBase Name
Rock sole

International Recognitions
Spain—Lenguado del Pacífico
France—Fausse limande du Pacifique

The rock sole has a rounded body and moderately deep, compressed eyes located on its right side. The eyed side is a light to dark brown or gray with darker mottling, which is sometimes yellow and red. Its blind side is mainly a whitish color, although there is sometimes a yellowish tinge near the rear. The rough spiny scales on its eyed side lend it the name "rough back." The dorsal fin runs from its eye to its tail. The caudal fin is slightly rounded. The rock sole is distinguished from other flatfish by having both an abrupt arch in its lateral line over its pectoral fin and a branch dorsal lateral line (i.e., it is "two-lined"). Although many flatfish can change pigment, the rock sole is distinguished by an exceptional ability to match the color of its background, making it virtually invisible. This unique ability is apparently dependent on eyesight, as blind fish cannot perform this feat. The yellowfin sole is similar to the rock sole but has yellow dorsal and anal fins and no dorsal branch.

North American Common Soles	Commercial Landings Scientific Name	Range	2008 US Landings $US (000)	MT	2008 Canada $Cdn (000)	MT
Yellowfin	*Limanda aspera*	N Pacific	54,744	141,237	N/A	N/A
Rock	***Lepidopsetta bilineata***	N& NE Pacific	27,425	52,979	696	574
Flathead	*Hippoglossoides elassodon*	N Pacific	10,781	25,274	N/A	N/A
Dover	*Microstomus pacificus*	NE& N Pacific	9,273	11,189	1,905	1,964
Rex (Witch)	*Glyptocephalus zachirus*	NE& N Pacific	2,360	4,103	330	415
Petrale (Brill)	*Eopsetta jordani*	NE Pacific	4,972	2,216	514	581
Total (includes other soles not shown)			**109,863**	**237,398**	**5,043**	**4,188**

LANDINGS AND VALUES

The rock sole ranges from southern California to the Bering Sea and St. Lawrence Island and then south to Korea and southern Japan. Although it usually prefers shallow waters (depths less than 600 feet), it can be found in waters up to 1,200 feet in depth. Whatever the water depth, the rock sole will usually be found on a pebbly or rocky ocean floor. This very tasty flatfish is sought by both the sport and commercial fishers. In Alaska, rock sole are fished commercially from mid-January to March prior to spawning. US landings of rock sole totaled 24,688 tonnes in 1989, valued at $7.3 million (not shown). This has increased to

Rock Sole US Landings by Year — Nominal Data Value in $US (000); Quantity in tonnes; (NMFS)					
	2004	**2005**	**2006**	**2007**	**2008**
Value	13,405	15,439	19,561	19,376	27,425
Quantity	29,256	28,252	34,247	34,362	52,979

Rock Sole Canadian (BC) Landings by Year — Nominal Data Value in $Cdn (000); Quantity in tonnes; (DFO)					
	2004	**2005**	**2006**	**2007**	**2008**
Value	1,353	1,036	1,235	970	695
Quantity	1,325	1,020	1,019	800	574

52,979 tonnes in 2008, valued at more than $27 million (see table). Rock sole was the largest single US sole species landed in 1989 and accounted for about half of the catch of 53,423 tonnes, closely followed by Dover sole at 20,250 tonnes. In contrast, in 2008, all sole landings (about 11 species) increased to 237,398 tonnes of which rock sole accounted for about 20% and yellowfin sole accounted for almost 60% of the catch (see table, previous page). Most of the yellowfin and rock sole catch is from Alaska. (Note that about 10,000 tonnes of unidentified flatfishes were also landed in Alaska in 2008.) BC sole species include rock sole, Dover sole, rex and petrale sole. Rock sole was the predominant species into the early 1990s; however, catches declined and Dover sole has been the larger catch in recent years. In 2008, 4,188 tonnes of sole species, valued at $5 million, and 11 tonnes of flounder (not shown) were landed in BC.

COMMERCIAL USES

Sole is a marketing name of several species of flatfish on the west coast and does usually not apply to the east coast; an exception is gray sole that is also marketed as (witch) flounder. Although the primary market for Alaska rock sole is roe-in females for Japan, some male rock sole is exported to China where it is filleted and even exported back to the US. Processing plants in the Pacific Northwest also fillet this species and market it specifically as "rock sole" because it is so well known for its fine quality. It is marketed fresh or frozen, whole and filleted. English sole and other flatfish are often marketed as "lemon sole," deriving this name from a slight lemon odor. Petrale sole is the most highly valued west coast sole, but landings are small.

LIFE CYCLE

The rock sole spawns between February and April, laying between 400,000 and 1.3 million bright yellow-orange eggs that sink to the bottom. The young begin life with an eye on either side of their head. However, within only a few days, one eye starts migrating toward the other until they are both close together on the right side of the body. At the same time the eye is migrating, the mouth becomes strangely twisted and the dorsal fin spreads forward until it almost reaches the mouth. A few days after this metamorphosis is complete, the young rock sole sinks to the ocean bottom where it spends the rest of its life swimming with its eyeless side on the bottom. Adults feed primarily on molluscs and crustaceans (e.g., clams, shrimps, small crabs, etc.) as well as worms, sandlances and small bottom fish. Unlike other flatfishes, the rock sole doesn't bury its body in the ocean floor—it is in almost constant motion in search of prey.

SPADEFISH

Atlantic Spadefish, *Chaetodipterus faber*

GENERAL

The Atlantic Spadefish is found in the family Ephippidae (spadefishes) that includes 8 genera and about 15 species. The genus *Chaetodipterus* includes the **Atlantic spadefish** and 2 other species, including the Pacific spadefish, *C. zonatus.* However, all present commercial catches of spadefishes are on the Atlantic and Gulf Coasts.

The spadefish is named after its spade-like body shape. They are known to float on their side and can be mistaken for floating debris.

PHYSICAL DESCRIPTION

Max length: 91.0 cm TL male/unsexed; (Ref. 7251);
Common length : 50.4 cm TL male/unsexed; (Ref. 26466);
Max. published weight: 9,000 g (Ref. 7251)

The spadefish has a deep, compressed body with a blunt snout and small mouth. It has no teeth on the upper mouth. There are 2 separated dorsal fins and a concave caudal fin with elongated rays on the anal and second dorsal. It can be irregularly striped with (4 to 6) black and white to silver vertical bands that fade with age. Juveniles are completely black. Scales are present on the head and fins.

The family is of the same suborder and is related to the surgeonfishes (family Acanthuridae -see entry in this book). It also looks similar to the blue and queen angelfishes (*Holacanthus* spp.) but, among other differences, the coloring, pointed beak and convex tail profiles of the angelfishes are different.

Also Known As
Porgy/ Moonfish/ Angelfish/ Tripletail/ Paguala

FishBase Name
Atlantic spadefish

International Recognition
Spain—Paguara
France—Disque portuguais
Japan—Shirogane-tsubameuo
Germany—Spatenfisch

LANDINGS AND VALUES

The Atlantic spadefish is found in western Atlantic as far north as Massachusetts and as far south to southern Brazil, but most commonly around Florida, the Bahamas, and in the Gulf of Mexico. These are a schooling fish often found in shallow waters around reefs, wrecks, harbors, grass beds, and mangroves, although they do school offshore as well. They are a minor commercial fishery in the US that landed 38 tonnes in 2008, valued at $47,000 (see table). They are not a reported fishery in Canada.

Spadefishes US Landings by Year — Nominal Data Value in $US (000); Quantity in tonnes; (NMFS)					
	2004	2005	2006	2007	2008
Value	40	40	26	48	47
Quantity	52	47	26	52	38

Endangered Status: Not evaluated (IUCN)
Aquaculture: The spadefish has been cultured in captivity, but not commercially.

COMMERCIAL USES

Spadefish are a minor commercial fishery but are considered a good food fish, usually marketed fresh. They are also present in the aquarium trade. Ciguatera poisoning has been reported.

LIFE CYCLE

They reach sexual maturity at one year and spawn in the spring and summer months from May to September on the inner shelf. Females can release up to a million eggs per season. Eggs are pelagic and fertilized externally.

The eggs hatch after approximately 24 hours. Larvae feed on a yolk sac for about two days before actively feeding. When the larvae become juveniles, the teeth and lateral line appear. Black stripes develop sequentially as the fish grow larger, starting with three at 2 cm and increasing to five at about 4 – 5 cm.

They feed on benthic invertebrates and plankton as well as jellyfish tentacles. Predators include sharks and other large fish such as the tripletail.

SQUIRRELFISH

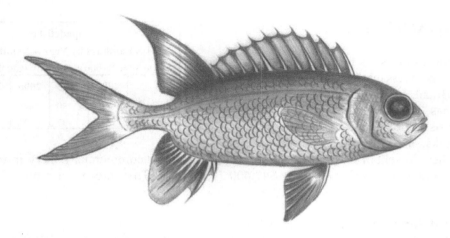

Squirrelfish, *Holocentrus adscensionis*

GENERAL

Which animal has quick, jerky motions, large, bright eyes and makes chattering-like sounds? The squirrelfish is found in subfamily Holocentrinae of the family Holocentridae (soldierfishes, squirrelfishes). The subfamily is comprised of 3 genera and approximately 37 species. There are two species in the genus *Holocentrus*; one is the **squirrelfish** and the other is the longspine squirrelfish, *H. rufus*. (Ref: *ITIS*)

FishBase indicates 84 species in the total Holocentridae family. *The Seafood List* (*TSL*) records 6 species under the market name squirrelfish.

The squirrelfish is capable of producing a warning sound by vibrating its swim bladder, which it uses to defend its territory. It also has venomous spines, but is not deadly to humans. It has large, squirrel-like red eyes that help it blend in with its reed environments.

Also Known As
Soldierfish/
Longjaw
Squirrelfish/
Squirrel/
Welshman

FishBase Name
Squirrelfish

International Recognitions
Spain—Candil
gallito

PHYSICAL DESCRIPTION

Max length: 61.0 cm TL male/unsexed; (Ref. 3634);
Common length: 25.0 cm TL male/unsexed; (Ref. 5217)

The squirrelfish's dorsal fin is spiny in front separated by a small membrane from long, soft rays in back. The dorsal spine is tinged yellowish-red, or translucent, with large rough scales. The anal fin matches the anterior dorsal fin in size and placement, but is rounded rather than angular. It has a slender keel, with a narrow, long, deeply forked caudal fin. Body coloration is red (sometimes orange or pinkish) on top and sides (sometimes mottled) and white below.

LANDINGS AND VALUES

In the western Atlantic, both the squirrelfish and longspine squirrelfish are distributed from North Carolina to Bermuda, the Gulf of Mexico and Caribbean, as far south as Brazil. They are typically near shore, reef-associated fishes with a depth range 0 - 180 meters, but usually stay close to the surface or shallow water. They are nocturnal and hide under ledges and within crevices during the day and prey on small crustaceans at night. Squirrelfishes are landed in Florida and North Carolina, but other species of squirrelfishes (e.g., *Sargocentron* spp. or *Myripristis* spp.) are found in Hawaii, where most of the commercial landings are found.

Squirrelfishes (Includes Hawaii) US Landings by Year — Nominal Data Value in $US (000); Quantity in tonnes; (NMFS)					
	2004	2005	2006	2007	2008
Value	123	118	108	135	260
Quantity	19	16	14	16	27

In 2008, 27 tonnes of squirrelfishes were landed in the US (including Hawaii), valued at $260,000 (see table). The Atlantic and Gulf landings of squirrelfish and longspine squirrelfish were approximately 1 tonne, valued at $1,900 (see table). They are not a reported fishery in Canada.

Endangered Status: Not evaluated (**IUCN**)

COMMERCIAL USES

The catch is not highly commercial because of the tough scales and multiple spines. Ciguatera poisoning has been reported. It is marketed fresh. There is also an aquarium trade.

Squirrelfishes US Atlantic and Gulf Coasts Landings by Year — Nominal Data Value in $US (000); Quantity in tonnes; (NMFS)					
	2004	2005	2006	2007	2008
Value	3.3	2.2	3.9	3.1	1.9
Quantity	1.4	1.1	2.0	1.4	0.9

LIFE CYCLE

Squirrelfish are nocturnal and live in reef crevices. They prey on small crustaceans. Fertilization is external and spawning occurs in open water. They are broadcast spawners and do not guard the eggs.

SURFPERCH

Barred Surfperch, *Amphistichus argenteus*

GENERAL

Also Known As
Surffish

FishBase Name
Barred surfperch

**International
Recognitions**
Mexico—Perca
Poland—Szumien
srebrny
Germany—Gebändeter
Brandungsbarsch

The surfperches are found in the family Embiotocidae (surfperches) that includes 13 genera and about 26 species. The genus *Chaetodipterus* includes the **barred surfperch** and 2 other species: the calico surfperch, *A. koelzi* and the redtail surfperch, *A. rhodoterus. The Seafood List* identifies 8 species of surfperches. All members of the family are found only in the Pacific Ocean, most of them in eastern Pacific subtropical waters of North and South America.

PHYSICAL DESCRIPTION

Max length: 43.0 cm TL male/unsexed; (Ref. 2850);
Common length: 30.0 cm TL male/unsexed; (Ref. 2850);
Max. published weight: 2,000 g (Ref. 2850);
Max. reported age: 9 years (Ref. 56049)

All surfperch are short with thin, deep bodies and large eyes. They have a single dorsal fin and tail fins that are deeply forked. They are usually brightly colored and have bars or striped patterns to their coloration.

Barred surfperch coloration is olive to yellow green on the dorsal changing to silver on the sides and belly with bronze to brassy yellow bars or spots along the side. Although similar to other perch in the area, the barred surfperch is distinguishable by its lower jaw being shorter than the upper and by the lack of any reddish coloration on its fins.

LANDINGS AND VALUES

Surfperch are found at the bottom of the water column in subtropical waters. In the eastern Pacific, the barred surfperch range extends from Bodega Bay in northern California to central Baja California. They are generally found in sandy bottom areas or along rocks or pier pilings, but can be caught in bottom trawls offshore to about 70 meters depth. They are not highly migratory.

Surfperches US Landings by Year — Nominal Data Value in $US (000); Quantity in tonnes; (NMFS)					
	2004	2005	2006	2007	2008
Value	165	105	71	29	33
Quantity	40	27	17	8	9

They can be trawl caught in up to 73m of water. However, surfperch are generally fished by surf fishermen and anglers on an incoming tide when they come in to feed. Common bait includes soft-shelled crabs, blood worms and cut fish. In 2008, nine tonnes were landed commercially in the US, valued at $33,000 (see table). In addition, 158 tonnes of various surfperch species were landed recreationally in 2008 in the US, of which about 60% was barred surfperch (not shown).

COMMERCIAL USES

They are an excellent gamefish. As tasty little fishes, they can easily replace rockfishes, snappers, seabasses, porgies and breams in any recipe. However, because they are small, they are best grilled whole (scaled and gutted), or crispy-fried Asian-style.

LIFE CYCLE

Mating occurs from fall to early winter. Fertilization is internal and reproduction is viviparous. Juveniles are born fully developed from March to July, ranging from less than 10 to more than 100 juveniles, with an average of 33 per female. They reach maturity at about 2 years and have an average life span of 6 yrs for males and 9 for females. They are not highly migratory. They are generally found in small schools and feed on sand crabs and other shellfish and invertebrates.

SWORDFISH

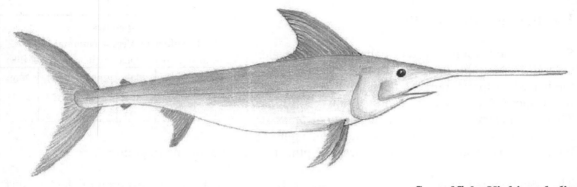

Swordfish, *Xiphias gladius*

GENERAL

At first glance, it would seem evident that swordfish belongs to the same family (Istiophoridae) as other billfishes like sailfish and marlin. However, the **swordfish** is the single species of the monotypic family Xiphiidae. Since the time of Aristotle, it has been famous for its formidable, sword-like weapon, as is implied by the scientific name *gladius* (sword). Known to penetrate metal-reinforced oak planks, this long rostrum is used by the swordfish to attack prey and, on rare occasions, whales, wooden fishing vessels and even research submarines. One swordfish landed off the coast of Chile by rod-and-reel weighed 1,180-pounds. There are now many conservation concerns about swordfish stocks, as well as the stocks of most other large fishes and mammals in the ocean.

PHYSICAL DESCRIPTION

Max length : 455 cm FL male/unsexed; (Ref. 40637);
Common length : 300 cm TL male/unsexed; (Ref. 9354);
Max. published weight: 650.0 kg (Ref. 4689)

Also Known As
Broadbill
Broadbilled
Swordfish
Espada
Emperado

FishBase Name
Swordfish

**International
Recognitions**
France—
espadon
Germany—
Schwertfisch
Spain—pez
espada
Italy—pesce
spada
Japan—mekajiki

The swordfish has two anal fins, the first much larger than the second, and pectoral fins that approximate the height of the first dorsal fin. The body of the swordfish is stout and only slightly compressed. Its caudal peduncle is moderate, with a strong lateral keel. The swordfish has a large mouth, with the upper jaw greatly flattened and prolonged into the famous sword shape. The bill is wider than it is deep. It projects beyond the lower jaw and is almost twice the length of the head. Swordfish have a dark metallic purple dorsal and a dusky underside. The sword is almost black on the top and lighter on its underside. The fins are dark and have a silvery sheen. It can be distinguished from other northern fishes by the lack of pelvic fins.

The most readily apparent physical characteristics of the swordfish, apart from the long, broad sword or rostrum, is its eminent size, its higher-than-long front dorsal fin and its broad, crescent-shaped tail fin. The streamlined and powerful swordfish can move at 60 miles per hour, making it the second fastest fish in the sea after the (Atlantic) sailfish (*Istiophorus platypterus*), clocked at 68 miles per hour.

LANDINGS AND VALUES

The swordfish is a world ocean traveler, frequenting all temperate and tropical waters. In warm waters it can swim in great depths, but tends to rise in temperate waters. Preferring water temperatures in a narrow vicinity of 53°F to 60°F, swordfish follow the warm Gulf Stream northward on the Atlantic Coast until meeting cooler, southward currents off Newfoundland. However, most are landed in temperate waters further south. On the Pacific coast they are found as far north as Oregon. In the commercial fishery, they are generally longlined using 40 mile sets with 1,000 hooks, each hook with a chemical

Swordfish – 50 % Hawaii US Landings by Year — Nominal Data Value in $US (000); Quantity in tonnes; (NMFS)					
	2004	**2005**	**2006**	**2007**	**2008**
Value	13,701	16,365	13,461	19,501	16,041
Quantity	2,742	3,022	2,711	3,578	3,391
Swordfish **Canadian Landings by Year — Nominal Data** Value in $Cdn (000); Quantity in tonnes; (DFO)					
	2004	**2005**	**2006**	**2007**	**2008**
Value	10,114	13,309	11,897	11,384	8,801
Quantity	1,203	1,584	1,405	1,348	1,383

light attached for attraction. The bait is often squid. Swordfish are nocturnal eaters and prefer bright moonlit nights to feed. They are also harpooned and trolled. Although the swordfish is a relatively small US fishery in terms of landed weight, it is a valuable commercially species with a landed value of approximately $16 million in 2008 (see table). In Canada, catches totaled almost 1,400 tonnes in 2008, valued at $8.8 million (see table). Marlin landings in 2008 were 885 tonnes, valued at around $2 million (not shown - see marlin entry in this book). Landings for sailfish and tarpon are incidental; they are not major commercial fisheries.

COMMERCIAL USES

The US is a major swordfish market. This market was damaged in 1970 when an unacceptable level of mercury was found in many commercial species, including swordfish. However, when the US FDA raised the permissible "action level" of mercury from 0.5 to 1.0 parts per million (ppm) in 1979, the fishery was restored. Presently, the FDA issues a warning advising pregnant women and young children not to consume swordfish, shark, tilefish and king mackerel. The Health Canada advisory is two-tiered: the permissible level is a standard of 0.5 ppm total mercury in all retail fish (including all canned tuna) with the exception of 1.0 ppm for fresh/frozen tuna, shark, swordfish, escolar, marlin, and orange roughy; these latter fish are subject to consumption advice. Generally, the advisory to pregnant or nursing women is to limit consumption to 1 meal (150g) per month and 1/2 this amount (75g) to young children A fat fish having firm flesh and excellent flavor, swordfish is available fresh or frozen, typically as steaks.

LIFE CYCLE

The swordfish spawns in warm waters and migrates to cooler waters to feed. In the western Atlantic, the spawning area is believed to be the southern Sargasso Sea. Peak spawning activity occurs from February to April. Little is known of their Pacific spawning grounds. Eggs are buoyant, transparent, and have a large oil globule, but little else is known of spawning behavior. The species is perceived to be fast-growing, with the females growing faster, larger and living longer than the males. Swordfish prey upon smaller fishes, such as mackerel, herring, hake, redfish, squid and barracuda, but will attack virtually any prey available. Ingested animals often show signs of sword slashes. Young swordfish are preyed upon by many species including tuna, shark and marlin, but larger specimens have few predators.

TANG OR SURGEONFISH

Blue Tang, *Acanthurus coeruleus*

GENERAL

Surgeonfishes are found in the family Acanthuridae (surgeonfishes, tangs) that has 6 genera and about 81 species. The genus *Acanthurus* has 42 species including the **blue tang**. *The Seafood List* recommends that one species, the goldenring surgeonfish (*Ctenochaetus strigosus*), be marketed only as "surgeonfish," while all other members of the genus *Ctenochaetus* spp., as well as all members of the genus *Zebrasoma* spp., be marketed only as "tang." Like the blue tang, 3 other species, all in the genus *Acanthurus*, including the doctorfish (*A. chirurgus*) *the yellow surgeonfish* (*A. xanthopterus*) *and the elongate surgeonfish* (*A. mata*) can be marketed as either surgeonfish or tang.

The name is derived from the Greek "acanthi" (thorn) and "oura" (tail), referring to the double spine on the caudal peduncle that resembles a surgeon's scalpel and can inflict painful wounds.

PHYSICAL DESCRIPTION

Max length: 39.0 cm TL male/unsexed; (Ref. 36453);
Common length : 25.0 cm TL male/unsexed; (Ref. 5217)

The blue tang is a rounded, deep-bodied, laterally-compressed fish. The snout is pointed, the eye is located high on the head and the small mouth is lower on the head. It has a continuous dorsal fin and smaller lunate caudal fin. On both sides of the caudal peduncle are two horizontal yellow caudal spines that fit into horizontal grooves and can be extended for use as defense. Coloration changes with age. Young tang are yellow, changing to a mixture of blue and yellow as juveniles. Adult fish are bright blue to purple-gray with a yellow caudal fin. They display grey horizontal lines along the flank and the blue anal and dorsal fins are banded with orange-brown diagonal stripes. At night, blue tangs display white vertical stripes. It is considered to have the most distinctive coloration of all western Atlantic surgeonfishes.

Also Known As
Blue Surgeon/
Surgeonfish/
Barbero/ Blue
Doctorfish

FishBase Name
Blue Tang
Surgeonfish

International Recognitions
Spain—Navajón
azul
France—Chirurgien
bayolle
Germany—Blauer
Doktorfisch

LANDINGS AND VALUES

In the western Atlantic, the blue tang is distributed from New York to Florida, the Gulf of Mexico, Bermuda and the Caribbean. It is found along reefs, seagrass beds, mangroves and inshore rocky areas. Feeding groups are often multi-species and the blue tang is associated with the doctorfish and the sergeant major (*Abudefduf saxatilis*) in Florida waters. Surgeonfishes, such as the blue tang and doctorfish, are landed in Florida, but other species of surgeonfishes (e.g., black surgeonfish, *Ctenochaetus hawaiiensis*) are found in Hawaii, where most of the commercial landings are made.

Surgeonfishes (Includes Hawaii) US Landings by Year — Nominal Data Value in $US (000); Quantity in tonnes; (NMFS)					
	2004	2005	2006	2007	2008
Value	109	121	111	154	146
Quantity	33	38	30	39	36

In 2008, 36 tonnes of surgeonfishes were landed in the US (including Hawaii), valued at $146,000 (see table). Florida landings of surgeonfishes in 2008 were approximately 100 kg, valued at approximately $600 (see table). They are not a reported fishery in Canada.

Endangered Status: Not evaluated (**IUCN**)

Surgeonfishes (Florida Only) US Landings by Year — Nominal Data Value in $US (000); Quantity in tonnes; (NMFS)					
	2004	2005	2006	2007	2008
Value	2.1	0.7	--	--	0.6
Quantity	0.4	0.2	0.0	--	0.1

COMMERCIAL USES

The landings are almost entirely Hawaiian. There is a minor commercial fishery and part may be used as bait. The flesh is malodorous and not prized for food, so they are usually collected for the aquarium trade.

LIFE CYCLE

Blue tang are found in small schools around reefs, seagrass beds, mangroves, and inshore rocky areas and are diurnal. They eat only algae, sometimes gleaned from cleaning the fins and flippers of sea turtles. They live in holes or crevices for protection from predators like large carnivorous fish. They are important for keeping algae populations in check, which could threaten the health of coral. They become sexually mature in their first year and spawning occurs in late afternoon or evening hours. Fertilization is external and eggs are small and pelagic; hatching in about 24 hours. After about 2 weeks, two-inch long juveniles settle to the bottom of the inshore habitat. When spawning, their color changes from a uniform dark blue to a pale blue in the front and a dark blue posterior.

TAUTOG

Tautog, *Tautoga onitis*

GENERAL

The **tautog** belongs to the large family of wrasses, Labridae, many species of which are small, colourful fish found in the Indo-Pacific Ocean. In North America, it is closely related to the cunner, *Tautogolabrus adspersus,* and is in the same family as the hogfish, *Lachnolaimus maximus.* Tautog historically had little market value, and was not commercially exploited. Commercial fishing began in earnest in the early 1980s when other traditionally more valuable species become less abundant. Recreational landings also increased rapidly at this time and tautog has now established itself in chowders and other foods at the dinner table. With their flat, grinding teeth, tautogs are well suited to crushing the hard shells of molluscs such as oyster; hence the name "oysterfish."

Also Known As
Blackfish/
Oysterfish/
Black Porgy/
Sea Dog/ Cub

FishBase Name
Tautog

International Recognitions
France—Matote noire/Tautogue noir
Denmark—Tautog-læbefisk

PHYSICAL DESCRIPTION

Max length : 91.0 cm TL male/unsexed; (Ref. 7251);
Max. published weight: 11.3 kg (Ref. 40637);
Max. reported age: 34 years (Ref. 6486)

The tautog is a portly fish with a blunt nose and a thick-lipped mouth that has large conical-shaped teeth in front and flat crushing teeth in back. The long dorsal fin originates over the gill and runs nearly to the tail. The first three-quarters of this fin possess a series of stiff, sharp spines followed by longer, rounded soft ray. The pelvic fins have one spine each. The coloration of the dorsal area ranges from dark green to black, mottling into a lighter background color on the sides. The greenish coloration in the fins is believed caused by this fish's diet, primarily blue mussels. The belly is slightly lighter than the sides, but the chin is white, leading to the name "white chin." The tautog is distinguished from the cunner, *T. adspersus,* which occurs in much the same areas, by its steep, rounded dorsal head, stouter body, scaled lower gill cover and the more posterior positioning of the pelvic fins.

TAUTOG

LANDINGS AND VALUES

Tautogs are distributed throughout hard, or rocky bottomed, habitats in nearshore waters along the Western Atlantic from Nova Scotia, to South Carolina. The most abundant population is believed to be located from Cape Cod to Delaware. Southern populations live farther offshore than more northern

Tautog US Landings by Year — Nominal Data Value in $US (000); Quantity in tonnes; (NMFS)					
	2004	2005	2006	2007	2008
Value	558	529	716	745	782
Quantity	134	121	158	153	141

populations, but most stay above 60m in depth. They migrate inshore during the spring and out to open water in the winter months. Tautogs prefer to hide under wrecks and pilings, or near jetties and steep rock outcroppings. In 2008, US commercial landings totaled 141 tonnes, valued at $782,000 (see table). In addition, about 1,600 tonnes were landed in the US recreational fishery in 2008 (not shown). Tautog is not presently a Canadian fishery; however, a very small amount of cunner (less than ½ tonne) is landed yearly (not shown).

COMMERCIAL USES

The tautog is gaining popularity as a food and game fish. The flavor has been linked to that of the red snapper. Traditionally, it has been used in chowders; but its firm, mildly-flavored flesh also lends itself well to baking and broiling, and can substitute for recipes developed for species such as striped bass. It is also has a demand in the aquarium trade.

LIFE CYCLE

Both sexes mature at 3 or 4 years of age. Female fecundity (number of eggs produced in a spawning season) is directly related to their size and weight. A one-pound female can produce about 30,000 eggs, while a five-pound female can produce about 200,000 eggs, per season. The fertilized eggs are buoyant and float for about 2 days before hatching. Within 4 days after hatching, the larvae will feed on microscopic plankton.

Spawning in Canadian waters was noted to occur in June-July, but appears to be more protracted in coastal waters near Virginia, where spawning is found from April to July. In Massachusetts, tautogs spawn from May until August, with peak activity occurring in June at water temperatures of 62 to 70 degrees F. Spawning usually takes place inshore in areas dominated by eelgrass beds. Although tautogs tend to aggregate in large groups most of the year, they seem to form small, discrete groups during spawning season. After reaching sexual maturity, many fish return to the same spawning area each year. They are a slow growing fish; males grow faster and live longer than females.

Tautogs feed during the day and rest in crevices at night. Prey includes gastropods, crustaceans, and molluscs.

TILEFISH OR GOLDEN TILEFISH

Blue Tilefish, *Lopholatilus chamaeleonticeps*

GENERAL

In 1882, an estimated 1 billion tilefish were observed dead or dying on the outer coast of New England. The species all but disappeared for 10 years. It is believed this decimation was caused by a sudden temperature change in the Gulf Stream current moving offshore. Tilefish are also noted for home building—constructing and occupying burrows in the bottom sediment.

The **blue tilefish**, often called the "golden tilefish" or just "tilefish," is a member of the Malacanthidae family and is related to the goldface tilefish (*Caulolatilus chrysops*), the blueline tilefish (*C. microps*), the ocean whitefish *(C. princeps)* and the sand tilefish *(Malacanthus plumieri)*.

Also Known As
Tilefish/
Golden Tilefish/
Blanquillo

FishBase Name
Great Northern
Tilefish

International Recognitions
France—tile
Japan— amadai

PHYSICAL DESCRIPTION

Max length: 125 cm TL male/unsexed; (Ref. 3276); 95 cm FL (female);
Common length : 90.0 cm TL male/unsexed; (Ref. 3276);
Max. published weight: 30.0 kg (Ref. 9988); Max. reported age: 35 years (Ref. 6086)

The tilefish has a moderately large mouth and a slightly projecting lower jaw with small barbel-like projections on each side. Canine teeth, accompanied by bands of smaller teeth, are found in both jaws. The eyes are located high on the head. The body is compressed with a long dorsal fin, a moderately truncated tail with pointed lobes, an anal fin, moderately large pelvic fins and pointed pectorals.

The blue tilefish is readily distinguished from other tilefish by the yellowish fleshy triangular tab on the top of its head, which is equal in height to that of its dorsal fin. Related to tropical fishes, the body color ranges from a brilliant bluish to olive green on its back and upper parts of its side, fading to a yellow or rose on its lower sides and belly. There are numerous yellow spots on its upper body and larger yellow spots on its dorsal and anal fins.

LANDINGS AND VALUES

The blue (or golden) tilefish is distributed throughout the north-western Atlantic Ocean and ranges from Nova Scotia to southern Florida. It is also found in the eastern Gulf of Mexico and as far as South America. It prefers depths of 270 to 900 feet and is found along the bottom of the ocean floor, particularly where there is clay, sand, or mud

All Tilefishes US Landings by Year – Nominal Data Value in $US (000); Quantity in tonnes; (NMFS)					
	2004	2005	2006	2007	2008
Value	4,809	5,222	6,457	6,068	6,483
Quantity	1,645	1,160	1,352	1,134	1,324

substrates. It usually inhabits a narrow zone along the continental slope and upper reaches of canyons where the water temperature ranges from 47 to 54°F. The tilefish supports a small, commercial longline fishery off the coast of New York and southern New England and also has significant landings around Florida. The US fishery had peak years from 1979 to 1981 of more than 4,000 tonnes, but this catch level has declined in more recent years. US catches (all tilefishes) in 2008 totaled 1,324 tonnes, valued at approximately $6.5 million (see table). The golden tilefish usually accounts for about 75%–90% of the catch (see table), followed by the blueline tilefish at about 10%–20% along with incidental amounts of goldface and sand tilefishes (not shown). Tilefish is also a small recreational fishery in the New York-New Jersey area where anglers often use weighted lines and electric reels. Canada reported commercial landings of 3 tonnes in 2008, valued at $8,000 (not shown).

COMMERCIAL USES

Tilefish, in general, have flaky, pinkish white flesh and a taste similar to lobster or crab. The meat remains moist after cooking; therefore, it is ideal for baking or broiling. Once cooked, the meat is tender and succulent. The golden tilefish is the best known, and commercially, the most valuable of all tilefishes. It is considered very flavorful when

Golden Tilefish US Landings by Year – Nominal Data Value in $US (000); Quantity in tonnes; (NMFS)					
	2004	2005	2006	2007	2008
Value	4,359	4,952	6,051	5,813	5,604
Quantity	1,435	1,058	1,193	1,032	1,037

baked, boiled, fried or served in chowder. Like king mackerel, swordfish and shark, tilefish is prone to mercury and PCB contamination and the FDA has issued an advisory on it. However, as a bottom fish, significant mercury contamination in tilefish may be localized to certain populations, particularly in the Gulf of Mexico.

LIFE CYCLE

Tilefish are highly fecund. It is believed that females may spawn several times from March to September. A tilefish weighing 20 pounds has been found to lay up to 9 million eggs, while one weighing 35 pounds might produce as many as 16 million. The incubation period is believed to be dependent on the water temperature. The larvae are assumed to remain near the surface until they develop into bottom-dwelling juveniles.

The tilefish grows rapidly during the first 4 to 5 years of its life, adding about 4 inches to its length each year. However, it is considered a slow-growing, long-lived species. It dines primarily on crustaceans and a variety of other marine organisms, including squid, marine worms, sea cucumbers, sea urchins and fishes. Size can vary considerably both between sexes and geographically. Female tilefish that do not fall prey to dogfish, conger eels, or other tilefish reach sexual maturity at 5 to 7 years of age.

TOADFISH

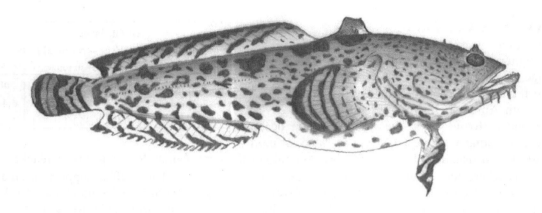

GENERAL

The Gulf toadfish belongs to subfamily Batrachoididae of the family Batrachoididae (toadfishes). There are 16 genera in the subfamily and about 52 species (*ITIS*). *The Seafood List* identifies 3 species marketed under name toadfish, the **Gulf toadfish**, the oyster toadfish (*O. tau*) and the Pacuma toadfish (*Batrachoides surinamensis*).

The Gulf toadfish is a solitary species and prefers to bury itself on the sand or hide among vegetation to ambush its prey. It is capable of surviving a range of conditions including changes in salinity, ammonia, and hypoxia and can survive out of water for small periods of time. It is able to make a toad-like sound by compressing its swim bladder, often followed by a short, high-pitched, whistle. Although it is not venomous it is often mistaken as such.

PHYSICAL DESCRIPTION

Max length : 30.0 cm TL male/unsexed; (Ref. 7251)

The gulf toadfish lacks scales and has a large head on a broad, flattened body with the lower jaw projecting further than the upper. There are tabs along the lower jaw with a posterior barbel and dark brown bars on the pectoral and caudal fins. It has a wide mouth with very sharp teeth. Three lateral lines run along the length of the fish with small pelvic fins and elongated anal and dorsal fins. The pectoral fins are large and fan-shaped. Coloration is brown to grey, variously mottled with some white. Dorsal and anal fins have brown diagonal banding. Males are larger than females.

Also Known As
Dogfish/
Mudfish/
Oysterdog

FishBase Name
Gulf toadfish

International Recognitions
Finland—
lahtikonnakala
Denmark—
Mexikansk
paddefisk
Spain—sapo de
boca blanca

LANDINGS AND VALUES

The Gulf toadfish is distributed through Florida, the Gulf of Mexico and the Bahamas, among rocky bay and tidal lagoons. It is a solitary species found at depths of about 250 meters (800 ft.). In the US, 16 tonnes were commercially landed in 2008, valued at $178,000 (see table). It is usually caught as bycatch in shrimp trawlers. In addition, another 27 tonnes were landed recreationally. It is not a fishery in Canada.

Toadfishes US Landings by Year — Nominal Data Value in $US (000); Quantity in tonnes; (NMFS)					
	2004	2005	2006	2007	2008
Value	3	2	3	9	178
Quantity	1	1	1	1	16

Endangered Status: It appears to be abundant in its habitats; however, due to the lack of directed fisheries, there are no regulations regarding the fishery of this species.

COMMERCIAL USES

Toadfish are not a targeted commercial species because of the poor quality of the meat. However, they are sometimes marketed fresh or live. Cases of ciguatera poisoning have been reported. They are sometimes used in scientific studies.

LIFE CYCLE

Gulf toadfish are found in subtropical waters. Spawning occurs between February and March when territorial males establish nests in protected areas using materials such as shells or sponges. Males attract females with long calls and after spawning, males guard and aerate the nest until the eggs hatch.

Prey includes smaller fish, molluscs, annelids and crustaceans. They are preyed on by larger fish like the barracuda as well as dolphins and sea turtles.

TRIGGERFISH

Gray Triggerfish, *Balistes capriscus*

GENERAL

The triggerfish is named for the tall dorsal spine that can be triggered as a predator defense and also used to wedge itself in rocky places for protection. The species is found in the family Balistidae (triggerfishes and filefishes). There are 12 genera in the family and about 42 species. *The Seafood List* recognizes 6 species marketed under the name of triggerfish, including the gray triggerfish and the queen triggerfish, *B. vetula*, which both range in similar waters.

PHYSICAL DESCRIPTION

Max length: 60.0 cm TL male/unsexed; (Ref. 7348);
Common length: 44.0 cm TL male/unsexed; (Ref. 47377);
Max. published weight: 6,150 g (Ref. 40637)

Triggerfish are tall, laterally-compressed fish with a small mouth, large incisor teeth, tough plate-like anterior scales and their trademark spiny dorsal fin. The second separate, soft-rayed dorsal fin is located directly opposite an almost identical anal fin. Adult gray triggerfish generally have three broad dark, but faint, bars on their body; as well as a pale, narrow band on the chin. Small blue spots are often found on the flanks and dorsal fins with irregular, short, ventral lines. General coloration is greyish to light brown that appears dull in open water and fades as they age. They do have a limited ability to change color to blend with surroundings. They are easily distinguished from the queen triggerfish by their comparably simple coloration.

Also Known As
Spotted Triggerfish/
Leatherjacket/
Turbot/ Cucuyo

FishBase Name
GrayTriggerfish

International Recognitions
France—baliste cabri
Spain—ballesta; cachua; escopeta
Portugal—cangulo; maracuguara
Italian—mola
Japanese—mongarakawahagi

LANDINGS AND VALUES

Gray triggerfish are found on both sides of the Atlantic Ocean. In the western Atlantic, triggerfish are found sub tropically from Nova Scotia, Canada, through Bermuda and the Gulf of Mexico to Argentina. They are found at depths from the surface to 100 meters, generally preferring depths to about 50

Gray Triggerfish US Landings by Year — Nominal Data Value in $US (000); Quantity in tonnes; (NMFS)					
	2004	**2005**	**2006**	**2007**	**2008**
Value	88	47	30	35	25
Quantity	40	21	15	18	12

meters. They are reef associated and also found in harbors, bays, lagoons and drifting with sargassum (brown algae) mats. They are usually solitary, but are sometimes found in small groups. In the US, approximately 12 tonnes of triggerfishes were landed in 2008, valued at $25,000. All of this was the gray triggerfish, but a very small amount of queen triggerfish is occasionally landed. In addition, almost 400 tonnes of triggerfishes and filefishes were landed recreationally in the US in 2008. It is not a reported fishery in Canada.

Endangered Status: Not evaluated (IUCN), but not believed to be vulnerable or threatened.

COMMERCIAL USES

Marketed fresh, smoked and dried/salted and considered a very high quality meat. It is also a popular recreational fishery. Additionally it is a popular aquarium species. Human concerns include reports of ciguatera poisoning.

LIFE CYCLE

Gray triggerfish build nests on the bottom substrate in summer. Spawning occurs when water temperature exceeds 21°C (70°F) when fish are mature (usually by 3 years of age). Reproduction is oviparous. Eggs are demersal and are guarded in nests, but hatch within a few days. Juveniles move to the surface and are often associated with sargassum mats. When juveniles have grown to 12-17cm they will descend to bottom reef habitats, usually in the autumn. Triggerfish are resistant to capture, repopulate quickly (females can lay 50,000 to 100,000 eggs) and compete with other species for resources.

They prey on invertebrates, molluscs and crustaceans. They use their strong teeth to crush the shells of mussels, urchins and barnacles. Juveniles may also feed on plankton. As juveniles, their major predators include large pelagic fishes such as tuna, marlin, sailfish and sharks. As adults, amberjack, grouper and sharks are major predators. Wrasses and red snappers can prey on unguarded eggs.

TRIPLETAIL

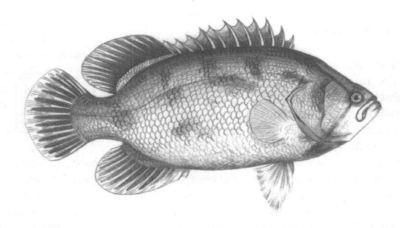

Tripletail, *Lobotes surinamensis*

GENERAL

The species **tripletail** is found in the family Lobotidae (tripletails). There is only one genus in the family and 2 species, including the (Atlantic) tripletail and the West Coast tripletail, *L. pacificus*; both species are listed in *The Seafood List* (*TSL*). In addition, there are 3 other species that are recognized under the market name tripletail (and also "tigerfish") in *TSL*. These 3 species are from a different family, Datnioididae, found in the western Pacific. These species look much like the tripletail with the distinctive tri-lobed fin structure, and evidently suit being presented under the same market name.

The species tripletail is characterized as being somewhat "lazy" (or perhaps uniquely cunning?) in that it is often observed floating on its side near the surface, hidden among other floating debris or algae.

PHYSICAL DESCRIPTION

Max length: 110 cm TL male/unsexed; (Ref. 7251);
Common length: 80.0 cm TL male/unsexed; (Ref. 5450);
Max. published weight: 19.2 kg (Ref. 40637)

Tripletails are a deep-bodied, laterally-compressed fish with a concave head and a large, oblique mouth set atop a slightly extended lower jaw. Their most distinguishing characteristic is the large soft rays of the dorsal and anal fins that are set back toward the caudal fin giving it an appearance of three tails; this is especially noticeable when the dorsal spine is retracted as may happen when the fish is out of water. Coloration can vary from dark brown through to reddish-bronze to greenish-yellow on top and sides; head and body variously mottled dark brown to black; pectoral fins translucent yellow, other fins darker than body. The caudal fin has a distinct yellow margin on the edge and there is dark brown stripe running from the eye to beginning of dorsal fin.

Also Known As
Falsher/
Chobie/
Lumpfish/
Strawberry Bass/
Black Perch

FishBase Name
Tripletail

International Recognitions
Spain—Dormilona
France—Croupia roche
Italy—Pesce foglia
Japan—Matsudai

LANDINGS AND VALUES

Tripletail US Landings by Year — Nominal Data Value in $US (000); Quantity in tonnes; (NMFS)					
	2004	2005	2006	2007	2008
Value	12	15	14	23	12
Quantity	4	3	4	5	2

The species tripletail is found tropically and sub tropically in all the world's oceans, but not in the eastern Pacific. Ironically, its counterpart species, the West Coast tripletail, only inhabits the Eastern Pacific (tropically). In the western Atlantic, the tripletail inhabits the brackish water of bays, muddy estuaries, and mouths of rivers from Canada along the US coast to Florida (including Bermuda), the Gulf of Mexico, and the Caribbean and south to Argentina. It is a semi-migratory pelagic fish that can often be found around pilings, wharfs, buoys and boats. In 2008, 2 tonnes of tripletail valued at $12,000, was landed in the US. Most of the catches in 2008 were caught on the Florida East Coast. The gear used was mostly hand lines and various nets. It is not a reported fishery in Canada.

Endangered Status: Not Evaluated (IUCN)

COMMERCIAL USES

Excellent tasting food fish and a hard fighting sport fish.

LIFE CYCLE

Little is reported on the reproductive activity of this fish. The tripletail spawns in the summer months. The larvae experience four stages of development and juveniles drift along with the current into shallow waters. The tripletail grows fast in its first year, which may offset high predation.

It feeds on a variety of prey including small finfish such as menhaden and anchovies, as well as benthic crustaceans including crabs and shrimp. Predators are mainly sharks and larger fishes.

TUNA

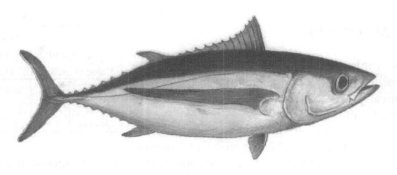

Albacore, *Thunnus alalunga*

GENERAL

The **albacore** is a tuna in the family Scombridae (tunas, mackerels and bonitos). Albacore taxonomy is uniquely described in terms of family, subfamily, tribe, genus and subgenus (*ITIS*). Tunas, mackerels, bonitos and wahoos are all in the same subfamily (Scombrinae) and the tuna tribe (Thunnini) has 5 genera. [Mackerels are found in the Scombrini tribe.] The albacore is in the genus *Thunnis*, subgenus *Thunnus* (*Thunnus*); along with the bigeye (*T. obesus*) and bluefin tunas (3 species–see bluefin tuna entry). The other subgenus *Thunnus* (*Neothunnus*) includes the blackfin tuna (*T. atlanticus*), the longtail tuna (*T. tonggol*) and yellowfin tuna (*Thunnus albacares*). Skipjack, spotted tunny, frigate and other tunas are found in other genera not described at the subgenus level.

PHYSICAL DESCRIPTION

Max length: 140 cm FL male/unsexed; (Ref. 3669);
Common length: 100.0 cm FL male/unsexed; (Ref. 9684);
Max. published weight: 60.3 kg (Ref. 40637); Max. reported age: 9 years (Ref. 72462)

Albacore are identified by their concave dorsal fin and very long pectoral fins (sometimes half the length of their body) and small scales. Coloration is metallic, dark blue on the dorsal side with silvery white counter-shading on sides and belly. Bodies are streamlined and torpedo shaped. They can swim at speeds over 50 miles per hour and can regulate both body temperature and metabolic rate. Albacore can be confused with juvenile bigeye tuna because of their long pectoral fins, but are distinguished by the lack of rounded tips in albacore.

Also Known As
Germon/
Longfinned
Tuna/ Albecor/
T. Germo

FishBase Name
Albacore

International Recognitions
Spain—Atún blanco
France—Germon
Italy—Alalunga
Germany—Thun
Japan—Binnaga

Common Tunas	Scientific Name	Range	US Landings (inc Hawaii)		Canadian Landings	
			1989 MT	2008 MT	1989 MT	2008 MT
Albacore	*Thunnus alalunga*	Worldwide	1,850	11,525	396	127
Bigeye	*Thunnus obesus*	Worldwide	1,553	6,430	57	134
Yellowfin	*Thunnus albacares*	Worldwide	20,649	2,667	11	170
Bluefin	*Thunnus thynnus*	Worldwide	1,019	302	603	579
Skipjack	*Katsuwonus pelamis*	Worldwide	6,024	416	N/A	N/A
Spotted Tunny	*Euthynnus alletteratus*	Atlantic	101	249	N/A	N/A
Total (includes all tunas, some not shown)			**31,179**	**21,730**	**1,067**	**1,009**

LANDINGS AND VALUES

Albacore tuna is an oceanic species preferring pelagic waters ranging in depth from the surface to 600m. They are distributed circumglobally including Mediterranean waters. They are known to concentrate at thermal boundaries and will often form mixed schools with skipjack, yellowfin or bluefin tuna. They also congregate under floating objects like sargassum mats. In 2008, 11,525 tonnes of Albacore valued at $30.3 million, was landed in the US (see table). Most of the catch (58%) in 2008 was landed in Washington State. The rest was mostly caught in Oregon (35%), Hawaii (3%) and California (3%). The gear used was mostly troll lines. The Canadian catch is much lower (see table) and reflects mostly BC landings. However, small landings of albacore are made on the Atlantic coast in both the US and Canada.

Albacore US Landings by Year — Nominal Data Value in $US (000); Quantity in tonnes; (NMFS)					
	2004	2005	2006	2007	2008
Value	28,846	22,186	25,148	22,912	30,282
Quantity	15,012	9,447	13,173	11,991	11,525

Albacore Canadian Landings by Year — Nominal Data Value in $Cdn (000); Quantity in tonnes; (DFO)					
	2004	2005	2006	2007	2008
Value	2,660	4,003	3,329	3,621	668
Quantity	765	1,096	1,148	1,334	127

Endangered Status: Stocks are managed through various international treaties for highly migratory species. **Pacific stocks**: neither northern nor southern stocks are thought to be presently endangered. The US Pacific fishery is Marine Stewardship Council (MSC) certified as sustainable and well managed. This fishery is by pole-line and troll and is the only certified sustainable tuna fishery in the world. **Atlantic stocks**: estimated below the biomass necessary to support maximum sustainable yield. **Aquaculture:** None in US or Canada.

COMMERCIAL USES

Albacore is prized and the fishery is economically significant. It is the only tuna species that may be marketed as "white meat tuna" in the US. Additionally, albacore is a sport fishery. Although most is canned as "white meat tuna" increasing amounts are being shipped frozen. They are also marketed fresh or smoked and eaten raw or cooked (steamed, broiled, fried or microwaved). Products of the MSC fishery are identifiable by the MSC blue and white fish "eco-label." Like many other top predators, albacore accumulates methyl mercury in its tissue over time. The average canned albacore "white" or "solid" tuna has 0.35 ppm of methyl mercury. This contaminant is linked with many ill health affects and is of particular concern for pregnant or nursing mothers and young children. A FDA mercury advisory for this group is to restrict weekly intake of albacore to 6 oz. (US). Similar Health Canada guidelines are inexplicable in the space allowed.

LIFE CYCLE

Spawning occurs from March to July and possibly multiple times per season in subtropical waters. Females can release up to 2.6 million eggs per spawning. Egg and larvae are pelagic. Eggs develop rapidly and hatch within 1 to 2 days. Juveniles grow quickly, over 1 inch per month, although growth slows with age. Sexual maturity is reached at 90cm. Life span is generally 11-12 years. Albacore prey primarily on smaller fishes and schooling stocks like anchovy, sardine, crustaceans and squids. They are voracious predators and can consume up to 25% of their body weight every day. Their predators include other large tuna, billfishes, sharks and humans.

TUNA

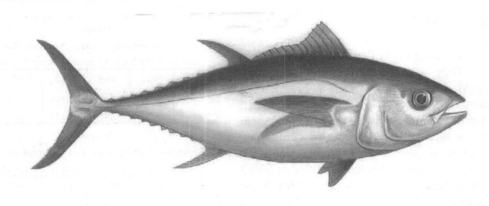

Bigeye Tuna, *Thunnus obesus*

GENERAL
Bigeye tuna, another member of the Scombridae family, is also known by its Hawaiian name "Ahi," in the central and western Pacific where most is landed. The same name is used for the yellowfin tuna (*T. albacares*), which is physically similar. The bigeye, yellowfin and skipjack (*Katsuwonus pelamis*) are world travellers and also caught in the Atlantic. All Pacific highly migratory tunas are managed by Inter-American Tropical Tuna Commission (IATTC), the Western and Central Pacific Fisheries Commission (WCPFC) and other international treaties. The relevant Atlantic organization is the International Commission for the Conservation of Atlantic Tunas (ICCAT).

PHYSICAL DESCRIPTION
Max length: 250 cm TL male/unsexed; (Ref. 27000); Common length: 180cm FL male/unsexed; (Ref. 168); Max. published weight: 210.0 kg (Ref. 9987); Max. reported age: 11 years (Ref. 30326)

Also Known As
Big Eye/
Ahi-b

FishBase Name
Bigeye tuna

International Recognition
Spain—Patudo
France—Thon
obèse
Italy—Tonno
obeso
Germany—
Großaugenthun
Japan—Mebachi

The bigeye tuna has a dark, metallic blue coloration on the back and sides with white lower sides and underbelly. Its first dorsal fin has a deep yellow coloration fading to a paler yellow coloring on the second dorsal and anal fins. Finlets are bright yellow edged in black. The yellowfin has the same coloration, but smaller eyes. Also see bluefin and albacore entries for additional descriptive data. The little tunny is similar to bonito (see bonito entry in this book).

LANDINGS AND VALUES
Bigeye is a subtropical oceanic pelagic fish, found in the Atlantic, Pacific and Indian Oceans, and preferring water temperatures between 17° and 22°C. In 2008, 6,430 tonnes of bigeye, valued at $52.6 million, was landed in the US (see table). Most of the catch (94%) in 2008 was in Hawaii, with the remained from Florida, North Carolina and New Jersey. Canadian catches of bigeye and yellowfin tuna were 134 tonnes and 170 tonnes, respectively in 2008 (see table). In the Pacific, smaller bigeyes are landed as a bycatch in the purse seine fishery, but adults are targeted with more deeply set longlines and handlines. Purse seines are used in directed fishing for skipjack and yellowfin, sometimes with fish aggregating devices (FADs).

Aquaculture: There is no current commercial aquaculture in the US or Canada for bigeye or other tunas.

Endangered Status: *Pacific bigeye, skipjack and yellowfin tunas* –stocks not overfished, but there is overfishing occurring in Pacific bigeye; *Atlantic Bigeye and Yellowfin Tunas* – not overfished, but concern with possible overfishing of Atlantic bigeye; rated as vulnerable (bigeye), least concern (yellowfin), not evaluated (skipjack and spotted tunny) by IUCN

COMMERCIAL USES

Most bigeye, yellowfin and skipjack is canned ("light meat tuna") for worldwide markets. Some is frozen for export and they are also sold fresh. Bigeye is highly prized in Japan where it is processed into sashimi. Tunas, like many other large fishes, carry a mercury poisoning advisory, especially for pregnant women and young children.

LIFE CYCLE

Bigeyes reach maturity between three and four years of age. Juveniles and small adults may school near the surface or under drifting debris making them particularly susceptible to purse seine fishing techniques. They may form mixed schools with other tuna such as yellowfin and skipjack. Adults stay in deeper water and can dive to 150 meters (500ft.). Mature adults are multiple spawners and can spawn every 1 or 2 days over several months. Their spawning is generally associated with the full moon. Females can have from 2.9 to greater than 6 million ova. Spawning occurs at or near the surface in tropical waters worldwide. Eggs and larvae are pelagic. They feed on a variety of fishes, cephalopods and crustaceans. They are preyed upon by large billfishes and toothed whales. Yellowfin and skipjack have similar reproductive cycles.

US landings of yellowfin were almost 2,700 tonnes in 2008, valued at almost $17 million (see table). US landings of skipjack and spotted tunny were 426 tonnes and 249 tonnes in 2008, respectively (see table). Only small landings of yellowfin and no landings for spotted tunny were reported in Atlantic Canada in recent years. There is a large US recreational fishery for yellowfin and skipjack (6,700 tonnes and 2,200 tonnes, respectively.)

Bigeye Tuna
US Landings by Year – Nominal Data
Value in $US (000); Quantity in tonnes; (NMFS)

	2004	2005	2006	2007	2008
Value	30,579	37,931	37,636	44,745	52,642
Quantity	4,702	5,214	5,077	6,180	6,430

Bigeye Tuna
Canadian Landings by Year – Nominal Data
Value in $Cdn (000); Quantity in tonnes; (DFO)

	2004	2005	2006	2007	2008
Value	1,025	1,334	2,251	1,648	1,536
Quantity	143	193	196	144	134

Yellowfin Tuna
US Landings by Year – Nominal Data
Value in $US (000); Quantity in tonnes; (NMFS)

	2004	2005	2006	2007	2008
Value	21,749	18,309	19,116	20,958	16,947
Quantity	4,263	3,417	3,372	3,735	2,667

Yellowfin Tuna
Canadian Landings by Year – Nominal Data
Value in $Cdn (000); Quantity in tonnes; (DFO)

	2004	2005	2006	2007	2008
Value	2,143	1,691	2,068	1,948	1,200
Quantity	303	240	293	276	170

Skipjack Tuna
US Landings by Year – Nominal Data
Value in $US (000); Quantity in tonnes; (NMFS)

	2004	2005	2006	2007	2008
Value	1,269	1,431	1,238	805	1,194
Quantity	712	962	443	336	416

Spotted Tunny
US Landings by Year – Nominal Data
Value in $US (000); Quantity in tonnes; (NMFS)

	2004	2005	2006	2007	2008
Value	124	118	202	230	196
Quantity	218	202	288	336	249

TUNA

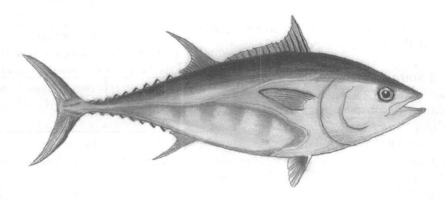

Bluefin Tuna, *Thunnus thynnus*

GENERAL

The **bluefin tuna** is the largest member of the mackerel family
Scombridae (mackerel, tunas and bonitos) and arguably the largest bony
fish in the sea. The bluefin is truly a giant species — one record bluefin
caught off Nova Scotia in 1979 weighed almost 1,500 lb. The bluefin is
also capable of great speed — bursts of 43 miles per hour. This
combination of size and speed made the bluefin a prized game fish, but it
is now mainly prized for its high value. The Pacific bluefin (*T.
orientalis*) [in *ITIS*, but not on *The Seafood List*] and the southern bluefin
(*T. maccoyii*) are 2 other (subgenus) species named "bluefin tuna." All
bluefin species are closely related to the albacore and bigeye and in the
same genus (different subgenus) as the blackfin tuna (*T. atlanticus*), the
longtail tuna (*T. tonggol*) and yellowfin tuna (*Thunnus albacares*).
[Skipjack, spotted tunny, frigate and other tunas are found in the same
subfamily, but other genera.]

Also Known As
Albacore/ Giant
Bluefin/ Northern
Bluefin Tuna/ Tunny/
Oriental Tuna

FishBase Name
Atlantic Bluefin Tuna

**International
Recognitions**
Spain—Atún rojo del
Atlántico
France—Thon rouge
de l'Atlantique
Italy—Tonne
Germany—Blauflossen
Thun
Japan—Kuromaguro

PHYSICAL DESCRIPTION

Max length: 458 cm TL male/unsexed; (Ref. 26340); Common length:
200 cm FL male/unsexed; (Ref. 168); Max. published weight: 684.0 kg (Ref. 26340); Max.
reported age: 15 years (Ref. 4645)

The distinct tail and finlets are the trademarks of the tuna and mackerel families. The bluefin
tuna has a dark, metallic blue dorsal fin, shading to silvery white on the sides and an almost
white underside. The bluefin's streamlined body is nearly round in the middle, tapering toward
each end. Both its second dorsal fin and anal fin are followed by a row of 8 to 10 yellow, black-
edged "finlets" leading to the base of the large and widely forked tail. The following distinguish
other tunas from the bluefin: 1) the skipjack has a short pectoral fin and three to five black
stripes on its sides; 2) the yellow fin has yellow on all fins, except for the second dorsal fin, and
a gold stripe on the side; 3) the bigeye has large eyes, yellow finlets and a pectoral fin reaching
below the second dorsal fin; 4) the albacore has a very long pectoral fin and no yellow on the
main fins.

LANDINGS AND VALUES

Most tunas, including the "bluefins," are found worldwide. However, the species bluefin (2 stocks) does not range outside of the North Atlantic, while the Pacific bluefin ranges in the North Pacific and southern bluefin ranges worldwide in the southern hemisphere. In North America bluefins are mostly caught from the Caribbean to Newfoundland on the Atlantic side, and a small amount in California (Pacific bluefin) on the Pacific side. Commercially, tunas are caught using pole and line, longlines and purse seines with incidental catches in

All Tunas US Landings by Year — Nominal Data Value in \$US (000); Quantity in tonnes; (NMFS)					
	2004	2005	2006	2007	2008
Value	89,952	86,358	86,760	93,929	107,023
Quantity	25,548	20,072	22,645	22,990	21,730

All Tunas Canadian Landings by Year — Nominal Data Value in \$Cdn (000); Quantity in tonnes; (DFO)					
	2004	2005	2006	2007	2008
Value	14,990	16,477	18,171	14,126	16,315
Quantity	1,752	2,134	2,369	2,249	1,009

gillnets and traps. More recently, bluefins have been landed using buoy-tended lines with a single hook and the line attached to the vessel (keg fishing). (Atlantic) bluefin have also been "ranched" by catching and holding them in "pounds" until they attain a larger market size. US landings of all tunas were 21,730 tonnes in 2008, valued at \$107 million (see table). About 50% to 60% of the US catch of tuna in recent years has been albacore (see entry). Bluefin have been averaging US landings of 200 to 500 tonnes in recent years. Canadian landings of all tuna in 2008 were 1,009 tonnes, valued at \$16.3 million (see table). Bluefin is the largest catch on the Canadian East Coast with 2008 landings of 579 tonnes, valued at \$12.9 million (see table). **Endangered Status:** Species of Concern (US). **Aquaculture:** On-going worldwide efforts and ranching.

COMMERCIAL USES

Bluefin tuna is seldom canned. It is usually sold directly to Japan (90% of market) where one tuna was reported selling for a record \$180,000. Bluefin is highly prized for its red meat and high oil content. It is thinly sliced and consumed raw in sushi and sashimi dishes. Tunas, like many other large fishes, carry a mercury poisoning advisory, especially for pregnant women and young children.

Bluefin Tuna US Landings by Year — Nominal Data Value in \$US (000); Quantity in tonnes; (NMFS)					
	2004	2005	2006	2007	2008
Value	7,033	5,962	3,114	3,576	4,801
Quantity	551	732	247	291	303

Bluefin Tuna Canadian Landings by Year — Nominal Data Value in \$Cdn (000); Quantity in tonnes; (DFO)					
	2004	2005	2006	2007	2008
Value	9,162	9,443	10,524	6,907	12,910
Quantity	540	603	731	495	579

LIFE CYCLE

The major spawning grounds in the western Atlantic are in the Gulf of Mexico. A female bluefin, depending on her size, can produce from 5 to 60 million eggs. When the young hatch, they are 1/10 of an inch long. Early growth is very rapid; within the first 3 months they can weigh as much as 1 pound and up to 9 pounds by the end of the first year. For the next 3 to 4 years, they will double in size annually. Growth continues at a fairly rapid rate until the bluefin reaches about 8 feet. Then the process begins to slow. Males are heavier than females of the same length while females tend to live longer. Often referred to as "warm-bodied," the bluefin is able to maintain a body temperature greater than the surrounding water, allowing it to roam widely in search of food such as herring, menhaden, hake, cod, bluefish, whiting, mackerel, squid and shrimp. Sharks, orcas and humans are the main predators of large tunas.

WAHOO

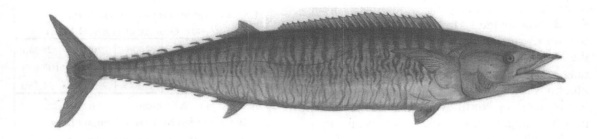

Wahoo, *Acanthocybium solandri*

GENERAL

Wahoo is a species in the Scombrinae tribe, subfamily Scombrinae of the family Scombridae (mackerels, tunas, and bonitos). It is closely related to the Spanish mackerels (*Scomberomorus* spp.) [*ITIS*]. Its common name is the same as its market name and it is the only species in *The Seafood List* that is marketed under wahoo.

It is a bullet-like fish with sharp teeth that can travel fast (up to 80 km per hour). [Also see tuna, mackerel and bonito entries in this book.]

PHYSICAL DESCRIPTION

Max length: 250 cm TL male/unsexed; (Ref. 30573);
Common length: 170 cm FL male/unsexed; (Ref. 9340);
Max. published weight: 83.0 kg (Ref. 168)

The wahoo has a long, sharply-angled snout with a mouth that resembles a beak and strong, finely serrated teeth. The dorsal is iridescent bluish-green fading to silvery on the sides that are covered in 24 to 30 dark blue vertical bars extending below the lateral line.

The wahoo may be distinguished from other mackerels by its sharp snout, bar configuration on its sides and by a fold of skin which covers the mandible when its mouth is closed.

Also Known As
Kinkfish/ Peto/
Guarapucu/ Ono/
Thazard Batard

FishBase Name
Wahoo

International Recognitions
Spain—Peto
France—Thazard-bâtard
Italy—Acantocibio
Japan—Kamasu-sawara

LANDINGS AND VALUES

The wahoo is found circumglobally in tropical and subtropical waters, including the Caribbean and Mediterranean seas. These are pelagic, oceanodromous and solitary fishes, occasionally forming small groups. In North America, they are fished in Hawaii and along the Atlantic and Gulf coasts.

Wahoo US Landings by Year — Nominal Data Value in $US (000); Quantity in tonnes; (NMFS)					
	2004	2005	2006	2007	2008
Value	2,488	2,483	2,555	2,345	2,445
Quantity	480	444	482	404	447

In 2008, 447 tonnes of wahoo, valued at $2.4 million, was landed in the US (see table). Most of the catch (85%) in 2008 was landed in Hawaii. The rest was mostly landed on the Florida West Coast and in Louisiana. They are generally caught incidentally in longline and trolling fisheries. In addition, more than 800 tonnes of wahoo was landed recreationally in 2008 in the US.

Endangered Status: Unknown.
Aquaculture Status: None known.

COMMERCIAL USES

It is an excellent eating fish with white, delicate, meat and marketed as fresh, frozen, spiced slices and salted. Cases of ciguatera poisoning have been reported.

LIFE CYCLE

Wahoos are fast growing and both sexes are capable of reproducing during the first year of life. Like all members of the tuna and mackerel family, they can spawn many times during the season and produce millions of eggs per year. Eggs and larvae are pelagic. They spawn year 'round in tropical waters, or in the summer months in subtropical waters, at temperatures greater than 68-75° F.

They prey on smaller fish and squid, which they are able to attack using their speed. They are prey for larger pelagic predators that can catch them.

WEAKFISH (& SEATROUT)

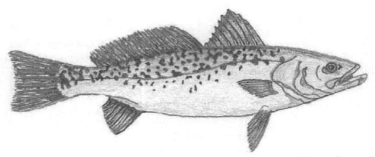

Weakfish, *Cynoscion regalis*

GENERAL

The species **weakfish** (same as the market name) is a member of the Sciaenidae family (drums or croakers) that are often capable of producing a drum-like or "croaking" sound by using special muscles on the wall of the swim bladder. There is a challenge in nomenclature here. *The Seafood List* recognises 5 species of weakfishes and 3 species of seatrouts, all in the same genus. The genus *Cynoscion* (weakfishes and seatrouts; 24 species [*ITIS*]) includes the **weakfish**, the striped weakfish (*C. striatus*) and the gray seatrout [*FishBase* name: acoupa weakfish] (*C. acoupa*); all marketed correctly as weakfish. The spotted seatrout [*FishBase* name: spotted weakfish] (*C. nebulosus*), the silver seatrout (*C. nothus*) and the sand seatrout [*FishBase* name: sand weakfish] (*C. arenarius*) are properly marketed as **seatrout**. The king weakfish (*Macrodon ancylodon*) is another species (different genus than the weakfish and seatrouts) that is also marketed (correctly) as weakfish.

Also Known As
Gray weakfish/
Seatrout/
Squeteague/
Gray Trout/
Saltwater Trout

FishBase Name
Squeteague

International Recognitions
Spain—Corvinata
real
France—Acoupa
royal

Two close relatives of the weakfish, the Atlantic croaker (*Micropogonias undulatus*) and the spot [*FishBase* name: spot croaker] (*Leiostomus xanthurus*), also represent valuable commercial, as well as recreational, species. Another croaker, the "corvina" or "gulf corvina" [*FishBase* name: Gulf weakfish] (*C. othonopterus*), is sometimes called seatrout, but should be marketed as croaker or corvina. The above "seatrouts," are not related to the freshwater, sea-running species of salmonids such as the brown trout (*Salmo trutta*) and brook trout (*Salvelinus fontinalis*), etc.

PHYSICAL DESCRIPTION

Max length: 98.0 cm TL male/unsexed; (Ref. 40637); Common length: 50.0 cm TL male/unsexed; (Ref. 3702); Max. published weight: 8,850 g (Ref. 40637)

The weakfish is greenish grey on its upper back and paler with metallic reflections on the sides. The pelvic and anal fins are yellowish and other fins pale or pale yellowish tinge. It has a projecting lower jaw and 2 canine-like teeth at the tip of the upper jaw. Both the weakfish and spotted seatrout have many black "spots" on the upper side, while the spotted seatrout also has spots on the second dorsal fin and caudal fin. The sand seatrout is not spotted. The Atlantic croaker resembles the seatrout except that it has diagonal narrow lines or rows of spots on its back and tiny barbels on the chin. The spot croaker, similar to the Atlantic croaker, has a distinct brownish spot on the shoulder.

LANDINGS AND VALUES

The weakfish can be found off the east coast of the United States, from Cape Cod to north Florida. It is a bottom-dwelling fish that primarily prefers to inhabit muddy bays, estuaries and shallow banks. The weakfish is usually caught from March to December, with the majority of the catch being harvested from March to May and September to November. It is often captured by seine and gill nets.

North American commercial catches of weakfish have traditionally dominated seatrouts with 1989 landings of 6,424 tonnes, valued at $7.3 million (not shown). This total has declined to 214 tonnes, valued at $570,000, in 2008 (see table). Commercial seatrout landings were 229 tonnes in 2008, valued at $756,000 (see table). The spotted seatrout is by far the most valuable species with an average ex-vessel price to fishermen almost double the price received for weakfish and sand seatrout. It also accounts for the major portion of seatrout landings, about 60% to 75% in recent years. Moreover, the drums and croaker family is one of the leading US recreation fisheries accounting for more than 25,000 tonnes landed in 2008, with the spotted seatrout and red drum each accounting for almost one-third of this total (not shown). Black drum, Atlantic croaker, spot and kingfishes make up most of the remainder in this group (not shown). [Also see drum, croaker and kingfish entries in this book.]

Endangered Status: Weakfishes are generally not evaluated or, if evaluated, are deemed "Least Concern." (IUCN).

Weakfish US Landings by Year — Nominal Data Value in $US (000); Quantity in tonnes; (NMFS)					
	2004	**2005**	**2006**	**2007**	**2008**
Value	1,259	1,078	1,090	984	570
Quantity	711	580	481	410	214

Seatrouts (Sand and Spotted) US Landings by Year — Nominal Data Value in $US (000); Quantity in tonnes; (NMFS)					
	2004	**2005**	**2006**	**2007**	**2008**
Value	435	457	676	871	756
Quantity	149	154	224	278	229

COMMERCIAL USES

The weakfish and seatrouts represent important game and food fishes throughout their range, popular with boat fishers, surfcasters and pier fishermen. Weakfish is marketed fresh and frozen and consumed pan-fried, broiled, steamed, microwaved and baked. Croaker also rates high as a white-fleshed ingredient in well-known, surimi-based brands in Japan, as these products require the strong, gel-forming capability that is offered.

LIFE CYCLE

Weakfish reproduction is oviparous, with high fecundity (Ref. 54406). Weakfish are adaptable to low salinity and are usually found in estuaries in summer where they feed and nurse. They feed on copepods, small crustaceans, small fishes (e.g., anchovies) and other weakfishes. They are prey to striped bass, bluefish, rays and other large fishes.

The gray seatrout (weakfish) spawns in early May and June, usually near the bottom in 18 to 30 feet of water. The eggs float to the surface and hatch in about 1 1/2 days. The fry grow rapidly and within 6 months are 4 to 6 inches long. The fish matures in 2 to 3 years at 10 to 13 inches in length. They are primarily a predaceous and bottom-feeding species living in shallow and brackish waters along the continental shelf. Prey includes molluscs and crustaceans.

WHITING, NORTH PACIFIC OR PACIFIC

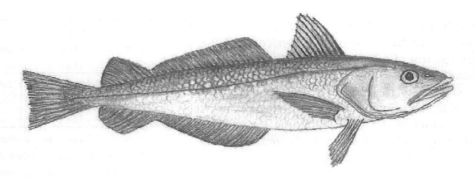

Pacific Whiting, *Merluccius productus*

GENERAL

Merluccius spp. were once classified as members of the cod family Gadidae, but are now classified as belonging to a separate family, Merlucciidae (Merluccid hakes). Whiting is a market name generally applied to Pacific hake, but it can also be correctly applied to other hakes such as (Atlantic) silver hake *(Merluccius bilinearis)*, New Zealand hake or "Hoki" (*Macruronus novaezelandiae*), and other hakes of the genus *Merluccius* that closely resemble each other. **Pacific whiting**, or North Pacific whiting, rather than Pacific hake, is now the correct US common name for *Merluccius productus.* Kingfish [*FishBase* name: kingcroaker] (*Menticirrhus* spp.) and Walleye pollock (*Theragra chalcogramma*) are sometimes (incorrectly) called whiting. *Micromesistius poutassou* is another, but different species, (cod family Gididae) correctly marketed as "blue whiting," presently landed in huge quantities in Northern Europe and Iceland.

Also Known As
California Hake

FishBase Name
North Pacific hake

International Recognitions
Spain—Merluza del Pacífico norte
France—Merlu du Pacifique nord
Italy—Nasello del pacifico
Germany—Pazifikhecht

PHYSICAL DESCRIPTION

Max length: 91.0 cm TL male/unsexed; (Ref. 1371); Common length: 60.0 cm TL male/unsexed; (Ref. 1371); Max. published weight: 1,190 g (Ref. 4883); max. reported age: 16 years (Ref. 56527)

Pacific whiting is similar to cod, except that it has a distinct "V-shaped" ridge on its head, two instead of three dorsal fins, and one dorsal and the anal fin deeply notched. Also, unlike the cod, it has no barbel. The body is elongated with a somewhat protruding lower jaw, dark mouth and sharp teeth, a somewhat slender head and a soft body. The color is silvery with a white bottom, shading to darker gray or brown on the back, which may have speckles. The Pacific whiting grows larger than its Atlantic cousin, the silver hake.

The Atlantic silver hake has a dusky blue mouth with black-edged upper fins and white-edged lower fins. The inside base and edge of the pectoral fins are blackish. Blue whiting has three dorsal fins like cod.

PACIFIC WHITING

LANDINGS AND VALUES

The Pacific whiting ranges from the coast of Asia to Alaska and down the Pacific coast to the Gulf of California. It is ocean-going, but mainly found over the continental shelf. Although a pelagic species, it is also often found at great depths, where it will bottom-feed. It can be caught with lines, but is most often harvested with otter trawls. Large runs can be caught, usually from late spring to early fall.

Until recent years, the soft, pasty flesh was not highly valued by North American consumers and much of the harvest went

Pacific Whiting US Landings by Year — Nominal Data Value in $US (000); Quantity in tonnes; (NMFS)					
	2004	**2005**	**2006**	**2007**	**2008**
Value	21,819	29,139	34,425	32,603	58,492
Quantity	215,214	258,220	253,142	206,175	240,986

Pacific Hake (Whiting) Canadian Landings by Year — Nominal Data Value in $Cdn (000); Quantity in tonnes; (DFO)					
	2004	**2005**	**2006**	**2007**	**2008**
Value	16,000	21,460	20,002	16,167	16,843
Quantity	65,978	88,494	82,482	66,668	69,452

overseas. However, with the decline of traditional species, its value has grown significantly and it is now a bright spot in the fishery. In 1989, the quantity of Pacific whiting landed in the US totaled 7,447 tonnes with a value of $1.1 million (not shown in table; also, this total may not include foreign sales). US landings increased to 240,986 tonnes in 2008, valued at more than $58 million (see table). Pacific whiting accounted for about 97 percent of the total US "hake" catch in 2008 with silver hake landings of 5,753 tonnes and red/white hake landings of 1,524 tonnes (not shown). Canadian landings of Pacific whiting in 2008 totaled 69,452 tonnes, valued at $16.8 million (see table). (Also see white hake entry in this book.) **Endangered Status:** Species of Concern – Georgia Basin (US).

COMMERCIAL USES

All whiting has somewhat delicate flesh. However, because the texture of the flesh is perceived as poorer quality, the Pacific whiting has not achieved the same price in the market as the Atlantic Coast whiting (silver hake). New production technologies and recently increased marketing efforts may change this.

Pacific whiting flesh is lean, white, coarser than cod, but less bland. The major markets in North America are for whole (sometimes smoked) fish and fillets. Whiting is also used for fish sticks and portions. About half or more is made into surimi for imitation shellfish products. Some export markets accept salted, dried whiting as a lower-priced cod substitute. Whiting roe is also a potential export product.

LIFE CYCLE

Whiting eggs float in the water column for a few days until they are hatched. They remain pelagic for three to five months before seeking the bottom. Growth is quite fast, but it takes up to three or four years for the fish to mature. Females grow faster than males and at maturity may be 4 to 6 inches longer than the males, which are about 10 to 12 inches at this time. They are voracious nocturnal predators, consuming many small fishes (including their own young), shrimp and squid. They are preyed on by sea lions, cetaceans, cod, pollock and dogfish.

WOLFFISH

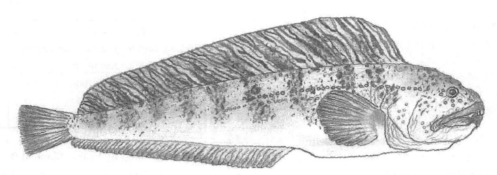

Atlantic Wolffish, *Anarhichas lupus*

GENERAL
Included in the Anarhichadidae family are the **Atlantic wolffish**, the northern wolffish (*A. denticulatus*) and the spotted wolffish (*A. minor*) on the east coast and the Bering wolffish (*Anarhichas orientalis*) and North Pacific wolf-eel (*Anarrhichthys ocellatus*) on the Pacific Coast - the latter is in *ITIS*, but not listed in *The Seafood List*. The Atlantic wolffish is by far the most abundant, in terms of landings, of the various Atlantic species, but all 3 are listed as Canadian "Species at Risk" (*SARA*) with the Atlantic wolffish subject to "Special Concern" and the other 2 listed as "Threatened." This is a local situation as these species are not on the World Conservation Union (IUCN) Red List.

Although these species were traditionally referred to as "ocean catfish," unlike the sea catfish and the freshwater catfish, members of the Anarhichadidae family do <u>not</u> have a barbel or an adipose fin. To fully differentiate ocean catfish from barbeled catfish, they are now marketed as "wolffish."

PHYSICAL DESCRIPTION
Max length : 150 cm TL male/unsexed; (Ref. 7251);
Max. published weight: 23.6 kg (Ref. 40637)

The Atlantic wolffish has an elongated, laterally compressed body with a blunt, heavy, somewhat rounded head and small eyes. Be careful—the mouth and throat of wolffish are literally filled with teeth. There are approximately six large, conical teeth at the front of its upper jaw, with a row of five or six canine-like teeth behind them and two rows of rounded molars in the lower jaw. Crushing teeth are located in the roof of its mouth and there are small scattered teeth in its throat. A long dorsal fin extends to the base of its caudal, which is small and slightly rounded. The anal fin is half the length of its dorsal fin and its pectorals are heavy and rounded. The wolffish may range in color from a dull olive-green to purplish-brown. There are usually 10 or more irregular, broken, vertical stripes down its sides, which may extend onto the dorsal fin, that distinguish this species from the spotted wolffish and northern wolffish.. The underside of the head and belly are a dirty white. The Pacific wolf-eel more closely resembles an eel than the other ocean wolffish species.

Also Known As
Catfish/ Striped Catfish/ Seacat/ Ocean Whitefish/ Rock Salmon/ Loup de Mer

FishBase Name
Atlantic wolffish

International Recognitions
France—loup atlantique
Germany—Gestreifter Seewolf
Spain—perro del Norte
Italy—lupo di mare

LANDINGS AND VALUES

The Atlantic wolffish is found on both sides of the North Atlantic Ocean. In North America, it can be found from southern Labrador and western Greenland to Cape Cod and as far south as New Jersey (although rarely). It generally inhabits water at depths of 50 to 500 feet along slopes where there is a hard (usually rocky) bottom. Other wolffish such as the northern wolffish and the spotted wolffish are now considered "threatened" through over-fishing and protected under the Canadian Species at Risk Act (SARA). The Atlantic wolffish is not presently considered threatened, but is under "special concern."

Atlantic Wolffish US Landings by Year — Nominal Data Value in $US (000); Quantity in tonnes; (NMFS)					
	2004	2005	2006	2007	2008
Value	135	132	120	100	83
Quantity	119	110	81	64	44

It appears that Atlantic wolffish stay closer to shore during the early spring and head for deeper water during the summer months. Directed fishing for wolffish in Canada is prohibited, but they are taken as a by-catch in the Atlantic trawl fishery for groundfish. Landings of wolffish species are often reported as sea/striped catfish. US landings in 1989 were 545 tonnes, valued at about $400,000 (not shown). Since then, catches and values for the US decreased to 44 tonnes in 2008, valued at $83,000 (see table). A small amount of wolf-eel is also landed each year in Oregon, usually less than 1 tonne (not shown). The 1989 Canadian catch was approximately 2,000 tonnes valued at $519,000 (not shown). Canadian landings have since decreased to only 82 tonnes; in total, valued at $31,000 in 2008 (see tables). **Endangered Status:** Atlantic wolffish is a Species of Concern (*ESA* and *SARA*); and northern wolffish and spotted wolffish are considered Threatened (*SARA*).

Atlantic Wolffish (AKA - Striped Catfish) Canadian Landings by Year — Nominal Data Value in $Cdn (000); Quantity in tonnes; (DFO)					
	2004	2005	2006	2007	2008
Value	19	16	11	10	15
Quantity	45	44	31	33	44

Unspecified Wolffish (*Anarhichas* spp.) Canadian Landings by Year — Nominal Data Value in $Cdn (000); Quantity in tonnes; (DFO)					
	2004	2005	2006	2007	2008
Value	62	57	29	40	16
Quantity	133	120	69	78	38

COMMERCIAL USES

The flesh of the wolffish is white and flaky and known for its high quality. It is available fresh and in frozen fillets. It has also been used in canned chicken haddie and in sticks and portions.

LIFE CYCLE

It appears that there is a wide variety in both the times and places of spawning of this species. Off eastern Newfoundland spawning takes place in September, whereas in the waters off Iceland spawning has been reported to occur in January and February. The pelagic, transparent eggs are deposited in a cohesive mass some distance from shore and are guarded by the male wolffish. Although there are not a large number of eggs laid, the survival rate is high. Once hatched the larvae remains on, or close to, the bottom until the yolk sac is absorbed. Although the larvae may drift somewhat with the current, the entire larval stage is usually spent near the area of hatching. With its strong teeth, the wolffish primarily feeds on echinoderms, molluscs, crustaceans and a small amount of fish (mostly redfish). It reaches maturity between the ages of 8 to 10 years at approximately 20 to 24 inches in length. Juvenile wolffish may fall prey to cod. SCUBA divers often sight wolffish sleeping beside large rocks on the bottom near shore. They are fairly docile, except when attacked, and then they can inflict a serious wound.

North American Salmons, Trouts and Chars
Family Salmonidae: Subfamily Salmoninae (and Coregoninae for Inconnu)
(Excludes Graylings [Subfamily Thymallinae] and most Whitefishes [Subfamily Coregoninae])
Including Scientific, Market and Common Names

Scientific Name	Market Name	Common Name	Also Known As	Max. Publ. Weight (kg)
Oncorhynchus spp.	Salmon or Trout	Pacific Salmons	Salmon Genus	
O. tshawytscha	Salmon	Chinook Salmon	King Salmon, Spring Salmon	61.4
O. keta	Salmon	Chum Salmon	Keta Salmon,	15.9
O. kisutch	Salmon	Coho Salmon	Silver Salmon, Med.-Red Salmon, Hoopid	15.2
O. gorbuscha	Salmon	Pink Salmon	Humpback Salmon, , Gorbuscha, Haddo	6.8
O. nerka	Salmon	Sockeye Salmon	Blueback, Red, Kokanee	7.7
O. mykiss	Trout, Rainbow	Rainbow Trout	Steelhead, Silver Trout	25.4
O. m. aguabonita	Trout	Golden Trout	Rainbow Trout (subspecies)	5.0
O. clarkii	Trout	Cutthroat Trout	Red-Throated Trout	18.6
O. chrysogaster	Trout	Mexican Golden Trout- T		N/A
O. gilae	Trout	Gila Trout - EN		N/A
O. g. apache	Trout	Apache Trout - CE	Gila Trout (subspecies)	2.3
Salvelinus spp.	Char or Trout	Chars	Char Genus	
S. alpinus	Char	Arctic Char	Alpine Char, Char, Charr	15.0
S. confluentus	Trout	Bull Trout - T		14.5
S. malma	Trout	Dolly Varden	Bull Trout, Brook Trout/Char	18.3
S. fontinalis	Trout	Brook Trout	Speckled Trout	9.4
S. namaycush	Trout	Lake Trout	Gray Trout, Great Lakes Char	32.7
S. agassizii	N/A	Silver Trout - E		N/A
Salmo spp.	Trout or Salmon	Atlantic Salmons	Trout Genus	
S. trutta	Trout	Brown Trout	Sea Trout	50.0
S. salar	Salmon	Atlantic Salmon	Sebago, Ouananiche	46.8
Stenodus spp.	Trout	Inconnu	Inconnu Genus	
S. leucichthys	Trout	Inconnu	Sheefish	40.0
Key		T - Threatened (at least in some areas); EN - Endangered;		
		CE - Critically Endangered; E - Extinct		

Note: The above table does not include many sub-species, as are found in rainbow and cutthroat trout populations; or hybrids (e.g., "splake" - hybrid lake trout / brook trout; "tiger trout" - hybrid brown trout / brook trout; and various rainbow trout hybrids with other species). Salmonidae species outside of North America also not included above.

Freshwater Finfishes

Listed Alphabetically

BASS

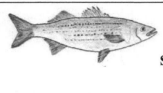

Striped Bass

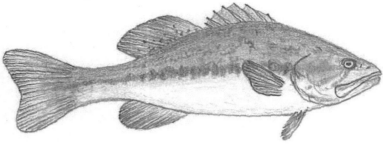

Largemouth Bass, *Micropterus salmoides*

GENERAL

Many fish legally marketed as freshwater bass in North America are actually from the sunfish family (Centrarchidae). These basses include several species of the genus *Ambloplites,* of which the rock bass *(Ambloplites rupestris)* is the most important; and several species of the genus *Micropterus,* of which the **largemouth bass** and smallmouth bass (*M. dolomieu*) are most important. The black crappie (*Pomoxis nigromaculatus*) is another sunfish (see entry in this book). In addition, there are several other fish marketed as bass from the family Moronidae (temperate basses). These fish include the anadromous striped bass (*Morone saxatilis*), the white bass (*M. chrysops*) and the yellow bass (*M. mississippiensis*). However, the white perch (*M. americana*), that is really a member of the striped bass genus (*Morone*), is properly marketed as perch or white perch in the US. (Also see "bass, sea" entry in this book.)

PHYSICAL DESCRIPTION

Max length: 97.0 cm TL male/unsexed; (Ref. 5723); Common length: 40.0 cm TL male/unsexed; (Ref. 556); Max. published weight: 10.1 kg (Ref. 4699); Max. reported age: 23 years (Ref. 46974)

The largemouth bass is a deep brownish green on its back which shades from a light green to a gray or cream color on its belly. (The color may vary in accordance with the water the fish inhabits; that is, the darker the water, the darker the fish.) There is a thin black band running laterally from the gills to the middle of the caudal. It can be distinguished from other black basses by the gaping jaw which extends beyond the rear of the eye, the deep notch between the two dorsal fins and the lack of scales at the base of the soft dorsal rays. In contrast, the smallmouth bass is smaller (up to 24 inches) with bronze reflections on its greenish-yellow sides and no scales at the base of its soft dorsal and anal fins. Striped bass are identified by the seven or eight continuous stripes extending from the gills to the tail. Coloring is light or olive green to steel blue, brown or black. The undersides are usually an iridescent white or silver. Like the striped bass, the small white bass has 6 or more stripes along its side while the rock bass is noted for its dark spot on each scale. The freshwater and temperate basses are in separate families from the sea basses (also see entry in this book).

Also Known As
Black Bass/
Largemouth
Osego Bass/
Chub/ Trout/
Jumper

FishBase Name
Largemouth
black bass

**International
Recognitions**
Spain—black
bass
France—perche
d'Amérique à
grand bouche
Italy—persico
trota
Germany—
forellenbarsch

LANDINGS AND VALUES

Originally, the largemouth bass was only found in the US, in freshwaters east of the Mississippi. However, due to successful stocking, it is now found in nearly every US state as well as southern Canada. It thrives in waters with plenty of vegetation and structural features from which to ambush prey. Generally, there is no commercial fishery for largemouth or smallmouth bass. However, there is a significant fishery for striped bass in US mid-Atlantic states, resulting in landings of 3,305 tonnes, valued at $15.5 million in 2008 (see table). White bass is another small commercial bass fishery in the US with landings

Striped Bass US Landings by Year — Nominal Data Value in $US (000); Quantity in tonnes; (NMFS)					
	2004	**2005**	**2006**	**2007**	**2008**
Value	11,385	15,917	14,327	15,612	15,491
Quantity	2,851	3,577	2,976	3,290	3,305

White Bass US Landings by Year — Nominal Data Value in $US (000); Quantity in tonnes; (NMFS)					
	2004	**2005**	**2006**	**2007**	**2008**
Value	187	221	255	338	320
Quantity	146	165	159	225	193

of 193 tonnes, valued at $320,000 in 2008 (see table). Canada landed 1,869 tonnes of white bass and 10 tonnes of rock bass in 2008, valued at $2.3 million and $19,000, respectively (see tables). There is a small US fishery of rock bass, averaging about 1 tonne and $2,000 per year and incidental landings of longtail bass (not shown). There is no commercial striped bass fishery in Canada.

Recreational bass fisheries: On the Atlantic coast striped bass is found from the Gulf of St. Lawrence to Florida and the northern Gulf of Mexico. As an introduced species, striped bass can also be caught from BC to the Baja Peninsula on the Pacific coast. Recreational landings of striped bass in the US in 2008 were almost 12,000 tonnes (10.4% of the total). In 2005, basses (generally large and small mouth) constituted 13% of all game fishing in Canada. **Aquaculture:** Striped bass is also a farmed species in the US with 2008 production of 5,434 tonnes, valued at $30.4 million (not shown).

White Bass Canadian Landings by Year — Nominal Data Value in $Cdn (000); Quantity in tonnes; (DFO)					
	2004	**2005**	**2006**	**2007**	**2008**
Value	2,562	2,316	1,687	2,020	2,322
Quantity	1,477	1,131	1,019	1,421	1,869

Rock Bass Canadian Landings by Year — Nominal Data Value in $Cdn (000); Quantity in tonnes; (DFO)					
	2004	**2005**	**2006**	**2007**	**2008**
Value	6	7	0	11	19
Quantity	7	8	0	11	10

COMMERCIAL USES

Striped bass is an exception, but the primary value of the various bass fisheries is the sport fisheries that support major recreation and tourism operations. Bass are an excellent eating fish.

LIFE CYCLE

Spawning largemouth bass prefer water temperatures from 63°F, to as high as 70°F. Accordingly, although spawning takes place in mid-winter in the southern US, it is April to June in the northern climates. Spawning occurs in shallow waters near weed beds, lily pads, floating vegetation and inlets. Dense weed beds not only provide cover, but also produce oxygen for the various aquatic life on which it feeds.

The striped bass is an anadromous species that spawns in freshwater rivers and streams. The young migrate to estuarine and nearshore waters where, as voracious predators, they grow quickly. Some may migrate great distances at sea before returning to freshwater to spawn. The striped bass and white bass have been hybrid to produce the "sunshine" bass in one cross (eggs from the white bass) and the "palmetto" bass in another cross (striped bass eggs). The sunshine bass more closely resembles the striped bass than the white.

BOWFIN

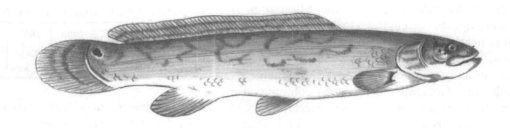

Bowfin, *Amia calva*

GENERAL

The **bowfin** (same market and common name) is the only species in the family Amiidae. It is an ancient species dating from the Jurassic period (approximately 180 million years ago) that is closely related to the gar, but younger in evolutionary terms (see gar entry in this book). It has a primitive skeleton made both of bone and cartilage, as well as a double skull. (Fishes of more recent ancestry have skeletons made entirely of bone). Its ability to survive out of water has been demonstrated to farmers after floods when they find bowfin in the mud while plowing their fields.

PHYSICAL DESCRIPTION

Max length: 109 cm TL male/unsexed; (Ref. 5723);
Common length: 53.4 cm TL male/unsexed; (Ref. 12193);
Max. published weight: 9,750 g (Ref. 4699);
Max. reported age: 30 years (Ref. 72462)

Bowfins have a stout, torpedo-like shape and a long dorsal fin. They are olive-colored dorsally with lighter sides and a whitish belly. Anal fins are bright green and caudal fin is light green with dark vertical bars. There is a distinctive bony plate located on the undersurface of the throat between the lower jaws. Females have a black spot on the upper base of their caudal fin while males have a black spot with a yellow ring around it. Fins are often bright green with some orange highlights on males. It seems that Bowfins are the lone survivors of an earlier primitive family of fish known mostly through fossils. They differ from the gar in having cycloid scales like most soft-rayed fishes, and the skin feels smooth and leathery. In contrast, the gar's scales are hard and diamond-shaped, like an armor coat.

Also Known As
Bowfish/
Dogfish/
Mudfish/
Grindle/ Cyprus
Trout/ Choupic

FishBase Name
Bowfin

**International
Recognitions**
France— amie

LANDINGS AND VALUES

Bowfin is a freshwater species found in the swampy, vegetated lakes and rivers of eastern North America, from southern Canada to Louisiana. Major drainages habituated include St. Lawrence River, Lake Champlain and the Mississippi River.

Bowfin US Landings by Year — Nominal Data Value in $US (000); Quantity in tonnes; (NMFS)					
	2004	2005	2006	2007	2008
Value	95	207	157	111	332
Quantity	62	98	64	47	132

In 2008, 132 tonnes of bowfin valued at $332,000, was landed. Almost all of the catch is typically in Louisiana, with a small amount from North Carolina. A caviar fishery has developed for bowfin in the Atchafalaya Basin of Louisiana. Sinking gill nets, along with hoop nets and trot lines are the gear used.

Endangered Status: Bowfins are not considered an endangered species. Their unique physiology is believed to have helped them to survive unfavourable environmental conditions

COMMERCIAL USES

Bowfins are generally considered to be poor eating and are not a highly commercial meat fish, except for the caviar, which is dark black and rivals sturgeon and paddlefish caviar in some minds. Some recipes are Cajun-based. Recreational fishers also enjoy the challenge of this prehistoric fish. There is also an aquarium demand.

LIFE CYCLE

The bowfin is unique in its ability to withstand high water temperatures in stagnant areas and during drought conditions is able to burrow into the mud. They have a unique gas bladder that allows them to extract oxygen from air.

Bowfins become sexually mature between 3 and 5 years. Females grow to be larger than males. They are somewhat migratory during spawning and lay eggs that stick to decaying vegetation and weeds. Spawning occurs in Winter in Louisiana or in the Spring further north. After the male constructs a bowl-shaped nest in shallow water, from 30,000 to 45,000 eggs can be layed. The male will guard the eggs and fry for several weeks. These are the only prehistoric fish to provide care for their young. They are aggressive protectors and will attack any intruders, including humans. Adult bowfins usually reach a length of about 2 feet and weigh 2-5 pounds, although they may occasionally reach weights of up to 12 pounds. (Cornell)

The bowfin is a voracious and opportunistic predator that preys on fish fry, larvae and small crustaceans as well as on frogs and insects. It uses both sight and scent to capture prey by gulping water.

BUFFALOFISH

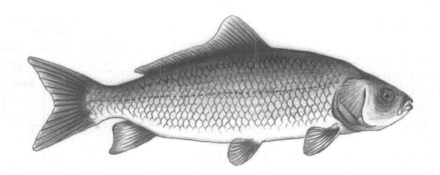

Bigmouth Buffalofish, *Ictiobus cyprinellus*

GENERAL
The buffalofish is a species in the family Catostomidae (suckers), subfamily Ictiobinae [*ITIS*]. There are 3 subfamilies, 14 genera and about 80 species in the family. The subfamily Ictiobinae includes 2 genera, including the *Ictiobus* spp. (buffalofishes) and the *Carpiodes* spp. (carpsuckers, quillbacks). All are somewhat carp-looking, none more than the bigmouth buffalofish. (Carp and sucker families are found in the same order; i.e., Cypriniformes.)

There are 5 species of buffalofishes in the genus *Ictiobus,* including the **bigmouth buffalofish,** the smallmouth buffalofish (*I. bubalus*) and the black buffalofish (*I. niger*) and 3 species of carpsuckers, including the **quillback** (*Carpiodes cyprinus*). The family also includes the **white sucker** (*Catostomus commersonii*) [see entry in this book]. Buffalofishes, quillback and white sucker represent the major species of suckers commercially landed in the USA and Canada.

PHYSICAL DESCRIPTION
Max length: 123 cm TL male/unsexed; (Ref. 40637);
Common length : 35.6 cm TL male/unsexed; (Ref. 12193);
Max. published weight: 31.9 kg (Ref. 4699);
Max. reported age: 20 years (Ref. 12193)

Bigmouth buffalofish can be gray, olive brown or slate blue dorsally with yellowish olive sides, white belly and dark fins. They have a large head and long dorsal fin, with a big, distinctively oblique and thin-lipped, toothless mouth angling upward when closed. The large blunt mouth differs from other sucker fish species in that it is not faced downward in typical sucker fish fashion.

Quillbacks (also known as carpsuckers and marketed as sucker) have golden-yellow scales, and are silvery on their sides with white bellies. They have an inferior mouth, and are bottom-feeders. They can grow to be 26 inches, but on average are between 12 to 17 inches. The first part of their dorsal fin is long and pointed (and where they get their name), but they do not possess any actual quills or barbs.

Also Known As
Redmouth Buffalofish/
Largemouth Buffalofish/
Buffalo Suckers

FishBase Name
Bigmouth Buffalo

International Recognitions
France—
poisson-taureau

LANDINGS AND VALUES

Bigmouth buffalofish are freshwater fish that inhabit lakes and rivers in the lower Great Lakes and Mississippi River basins from Ontario to Saskatchewan south to Louisiana. They generally live in deeper lakes and rivers to depths of 10 meters or more, where possible. (The smallmouth buffalofish overlaps this range as well.) The species has also been introduced elsewhere in North America as well as outside North America. There is some interest in aquaculture with the species.

Buffalofishes US Landings by Year — Nominal Data Value in $US (000); Quantity in tonnes; (NMFS)					
	2004	**2005**	**2006**	**2007**	**2008**
Value	639	741	903	884	815
Quantity	1,605	1,800	1,866	1,913	1,645

Quillback US Landings by Year — Nominal Data Value in $US (000); Quantity in tonnes; (NMFS)					
	2004	**2005**	**2006**	**2007**	**2008**
Value	61	45	30	54	63
Quantity	158	133	139	126	130

Quillback inhabit warm, freshwater rivers and streams of the Great Lakes, St. Lawrence River, Hudson Bay and Mississippi River basins from Alberta to Quebec in Canada and south to Louisiana.

In 2008, 1,645 tonnes of buffalofishes valued at $815,000, was landed in the US. Most of the catches in 2008 were in Louisiana. The rest was landed in Michigan and Ohio. In the same year, 130 tonnes of quillback was landed, valued at $63,000; mostly in Michigan and Ohio (see tables). The gear used was mostly hoop nets, fyke nets and gill nets. There is no reported Canadian commercial fishery.

Endangered Status: Special Concern, Saskatchewan – Nelson River population (*SARA*).

COMMERCIAL USES

Buffalofish are considered good eating and are a highly valued commercial freshwater species, even though they are quite boney. Quillbacks are caught commercially for bait in the spring, during spawning, but are not used for human consumption.

LIFE CYCLE

Bigmouth buffalofish migrate upstream to spawn in springtime, usually between April and June. They are oviparous and produce eggs that are laid in turbid, shallow water vegetation or over sand and gravel bottoms. Females may mate with several males. Bigmouths are filter feeders and prey on different species of copepods, including cladocera and cyclopoid, and midge larvae.

Quillbacks spawn in the spring in gravel or sandy bottom streams and rivers. Adult females can lay up to 64,000 eggs in one season. They broadcast their eggs that have an adhesive casing. The eggs settle in the gravel and hatch alone. Quillback are a long-lived species, with the oldest fish on record being 11 years old.

BURBOT

GENERAL

Burbot is a member of the cod family Gadidae, subfamily Lotinae (cuskfishes) [*ITIS*]. It is the only species listed in *The Seafood List* under the burbot market name and has the same common name, although there is speculation that the North American and Western Eurasian species may differ. They are also the only freshwater member of the cod family. The name burbot is derived from the Latin 'barba' or beard referring to its chin barbel. Some scientists believe burbots were trapped inland when an arm of a prehistoric sea receded.

PHYSICAL DESCRIPTION

Max length: 152 cm TL male/unsexed; (Ref. 27547);
Common length: 40.0 cm TL male/unsexed; (Ref. 1371);
Max. published weight: 34.0 kg (Ref. 27547);
Max. reported age: 20 years (Ref. 556)

Burbot have an elongated body with yellowish or tan skin and dark brown or black patterned camouflage on the head, sides and dorsal and caudal fins. A broad anterior portion tapers to a more laterally compressed tail region with a rounded caudal fin. They have large mouths and numerous rows of teeth. Two small barbels on the anterior of each nostril and one on the chin are its namesake "beard." Imbedded scales give them a slimy feel.

Similar looking to the European ling (*Molva molva*) and a little like its close relative the cusk (*Brosme brosme*), both marine fishes, burbot have two dorsal fins from their back to their tail (rather than one continuous dorsal fin in the cusk), a short anterior fin and a long posterior fin. The anal fin is also half the length of the body and the caudal fin is rounded. The pelvic fins are light colored, while pectorals are darker colored.

Also Known As
Eelpout/ Ling/ Freshwater Cod/ Lawyers/Lotte

FishBase Name
Burbot

International Recognitions
Spain- lota
France-palmo
Germany-
trüsche; quappe
Russia-nalim

LANDINGS AND VALUES

Burbot are found circum-globally in northern and Arctic regions of the Northern Hemisphere. In North America, burbot are widely distributed throughout Alaska, Canada and the northern US (above 40° latitude), including the Great Lakes. It is somewhat peculiarly missing in the extreme eastern regions of Canada (e.g., Nova Scotia). In the middle of the 20th century, burbot populations in the Great lakes declined due to the invasion of the sea lamprey and there is no record of US commercial catches between 1961 and 1985. However, burbot are returning to the Lakes in increasing numbers. In 2008, 6 tonnes of Burbot valued at $5,000, was commercially landed in the US (see table). Most of the catch in 2008 was in Wisconsin. Similar low numbers exist in Canada (see table).

Burbot US Landings by Year — Nominal Data Value in $US (000); Quantity in tonnes; (NMFS)					
	2004	2005	2006	2007	2008
Value	10	8	8	7	5
Quantity	10	7	8	7	6

Burbot Canadian Landings by Year — Nominal Data Value in $Cdn (000); Quantity in tonnes; (DFO)					
	2004	2005	2006	2007	2008
Value	1	2	0	0	0
Quantity	2	4	0	1	0

Recreational Fishery: There are no records on gamefish catches of burbot in the US or Canada; however, the species was long regarded as a "trash fish" by many anglers. More serious fishmen generally regard it as an excellent eating fish. Likely, many are caught in this fishery, although some may be released.

COMMERCIAL USES

Burbot are not considered a great recreation fishery not only for the reason mentioned above, but also because they are usually active only at dawn and dusk. In Europe, they have been a source of oil and liver (sold smoked or canned). They have also been processed into fishmeal. The meat flavor is as tasty as its saltwater cousins; but significant human demand seems presently limited, especially to Scandinavian countries that prize the liver. The Alaska Department of Fish and Game recommends skinning burbot to get at the meat; hence, perhaps the look and feel of the fish is a barrier to greater consumption.

LIFE CYCLE

Burbot spawn in shallow water, over gravel, under the ice in winter. They do not build nests or care for young, and return to deepwater shortly after spawning. They are sexually mature at 6 to 7 years, although they are reported more slow-growing in the most northern part of their range. They can form spawning "fish balls" of up to a dozen individuals and produce over 1 million eggs in a spawning session.

Burbot prefer to live among roots, vegetation, crevices or under rocks. They are crepuscular (i.e., active at twilight) and nocturnal and are usually found at the bottom of deep lakes or slow moving rivers. They feed on invertebrates, small fish and fry like whitefish, sculpins, lamprey and other burbot and have been known to eat mice or shrew.

CARP

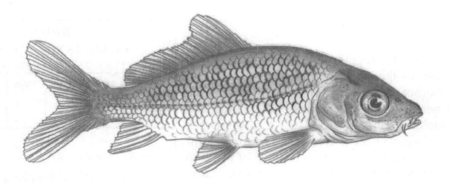

Common Carp, *Cyprinus carpio*

GENERAL

Common Carp is a member of the family Cyprinidae (carps and minnows), which consists of the carps, the true minnows, and their relatives. They are also often referred to as the cyprinids. Cyprinids are the largest family of fresh-water fish, with almost 2,900 species (including subspecies) in about 320 genera. Most cyprinids are native to eastern Europe and Asia. Although Africa has some Cyprinid species, they are uncommon in North America and very scarce in Central and South America. Moreover, the native North American species tend to be very small fishes (e.g., freshwater shiners, chubs, dace and minnows). The **common carp** was an early introduced species, possibly from Europe, that is now found throughout the Mississippi River Drainage as well as the Great lakes and elsewhere. More recently introduced Asian species include the silver carp (*Hypophthalmichthys molotrix*), bighead carp (*H. nobilis*), black carp (*Mylopharyngodon piceus*) and grass carp (*Ctenopharyngodon idella*). The latter two species, although recognized food fish, are not listed in *The Seafood List*. In the US, silver carp have become celebrated for leaping into the air when frightened by powerboats. There are efforts to bar them from the Great Lakes.

Also Known As
European Carp/
German Carp/
Mirror
Carp/Carpe

FishBase Name
Common Carp

International Recognitions
Spain—Carpa
France—Carpe commune
Italy—Carpa
Japan—Koi
Germany—Karpe

PHYSICAL DESCRIPTION

Max length: 110 cm SL male/unsexed; (Ref. 59043);
Common length: 31.0 cm TL male/unsexed; (Ref. 3561);
Max. published weight: 40.1 kg (Ref. 72380); Max. reported age: 38 years (Ref. 72479)

Carps are the largest members of the Cyprinidae family. The common carp is a stocky built, large-scaled species with two barbels on each side of the upper jaw. Scales are usually bronze in color, with a dark spot at the base. However, coloration can vary significantly from bronze on top and sides to yellow-white, undersides. They have a long dorsal fin, starting at mid-body, and running to the tail; one serrated spine at the front of the dorsal fin; 17-21 branched dorsal fin rays and a forked caudal fin. Their pharyngeal teeth are robust and molar like. Wild carp are often distinguished by a less stocky build than those raised in captivity. The goldfish (*Carassius auratus*), and the grass carp are similar looking to the common carp; however, both lack barbels and the latter is longer and has a much shorter dorsal fin.

Landings and Values

Common carp are a fresh to brackish water species now distributed throughout subtropical US waters as an introduced species. They prefer warm, deep, slow-flowing or still waters in soft bottom, well vegetated rivers and lakes. Common carp are now abundant throughout the Great Lakes and small numbers of bighead and grass carp have been found there too. Bighead, silver, and grass carp are already known to be well-established in the Mississippi River. Grass carp, like blue tilapia (*Oreochromis aureus*) was initially introduced, and is still used in many states, as an effective bio-control for unwanted aquatic plants, many of which are also introduced/invasive

Common Carp US Landings by Year — Nominal Data Value in $US (000); Quantity in tonnes; (NMFS)					
	2004	2005	2006	2007	2008
Value	195	151	185	261	204
Quantity	430	392	546	612	524

Grass Carp US Landings by Year — Nominal Data Value in $US (000); Quantity in tonnes; (NMFS)					
	2004	2005	2006	2007	2008
Value	9	10	13	24	13
Quantity	20	23	32	55	32

species. When used for weed control, carps are usually introduced as sterile "triploid" fish to reduce the probability of reproduction. Commercial landings of common carp and grass carp are provided in the associated tables for recent years. Most US landings are in Louisiana, Michigan and Ohio. The US also landed 25 tonnes of unspecified carp/minnows, valued at $267,000 in 2008 (not shown).

Commercial Uses

The common carp is relished as a food fish and a gamefish in parts of Europe and it has been widely cultivated for centuries; however, it has not really caught on in North America. As a bottom feeder, some people think it has a muddy flavor. In Europe, before eating, the fish are often placed in clean running water to improve the flavour. The meat is

Carp Canadian Landings by Year — Nominal Data Value in $Cdn (000); Quantity in tonnes; (DFO)					
	2004	2005	2006	2007	2008
Value	241	223	197	194	122
Quantity	517	502	431	362	259

even canned in sauces, like sardines. In some cases, carp have become invasive species that compete with native fishes or disrupt the environment. In particular, the common carp stirs up riverbeds, reducing the clarity of the water and making it difficult for native plant and animal life to grow. Carps are considered something of a gamefish (due to large sizes) and there is also an aquarium trade for some species (e.g., goldfish). Grass carp and other Asian species are considered more palatable, with some invasive concerns. Grass carp, renamed as "white Amur," to avoid negative associations with the name "carp," are considered one of the world's most important aquaculture species. Carp can be consumed steamed, pan fried, broiled or baked.

Life Cycle

Common carp are most active at dawn and dusk and feed on a variety of benthic organisms and plants. They spawn along shores and backwaters and will often migrate significant distances. Eggs are not guarded or layed in nests. Larvae only survive in very warm waters among shallow, submerged vegetation. They commonly feed on zooplankton, plants and algae found on the bottom, sometimes tearing plants from the bottom and muddying the water. They are a hardy species that can live out of water for quite some time.

Grass carps feed on aquatic plants and submerged grasses; as well as detritus, insects and other invertebrates—which is good if there are only invasive weeds and the population is sterile. Bighead and silver carp feed by filtering plankton from the water. **Endangerment Status:** Habitat destruction has led to the decline of several native cyprinid species in the US southwest.

CATFISH

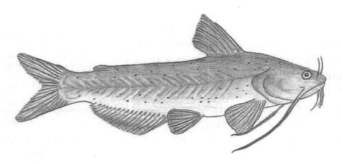

Channel Catfish, *Ictalurus punctatus*

GENERAL

There are 33 catfish families (order Siluriformes) in total worldwide and thousands of species. However, the **channel catfish** is one of the best known freshwater species in North America, although it occasionally enters salt water of low salinity. It is one of a large group of North American catfishes (family Ictaluridae) of which there are 45 species, including the flathead catfish (*Pylodictis olivaris*), blue catfish (*Ictalurus furcatus*) and the smaller black bullhead (*Ameiurus melas*), brown bullhead (*A. nebulosus*) and yellow bullhead (*A. natalis*). Catfishes from the genus *Noturus* (madtoms) such as the stonecat (*N. flavus*) and the brindled madtom (*N. miurus*) have especially venomous pectoral fins that can inflict a painful, though not dangerous, sting. Although catfishes are often considered freshwater fishes, a large family of sea catfishes (Ariidae) also exists. Sea catfishes include the (*Bagre marinus*) and the (*Ariopsis felis*). Sea catfishes should not be confused with ocean catfishes (i.e., wolffishes—see entry in this book) that belong to a different order (Perciformes).

Also Known As
Spotted Cat/
White Cat/ Lake
Catfish/Poisson
Chat

FishBase Name
Channel Catfish

International Recognitions
France —barbue
d'Amérique
Spain—bagre de
Canal
Italy—pesce
gatto
punteggiato
Japan—namazu

PHYSICAL DESCRIPTION

Max length: 132 cm TL male/unsexed; (Ref. 26550);
Common length: 57.0 cm SL male/unsexed; (Ref. 59043);
Max. published weight: 26.3 kg (Ref. 4699);
Max. reported age: 24 years (Ref. 59043)

Typically, catfishes have naked skins and their dorsal and pectoral fins are characterized by well-developed serrated spines. The most distinguishing characteristic is barbels (fleshy, sensory appendages) near the mouth. The number of barbels varies with the species: channel and bullhead catfish have four pairs of barbels; sea catfishes have four to six barbels. The channel catfish has a slender, smooth, scale-less body, an adipose fin, four pairs of barbels and a deeply forked tail. Catfishes vary in length from a few inches (e.g., madtoms) to several feet. The blue, channel and flathead catfishes are the larger of the species in North America. Channel and blue cats both have a distinctly forked tail whereas bullheads and flatheads have rounded tails. The blue catfish has a distinctly blue color, while the flathead has a noticeably flatter head.

LANDINGS AND VALUES

The catfish is a bottom-feeding fish and its habitat includes ponds, lakes, or rivers and creeks with slow- to moderate-running currents over gravel, sand, or rock bottoms. Catfishes are often scavengers and feed on a variety of marine life, including clams and crustaceans, as well as insect larvae. In the US, the channel catfish ranges throughout the eastern and central states. In Canada, it is found from as far west as southern Alberta and as far east as southern Quebec. In many instances, catfish species have been introduced by humans, as was the case of the white catfish in California. Both a commercial and a sport fish, the channel catfish is also the one most often produced in aquaculture. US catfish and bullhead landings (*Ictalurus* spp.) were 3,979 tonnes in 2008, valued at $4.3 million (see table). Canadian catfish landings were only 326 tonnes in 2008, valued at $281,000 (see table). **Aquaculture:** Farmed catfish are raised in big, shallow ponds and, unlike many other farmed fish, will accept a grain-based diet. US commercial landings are overshadowed by catfish farming that produced 233,564 tonnes in 2008, valued at a whopping $390 million (see table). In comparison, the next largest 2008 farmed species in the US was crawfish at 53,285 tonnes, followed by salmon at 16,714 tonnes, trout at 16,213 tonnes and tilapia at 9,072 tonnes (not shown). **Endangered:** Northern Madtom (*N. stigmosus*) – *SARA*.

All Freshwater Catfish and Bullheads US Landings by Year — Nominal Data Value in $US (000); Quantity in tonnes; (NMFS)					
	2004	2005	2006	2007	2008
Value	6,703	3,859	4,767	4,309	4,315
Quantity	6,313	3,876	3,803	3,926	3,979

All Catfish and Bullheads US Aquaculture by Year — Nominal Data Value in $US (000); Quantity in tonnes; (NMFS)					
	2004	2005	2006	2007	2008
Value	439,158	428,476	441,264	424,596	390,052
Quantity	285,970	274,664	258,049	255,781	233,564

COMMERCIAL USES

Catfish tolerate low oxygen levels and are sometimes marketed live. They are also sold fresh (head on and dressed), frozen whole, prepared and, to a lesser extent, filleted. They are a sweet tasting fish and are excellent in portions and sticks.

All Freshwater Catfish and Bullheads Canadian Landings by Year — Nominal Data Value in $Cdn (000); Quantity in tonnes; (DFO)					
	2004	2005	2006	2007	2008
Value	303	264	281	283	281
Quantity	329	304	327	327	326

LIFE CYCLE

With the channel catfish, spawning occurs in the spring when water temperatures reach about 80°F. After the eggs are deposited by the female the male fertilizes them and then chases the female away. The male continues to care for the eggs until they are hatched, about 7 days later. Farmed freshwater channel catfish take about 16 to 18 months to grow to a market size of 1 to 1.5 pounds, but can grow much larger. A record size for both catfish and freshwater fish was a Mekong giant catfish landed in Thailand in June, 2005 that weighed in at 646 pounds (293 kg). Some catfishes, like the hardhead, have an unusual life cycle as, like many tilapia and cardinal fishes, they are mouth brooders. The fertilized eggs are carried in the mouth of the male fish until they hatch, up to nine weeks after spawning. After hatching, the juveniles may remain in the fish's mouth for a few more weeks, until they are mature enough to be independent. Throughout this brooding process, the fish goes without food.

CHAR

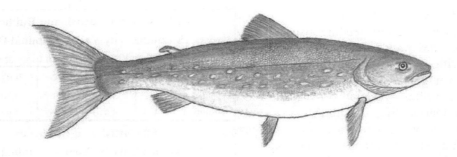

GENERAL

The **Arctic char** is an international fish living in the circumpolar waters of North America, Europe and Asia. It is a member of the Salmonidae family (see Salmonidae Table). There are two principal groups of Arctic char: the landlocked variety, living entirely in fresh water; and the anadromous, which make annual migrations to the ocean.

The Arctic char is a product of clean, clear and cold northern waters and is appreciated for its delicate flavor and as a challenging sport fish. Closely related species include the lake trout (*S. namaycush*), (eastern) brook trout (*Salvelinus. fontinalis*), the Pacific brook trout or Dolly Varden (*S. malma*) and the bull trout (*S. confluentus*), all of which are included in the char genus *Salvelinus*. An average arctic char weighs between 3 and 5 pounds, although 30-pound specimens are known.

(For additional information on char, see entries in this book on lake trout, inconnu/trout and Atlantic salmon.)

Also Known As
Common Char/
Alpine Trout/
Alpine Char/
Sea
Trout/Omble
D'Artique

FishBase Name
Charr

**International
Recognitions**
Germany—
Saibling
Spain—
salvelino
Italy—salmerino
artico

PHYSICAL DESCRIPTION

Max length: 107 cm TL male/unsexed; (Ref. 40637);
Common length: 40.0 cm TL male/unsexed; (Ref. 4779);
Max. published weight: 15.0 kg (Ref. 4779); Max. reported age: 40 years (Ref. 46974)

The Arctic char has a slender body, silver in color, with deep green or blue shading on the back and upper sides and along the pale-edged fins. Sometimes there is a scattering of small pink dots along, and below, the lateral line. The Arctic char has very fine, deeply embedded scales which give it a slippery, smooth surface. The teeth are located only in the central forward part of the mouth. Another branch of the Salmonidae family (salmons and trouts), the char has an adipose fin characteristic of this group. Lake trout have a deeply forked tail while Arctic char, Dolly Vardens and eastern brook trout have a slightly forked tail. Small char and brook trout look very similar, but brook trout have irregularly shaped black markings on both caudal (tail) and dorsal fins.

ARCTIC CHAR

LANDINGS AND VALUES

In North America, the Arctic char is primarily found in northern Canada. Char is caught year-round in rivers and lakes near entry points to the sea. It is particularly abundant in Labrador. In some areas, populations have become landlocked. Although spawning runs vary according to location, they are usually in September or October, when the water is at

Arctic Char Canadian Landings by Year — Nominal Data Value in $Cdn (000); Quantity in tonnes; (DFO)					
	2004	2005	2006	2007	2008
Value	0	9	79	52	32
Quantity	0	5	.39	29	18

a mean temperature of about 39°F. They are also fished through the ice in winter. Commercially, char is primarily caught by gill nets and traps. For those lucky enough to reach its habitat, it is a popular sport fish. Arctic char is also cultured in both fresh and salt water. In 1988, Canadian landings were 88 tonnes, valued at $570,000 (not shown). Landings in 2008 were 18 tonnes, valued at $32,000. It is 100% a northern territorial fishery. **Aquaculture:** An increasing amount of Arctic char is farmed; mostly in Iceland, Norway, Canada and the US.

COMMERCIAL USES

Historically, the char supported the Eskimo populations of northern Canada, providing food for both human and dog. It was eaten raw, salted, dried and smoked. Today, Arctic char is a highly valued food source, available fresh or frozen, dressed or as steak. It can also be smoked. Arctic char is considered a delicacy in many parts of the world. It is a fatty fish with amber to reddish flesh, depending on its diet. Reddish flesh commands the highest price and it can be substituted in any salmon recipe. The Arctic char has developed as a strong sport fishery supporting many northern communities, having earned a reputation as a formidable fighter.

LIFE CYCLE

The Arctic char life cycle is very similar to salmon. Spawning adults, especially males, become brilliant orange-red to bright red on the ventral side and on the pectoral, pelvic and anal fins. They usually spawn in cool streams in September or October. However, if the char lives farther south, spawning takes place later. The female char finds a bed of gravel or broken rock in a stretch of river or lake bottom deep enough to protect the eggs from the winter ice. Then she releases between 3,000 and 7,000 eggs simultaneously with the male's release of milt. The eggs incubate during the winter at water temperatures between 32 and 36°F and hatch during the first week of April. Timing varies, depending on such factors as light, water temperature and location. The alevin remain hidden in the gravel until their food sacs are gone, usually in mid-July. Most of their growth occurs in the first few years. The anadromous char usually begin migration to the sea at age four or five. Each spring or summer they migrate to the ocean to feed and they return to their native rivers in the fall. Char from many different rivers mingle while at sea and when the time comes to return, they separate and go back to their native streams. However, growth is slow in the cold arctic waters and the char also stop eating in winter, living off the summer fat reserve, which further slows their growth. At 8 to 10 years of age, the char finally reach sexual maturity, but then may only spawn every 2 or 3 years and may not migrate during reproduction years. In freshwater the char feeds on planktonic crustaceans, amphipods, molluscs, insects and other fishes and has almost no predators. At sea, it usually stays close to the river mouth, but if food is scarce it will move offshore. Capelin, arctic cod and shrimp are part of its sea diet, while it is prey to seals and white whales.

CRAPPIE

Black Crappie, *Pomoxis nigromaculatus*

GENERAL

Black crappie is found in the family Centrarchidae (sunfishes) that has 9 genera and about 32 species, including the rock basses (*Ambloplites* spp.) and the largemouth and smallmouth basses (*Micropterus* spp.). All species of the family are native only to North America. The genus *Pomoxis* consists of the black crappie and the white crappie (*P. annularis)*; both are listed in *The Seafood List*. The crappie is a relatively small, excellent eating fish, closely related to the freshwater basses (also see bass entry in this book).

PHYSICAL DESCRIPTION
Max length: 49.0 cm TL male/unsexed; (Ref. 5723);
Common length: 27.5 cm TL male/unsexed; (Ref. 12193);
Max. published weight: 2,720 g (Ref. 40637);
Max. reported age: 15 years (Ref. 46974)

Crappies have a rounded, compressed body with a small head and an arched back. They have a large mouth with an extending lower jaw. Black crappies have a greenish back and silvery sides with black blotches. The dorsal, anal, and caudal fins also are marked with dark striping. The large dorsal and anal fins begin about mid-body and are of almost identical shape and size. It is identifiable by the seven or eight spines on the dorsal fin.

White Crappie:
Max length: 53.0 cm TL male/unsexed; (Ref. 5723);
Common length : 25.0 cm TL male/unsexed; (Ref. 12193);
Max. published weight: 2,350 g (Ref. 4699);
Max. reported age: 10 years (Ref. 12193)

The white crappie is similar to black crappie but lighter, without a black spotted pattern and with several dark vertical bars on the side. Also, unlike the black crappie, it has only 6 spines on the dorsal fin.

Also Known As
Calico Bass/
Oswego Bass/
Strawberry Bass/
Grass Bass/
Specks/Crapet

FishBase Name
Black crappie

International Recognitions
Mexico—Mojarra negra
Denmark—Sort crappie
Portugal—Perca-prateada

LANDINGS AND VALUES

It is thought that the black crappie originally ranged in freshwaters bordering the Atlantic and Gulf coasts, from Virginia to Florida including the St. Lawrence, Great Lakes and Mississippi River basins. However, the species has now been widely introduced, and cultured, throughout the US. The original white crappie range is thought similar to the black crappie, but may have extended further north (New York and Ontario) and west (Minnesota and South Dakota). Crappies usually occur in warm, clear, vegetated lakes, ponds, streams and rivers. They prefer clear, still water; open areas with nearby cover and access to deeper water in winter and summer. In the spring

Crappies US Landings by Year – Nominal Data Value in $US (000); Quantity in tonnes; (NMFS)					
	2004	**2005**	**2006**	**2007**	**2008**
Value	1	8	10	3	9
Quantity	0	2	3	1	3
Sunfishes (other than rock and white basses) Canadian Landings by Year – Nominal Data Value in $Cdn (000); Quantity in tonnes; (DFO)					
	2004	**2005**	**2006**	**2007**	**2008**
Value	173	319	216	228	193
Quantity	70	117	109	89	78

and fall they come nearer to shore and tend to stay in deeper water during the summer. They can also be fished through the ice in winter.

In the US, 3 tonnes were commercially landed in 2008, valued at $9,000 (see table). These catches were reported from Maryland and Michigan. In Canada, 78 tonnes were landed in 2008, valued at $193,000 (see table).

COMMERCIAL USES

Black crappies are excellent game fish highly regarded by sport fishers. They congregate in large schools, especially before spawning, and will take many types of bait and lures. They can be deep fried, baked or broiled.

LIFE CYCLE

Spawning behaviour for the two crappie species is similar. They mature early and a large female may produce over 100,000 eggs. Spawning occurs between April and June in circular nests fanned by males over gravel or soft muddy bottoms. Fertilization is external, possibly with more than one male and in different nests. The males guard the nest, eggs, and young. Crappies form schools and feed nocturnally, and at dawn and dusk, on planktonic crustaceans and smaller fish. They are prey for other larger fishes such as muskie and walleye.

EEL, FRESHWATER

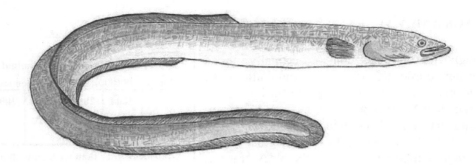

American Eel, *Anguilla rostrata*

GENERAL

Many mysteries still exist about the American eel. Why do they all migrate to the Sargasso Sea, far out in the Atlantic Ocean, to spawn? Even more curious, how do they get there and what happens to them afterward? Very few adult eels have been captured in the open ocean and none in the breeding grounds (where they are presumed to die after spawning). The eel is also sensitive to electric and magnetic fields: in a direct current electric field (e.g., that produced by a battery), it always points towards the positive electrode. Also worth noting is that a toxin in the eel's blood will affect the human nervous system. The **American eel** is a species in the family Anguillidae (freshwater eels) that is comprised of just one genus and 19 species (*ITIS*). The slime eel, or hagfish, *Myxine glutinosa*, and the conger eel, *Conger oceanicus* are a very different species (see entries in this book).

PHYSICAL DESCRIPTION

Max length: 152 cm TL male/unsexed; (Ref. 26938); 122 cm TL (female); Common length: 50.0 cm TL male/unsexed; (Ref. 3242); Max. published weight: 7,330 g (Ref. 4699); Max. reported age: 43 years (Ref. 40922)

The American eel is an elongated, serpent-like creature, with a single continuous dorsal fin. Immature adult eels are yellowish to greenish olive-brown in color. Older, mature eels turn silver when their sexual organs develop fully. To avoid detection, or to help in stalking prey, eels can alter their color to match the environment. The American eel differs only slightly from the European eel by having fewer vertebrae, a larger overall size and a shorter larval stage. It differs greatly from hagfish that have a distinctly jawless mouth, peculiar barbels and only one nasal aperture.

LANDINGS AND VALUES

The American eel ranges along the North American coast from Labrador and Greenland south to the Gulf of Mexico and the northern coast of South America. However, eels spend most of their lives in or near fresh water — in streams, rivers, lakes, or saltwater estuaries. Most of the fishing effort occurs in the fall migration period when the large silver eels move downstream to the sea. This movement usually happens at night and, it seems, the more miserable the weather, the larger the migration.

Also Known As
Common Eel/
Atlantic Eel/
Silver Eel/
Freshwater Eel/
Anguille

FishBase Name
American eel

International Recognitions
Germany—
Amerikanischer
Aal
Spain—anguila
americana
Italy—anguilla
americana

Eels are usually caught in various types of traps and weirs set up along rivers, but they are also fished, speared and caught in baited traps or "eel pots." The US catch in 2008 was 357 tonnes, valued at almost $3 million (see table). Canadian catches were about 550 tonnes in recent years, (except for 2008), with a value averaging $3 to $3.5 million (see tables). However, catches can fluctuate widely, both for supply and demand reasons. Pollution in European Rivers in the mid-1980s caused European consumers to be wary of buying eels, even the North American product, and this affected exports for a while. This appears to have ended now. **Endangered Status:** Identified as Special Concern by COSEWIC and is considered for listing under the Canadian *Species at Risk Act* (SARA). **Aquaculture:** Because eels adapt easily to captivity and are easy to feed, eel farming has made some inroads in North America. Asians, particularly the Japanese, have been farming eels successfully for many years.

American Eel US Landings by Year — Nominal Data Value in $US (000); Quantity in tonnes; (NMFS)					
	2004	**2005**	**2006**	**2007**	**2008**
Value	1,279	2,851	1,566	2,852	2,998
Quantity	332	396	338	358	357

American Eel Canadian Marine Landings by Year — Nominal Data Value in $Cdn (000); Quantity in tonnes; (DFO)					
	2004	**2005**	**2006**	**2007**	**2008**
Value	2,758	3,832	3,076	4,625	883
Quantity	441	409	458	436	187

COMMERCIAL USES

Since their larger size and higher fat content make them a superior smoked product, (mature) silver eels are preferred to yellows. Also, live eels, rather than frozen ones, are preferred in the export market. They are shipped by air freight and once at their destination, local processors either keep them alive

American Eel Canadian Freshwater Landings — Nominal Data Value in $Cdn (000); Quantity in tonnes; (DFO)					
	2004	**2005**	**2006**	**2007**	**2008**
Value	1255	978	908	1041	1041
Quantity	183	156	146	158	158

or prepare them to be jellied, smoked, canned, or marinated. Smoked eels have traditionally been considered a delicacy in Europe and command a high price. In North America, eels are usually sold live or fresh. Hagfish are valued for their skins, which are processed into eelskin leather boots, bags, wallets and other products in Korea. Additionally, Koreans consume millions of pounds of hagfish meat each year.

LIFE CYCLE

The American eel is catadromous, spending from 5 to 10 years in the coastal and freshwater areas of North America before returning to the sea to spawn and die. Towards autumn, mature eels in North America (and Europe) leave lakes and estuaries in preparation for the return to their spawning grounds— the Sargasso Sea. Their migration routes and spawning behavior at sea are not presently understood. (It is also not known why some eels stay in coastal areas and never enter freshwater systems, or why females are most likely to predominate in the upper reaches of a river system.) Female eels can produce from 5 to 20 million eggs. Young eels float to the surface and drift with the tides and currents until they make their way to coastal areas. It is not believed that they home to any particular river since they have little swimming ability at this stage, but eels taken from one river to another have been able to find their way back to their home river. As young eels, or elvers, they are dark brown to black, but will turn silver and get much fatter as they mature and prepare to migrate back to the spawning grounds.

GAR

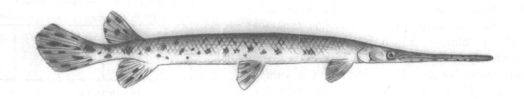

Longnose Gar, *Lepisosteus osseus*

GENERAL

Gars belong to the family Lepisosteidae (garfishes) in the same order as the bowfin (order Neopterygii), a distant, but more recent relative. The family includes 2 genera and 7 species (*ITIS*), including the alligator gar (*Atractosteus spatula*), the only other gar listed in *The Seafood List*. All 7 species are only native to either North or Central America, although the **longnose gar** is native to both. Gar can withstand water with low oxygen levels because they are able to take in added oxygen by swimming to the surface and gulping air into their swim bladders. They can also live out of water for hours as long as they remain moist. Alligator gars grow to the largest size of all gars with a maximum published weight of 137.0 kg (Ref. 58490).

PHYSICAL DESCRIPTION

Max length: 200 cm TL male/unsexed; (Ref. 40637);
Common length: 17.5 cm TL male/unsexed; (Ref. 12193);
Max. published weight: 22.8 kg (Ref. 4699);
Max. reported age: 36 years (Ref. 12193)

The longnose gar is a long, slender, graceful fish that is distinguished by a long needle-like nose, (much longer than other gars) and razor-sharp pointed teeth in both its upper and lower jaws. The dorsal fin is placed very far back on body, just before the tail and there are sets of pectoral, median and anal fins. Scales are hard (ganoid) and diamond shaped like an armor coat. The body is olive brown, usually with spots and is silvery on the belly. The caudal fin is rounded and all fins have dark spots.

Also Known As
Gar Pike/
Garfish/ Billfish/
Ohio Gar

FishBase Name
Longnose gar

International Recognitions
Spain—Catán aguja
France—Lépisosté osseux
Germany— Gemeiner Knochenhecht

LANDINGS AND VALUES

Gars US Landings by Year — Nominal Data Value in \$US (000); Quantity in tonnes; (NMFS)					
	2004	2005	2006	2007	2008
Value	553	395	513	735	607
Quantity	360	246	280	363	315

Most North American gars seem to be prevalent in Mississippi River drainages, although the Florida gar is found only in the southeast US. The longnose gar's range tends to be more a little further north (24°N - 47°N latitude) and significantly further east (69°W- 97°W longitude) than the alligator gar (20°N-44°N and 82°W-101°W). They are usually found in sluggish rivers, streams, backwaters and swamps. Gars are somewhat sluggish when not on the hunt and can be seen basking in the sun while they await their prey. While sunning themselves, they are often gulping air. In the US, 315 tonnes of gars were landed in 2008, valued at \$607,000 (see table). Most of these gars were landed in Louisiana (88%), followed by Texas (10%) and North Carolina.

Endangered Status: Gars appear to be thriving in the US due to dams and other river diversions that provide a preferred environment. In Canada, the spotted gar (*Lepisosteus oculatus*) is listed as "threatened" under the *Species At Risk Act* (*SARA*).

COMMERCIAL USES

Years ago, the gar was appreciated as a food source in local communities where it was indigenous. However, this changed after the age of supermarkets and new species (such as cod, whiting and farmed catfish) permeated the interior of North America. Then gars slowly took on the reputation of a "trash fish" and a species that depleted other gamefish such as bass and crappie. The perception that gar is a poor food fish was mainly driven by; 1) a tough "hide" that has to be skinned using saws and scissor tools, 2) the presence of poisonous eggs, and 3) sharp teeth and the potential for serious wounds. However, both the presence and price of the species has been elevated in local markets in recent years as knowledge on how to fillet the excellent, boneless, white meat has grown. It is now considered a prized restaurant menu item in some southern US localities. Gar meat is sometimes ground-up, or chunked and boiled, and mixed to form spicy meat patties. Gar can also be smoked. Even where the meat is not highly prized, it is often considered a great recreational fish as it can put up a magnificent fight and/or provide record sizes. There is also an aquarium trade for this unique species.

LIFE CYCLE

Longnose gar spawn in spring in shallow sloughs and streams. A single female is often accompanied by several males. Although nests are not prepared, gravel is cleared in the spawning activity. Females can deposit a portion of eggs at several different locations. The eggs adhere to the gravel, hatching in about 1 week. Yolk-sac fry have an adhesive disc on their snouts and attach themselves to submerged objects until the yolk sac is absorbed. When young, they look like tiny floating sticks on the surface of the water. Fry feed primarily on insect larvae and small crustaceans such as water fleas, but quickly move onto larger prey. Adult gars prey on smaller fish, crustaceans and frogs. In Minnesota they have been found to consume minnows and carp, not especially other game fish.

PERCH, LAKE OR YELLOW

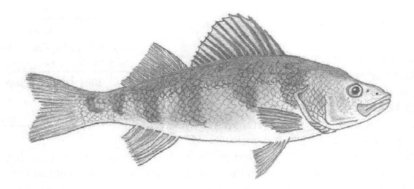

Yellow Perch, *Perca flavescens*

GENERAL

Although perch is a name used commonly for many species perhaps distantly related, it properly refers to members of the freshwater perch family, Percidae. In North America, this includes the walleye, the sauger, about 200 mostly small darter fish and the **yellow perch**. (Also see walleye and sauger entries in this book.)

Classed also as a sport fish, its white, flaky, very tasty flesh makes the yellow perch a prominent commercial species, particularly in the Great Lakes region.

PHYSICAL DESCRIPTION
Maximum Size: 50.0 cm TL (male/unsexed; Ref. 9988);
Maximum Published Weight: 1.9 kg (Ref. 40637);
Maximum Reported Age: 11 years

The yellow perch can be distinguished from the other perch species by its short, stubby, hunch-backed body, marked with six to eight broad, dusty, vertical bars. The yellow perch has two well-separated dorsal fins: the first spiny-rayed, the second soft-rayed. Its head is moderately deep and rounded at the tip, having a rather large mouth and bright yellow to green eyes.

The sides, to below the pectoral fins, are yellow to yellow green, with a dusty olive green back and a white belly. Spawning males exhibit more intense colors: bronze green to bright yellow bars, as well as darker lower fins suffused with orange to bright red. The young are transparent at first, later turning silvery or a dull, pale green.

Also Known As
Ring Perch/
Striped
Perch/Perchaude

FishBase Name
American
yellow perch

International Recognitions
France—
Perchaude
Germany—
Amerikanischer
Flußbarsch
Spain—
Amerikanischer
Flußbarsch
Italy— Persico
dorato

LANDINGS AND VALUES

The yellow perch is primarily a lake fish, but it also inhabits ponds and slow-running rivers and streams in most of the northern United States and throughout Canada. The Great Lakes have the greatest abundance of yellow perch and it is this stock that supplies almost the entire commercial fishery. Canadian landings in 2008 totaled 3,713 tonnes at a value of $9.1 million; while US landings in 2008 totaled 994 tonnes, valued at $4.9 million (see table). Yellow perch is caught commercially by gillnets, poundnets and trapnets. Anglers use various types of gear, with both live and artificial bait and lures.

Yellow Perch US Landings by Year — Nominal Data Value in $US (000); Quantity in tonnes; (NMFS)					
	2004	**2005**	**2006**	**2007**	**2008**
Value	2,461	2,904	3,675	2,820	4,935
Quantity	746	813	790	580	994

Yellow Perch Canadian Landings by Year — Nominal Data Value in $Cdn (000); Quantity in tonnes; (DFO)					
	2004	**2005**	**2006**	**2007**	**2008**
Value	12,694	14,973	18,308	13,958	9,144
Quantity	3,603	4,034	5,307	4,188	3,713

COMMERCIAL USES

Most of the commercial catch is marketed in the United States as fillets, but there is a growing market in Canada, where it is marketed as fresh and frozen whole fish and fillets. Its firm, white flesh and sweet taste make it an excellent pan fish.

Perch are not a fighting fish like trout, but these full-bodied, large-finned panfish are a favorite treat and a relatively easy target for anglers.

LIFE CYCLE

The yellow perch spawns in the spring, usually from mid-April to early May, in water temperatures of about 48 to 54°F. In some areas, spawning may extend into July. To spawn, adults migrate shoreward into the shallow depths of lakes and sometimes tributary rivers. The smaller males move to the spawning grounds first, followed by the females. Spawning takes place at night or in early morning, usually near rooted vegetation, submerged brush or fallen trees, but also over sand or gravel. Spawning is thought to involve a single large female and many smaller males swimming about in a long compact queue, the first males with their snouts pressed against the female.

The eggs are released in a unique, gelatinous, accordion-folded string or tube. Transparent at first, they are about 0.14 inch in diameter. Hatching usually takes place in 8 to 10 days, although it can take as long as 27 days in cooler waters. The young fish are inactive for about the first five days, until the yolk sac has been absorbed.

The diet of yellow perch consists of insects and other small organisms. Larger perch also eat other fish. Growth is rapid at first, but also extremely variable, depending upon the population size and habitat. The age of yellow perch can be determined by their scales.

PIKE

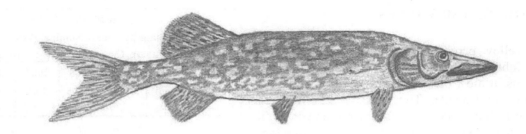

Northern Pike, *Esox lucius*

GENERAL

Northern pike or "pike" is a member of the pike family (Esocidae) and closely related to the muskellunge or "musky" (*Esox masquinongy*) and "pickerels," such as the chain pickerel (*Esox niger*). (Muskellunge and pickerel are the preferred market names for these latter mentioned species, although both are often referred to as "pike" or, in the case of muskellunge, also "great pike.") The northern pike has been deemed the wolf of fresh waters because it is a tough and serious predator. The pike has also gained a reputation as an excellent game fish in waters where it is native. However, where it has been newly introduced (often illegally or accidentally), it is also often considered an invasive species because it can devastate an entire ecosystem. In some such cases Alaskan officials, for example, have designated the pike as a "salmon and trout-eating machine" and encourage year-round fishing expeditions, with no catch limits — spears included.

PHYSICAL DESCRIPTION

Max. Size: 137 cm FL (male/unsexed; Ref. 40637); 150 cm TL (female);
Max. Published Weight: 35 kg; Max. Reported Age: 30 years

The northern pike has a long, slender, powerful body, with a long, broad, flattened snout. Its dorsal and anal fins are placed far back on its body, near the tail. The roof and jaws of its large mouth show broad bands of sharp, pointed teeth. It has five large sensory pores on each side of its lower jaw. The pike blends in perfectly with its surroundings. Its back and upper sides are green to olive brown, becoming lighter on the lower sides and shading to white over the belly. The sides of adults are marked with longitudinal rows of yellow to whitish bean-shaped spots. The scales are very small, and while the cheeks are scaled, the lower half of its gill cover is not.

The differences among pike, musky and pickerel are mainly in size and coloring. Musky have greenish-grey to silvery sides with dark spots or diagonal bars. They grow up to 6 feet and weigh as much as 100 pounds. They have 6-9 large sensory pores on each side of the lower jaw.

The chain pickerel has dark, chainlike markings on its sides and is smaller than the pike and musky, growing to about 2 1/2 feet and 10 pounds. It has 4 large sensory pores on each side of the lower jaw. The walleye (sometimes called walleye-pike) is not a member of the pike family.

Also Known As
Jack/ Snake/
Jackpike/
Jackfish/ Grass
Pike/Brochet

FishBase Name
Northern pike

International Recognitions
France—
Brochet du nord
Germany—
Grashecht
Spain— Lucio
Italy— Luccio
Japan—
Kawakamasu

LANDINGS AND VALUES

The northern pike is circumpolar, found in lakes, ponds and quiet streams in the northern hemisphere. In North America, it is found in rivers and lakes from Alaska to Labrador, throughout Canada, New England, much of New York, the northern Ohio Valley, the Great Lakes and southward to Missouri and Nebraska. It is a solitary fish, but migratory behavior is not clearly established. They usually prefer clear, warm, meandering, heavily vegetated rivers and streams and the weedy bays of lakes. In the spring and fall, they generally live in shallower waters, moving to deeper water at the height of summer. Upper lethal water temperature is around 30°C (86°F). Primarily a freshwater fish, they can tolerate salinity and have been found in brackish waters.

Pike Canadian Landings by Year — Nominal Data Value in $Cdn (000); Quantity in tonnes; (DFO)					
	2004	2005	2006	2007	2008
Value	1,203	855	965	1,035	1,605
Quantity	1,938	1,418	1,572	1,697	1,951

Pike are landed year-round. The largest commercial catches are taken in Manitoba, followed closely by Saskatchewan. Most of the catch is incidental to other fishing operations carried out with gillnets, poundnets and seines. Anglers troll for the pike with spoon hooks and other artificial baits or with live fish bait. Canadian commercial catches average about 1,400 to 1,950 tonnes per year, with 2008 landings valued at $1.6 million. Pike is not a reported commercial fishery in the US. Pickerel and musky are primarily game fisheries with no recorded commercial landings in either the US or Canada, although some landings may be reported as pike. **Aquaculture:** Northern pike does not culture well as it will not accept artificial food.

COMMERCIAL USES

The northern pike is marketed fresh and frozen as a whole fish. The flesh is firm, white and finely textured. The taste is considered excellent, but for the best flavor, the fish should be skinned before cooking. It can be infested with parasites, including the broad tapeworm, so should be thoroughly cooked. It is also a valuable game fish.

LIFE CYCLE

The northern pike spawns soon after the ice melts, in April or early May, when the water temperature is near 45°F. Generally, the northern pike spawns during daylight hours, in heavily vegetated flood plains of rivers, and in marshes and bays of large lakes. A large female, accompanied by one or two smaller males, swims through vegetation in water often no deeper than 2 cm (3/4 inches). Facing each other in close approximation, the fish roll on their sides. Then, during rapid vibrations of their bodies, the eggs and milt are extruded simultaneously. After spawning, the fish wave their tails to scatter the settling eggs.

Mature females can release 10,000 to 100,000 eggs, depending on size. About 50 percent of these get fertilized and the eggs hatch in 12 to 14 days. Growth is dependent on latitude. Although rate of growth decreases after maturity, weight increases until old age. Northern pike in the southern parts of their range spawn occasionally at one year of age, while most spawn initially at two years. In the far north, sexual maturity occurs by age six in females and age five in males. The young feed on small crustaceans and insects, while adults feed mainly on fishes, including young pike, but also frogs and crayfish. Eggs and young pike are preyed upon by aquatic insects, fishes, birds and mammals.

SAUGER

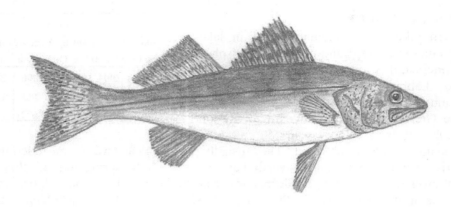

Sauger, *Sander canadensis*

GENERAL

A member of the perch family, Percidae, the **sauger** is a smaller version of its close relative the walleye, which it strongly resembles in both appearance and life cycle. It is an important commercial and sports fishery in north-central North America and is sometimes marketed as Canadian pike, but this is a misnomer as it is not a pike at all..

Sauger and walleye are known to interbreed. This explains the size of larger sauger, called "saugeye."

PHYSICAL DESCRIPTION

Max length: 76.0 cm TL male/unsexed; (Ref. 5723);
Common length: 35.8 cm TL male/unsexed; (Ref. 12193);
Max. published weight: 3,960 g (Ref. 4699);
Max. reported age: 18 years (Ref. 72496)

The body of the sauger is almost cylindrical, with a long, pointed head. The back and sides are dull brown or grey, flecked with yellow, shading to white underneath. It is distinguished from the walleye by its smaller size, the rough scales on its cheeks, and by the two to three rows of distinct black spots on its spiny dorsal fin.

The best identifying characteristic of saugeye, a cross of the walleye and sauger, is the dark bars on the dorsal fin. The saugeye also has sharp canine teeth, dark blotches on the sides and a white tip on the lower tail.

Also Known As
Eastern Sauger/
Sand Pike/ Sand
Pickerel/ Gray
Pike/ Canadian
Pike/ Pike
Perch/ Doré
Noir

FishBase Name
Sauger

International Recognitions
France— Sandre
canadien
Germany—
Kanadischer
Zander
Spain—
Lucioperca
canadiense

SAUGER

LANDINGS AND VALUES

Sauger is found from the St. Lawrence-Champlain River system westward to the Hudson Bay watershed. Most of the catch is taken in the central Manitoba-Minnesota-Nebraska area. Manitoba leads catches in Canada where sauger fishing is carried out almost year-round. Saugers tend to prefer large, turbid, shallow lakes and large, silty, slow-flowing rivers,

Sauger Canadian Landings by Year — Nominal Data Value in $Cdn (000); Quantity in tonnes; (DFO)					
	2004	2005	2006	2007	2008
Value	1,866	1,018	491	298	739
Quantity	639	344	172	105	215

where they can be protected from predators and use the advantage of their better eyesight over prey. In the commercial fishery saugers are caught primarily by gillnet and poundnet. Although saugers are fished for sport, they are too small to be in great demand. It is probable that many saugers are reported as (small) walleye, however.

In Canada, 2,730 tonnes of sauger was landed in 1989 (not shown). More recent years have shown a decline with 215 tonnes landed in 2008, valued at $739,000 (see table). Commercial landings for sauger in the US are not reported.

COMMERCIAL USES

Sauger is marketed as fresh or frozen, whole dressed or as fillets. Much of the catch is exported from Canada to the United States. It is a lean fish with a firm white flesh that is sweeter and finer in texture than that of the walleye.

LIFE CYCLE

The sauger is believed to follow much the same life cycle as the walleye. They spawn in a two-week period, usually beginning in the last week of May or the first week of June. Like the walleye, sauger may spawn in the same shoals of gravel or rubble in large turbid lakes or rivers each year. The males arrive on the spawning grounds first, followed by the females. Spawning takes place during the night, in water depths of 2 to 12 feet at temperatures of between 39° and 43°F. No nest is built; the eggs are fertilized by one or more males as they are shed and fall between the gravel and rocks.

A female will lay from 15,000 to 40,000 eggs per pound of her weight. At a mean water temperature of 46°F, the eggs will hatch in 25 to 29 days. The young spend 7 to 9 days on the bottom, where they absorb the attached yolk sac. The growth rate varies with the location, being faster in Prairie lakes than in lakes found further north.

Generally, they will stay close to bottom, hunting at night in schools for smaller fish, aquatic insects and crayfish. Although the growth rate in the first few years is rapid, it is slower overall than that of the walleye. Saugers are thought to be preyed on by walleye, northern pike, yellow perch and other sauger.

Saugeye: Most hybrid species do not reproduce, but saugeye do occasionally reproduce with sauger or walleye, creating potential genetic problems in the fishery.

SMELT OR AMERICAN SMELT

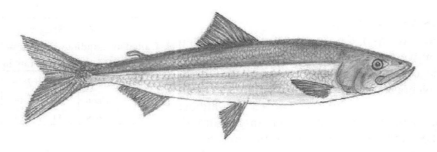

Rainbow Smelt, *Osmerus mordax*

GENERAL

The rainbow or American smelt belongs to the family Osmeridae, along with about 15 species of smelts worldwide. These include the eulachon (*Thaleichthys pacificus*) the delta smelt (*Hypomesus transpacificus*) and the capelin (*Mallotus villosus*). It is also more distantly related to the herring smelts of the family Argentinidae (Argentines). The **rainbow smelt** is a far-ranging fish, which can be found in the ocean, and in rivers and lakes throughout North America. It was originally native to Lake Ontario, but was introduced into the rest of the Great Lakes around 1912 — and subsequently to other large river systems in North America. Smelt fishing, both commercial and sport, is as active today as it ever was: from ice fishing on lakes for sport to the grand trawlers of the Great Lakes. (Also see capelin entry in this book.)

Argentines (*Argentina* spp.) are long known to Europeans; however, at least one species, the great silver smelt, *Argentina silus*, (up to 70 cm long), is occasionally landed in Western Atlantic waters as is the lesser silver smelt (*A. sphyraena*). These are marine species that do not inhabit freshwater.

Also Known As
Spirling/
Saltwater Smelt/
Freshwater
Smelt/ Icefish/
Eperlan

FishBase Name
Rainbow smelt

**International
Recognitions**
France—
Éperlan arc-en-
ciel
Germany—
Regenbogenstint
Spain—
Eperlano arco
iris

PHYSICAL DESCRIPTION

Max length: 35.6 cm TL male/unsexed; (Ref. 1998); max. reported age: 7 years (Ref. 52222)

Once classed in the same order as salmons, it is easy to see that smelts have similarities with these fishes, such as being anadromous and having the characteristic adipose fin of the salmoniformes. The rainbow smelt is a slender, sliver-colored fish with an olive to green back. Out of the water, the sides take on an iridescent purple, blue, or pink hue. It is very similar-looking to the capelin, but the capelin has a larger adipose fin and a projecting lower jaw. It is a large smelt species. The Arctic smelt may be a subspecies (*Osmerus mordax dentex*).

LANDINGS AND VALUES

Today's smelt fisheries are mostly concentrated in the Great Lakes, but smelt are still fished commercially off both coasts, especially California, the New England States and Eastern Canada Smelt enter freshwater during the fall and winter months, but the majority of the East Coast catch is caught in the winter, through holes in the ice. Eastern fishers use gillnets, bagnets and boxnets in this fishery. The Great Lakes trawler fishery allows for higher catches than with the fixed-type of gear used on the coasts.

Sport fishery enthusiasts in the Great Lakes often use dip nets, while coastal fishermen tend to use hook and line from docks in the summer and jigs and spears during the winter ice-fishing season. Regulations over the smelt fishery vary from place to place, but include restrictions on the type of gear used, the allowed mesh size and the open seasons. Management plans for these stocks generally do not exist due to the lack of information required to scientifically base any type of decisions. Data on estimates of reproductive and mortality rates, exploitation rates and current population size are difficult to obtain. In the US, landings for both marine and inland fisheries of various smelts, including

All Smelts & Eulachon (Marine & Freshwater)
US Landings by Year – Nominal Data
Value in $US (000); Quantity in tonnes; (NMFS)

	2004	2005	2006	2007	2008
Value	417	341	559	606	1,102
Quantity	410	352	529	576	437

Smelts (Marine)
Atlantic Canada Landings by Year – Nominal Data
Value in $Cdn (000); Quantity in tonnes; (DFO)

	2004	2005	2006	2007	2008
Value	896	934	741	664	394
Quantity	997	1,088	927	822	580

eulachon, totaled 437 tonnes, valued at $1.1 million in 2008 (see table). Canadian landings reflect separate coastal and inland catches for mainly rainbow smelts. The sea fishery in Canada was 580 tonnes in 2008, valued at $394,000 (see table). The inland fishery was 3,651 in 2008, valued at $1.9 million (see table). Small and sporadic landings of eulachon were recorded in BC and of argentines on both the US and Canada East Coast, over the last 5 years (not shown).

Endangered Status: Rainbow smelt is designated Species of Concern on both coasts and the Pacific eulachon is also designated as Threatened (US). **Aquaculture:** Some interest in farming smelt as valuable bait fish in sport fisheries.

COMMERCIAL USES

The greatest portion of the commercial catch is made up of 2- to 3-year old smelt. They are very good to eat and make a fine export product. Smelt are generally broiled or fried and garnished with butter, salt and pepper. The smelt can often be bought fresh in local markets, but the US and Japan have both imported smelt from Canada in the past. Sea smelt get more value per pound due to the popular belief they have a

Freshwater Smelt
Canadian Landings by Year – Nominal Data
Value in $Cdn (000); Quantity in tonnes; (DFO)

	2004	2005	2006	2007	2008
Value	3,121	1,657	467	2,273	1,884
Quantity	5,886	3,124	920	4,390	3,651

better quality than the landlocked, or non-anadromous variety. This species is also an excellent sport fish in all of its habitats. Argentines are used for fishmeal or food stuffing in Europe and also marketed commercially as frozen silver smelt, whole or headed and gutted.

LIFE CYCLE

Sea smelts inhabit near-shore areas and return to fresh water to spawn in the fall and winter. However, both the lake and ocean varieties migrate upstream to fresh water spawning grounds. Ideally, the eggs are laid on a gravel bottom, to which they stick, in a place where there is an open current for nourishment. Most smelt are able to spawn at 2 to 3 years of age and tend to return to their home spawning grounds. The best water temperature for spawning is from 39 to 45°F. A 2-ounce female may lay 50,000 eggs. Shortly after spawning, most of the males die. The eggs take from 20 to 50 days to hatch, depending on the temperature. The smelt's principal food is shrimplike crustaceans, but they also other zooplankton, insect larvae, aquatic worms and small bits of fish. The females generally grow more quickly than the males. They are a schooling species, and being sensitive to light, tend to stay near the bottom during the day.

STURGEON

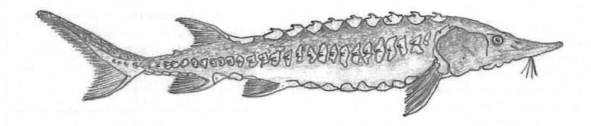

Lake Sturgeon, *Acipenser fulvescens*

Also Known As
Freshwater
Sturgeon
Rock Surgeon
Bony Sturgeon,
Esturgeon

FishBase Name
Lake Sturgeon

**International
Recognitions**
France—
Esturgeon jaune
Spain— rión
lacustre

GENERAL

As a group, sturgeons (family Acipenseridae) are one of the most prehistoric of fishes, known to have lived 65 million years ago. The **lake sturgeon** is one of 4 genera and 29 species that are widely distributed throughout North America, Europe and Asia. It is also one of the largest and longest lived of all purely freshwater species. A record exists of one lake sturgeon landed in Lake Superior weighing 310 pounds and measuring 8 feet. Other notable North American species include the white sturgeon (*A. transmontanus*), also called the "Oregon" sturgeon, and the Atlantic sturgeon (*A. oxyrinchus*); both of which are "anadromous" and found in fresh and saltwater. Atlantic sturgeons are generally larger than lake sturgeons, reaching over 200 pounds in weight and six to eight feet in length, but specimens up to 14 feet long and 800 pounds have been reported from New Brunswick, Canada. The largest recorded white sturgeon was a 468 pound specimen landed in San Francisco Bay, but others have been reported much larger. *FishBase* records suggest the Beluga sturgeon (*Huso huso*), already famous for its caviar, is the largest sturgeon and the largest European freshwater fish with a maximum published weight of 3,200 kg and a maximum size of 8 m (Ref. 59043).

PHYSICAL DESCRIPTION

Maximum Size: 274 cm TL (male/unsexed; Ref. 5723); Maximum Published Weight: 125.0 kg (Ref. 3672); Maximum Reported Age: 152 years (Ref. 72475)

All members of the sturgeon family have cartilaginous skeletons, with thick-set, torpedo-shaped bodies and can be distinguished from other fish by five rows of shield-like bony plates or "scutes;" one along the back and two along each side, which protect the body against attacks from predators. Other notable features include a long, pointed snout with four barbels, and a round, protrusive, sucking mouth. The lake sturgeon has a shark like tail fin, with the upper lobe being longer than the lower. The lake sturgeon's color changes with age. The young have large, black splotches on their sides, back and snout, but these disappear as they grow older. The adults are a uniform olive-brown to grey on the back and sides, shading to white below.

LANDINGS AND VALUES

The lake sturgeon was once abundant in the large rivers and lakes of central and eastern North America, especially the Great Lakes. However, early exploitation, pollution and the impact of the lamprey eel drastically reduced stocks. Lake sturgeon are now found primarily in northern Canada, especially in northern Quebec, but also Ontario and the western provinces, where the numbers have been stable for many years.

The lake sturgeon is a bottom-dwelling fish and its usual habitat lies in the shoal areas of large lakes and rivers, where it uses its sensitive feelers to find food. US landings of sturgeon (all white in 2008) were 164 tonnes, valued at $799,000 (see table). Canada has both freshwater and marine landings; freshwater sturgeon landings in 2008 were 114 tonnes, valued at $505,000 (see table). About 65% of the 2006 freshwater catch was lake sturgeon and the balance was Atlantic sturgeon.

Endangered Status: Lake sturgeon is recognized as endangered, threatened or of special concern in 19 of 20 states and is protected in most parts of the Canadian Great Lakes; also considered endangered by COSEWIC and under consideration for *SARA* status in 8 regions of Canada. The green sturgeon (*A. medirostris*) is listed as under Special Concern in Canada and Threatened in the US. The white sturgeon is listed as Endangered in the Kootenay, Nechako, Upper Columbia and Fraser Rivers (*SARA*).

Aquaculture: Sturgeon is farmed in many countries.

Sturgeon (Green and White) US Landings by Year – Nominal Data Value in $US (000); Quantity in tonnes; (NMFS)					
	2004	**2005**	**2006**	**2007**	**2008**
Value	668	762	714	665	799
Quantity	170	191	162	143	164

Sturgeon (Atlantic Coast, nei) Canada Marine Landings by Year – Nominal Data Value in $Cdn (000); Quantity in tonnes; (DFO)					
	2004	**2005**	**2006**	**2007**	**2008**
Value	243	426	306	387	0
Quantity	39	48	40	54	0

COMMERCIAL USES

Because of the short supply, lake sturgeon is an expensive fish. Most of the catch is marketed in the US, where it is considered a gourmet's delight. The firm white flesh is rich in flavor and also very tasty as a smoked product. Sturgeon is the source of "real" caviar of which the Beluga and other Caspian Sea sturgeons are considered the best source.

All Sturgeon (Lake ~65% , ~35% Atlantic) Canada Freshwater Landings by Year – Nominal Data Value in $Cdn (000); Quantity in tonnes; (DFO)					
	2004	**2005**	**2006**	**2007**	**2008**
Value	505	522	502	502	505
Quantity	131	128	112	112	114

Under US law, only eggs produced by members of the sturgeon family (Acipenseridae) can be called "caviar," while other "caviar" must include the fishes' name. The female lake sturgeon can supply caviar, but to protect the species, it is not usually fished until after spawning.

LIFE CYCLE

The spawning migration for this fish takes place shortly after the ice breaks up in the spring. They spawn in depths of 2 to 15 feet, in areas of swift rapids, or at the base of falls which prevent further migration. During spawning, they lie in groups of two or three, with one or two males for each female. No nests are made, so the adhesive eggs are scattered over the bottom, sticking to logs and rocks. The ripe eggs are black in color and are about 0.12 inches in diameter. The number of eggs released is usually between 100,000 and 1 million, depending upon the size of the female. At a mean temperature of 64°F some eggs are hatched in 5 days, while all would be hatched within 8 days. The young are nourished by a large yolk sac for a period of 9 to 18 days, at the end of which they resemble miniature lake sturgeon. Growth is rapid in their first year, but slower to maturity. For the male of the species, sexual maturity is reached by the age of 8 to 13 years, but first spawning generally does not occur until later. The female's first spawning is between the ages of 14 to 23 years and then spawning only occurs every four to six years. Hence, fishing pressure must be moderate. Lake sturgeons are omnivores and will consume anything edible.

SUCKER

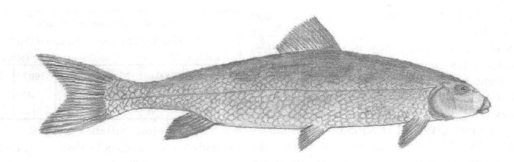

White Sucker, *Catostomus commersonii*

GENERAL

There are about 80 species of sucker (family Catostomidae) native to North America, with the longnose sucker (*C. catostomus*) and the **white sucker** having the widest distribution. "Mullet" or "black mullet" are incorrect names sometimes given by fishermen to the white sucker. This sucker or "mullet" should not be confused with the striped mullet and other "true" mullets that belong to a totally different family of fish, the Mugilidae, most of which normally inhabit salt water.

The bigmouth buffalofish (*Ictiobus cyprinellus*) is another species in the sucker family found in North America, but is of a different subfamily (Ictiobinae). (Also see buffalofish entry in this book.)

PHYSICAL DESCRIPTION

Maximum Size: 65.0 cm TL (male/unsexed; Ref. 10294);
Maximum Published Weight: 2.94 kg (Ref. 4699); Maximum Reported Age: 12 years
Most suckers have relatively large scales and a ventral mouth located on the lower body surface. Large lips covered with small, nipple-shaped protuberances are used to suck up food from the bottom. The fleshy lips also enable these fish to attach to rocks in quick flowing water. Most species are less than two feet in length.

White suckers have a robust, torpedo-shaped body, which is olive brown to grey on the back and upper sides, becoming much darker at spawning time. The lower sides are cream, shading to white over the belly.

The longnose sucker is dark olive, or grey to dark grey, on the back and cream to white on the lower sides and ventral surface of head and body. Spawning male longnose suckers can be quickly identified by a bright red stripe along their sides.

Sea mullets of the family Mugilidae have two dorsal fins and no lateral line on the body.

Also Known As
Black Sucker/
Buffalofish/
Brood Sucker/
Freshwater/Mulet

FishBase Name
White Sucker

International Recognitions
France— Cyprin-
sucet
Germany—
Weißer Sauger

LANDINGS AND VALUES

The white sucker is found only in North American waters. It is found in lakes and rivers from east to west; as far north as the Yukon and Alaska and as far south as North Carolina.

The end of the winter signals its spawning run up the rivers and streams from the lakes below. At this time, both commercial and sport fishermen catch the white sucker using weirs, dip nets, hoopnets and poundnets. At other times of the year, it is caught by commercial fishermen using gillnets. It can also be caught with hook and line baited with worms, grubs and other bait.

Suckers US Landings by Year — Nominal Data Value in $US (000); Quantity in tonnes; (NMFS)					
	2004	2005	2006	2007	2008
Value	56	38	42	21	22
Quantity	127	61	76	36	34

Suckers Canadian Landings by Year — Nominal Data Value in $Cdn (000); Quantity in tonnes; (DFO)					
	2004	2005	2006	2007	2008
Value	756	793	764	580	710
Quantity	0	2,419	2,313	1,637	1,898

The white sucker can inhabit shallow waters and is able to withstand the turbidity, stagnant water and alkalinity of tiny Prairie lakes that would kill most other fish species. US landings in 2008 were 34 tonnes, valued at $22,000 (see table). Canadian sucker landings totaled 1,898 tonnes in 2008, valued at $710,000 (see table).

COMMERCIAL USES

"White sucker" is seldom seen in the marketplace because the name lacks market appeal. As a result, it is often processed in a variety of ways under the name "mullet" (or "mulet" in Quebec). It is marketed mainly as headless, dressed, whole fish and as minced frozen fish. As a fat fish, a small amount is filleted and smoked for export. At one time, the primary use was in the preparation of pet food; however, it is now a more highly valued food fish for its soft-textured sweet white meat. It can be prepared as fish sticks, or used in soups and chowders. Longnose suckers are considered as tasty, or tastier, than whites, although perhaps bonier.

Minnow-sized suckers are also used as live bait by anglers and as food for game fish reared in hatcheries. Suckers may represent an under-utilized species.

LIFE CYCLE

As the winter snow melts away, mullet head toward fast-flowing rivers and streams for a hectic week of spawning activity. The fry hatch within a few days of being laid and then drift downstream with the currents, gathering in schools along the shorelines of cold, larger freshwater lakes and rivers.

Primarily bottom feeders, they aim their fleshy mouth downward to vacuum up worms, clams and, perhaps, fish eggs. Suckers are important in the diet of other species such as northern pike, muskellunge and walleye, as well as birds, bears and other mammals.

TROUT (& TROUT AQUACULTURE)

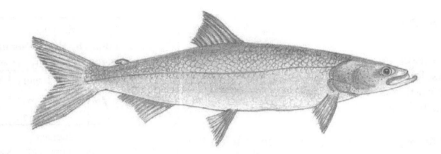

Inconnu, *Stenodus leucichthys*

GENERAL

Neither inconnu nor rainbow trout are "trout" in the strictest sense, but rather, close relatives approved to be marketed under this name. Most trout marketed in the US and Canada is now farmed rainbow trout.

Inconnu, French for "unknown," is what the early explorers called this fish. The voyageurs believed it to be a crossbreed of the whitefish and the lake trout. The scientific name, *S. leucichthys*, translates as "narrow-toothed whitefish" and inconnu was long considered the largest and fastest-growing member of the subfamily Coregoninae (whitefishes) of the Salmonidae family. This subfamily also includes the lake herring or "ciscos." Meanwhile, the rainbow trout (*Oncorhynchus mykiss*) is classified as a Pacific salmon (subfamily, Salmoninae). In *The Seafood List* (the guide to acceptable market names) both inconnu and rainbow trout are recognized as **trout,** for marketing purposes. However, the preferred market name for Arctic grayling (*Thymallus arcticus*), also a North American member of the Salmonidae family (subfamily, Thymallinae) is grayling, and not trout or whitefish.

PHYSICAL DESCRIPTION

Maximum Size: 150 cm TL (male/unsexed; Ref. 4574);
Maximum Published Weight: 40.0 kg (Ref. 10318); Maximum Reported Age: 22 years
It is a long fish, with a large, wide mouth containing many small, densely packed teeth. Its body, looking somewhat like a salmon, is silvery with darker shading over the back and the trademark small adipose fin of the salmonids behind the dorsal. Its scales, like those of the whitefish, are large and conspicuous. It is distinguished from whitefish by its distinctly projecting lower jaw.

LANDINGS AND VALUES

The inconnu is most abundant in large, muddy, northern rivers and lakes. In North America, it is located in the Northwest and Yukon territories and in Alaska. In coastal areas, the inconnu is anadromous, ascending from the sea to spawn in freshwater streams. However, the inland lakes fish are freshwater dwellers all their lives, migrating up small streams in summer and returning to the lake in fall. The inconnu is usually fished on its downstream migration, back to lake or ocean.

Also Known As
Nelma
Fighting
Sheefish
Caspian Inconnu
Sheefish

FishBase Name
Sheefish

**International
Recognitions**
France—
inconnu
Germany—
Weisslachs

The main fishery is on the Mackenzie River drainage system, including Great Slave Lake, using gillnets. The last reported commercial catch of inconnu was in 1989, totalling 63 tonnes, valued at approximately $125,000 (not shown). Inconnu was never a commercial fishery in the US. This leaves the lake trout (really a char) as the only significant commercial "trout fishery" left in North America.

Rainbow Trout

Trout Aquaculture: Aquaculture production is now the source of most commercial trout in North America, especially rainbow trout. Rainbow trout that migrate to the ocean (like salmon) or are farm-raised in saltwater are usually called "steelheads," and may vary in size and color, but there is essentially no other difference from the landlocked variety. There are, however, many sub-species of rainbow trout (e.g., Oregon claims three). Rainbow trout have been artificially introduced to many regions, including eastern North America. In fact, researchers now believe the rainbow trout was originally indigenous to the eastern Pacific peninsula of Kamchatkan, in Russia, before migratory steelheads populated the Pacific coast of North America. In 2008, US "trout" aquaculture production was 16,213 tonnes, valued at $49.8 million, while Canadian production was 7,785 tonnes, valued at $40.3 million (see tables). (Also see lake trout entry in this book.)

Endangered Status: Various trout species (e.g., steelhead/rainbow and cutthroat) are designated as Threatened or Endangered in many West Coast rivers and drainages in both the US and Canada.

All Trout Aquaculture US Production by Year — Nominal Data Value in $US (000); Quantity in tonnes; (NMFS)					
	2004	2005	2006	2007	2008
Value	57,082	65,469	57,664	58,960	49,774
Quantity	24,937	27,504	22,525	22,249	16,213

All Trout Aquaculture Canadian Production by Year — Nominal Data Value in $Cdn (000); Quantity in tonnes; (DFO)					
	2004	2005	2006	2007	2008
Value	22,086	21,363	19,743	23,570	40,330
Quantity	4,858	4,857	4,374	5,044	7,785

COMMERCIAL USES

In the past much of the commercial inconnu catch was exported to the US smoked fish market. The flesh is white, soft and has a rich flavor. Its high oil content makes it excellent for smoking. Its greatest untapped value presently is as a sports fishery; it is an excellent game fish. Farmed rainbow trout can usually be found whole, dressed, fresh or frozen in supermarkets across North America.

LIFE CYCLE

Inconnu spawning is believed to take place in late summer or early autumn, but there is little information concerning spawning behavior or spawning areas. It is suspected that individual fish may spawn only once every couple of years. The number of fertilized eggs is thought to be somewhere between 125,000 and 325,000. The rivers that exhibit large inconnu runs include the Big Buffalo and Taltson rivers; while the Slave, Little Buffalo and Hay rivers have smaller runs. The upstream, presumably pre-spawning migration is prolonged and apparently continues all summer. Young juveniles are thought to remain in Big Buffalo River for at least two years before descending into Great Slave Lake. In Great Slave Lake, the inconnu mature in 7 to 10 years at 22 to 27 inches. Hybridization of inconnu and various whitefishes (*Coregonus* spp.) is believed to be due more to the broadcasting of eggs and sperm rather than the pairing of species or genera.

TROUT

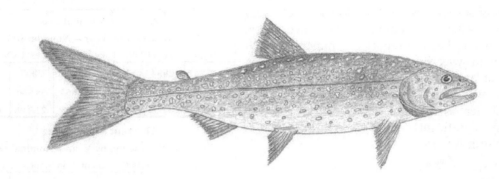

Lake Trout, *Salvelinus namaycush*

GENERAL

The **lake trout**, like the brook trout, belongs to the char (*Salvelinus*) branch of the Salmonidae family (see the Salmonidae Table). For clarification, the brown trout and the Atlantic salmon belong to the trout branch (genus *Salmo*), while the Pacific salmons and the rainbow trout belong to the salmon genus (*Oncorhynchus*). The rainbow trout, formerly *Salmo gairdneri*, was reclassified as a Pacific salmon (*Oncorhynchus mykiss*) in 1989, but the species is still called rainbow trout, generating heated discussions in many fishing camps. Similarly, the lake trout is a char and not a "true trout," but the differences do not spoil the sportsman's delight or the gourmet's palate; and the preferred market name for lake trout (char?) is "trout." The largest lake trout on record weighed about 40 kg (102 pounds).

PHYSICAL DESCRIPTION

Maximum Size: 150 cm TL (male/unsexed; Ref. 40637);
Max. Publ. Weight: 32.7 kg (Ref. 40637); Max. Reported Age: 50 years
The lake trout's color varies from near black to light green, depending on the water temperature and ambient light conditions. The color shades to pale yellow on the belly. Colder water will produce a red flush along the lower sides and an orange tinge along the edges of the lower fins. Fish from larger lakes tend to have a silvery cast. The long body is scattered profusely with light-colored dots and large, bean-shaped splotches on the flat part of the head, the dorsal fin and the tail. Unlike most members of the Salmonidae family, the lake trout has a deeply forked tail. Its teeth grow on both upper and lower jaws, on the roof of the mouth and even on the tongue. Rainbow trout generally have a sheen on their sides that reflects red and green, hence the name "rainbow." The tail is only slightly forked.

LANDINGS AND VALUES

The lake trout can be found in lakes and rivers across North America from the far north of the Northwest Territories south to Vermont. At one time, the Great Lakes teemed with these trout, but over-fishing, pollution and the lamprey eel dramatically reduced populations. Although stocked, self-sustaining populations are now primarily limited to Lake Superior.

Also Known As
Siscowet/ Splake/ Gray Trout/ Salmon Trout

FishBase Name
Lake trout

International Recognitions
France— Touladi
Germany— Amerikanische Seeforelle
Spain— Trucha lacustre
Italy— Trota di lago americana

The lake trout's slow growth and slow maturation rate mean that they are often taken before they reach maturity and before they have a chance to spawn. About 50 percent of Canadian landings come from Saskatchewan with the balance (and most US) catches from the Great Lakes Region, especially Lake Superior. Lake trout is usually caught by rod and reel, but it can be netted, hook and line jigged through the ice, or, in commercial ventures, gillnetted. There is only a small commercial exploitation of lake trout, since, even with hatcheries operating in both the Canada and the US, the population has been slow to increase. Canadian landings were 522 tonnes in 2008, valued at $424,000; while the US catch was 302 tonnes, valued at $240,000 (see table). **Aquaculture:** Lake trout is not farmed; for information on farmed trout, see the entry on trout/inconnu (& trout aquaculture) in this book.

Lake Trout US Landings by Year — Nominal Data Value in $US (000); Quantity in tonnes; (NMFS)					
	2004	2005	2006	2007	2008
Value	195	165	168	218	240
Quantity	186	188	219	266	302

Lake Trout Canadian Landings by Year — Nominal Data Value in $Cdn (000); Quantity in tonnes; (DFO)					
	2004	2005	2006	2007	2008
Value	587	486	447	384	424
Quantity	790	653	600	452	522

COMMERCIAL USES

Lake trout is available fresh or frozen, dressed, head dressed, or in tray-packed steaks and I.Q.F. (individually quick frozen) fillets.

LIFE CYCLE

The lake trout is the largest fish in the salmon family. It is also the greediest, with the least discriminating tastes, eating everything from plankton and small insects to fish and small mammals. The trout will also prey on smaller members of its own kind. The lake trout thrives in cold water, from temperatures of 40 to 50°F. It cannot withstand a high degree of salinity and thus inhabits lakes, rivers and streams. In the warm summer months, it tends to stay on the bottom where it is much cooler and darker, but may swim near the surface in colder months. The lake trout is a very local fish: it will generally stay in the same area it was hatched and usually spawns in its original spawning grounds. Most rarely travel further than 15 miles during their entire lives.

Water temperature affects the growth rate of lake trout. In southern areas, it reaches sexual maturity in about 6 years, while it may take up to 12 years in more northern regions. It appears to spawn every second autumn, with less frequency farther north. Females lay from 1,000 to 15,000 eggs, which hatch between March and June. The young fry are characterized by a reddish tinge and parr marks.

Under controlled conditions, trout can interbreed, though this behavior is very rare in the natural environment. Scientists have found a few good crossbreeds, such as the "splake," a cross between a brook trout and a lake trout. This breed combines the early maturation and fighting nature of the brook trout with the size and deep swimming characteristics of the lake trout, to produce a top quality sports fish.

WALLEYE

Walleye, *Sander vitreus*

GENERAL

With the many names it is sometimes known by, it would seem the **walleye** must belong to the pike or pickerel family. However, it is actually one of the 14 species of true perch (Percidae) found in North America's inland water system. Closely resembling the smaller sauger, and similar to the yellow perch, the walleye is easily identified by its glassy, opal eyes, which assist nocturnal foraging.

A major commercial and sport fishery, the walleye is (along with the yellow perch, whitefishes and catfishes) one of the most economically valuable of the freshwater species. Sport fishermen prize the walleye for its fighting spirit and as an incomparable food fish.

Except for the name "walleye," there is no close relation between the walleye and the walleye (or Alaska) pollock, which is a totally different species found in the Pacific Ocean (see entry on walleye pollock). The scientific name for walleye is currently listed as *Sander vitreum* in *The Seafood List*, an apparent mis-spelling.

PHYSICAL DESCRIPTION
Maximum Size: 107 cm FL (male/unsexed; Ref. 1998);
Maximum Published Weight: 11.3 kg (Ref. 4699); Maximum Reported Age: 29 years

The body of the walleye is elongated, thickset and robust with a cone-shaped head and a mouth well-armed with teeth. It has two dorsal fins, distinguishing it from the pike, which has only one. The front fin has sharp spines; the rear fin does not. The walleye is bright golden to brownish green, flecked with gold or yellow, shading to white over the belly. The lower lobe of its tail fin has a milky white tip.

The eyes of the walleye are large and silvery from light reflected by a light-sensitive layer. This feature gives the fish a glassy-eyed or "wall-eyed" appearance, as the name implies.

Also Known As
Walleye Pike/
Yellow Pickerel/
Yellow Pike/
Pickerel

FishBase Name
Walleye

International Recognitions
France— Sandre américain
Germany— Amerikanischer Zander
Spain— Lucioperca americana

LANDINGS AND VALUES

The walleye is found in lakes and rivers from Quebec to British Columbia, and from the Great Lakes north to the mouth of the Mackenzie River in the Northwest Territories. The walleye is most abundant in Manitoba, followed by Ontario and Saskatchewan. Commercial catches are caught primarily with gillnets set from boats during the summer and beneath the ice in the winter. In some locations stationary poundnets are also used. Anglers use many methods to catch walleye, including still fishing, drifting and jigging. Caught on a fishing line, the walleye puts up a prolonged and spirited fight.

Walleye US Landings by Year — Nominal Data Value in $US (000); Quantity in tonnes; (NMFS)					
	2004	2005	2006	2007	2008
Value	45	61	29	19	94
Quantity	12	18	14	9	22

Walleye Canadian Landings by Year — Nominal Data Value in $Cdn (000); Quantity in tonnes; (DFO)					
	2004	2005	2006	2007	2008
Value	26,130	31,521	32,534	30,528	28,643
Quantity	6,945	8,855	10,245	8,984	8,288

Walleye are capable of enduring a wide range of environmental conditions. They appear to prefer large, shallow, turbid lakes but also thrive in clear lakes and rivers if they are deep enough to protect their light-sensitive eyes. Canadian (commercial) landings in 2008 were 8,288 tonnes, valued at $28.6 million (see table). US landings were relatively minor, with the Great Lakes region reporting only 22 tonnes in 2008, valued at $94,000 (see table).

COMMERCIAL USES

Walleye is marketed in fillets in both fresh and frozen form and as whole, dressed fish. It is highly valued for its firm, finely flaked flesh, which has a succulent texture and a sweet taste.

LIFE CYCLE

Spawning occurs in the spring to early summer, depending on the latitude and water temperature. Normally, spawning begins when the water temperature reaches between 45 and 48°F; however, spawning has been known to occur in water with a mean temperature of 52°F. The spawning grounds are generally rocky areas in flowing rivers and streams, below impassable falls and dams. Males move toward the spawning grounds first. Spawning takes place at night, at depths of about 6 feet, with either one large female and two males, or two females and several males.

The female rolls on her side and releases the eggs at the same time the males release milt. The fertilized eggs are heavier than the water and sink into the crevices of the stream or lake bottom, where they stick to stones and debris. The maximum number of eggs released by a single female has been estimated to be around 600,000.

The eggs hatch after 12 to 18 days. Ten to 15 days after that, the young disperse into the upper layers of the open water. By the latter part of the summer, the young have moved toward the bottom. Growth is fairly rapid in the southern areas and somewhat slower farther north. Also, females tend to grow more quickly than males.

WHITEFISH

Lake Whitefish, *Coregonus clupeaformis*

GENERAL

Lake whitefish is one of many species of the genus *Coregonus,* commonly referred to as whitefishes, and a member of the Salmonidae family. In North America, lake whitefish is the most commercially important whitefish and, next to the perches, the most valuable freshwater capture fishery. There are 14 species in the *Coregonus* genus native to North America (8 listed in *The Seafood List*; 3 under the market name "whitefish") and it is generally difficult to distinguish them from each other, except by size. One closely related species, the lake herring (*C. artedi*), is marketed as "cisco" or "tullibee," while even smaller whitefishes are usually marketed as "chubs" or "bloaters." Lake whitefish has been extolled since the days of the early explorers for its exceptionally fine flavor.

PHYSICAL DESCRIPTION
Maximum Size: 100.0 cm TL (male/unsexed; Ref. 9988);
Max. Published Weight: 19.0 kg (Ref. 28850); Max. Reported Age: 50 years

Also Known As
Inland
Whitefish/
Labrador White
Fish/ Shad

FishBase Name
Lake whitefish

**International
Recognitions**
France—
Corégone de lac
Germany—
Felchen
Spain—
Coregono de
lago
Italy—
Coregone

The lake whitefish is characterized by a long, deep body and relatively small head, tapering to a blunt snout overhanging the lower jaw. Older fish develop a fleshy bump at the shoulders, which makes the head appear even smaller. Like other salmonids, whitefish have an adipose fin situated on the dorsal to the front of a deeply forked tail. As their name implies, lake whitefishes are silvery white, with darker-hued backs that range from light olive to dark brown, often tinged with green. The cisco is more streamlined than the whitefish and has a smaller pelvic fin, resembling a sea herring.

LANDINGS AND VALUES

The lake whitefish is found in many North American freshwater areas, from the Atlantic coast westward to British Columbia and Alaska. In Canada, the largest producers are Manitoba, Alberta and Saskatchewan, while Michigan and Wisconsin are the largest in the US. The lake whitefish is commercially fished by gillnets set in open water during the summer and below the ice in the winter. In some areas, trapnets and poundnets are used.

In 2008, the US catch of lake whitefish was 4,332 tonnes, valued at $8.1 million; while the Canadian catch was 6,497 tonnes, valued at $10.8 million (see tables). Other whitefish (tullibee) catches increased the 2008 US total by 620 tonnes, valued at $1.2 million; while the Canadian catch of tullibee was 284 tonnes, valued at $271,000 (see table). Landings for the round whitefish, (formerly *C. cylindraceus,* now classified as *Prosopium cylindraceum*), are reported separately in the US, but these landings are generally incidental (5 tonnes in 2008, valued at $7,000). In recent years, the whitefish has become an active sport fishery in many areas. Anglers catch it on a small hook, usually baited with salted or fresh minnows, or shiners. **Endangered Status:** The shortnose cisco (*C. zenithicus*) is endangered (*SARA*) and the shortjaw cisco (*C. reighardi*) is threatened (COSEWIC). A primitive whitefish called the Atlantic (or Acadian) whitefish (*Coregonus huntsmani*), found only in an isolated part of Nova Scotia, is also considered an "endangered" species in Canada and "vulnerable" on the IUCN Red List.

Lake Whitefish US Landings by Year — Nominal Data Value in $US (000); Quantity in tonnes; (NMFS)					
	2004	**2005**	**2006**	**2007**	**2008**
Value	6,801	6,769	6,754	7,819	8,119
Quantity	3,847	3,874	4,244	4,548	4,332

Tullibee (Lake Herring/Cisco and Chubs) US Landings by Year — Nominal Data Value in $US (000); Quantity in tonnes; (NMFS)					
	2004	**2005**	**2006**	**2007**	**2008**
Value	1,773	1,345	1,548	1,677	1,175
Quantity	1,117	1,005	1,058	877	620

COMMERCIAL USES

The lake whitefish is a medium-fat fish with large flakes of white flesh and a delicate, sweet flavor. It can be used in most salmon and trout recipes and is also excellent smoked. It is marketed fresh and frozen, whole, dressed and as fillets, but is also available in minced blocks, IQF and as tray-packed fillets. There is a strong demand for the roe, which is marketed as "golden caviar."

Lake Whitefish Canadian Landings by Year — Nominal Data Value in $Cdn (000); Quantity in tonnes; (DFO)					
	2004	**2005**	**2006**	**2007**	**2008**
Value	10,790	8,786	9,145	9,423	10,777
Quantity	8,537	7,158	7,098	6,648	6,497

Tullibee (Lake Herring/Cisco and Chubs) Canadian Landings by Year — Nominal Data Value in $Cdn (000); Quantity in tonnes; (DFO)					
	2004	**2005**	**2006**	**2007**	**2008**
Value	70	66	261	279	271
Quantity	136	99	278	262	284

LIFE CYCLE

The lake whitefish spawns in the fall, usually in November and December, in the Great Lakes region and earlier in more northern areas. Spawning begins when the water temperature drops to approximately 46°F with peak activity occurring at even lower temperatures. Usually, spawning occurs in shallow water, at depths of less than 25 feet although spawning in deeper water has been reported. Spawning usually takes place over a hard or stony bottom but it can occur over a sandy bottom. The number of eggs deposited by a female varies from population to population and tends to increase with the size of the female.

Eggs and milt are deposited randomly over the spawning grounds by the parent fish. The parent fish become quite active and may jump and thrash about, especially during the night. The eggs remain on the spawning grounds until they hatch, in April or May. After hatching, the larvae are known to form aggregations above steep shorelines. The young whitefish generally leave the shallow inshore waters by early summer and move out into deeper water. The growth rate varies from lake to lake but is fairly rapid overall. The males mature and die earlier than the females.

Representative North American Shellfish Species

Including *Scientific Names*, MARKET NAMES, Common Names and Aliases

Scientific Name	MARKET NAMES	Common Name	Also Known As
Phylum Mollusca	INVERTEBRATES	Molluscs	Shellfishes (Clams, Snails, Squids, etc.)
Class Bivalvia (or Class Pelecypoda)	BIVALVES	Pelecypods or Bivalves	Shellfishes (Clams, Mussels, Scallops, etc.)
Mya arenaria	CLAM, SOFTSHELL	Softshell Clam	Steamer, Maninose
Mercenaria mercenaria	CLAM OR QUAHOG	Northern Quahog	Hardshell, Littleneck, Quahog
Spisula solidissima	CLAM, SURFCLAM	Atlantic Surfclam	Bar Clam, Hen Clam, Sea Clam, Strip Clam, Skimmer Clam
Panopea abrupta	CLAM, GEODUCK	Pacific Geoduck	
Venerupis philippinarum	CLAM, LITTLENECK	Japanese Littleneck Clam	Manila clam
Mytilus edulis	MUSSEL	Blue Mussel	Common Mussel, Bay Mussel
Crassostrea virginica	OYSTER	Eastern Oyster	Virginia Oyster, Malpeque Oyster
Placopecten magellanicus	SCALLOP	Sea Scallop	Giant Scallop, Deep-sea Scallop
Clinocardium nuttallii	COCKLE OR COCKLE CLAM	Common Cockle	Nuttall Cockle, Heart Cockle, Basket Cockle
Class Gastropoda	GASTROPODS	Gastropods or Univalves	Shellfish, Sea Snails, Escargot, Scungilli
Haliotis rufescens	ABALONE	Red Abalone	Sea Ear, Ear Shell, Venus Ear Shell
Strombus gigas	CONCH	Queen Conch	Pink Conch
Busycotypus canaliculatus	WHELK	Channeled Whelk	Sea Snail, Conch, Bulot Shell
Littorina littorea	PERIWINKLE	Common Periwinkle	Buckie, Whelk
Class Cephalopoda	CEPHALOPODS	Cephalopods	Squid, Octopus, Calamari
Loligo pealeii	SQUID	Longfin Squid	Calamari, Winter Squid, Boston Squid
Octopus vulgaris	OCTOPUS	Common Octopus	Pieuvre, Pulpo Comun
Enteroctopus dofleini	OCTOPUS	North Pacific Giant Octopus	
Phylum Arthropoda	ARTHROPODS	Arthropods	Crustaceans, Spiders, Insects
Class Crustacea	CRUSTACEANS	Crustaceans	Crustaceans - Lobster, Crab, Shrimp
Homarus americanus	LOBSTER	American Lobster	Maine Lobster, Atlantic Lobster
Cancer magister	CRAB	Dungeness Crab	Pacific Edible Crab, California Crab
Farfantepenaeus aztecus	SHRIMP	Brown Shrimp	Redtail Shrimp, Brownies
Cancer borealis	CRAB	Jonah Crab	
Menippe mercenaria	CRAB, STONE	Florida Stone Crab	
Class Merostomata	MARINE CHELICERATES	Merostomata	Spiders, mites, ticks, horseshoe crabs
Limulus polyphemus	CRAB, HORSESHOE	Horseshoe Crab	King Crab
Phylum Echinodermata	ECHINODERMS	Echinodermata	Echinoderms
Class Echinoidea	ECHINOIDS	Echinoids	Sea Urchins, Sand Dollars
Strongylocentrotus franciscanus	SEA URCHIN	Red Sea Urchin	Urchin
Class Holothuroidea	HOLOTHUROIDS	Holothuroids	Sea Cucumbers
Parastichopus californicus	SEA CUCUMBER	California Stichopus	Sea Slug, Bechedemer
Phylum Porifera			
Class Demospongiae	SPONGES	Sponges	
Spongia graminea	SPONGE	Grass Sponge	

Shellfishes

Listed Alphabetically

ABALONE

Red Abalone, *Haliotis rufescens*

GENERAL

Abalones (family Haliotididae) are one of several marine snails (called gastropods) of high commercial importance; in fact, they are one of the single most valuable molluscs in the world today - if you can find them. A number of abalone species exist along the Pacific coast. The most important include the large near-shore **red abalone** and the pinto or "northern" abalone (*H. kamtschatkana*). Other Pacific abalones are the black abalone (*Haliotis cracherodii*); the green abalone *(H. fulgens)*; the pink abalone (*H. corrugata*), the threaded abalone (*H. assimilis*) the flat abalone (*H. walallensis*) and the deeper sea "white" abalone (*H. sorenseni*). Both the white and black abalones have been fished so extensively they have been almost extirpated and both are designated Endangered Species under the *ESA* (US).

Also Known As
Sea Ear
Ear Shell
Venus Ear Shell

SeaLifeBase Name
Red abalone

International Recognitions
Spain—Abulón colorado
France—Ormeau rouge

PHYSICAL DESCRIPTION

Max size 11.76"; Commonly size 6-8" (world's largest abalone) Weight: up to 2.3 kg (5 lb.)

These flattish, oval-shaped snails (also see whelk entry in this book) are distinguished by a body whorl and a row of holes (pores) that run parallel to the outer edge of their shells (through which the animal ingests water and expels waste products). A meaty foot is able to attach tightly to rocky surfaces by means of extended sensory tentacles.

The red abalone, by abalone standards, is one of the largest, potentially growing up to 12 inches. The outer shell is dull reddish-brown; the inside, however, is a polished pink, with bluish and copper tones as well. The interior outer rim is often red. There are 3 to 4 outer pores. The foot and tentacles are usually black and the sole (of the foot) is grayish-brown. The smaller pinto abalone generally measures from 4 to 6 inches and has an irregular, narrow outer shell that is a mottled brown and grey. There are 3 to 6 open pores and the pore edges are elevated above the shell surface. A groove in the shell can parallel the line of pores. The inner shell is pearly-white with faint pale-green reflections. Pinto abalone tentacles are yellowish-brown to sometimes green and thin.

LANDINGS AND VALUES

The red abalone occurs along the Pacific Coast of North America, from Bodega Bay, California, south to Mexico. The snail's natural habitat is rocky areas of moderately deep waters (intertidal zone and sub-tidally down to at least 100 feet). Its size, abundance and closeness to shore made it a preferred commercial and recreational species.

However, production of all abalones in the US petered-out in the 1990s and the abalone fishery in California was finally closed to all commercial fisheries in 1996, as well as most recreational fisheries, pending recovery efforts. The pinto or northern abalone is the only species native to Washington, BC and Alaska waters. Canadian northern abalone landings in 1989 were

Abalones US Landings by Year — Nominal Data Value in $US (000); Quantity in tonnes; (NMFS)					
	2004	2005	2006	2007	2008
Value	5	5	5	5	3
Quantity	1	1	1	1	--

approximately 49 tonnes, valued at nearly $1.2 million. However, the BC fishery was deemed at risk and closed in 1990, followed by Washington State in 1994 and Alaska in 1995. Stocks in Canada continued to decline throughout the 1990s and a recovery strategy for northern abalone was initiated in 2001. Traditionally, almost all abalone was harvested manually by divers who removed the molluscs from rocks with a curved bar or chisel. The high price of the product results from two factors: the high cost of harvesting and its scarcity. Most abalones are slow-growing, and recruitment to maturity is slow, so that larger animals are often harvested before they spawn. **Endangered Status:** Except for red abalone, most abalones are designated "species of concern" or "endangered" in the US and Canada (e.g., pinto abalone). **Aquaculture:** With only minor commercial landings (see table) US commercial abalone is now almost totally farmed. US production in 1989 totaled 28 tonnes (meats), valued at $331,000 (not shown). By 2007, it is reported there were 13 abalone farms on the coast of California where the farmed abalone size was normally 75 to 100mm. The largest farm produced over 100 tons and the smaller farms less than 10 tons. (Fishtech Inc.)

COMMERCIAL USES

The red abalone is the favored cultured species. The only edible part of the animal is the muscular foot, which makes up roughly 40% of the fleshy contents of the shell. To prevent toughness, the flesh is usually pounded gently to break down muscle fibers and then cooked for only a short time. Abalones are sold live-in-shell, fresh or frozen, mainly for sushi and sashimi in Japan and Korea, and as a delicacy in local upscale restaurants.

LIFE CYCLE

Triggered by ocean conditions, local populations of males and females spawn together simultaneous and seed and sperm are "broadcast" into the water. Females may lay up to 12 million eggs—an exceptionally high level of fecundity, which scientists believe may be necessary to offset mortality rates. Eggs fertilized in the water become active larvae in a few days and may be carried away by currents. Within two weeks the larvae settle to the bottom, where they feed on microscopic algae and bacteria. As the juvenile abalone grows, it becomes less mobile and tends to attach itself to one location (although it can move quickly when approached by a sea star). Movement is somewhat dictated by the available crevice space and shelter. As the abalone becomes more sedentary it feeds on algae and plant matter taken from the water, rather than directly on kelp. Octopus, crabs, sea stars, fishes, shore birds and animals prey on small abalones. Larger abalones have fewer predators, but sea otters (in particular), wolffish and some octopus can rapidly destroy colonies. Growth is somewhat dependent upon food supply and water temperature, but it generally takes 4 to 5 years for a red abalone to reach a market size of 4 to 5 inches.

CLAM, SOFTSHELL

Softshell Clam, *Mya arenaria*

GENERAL

The **softshell clam** (family Myidae) is one of the most abundant of all species of clams and is the most predominantly harvested clam in inter-tidal waters on the Atlantic coast. The earliest fossil record of the soft-shell clam dates back approximately 25 million years ago. In the past the clam was used in various ways by the Native Indians and early settlers; for example, food, fertilizer (calcium carbonate), jewelry, dishes and as a form of currency. Although there are 9 species in the genus *Mya*, the *M. arenaria* is the only clam listed under market name "softshell" in *The Seafood List*.

PHYSICAL DESCRIPTION

Max length : 10.0 cm TL male/unsexed; (Ref. 7726)

The color of the clam shell is usually chalky white. It is grey or yellow in younger clams due to an outer covering called the periostracum that tends to disappear with age, leaving a white appearance. However, because of the high organic content of some muds, a clam may also appear almost black. The clam's outer surface is covered with elliptical markings that represent the clam's annual growth rings. A neck capable of extending greatly is located at one end (posterior) of the clam. This neck contains two siphons, one for taking in water and the other for expelling it. At the opposite end of the clam's neck is its foot. The foot is a muscular tongue-shaped structure capable of great expansion and contraction that allows the clam to burrow quickly into the sediment. The soft-shell clam has a more elliptical shell than hard-shell clams and the shell is much thinner, usually cracking easily under pressure.

LANDINGS AND VALUES

The soft shell clam is found in bays and estuaries, both inter-tidally and sub-tidally, to depths of approximately 10 meters (30 feet). These clams usually bury themselves in fine sands mixed with clay and mud, or in black muds of high organic content. In the western Atlantic, the soft shell clam is most abundant from Chesapeake Bay northward and is scarce south of North Carolina. It was accidentally introduced to the Pacific coast about 100 years ago with oyster seed and has now spread from California to Alaska.

Also Known As
Steamer/
Maninose Clam

**SeaLifeBase
Name**
Softshell clam

**International
Recognitions**
Spain—Mye des
sables
France—Almeja
de can

The clam hack or hoe is used to retrieve clams at low tide. Maine has traditionally been the major US producer with landings of 3,444 tonnes of meats in 1989, valued at almost $24 million. Harvests have since declined through over-harvesting, pollution and predators, such as the green crab, an aquatic invasive species that has recently found its way to Canadian waters too. US landings of soft shelled clams (meats only) in 2008 were 1,789 tonnes, valued at almost $22.5 million (see table). The Canadian harvest of 1,014 live tonnes and $2 million represents Atlantic coast only (Pacific landings are too small to be reported). **Aquaculture:** Soft-shell clam enhancement projects are used in the industry. (See quahog entry in this book for additional clam aquaculture information.)

Soft-Shell Clams (meats) US Landings by Year — Nominal Data Value in $US (000); Quantity in tonnes; (NMFS)					
	2004	2005	2006	2007	2008
Value	19,112	22,823	23,158	24,349	22,469
Quantity	1,401	1,597	1,768	1,770	1,789

Soft-Shell Clams (live) Canadian Landings by Year — Nominal Data Value in $Cdn (000); Quantity in tonnes; (DFO)					
	2004	2005	2006	2007	2008
Value	7,867	6,973	4,379	3,175	1,998
Quantity	3,625	2,874	2,102	1,555	1,014

COMMERCIAL USES

Clams were first used in the mid-1800s as bait for fishers who caught cod, mackerel and halibut. Over the years, however, clams have become a delicacy. Clam beds are periodically afflicted by paralytic shellfish poison (PSP) and beds become closed to harvesting. However, once in clean saltwater, the clam will normally purify itself in about 48 hours. (Also see "shellfish sanitation" in the glossary.) Clams are available fresh shell-on or shucked, frozen, battered, IQF and are also available canned. Clams can be steamed, baked, deep-fried and used in chowders, quiches, casseroles, paellas and hors d'oeuvre. Clam hunting is also a popular leisure activity—the traditional clam bake.

LIFE CYCLE

Soft-shell clams are dioecious (the sexes are separate). Clams mature at two or three years of age. With the onset of summer, the cream- to yellow-colored gonads develop rapidly. Peak spawning takes place in mid-summer and, like many other inter-tidal invertebrates, spawning is linked to tidal cycles and water temperature. The eggs and sperm are released from the clams' expelling siphon into the water column where they unite. The larvae grow into juvenile clams and these attach themselves to the sediment by "byssal" threads. After reaching a size of 6 mm, they release their byssal threads and establish a permanent burrow. As the clam grows larger, it burrows deeper, using its highly extendable, mobile foot. Young clams may grow as much as 1 inch per year, but growth slows in older, larger clams to about 1/3 inch per year. Clams have many predators, including ducks, cormorants and gulls (which are known to carry clams inland, to be dropped and broken to get at the meat inside). Some large fish such as rays, cod and flounders will swallow clams whole.

CLAM OR QUAHOG

Northern Quahog, *Mercenaria mercenaria*

GENERAL

The **northern quahog** or "hard clam" (as it is usually called), is a bivalve mollusk (family Veneridae) with a variety of names in the commercial trade. Small hard clams are typically called "little necks," while slightly larger ones are "cherrystones" and the largest are "chowders." Recently, very small little necks have been called "pasta necks," and a size called "top neck" has been introduced between little neck and cherrystone. Although the minimum size of a little neck is set by law in some areas, all size categories can be flexible and cause market confusion. The little neck name refers to its siphon size and its association with Little Neck Bay, New York. The cherrystone name is derived from Cherrystone Creek, Virginia. A clue to the value of this species lies in its Latin name, 'mercenaria" referring to money, as beads were formed from the shell and made into wampum belts by aboriginal tribes. Hard clam stocks have been affected by overharvesting in some areas, but a very large and successful aquaculture industry has developed for little neck sizes. Hard clams can accumulate toxins, but in practice there is little evidence they do so. The main problem is sewage pollution, but stringent measures are in place to control contamination (see "shellfish sanitation" in the glossary).

Also Known As
Hard Clam
Hardshell/
Littleneck

SeaLifeBase Name
Northern quahog

International Recognitions
Spain—Chirla mercenaria
France—Praire

PHYSICAL DESCRIPTION

Max length: 13.0 cm TL male/unsexed; (Ref. 7726)

The hard clam has a heavy, slightly oblong shell, and the exterior is typically dull white in color. The shell can be stained by sediments, and a color variant known as a "notata clam" has zigzag brown markings. These markings are particularly abundant in many cultured clams. The interior is white, with either white or purple muscle scars and posterior border. It is the purple of these clams that made the most valuable wampum. The southern quahog *Mercenaria campechiensis* is a close relative of the northern quahog, but with a typically heavier and broader shell. Landing information for both species appears to be grouped. Both of these quahogs also resemble the ocean quahog (*Arctica islandica*) or "mahogany clam," but this is a different species found mainly in deeper waters.

LANDINGS AND VALUES

Hard clams can be found from the Gulf of St. Lawrence south to the Gulf of Mexico, with southern quahogs found from Virginia south with most landings reported in Florida. These are typically shallow water clams, inhabiting areas from inter-tidal to moderately deep water in protected bays and estuaries. At times some are found on the continental shelf. The clam buries itself beneath the sediment and must be dug out for harvest.

Hard clams may be harvested by mechanical dredging, but most states limit harvesting to "hand" methods, such as patent tongs and bull rakes. The former are typically winched from boat side and grab a portion of the bottom, which is washed, brought on board and sorted. The other is a true hand method using a large toothed basket attached to a pole with a handle that is "rocked" through the bottom to extract the clams. Total hard clam production in the US in 2008 was 3,071 tonnes (meats), valued at almost $49 million (see table). This 2008 total does not include 1) ocean quahog landings of 304 tonnes, valued at approximately $2.2 million, 2) unspecified quahog landings of 293 tonnes, valued at almost $4.3 million and 3) unspecified clam and bivalve landings of 36,269 tonnes (65% from New Jersey and 22% from Massachusetts), valued at $47 million. The latter probably represents mostly ocean quahog landings, but may include some hard clams. Typically, about 20% of hard clam landings are in waters where the southern quahog is found. Canadian landings of hard clams totaled 738 tonnes in 2008, valued at $1 million (see table). Canada's catch of ocean quahog is incidental (2 tonnes, valued at $2,200 in 2008 - not shown). **Aquaculture:** US clam aquaculture was valued at $88 million in 2008 (see table). On the US East Coast most culturing is hard clams, but there is softshell as well; on the West Coast (including Canada) it is primarily littlenecks, "manilas," and geoducks, with interest in abalone. Hard clam aquaculture is now found in most coastal states. The focus is on the small, valuable sizes for the half-shell trade.

Quahog - Hard Clam (excludes Ocean Quahog) US Landings (meats) by Year — Nominal Data Value in $US (000); Quantity in tonnes; (NMFS)					
	2004	2005	2006	2007	2008
Value	0	934	834	52,536	48,988
Quantity	0	79	75	4,005	3,071

Quahog - Hard Clam (excludes Ocean Quahog) Canadian Landings (live) by Year — Nominal Data Value in $Cdn (000); Quantity in tonnes; (DFO)					
	2004	2005	2006	2007	2008
Value	2,016	2,352	1,417	991	995
Quantity	1,005	1,356	814	571	738

COMMERCIAL USES

Most large hard clams and ocean quahogs are used for chowder, but a portion is minced for use in stuffed clams, cakes, fritters, etc. Small hard clams are valued for their tenderness and compete in the "steamer" market with softshell clams, but most little neck and cherrystones are consumed raw on the half shell. There is a trend for the smallest sized farmed products to be marketed as "pasta necks" and these, plus some little necks, are used in preparations requiring clams in the shell (on pasta, bouillabaisse, bisque, paella, etc.).

LIFE CYCLE

Hard clams in northern waters typically spawn from June to August; farther south, there may be an early spring and late fall spawn. The sexes are separate. Each female can produce tens of millions of eggs each year. The larvae spend about 2 weeks in the plankton stage and then set on the bottom, attaching to sand grains or other hard objects with a byssal thread. As the small clam grows the byssus gland atrophies and the quahog burrows into the sand, its prominent shell ridges serving as an anchor. Quahogs mature sexually after 2 or 3 years, at a shell size of about 3 inches. All quahogs have a male phase with about half becoming female at maturity. Spawning is more variable as they age.

US Clam Aquaculture Production Value in $US (000); Quantity in tonnes; (NMFS) (meat wt.)					
	2004	2005	2006	2007	2008
Value	73,339	72,783	75,357	65,754	88,088
Quantity	9,511	5,699	5,129	4,873	5,180

Canada Clam Aquaculture Production Value in $Cdn (000); Quantity in tonnes; (DFO) (live wt.)					
	2004	2005	2006	2007	2008
Value	7,371	8,463	8,906	9,713	8,614
Quantity	1,599	1,856	1,707	1,869	1,628

CLAM, SURFCLAM (& OTHER ATLANTIC CLAMS)

Atlantic Surfclam, *Spisula solidissima*

GENERAL

The **Atlantic surfclam** (family Mactridae) is the largest clam on the Atlantic coast. It is also one of the most active; when attacked by predators, it can actually jump to safety by pushing off the bottom with its foot. Surfclams, as the name implies, were originally harvested on sandy shores where they were deposited by the surf. As these areas became commercially exploited, the fishery moved further offshore. A close and valuable relative of the Atlantic surfclam is the Arctic surfclam, *Mactromeris polynyma* (also known as "Stimpson's surfclam"), landed in Canadian waters. A small amount of other surfclams (*Mactromeris* spp.), as well as jackknife and razor clams (*Ensis* spp., *Solen* spp., *Siliqua* spp.) [all usually marketed as razor clams] and venus clams (*Chione* spp.) are also harvested in both the US and Canada, on both coasts. The northern propellerclam* (*Cyrtodaria siliqua*), [closely related to the geoduck – see entry] is also harvested in Canadian waters, often as a by-catch of the offshore fishery. (See New References section in the Appendix for additional information on razor clams; also see the glossary for information on shellfish sanitation.)
[*not listed in *The Seafood List*]

Also Known As
Bar Clam/
Hen Clam/
Sea Clam

SeaLifeBase Name
Atlantic Surfclam

International Recognitions
Spain—Almeja blanca
Global—Mactre solide

PHYSICAL DESCRIPTION

Max length : 20.0 cm TL male/unsexed; (Ref. 7726)
The surfclam is triangular-shaped with a thick chalky shell that has a shiny, yellowish brown coating. It has a relatively short siphon and a large muscular foot for propulsion and burrowing. The Arctic surfclam closely resembles the Atlantic surfclam, but is smaller (seldom exceeding 10 cm) and has a reddish colored meat, rather than the yellowish color of the Atlantic surfclam.

Common Types	Atlantic Coast Clams Scientific Name(s)	Coastal Range	US Landings 2008 ($000)	US Landings 2008 MT-meats	Canada Landings 2008 ($000)	Canada Landings 2008 MT- live
Atl. Surf	*S. solidissima*	Mid-Atlantic	7,962	5,019	638	619
Arctic Surf	*M. polynyma*	N. Atlantic	N/A	N/A	28,913	20,016
Quahogs	*M. mercenaria, A. islandica*	Atlantic/Gulf	55,959	3,668	997	740
Softshell	*Mya arenaria*	Atlantic	21,979	1,535	1,998	1,014
Razor, Prop.	*Ensis* spp., *Cyrtodaria siliqua*	Atlantic	428	33	32	17
Clams (nei)	Clams or Bivalves (Other)	Atlantic	46,940	36,269	--	--
Total	(includes blood arc clam)		**133,293**	**46,535**	**32,578**	**22,406**

LANDINGS AND VALUES

The Atlantic surfclam is not especially plentiful in Canadian waters but is heavily exploited in the US, especially between Long Island and Virginia. New Jersey often accounts for about two-thirds of the landings. The preferred habitat is clean sandy shores at the extreme low water mark so they are not left high and dry. The surfclam can be found from the low tide mark down to 150 feet. The Arctic surfclam prefers colder northern waters and is primarily a Canadian offshore catch. Surf-clams are now landed by large vessels using hydraulic dredges that can blow the clams out of their burrows before scooping them up.

Atlantic Surfclam US Landings (meats) by Year — Nominal Data Value in $US (000); Quantity in tonnes; (NMFS)					
	2004	2005	2006	2007	2008
Value	32,603	30,009	31,536	34,103	7,962
Quantity	26,621	24,942	24,077	25,305	5,019

Atlantic Surfclam (Bar) Canadian Landings (live) by Year — Nominal Data Value in $Cdn (000); Quantity in tonnes; (DFO)					
	2004	2005	2006	2007	2008
Value	877	1,077	986	1,054	638
Quantity	932	932	881	928	619

Sometimes, suction pumps are used to bring the clams to the surface. The surfclam and ocean quahog fishery was one of the first in the US and Canada to be managed by individual transferable quotas (ITQs). Each company receives a right to catch a certain number of clams each year, depending upon prior performance. The rights to harvest can be sold or leased to other companies.

US landings of Atlantic surfclams totaled 5,019 tonnes (meats) in 2008, valued at approximately $8 million (see table). Canadian landings of Atlantic surfclams totaled 619 tonnes in 2008, valued at about $638,000 (see table). Canadian landings of Arctic surfclams totaled 20,016 tonnes in 2008, valued at approximately $29 million (see table).

Arctic Surfclam (Stimpson's) Canadian Landings (live) by Year — Nominal Data Value in $Cdn (000); Quantity in tonnes; (DFO)					
	2004	2005	2006	2007	2008
Value	30,580	22,580	29,387	26,690	28,913
Quantity	24,038	19,310	21,925	18,825	20,016

In addition, Atlantic Canada harvested 17 tonnes of razor clams and propellerclams in 2008, valued at $32,000; although the propellerclam total was down from almost 2,300 tonnes in 2005 (not shown).

COMMERCIAL USES

Almost all Atlantic surfclams are canned or minced for chowders. The meats are often frozen in 4-inch-thick sheets called "blankets" for the institutional market or the secondary food processor. The foot is occasionally cut into strips and deep-fried. Although the shell looks very similar to the Atlantic surfclam, the Stimpson's surfclam is a different animal altogether. The meat is a cherry red color and more closely resembles a native Japanese clam. Its bright color and rich flavor has not been accepted in traditional surfclam markets in North America; hence, it is primarily an export product to Japan, where it is called "hokkigai," and served as sushi. However, as with any quality shellfish, that could change in the future.

LIFE CYCLE

Most Atlantic surfclams begin spawning within their first two years; some as early as 6 months. Spawning usually occurs in June, July and August. As with other clams, the larvae drift as plankton for a few weeks before settling to the sandy bottom where they use their large foot to burrow into the sand. It is a fast-growing clam, adding as much as 1 inch each year, thus reaching market size in 3 to 4 years. The species is fecund and resilient to fishing pressure.

CLAM, GEODUCK (& OTHER PACIFIC CLAMS)

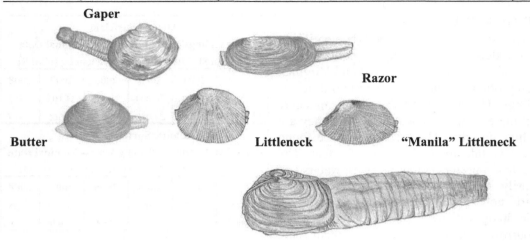

Gaper

Razor

Butter   Littleneck   "Manila" Littleneck

Pacific Geoduck, *Panopea abrupta*

GENERAL

The **Pacific geoduck** is the largest of the North American bivalves (family Hiatellidae) whose name (pronounced "gooey-duck") is believed derived from the Nisqually Indian phrase for "dig deep." (This clam typically burrows 2 to 3 feet into the mud of inter-tidal and sub-tidal waters.) Other Pacific bivalves harvested for their tasty meats include the 1) gaper clams such as the Pacific gaper (*Tresus nuttallii*) and the fat gaper (*T. capax*); also called "horse" clams and marketed correctly as surfclams; 2) butter clams, such as the Washington Clam (*Saxidomus nuttalli*) and the butter clam (*S. gigantean*), marketed correctly as butter clams; 3) razor clams, such as the Northern razor (*Siliqua patula*); and 4) littleneck clams such as the Pacific littleneck clam (*Protothaca staminea*) and the Japanese littleneck clam (*Venerupis philippinarum*) - the latter often referred to, incorrectly, as the Manila clam – are both correctly marketed as littleneck clam* (different from the East Coast "little necks"). *The Seafood List* also recognizes the genus *Tapes* spp. as "littleneck clam," although *T. variegate* is not listed in *ITIS* (even as a synonym) and *T. rhomboides* appears to be a European variety. [Also see "shellfish sanitation" in the glossary.]

Also Known As
Geoduck Clam
Pacific Gweduc

SeaLifeBase Name
Pacific geoduck clam

International Recognitions
Spain—Panopea del Pacífico
Global—Panopée du Pacifique
Japan—miru-gai

PHYSICAL DESCRIPTION

Common length: 21.2 cm SHL male/unsexed; (Ref. 78831) Common Weight: (1.4 to 2.3 kg);

Common Types	Pacific Coast Clams Scientific Name(s)	Coastal Range	US Landings 2008 ($000)	MT-meats	Canada Landings 2008 ($000)	MT- live
Geoduck	*Panopea abrupta*	Mid-Pacific	44,324	1,308	29,715	1,562
"Manila"	*Venerupis philippinarum*	Mid-Pacific	21,584	570	1,559	498
Littleneck	*Protothaca staminea*	Mid-Pacific	91	15	4	2
Butter	*Saxidomus* spp.	Mid-Pacific	23	8	73	79
Gaper	*Tresus* spp.	N. Pacific	11	2	--	--
Razor	*Siliqua patula*	Mid-Pacific	398	45	305	174
Softshell	*Mya arenaria*	Mid-Pacific	489	254	--	--
Total	**(totals are rounded)**	--	**66,922**	**2,201**	**31,656**	**2,315**

PACIFIC GEODUCK

The geoduck has a thick, oblong, coarse shell that is rounded at front and more square-like at the rear. The shell has notable wavy growth lines and is a creamy-white color with a thin yellowish coating. The siphons are too large to retract and the rough, brown neck is usually bulging out of its small shell. Approximately 50% of its total weight is made up by the "neck," which is necessarily long for deep burrowing. Gaper ("horse") clams can be confused with geoducks; however, gapers have pads and tentacles on the siphon tip and the color is dark green or black. The Japanese littleneck ("manila") is longer and flatter than the native Pacific littleneck.

Pacific Geoduck (meats) US Landings by Year — Nominal Data Value in $US (000); Quantity in tonnes; (NMFS)					
	2004	2005	2006	2007	2008
Value	28,076	30,984	26,417	36,960	44,324
Quantity	1,073	1,130	1,327	1,156	1,308

Geoduck Clam (live) Canadian Landings by Year — Nominal Data Value in $Cdn (000); Quantity in tonnes; (DFO)					
	2004	2005	2006	2007	2008
Value	34,373	31,650	32,206	30,431	29,715
Quantity	1,797	1,560	1,560	1,560	1,562

LANDINGS AND VALUES

The geoduck can be found along the Pacific coast from Alaska to the Gulf of California. Originally it was only fished recreationally. However, it is now fished commercially year-round by divers using high pressure water jets and efforts to farm it are underway. In terms of quantity, geoduck landings are not huge relative to clam landings on the east coast; however, they are a valuable species accounting for a significant percentage of overall clam value. In 2008, US landings totaled 1,308 tonnes (meats), valued at approximately $44.3 million (see table). Canadian landings totaled 1,562 tonnes (live) in 2008, valued at almost $29.7 million (see table). **Aquaculture:** See quahog entry.

COMMERCIAL USES

Geoduck is usually sold live to the Chinese market. It can also be marketed shucked and frozen, or fresh in the shell. Frozen siphon and body meat are usually sold separately. Most is exported to China. The body of the geoduck can be sliced into cutlets that are battered and fried for the restaurant trade. Minced meat (siphon and foot skinned) is well-suited for chowders, fritters, or stuffed clams. Horse clams and butter clams are often used in chowders and fritters; some butter clam is canned. Manilas and littlenecks are steamer clams; most are sold live. However, a small portion of the market is for frozen meats.

LIFE CYCLE

Geoducks spawn in the summer, releasing eggs and sperm into the water. Generally, spawning activity occurs simultaneously with all animals spawning at once when water conditions are optimal. Fertilization occurs in the water column. Fertilized eggs drift as larvae for about 2 months and then settle to the bottom to begin life as clams. The young clams are still able to travel by burrowing back out of the sediment and detaching threads that act as a parachute so they can drift with the current. Geoducks, like all clams, derive their nourishment from siphoning and filtering microscopic plant and animal life from the water. Growth is registered by the rings formed on its shell. They grow very quickly for the first 10 years, then shell growth stops (in length) while body weight continues to increase. They can be harvested after 5 years, but can live up to 168 years. As they get older, they are not able to move freely; in fact, once a mature geoduck is dug up, it can no longer use its foot to burrow back into the sediment. Mature geoducks have few natural enemies as most sea stars and other predators cannot reach them. Although rare, a cousin of the Pacific geoduck, the Atlantic geoduck (*Panopea bitruncata*) is found in moderately shallow water on the Atlantic coast from North Carolina to Florida.

COCKLE OR COCKLE CLAM

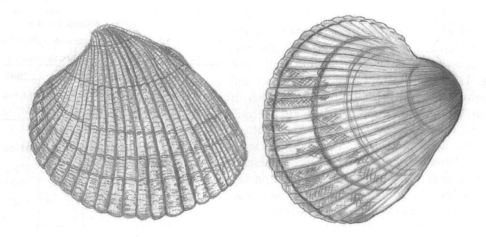

Common Cockle, *Clinocardium nuttallii*

GENERAL

Cockles are found in the family Cardiidae that has 15 genera and about 166 species. The family includes the **common cockle** and the Greenland cockle (*Serripes groenlandicus*), both of which are marketed as either cockle or cockle clam; the California cockle (*C. californiense*), and the Atlantic giant cockle (*Dinocardium robustum*), both of which are marketed only as cockle. Altogether, *The Seafood List* identifies 7 species that are marketed only as "cockle" and 2 species that are marketed as either "cockle" or "cockle clam." *The Seafood List* also identifies another species, *Cerastoderma edule*, under the name "common cockle," which may change in the future as normally each species has an unique common name. Also note that the *SeaLifeBase* name for common cockle is the Nuttall cockle – a name that is still well understood in North America. However, these are no doubt small problems for the scientists working to clarify complex shellfish taxonomies.

Also Known As
Nuttall Cockle
Heart Cockle/
Basket Cockle

SeaLifeBase Name
Nuttall cockle

International Recognitions
UK—basket cockle

PHYSICAL DESCRIPTION
Accounts of Alaskan specimens living up to 19 years;
Height up to 14 cm, but usually less than 5 cm.

Cockles, in general, have broad, high shells with radial ribs, two adductor muscle scars nearly equal in size and cardinal and lateral hinge teeth. Generally a cockle is a shell that is higher or not "noticeably" less high (dorsal to ventral distance) than it is long (anterior to posterior end). The **common cockle** is thick and has more than 30 distinct radial ribs covering the entire valve that interlock with one another at the ventral margins of the valve. The shell is usually a yellowish-cream to brownish color, mottled with darker brown or orange bands or blotches. The siphon is short, and, when buried in the sand, siphon edges appear white with white hairs extending from their tips. A side view reveals a heart-shaped profile. It is distinguishable from many other species by having radial ribs and by having greater height than length.

LANDINGS AND VALUES

In the North Pacific, the common cockle is distributed from Japan across the Bering Sea to Alaska and as far as San Diego, California in fine-mud sands of low intertidal and shallow sub tidal zones. It stays slightly buried in the substrate and is occasionally found in eelgrass beds. It is also reported in Venezuela (*SeaLifeBase*), putting it into a tropical shellfish category and perhaps suggesting its range may be more widespread than so far reported.

Nuttall Cockle US Landings (meats) by Year – Nominal Data Value in $US (000); Quantity in tonnes; (NMFS)					
	2004	**2005**	**2006**	**2007**	**2008**
Value	53	42	50	72	74
Quantity	23	16	20	24	26

(Greenland) Cockle (Atlantic Landings) Canadian Landings (live) by Year – Nominal Data Value in $Cdn (000); Quantity in tonnes; (DFO)					
	2004	**2005**	**2006**	**2007**	**2008**
Value	4,402	6,953	11,209	1,237	143
Quantity	4,783	7,387	10,362	1,144	125

In 2008, 26 tonnes of common (Nuttall) cockle, valued at $74,000, was landed in the US (see table). Almost all of the catches in 2008 were landed in Oregon. The Greenland cockle is reported as distributed in the western North Atlantic and surrounding the Canadian Archipelago. Canadian landings (Newfoundland) were 125 tonnes in 2008, valued at $143,000. This total was down considerably from previous years (see table).

Aquaculture: Alaska and BC are reportedly developing cockle aquaculture.

COMMERCIAL USES

Marketed fresh, frozen and canned (Newfoundland). Cockles are similar to clams and are consumed the same way: steamed, baked, broiled, etc.

LIFE CYCLE

Cockles live in sand and mud sediments close to shore (intertidal to 30 meters, preferably in sheltered bays where the salinity doesn't vary much). Unlike most bivalves, common cockles are simultaneous hermaphrodites and reach sexual maturity in about two years. Spawning occurs in summer months. They can live up to 16 years.

They are filter feeders and can pump up to 2.5 litres of water per hour, per gram of body weight. Their predators include gulls, sunflower star, and Dungeness crabs. They are able to slow feeding in winter, almost ceasing to eat entirely and can avoid predation (i.e., sea stars) by leaping away (extending foot rapidly). They are also occasional host to pea crabs in their mantle cavity.

CRAB, BLUE

Green Crab

Blue Crab, *Callinectes sapidus*

GENERAL

Ancient civilizations often revered the crab and it even became a sign of the zodiac (Cancer). In more recent years it has become the symbol for anti-pollution and resource management initiatives in Chesapeake Bay. With both a large commercial and recreational fishery the **blue crab,** family Portunidae (swimming crabs), has become one of the most popular crabs in history. Alternatively, the green crab (*Carcinus maenas*), has become one of the most unpopular crabs in many parts of its range. Blue crabs are also in the same superfamily (Portunoidea) as deepsea crabs (*Chaceon* spp.).

PHYSICAL DESCRIPTION

Max length : 22.7 cm WD male/unsexed; (Ref. 367)

Width: up to 9 in. (22.5 cm) Age: 2.5 to 3 years

As the name suggests, the blue crab is usually an olive or bluish-green color above with bright blue claws beneath. The shell is more than twice as wide as it is long, with nine marginal teeth and hind legs that are paddle-shaped. Whereas, the abdomen ("apron") of the male abruptly tapers to a long, slender cylinder-shape, that of the female is broadly rounded, facilitating easy identification of sexes. As with all crabs, the blue crab has an exoskeleton, including a single heavy carapace or "shell" that covers the fused head and thorax region.

The small green crab is native to northern Europe, but was introduced to North America, as well as other regions circumglobally. Max. carapace width: 7.7 cm; commonly 5 cm (Ref. 2779).

Also Known As
Hardshell Crab/
Softshell Crab

SeaLifeBase Name
Blue crab

International Recognitions
Spain—Cangrejo azul
France—Crabe bleu

NA Crabs Common Names	Scientific Name(s)	Coast Location	All US Landings (MT)		All Canadian Landings (MT)	
			1989	2008	1989	2008
Blue (all forms)	*Callinectes sapidus*	East	95,796	71,392	N/A	N/A
Snow/Tanner	*Chionoecetes* spp.	East/West (N)	74,058	29,973	22,364	93,866
Dungeness	*Cancer magister*	West	20,442	22,654	1,522	6,445
King	*Paralithodes* spp.	West (N)	11,097	12,341	NA	--
Jonah, Rock spp.	*Cancer* spp. (excl. Dungeness)	East/West	1,612	6,914	1,722	7,496
Deepsea GoldRed	*Chaceon* spp.	East	7	220	N/A	--
Stone	*Menippe* spp.	East (SE)	2,411	2,823	N/A	N/A
Spider/Toad	*Hyas* spp. nei	East (NE)	4	3	N/A	583
Total Crabs (includes others not shown)			**210,304**	**148,888**	**25,617**	**108,391**

BLUE CRAB

LANDINGS AND VALUES

The blue crab can be found along the Atlantic Coast as far north as Nova Scotia (though rare) and southward to northern Argentina and throughout the Gulf of Mexico. It is most abundant in Chesapeake Bay. Individual blue crabs have been sighted along the European coast and in the Mediterranean Sea. It is

Blue Crab (includes soft and peelers) US Landings by Year — Nominal Data Value in $US (000); Quantity in tonnes; (NMFS)					
	2004	**2005**	**2006**	**2007**	**2008**
Value	145,905	140,818	126,043	148,788	162,660
Quantity	79,181	72,232	75,357	68,572	71,392

believed that such crabs simply "hitchhiked" across the ocean on various seafaring vessels and are not native to those waters. In the same way, it is believed the green crab, an invasive species, was introduced to North America. The blue crab is found in coastal areas from the shoreline to depths of approximately 300 feet. They are abundant in coves, bays and estuaries to depths of more than 100 feet. The blue crab is fished commercially using crab pots or traps, baited long-lines or a light dredge in colder months when crabs are minimally active. It is the softshelled crab (i.e., those recently molted) that commands the highest price followed by the "peelers" (those about to molt). US landings in 1989 totaled 95,796 tonnes, valued at $90.1 million (not shown). In 2008, US landings totaled 71,392 tonnes, valued at $162.7 million (see table). The "soft" and "peeler" combinations in 2008 accounted for only 937 tonnes (1.3%) of the catch, but $6.1 million (3.8%) of the value (not shown). However, true value is much under-stated as the blue crab is also a major sport fishery. In 2008, 74 tonnes of green crab was also landed in the US, valued at $164,000 (not shown).

COMMERCIAL USES

The most common method of commercial processing is to cook blue crabs live in a steam retort at temperatures ranging from 240 to 250°F. Once cooked, the crabs are air-cooled to ambient temperature and then placed overnight in refrigerated coolers. The following day, the meat is hand-picked from the crab, contributing to the high cost of this product. The typical shelf-life of picked meats is about 7–10 days. However, pasteurization and refrigeration can extend this to 6 months or more. The green crab is edible, but except for bait and research, is difficult to market.

LIFE CYCLE

Blue crabs can reach sexual maturity as early as 10 months and usually no later than 18 months (as compared to 2- to 7-years for other crab species) and produce from 700,000 to two million eggs; factors that help maintain its heavy fishing pressure. The female crab mates only once during her lifetime, but can store sperm for future spawnings and may spawn several times in a single season. Prior to the molt that changes a juvenile to an adult, the female crab moves to less saline waters and is grasped by a male, under which she is cradled until molting. While in the soft stage the male deposits sperm in the seminal receptacles located inside the female. The female is released after its shell hardens. In the spring and summer months, 1-9 months following copulation, the female ovulates and the eggs pass through the seminal receptacles where they are fertilized. The eggs are then extruded and attach to the swimmerets (hairy appendages on the abdomen) for 7-10 days. The eggs hatch into planktonic zoea, which are approximately 1/24 inches long. After 31 to 49 days as zoea, the crab metamorphoses to a single megalops stage. The crab remains in this stage for 6 to 20 days and then transforms into the first crab stage. Adulthood is reached 10 to 18 months after hatching. Omnivores that feed on shellfish, fish, worms, plants and detritus; they are preyed on by drum, striped bass and croaker.

The green crab inhabits shallow water from the intertidal range down to 200 meters on both coasts; its destructive impact has affected the soft-shell clam, oysters and native crab fisheries.

CRAB, DUNGENESS

Dungeness Crab, *Cancer magister*

GENERAL

One of nearly three dozen true crab species that inhabit the west coast, the Dungeness crab is highly prized both as a sport and commercial shellfish. Its common name is derived from a fishing port located near Puget Sound, Washington. The scientific name literally means chief, or main, crab. The **Dungeness crab** is a member of the family Cancridae (rock crabs) that includes only one genus and 14 species; some of which are found on both coasts.

PHYSICAL DESCRIPTION

Carapace width: Max. 23 cm (male); Max. weight 2.0 kg (male)

Like all crabs, lobster and shrimp, the Dungeness crab belongs to the decapod order of crustaceans, having ten legs of relatively even length. Like most crabs, the male is larger than the female, often growing to a width of 10 inches and weighing as much as 4 pounds. The primary color of the Dungeness crab is sandy to medium brown. Two other species, the red rock crab* (*C. productus*) and the graceful rock crab* (*C. gracilis*), are sometimes confused with the dungeness. However, the dungeness can be distinguished from other West Coast crabs by the white-tipped pincers on its claws (chelipeds) and the sawtooth edges of the claws and upper pincers, with more than a dozen teeth along each edge. The Dungeness crab is also similar to the Atlantic rock or "purple" crab (*C. irroratus*) and the Jonah or "white" crab (*C. borealis*) found on the East Coast, although these species do not grow as large. (* Not listed in *The Seafood List*.)

Also Known As
Market Crab

SeaLifeBase Name
Dungeness crab

International Recognitions
Spain—Buey del Pacífico
France—Dormeur du Pacifique
Italy—Granciporro

NA Rock Crabs Common Names Crabs	Scientific Name(s)	Coast Location	US Landings 2008 Value ($000) MT	Quant MT MT	Canadian Landings 2008 Value ($000) MT	Quantity MT MT
Dungeness	*Cancer magister*	West	118,733	22,655	36,537	6,445
Jonah	*Cancer borealis*	East	5,033	4,185	331	385
Atlantic Rock	*Cancer irroratus*	East	2,172	2,176	5,654	7,111
Red Rock	*Cancer productus*	West	1,633	554	N/A	N/A
Graceful Rock	*Cancer gracilis*	West	N/A	N/A	N/A	N/A
Yellow Rock	***Cancer anthonyi***	West	N/A	N/A	N/A	N/A
(Pacific) Rock	***Cancer antennarius***	West	N/A	N/A	N/A	N/A
Other nei	Unidentified crabs	East (98%)	3,710	1,886	0	0
Total Rock Crabs (includes other crabs nei)			**131,281**	**31,455**	**42,522**	**13,941**

DUNGENESS CRAB

LANDINGS AND VALUES

The Dungeness crab ranges from the Aleutian Islands to Monterey Bay, California. (They are not found on the Atlantic coast.) They live primarily in bays, inlets and estuaries, and on the continental shelf between the low tide level and depths of 600 feet. Most fishing activity taking place in depths of 15 to 170 feet. Their preferred habitat is open sandy bottom areas with good water exchange, although they may utilize eelgrass beds for molting, mating or travel. They bury themselves in the

Dungeness Crab **US Landings by Year — Nominal Data** Value in $US (000); Quantity in tonnes; (NMFS)					
	2004	**2005**	**2006**	**2007**	**2008**
Value	120,713	101,843	148,983	133,012	118,736
Quantity	32,974	29,785	40,322	25,852	22,655

Dungeness Crab **Canadian Landings by Year — Nominal Data** Value in $Cdn (000); Quantity in tonnes; (DFO)					
	2004	**2005**	**2006**	**2007**	**2008**
Value	48,019	28,067	21,306	34,398	36,537
Quantity	9,429	5,415	3,870	6,210	6,445

sand when they are not actively feeding or traveling. Dungeness crabs are fished using circular stainless meshed traps from 30" to 40"in diameter and from 8" to 12" deep. Peak landings for the BC and Alaska coast occur over the late spring and summer. The winter fisheries in California and Oregon reflect the earlier molting period in warmer southern waters. The fishery along the entire Pacific coast is managed by size (often 6.5"), sex (males only) and season (often year-round with some winter closures) although quotas are in place for some jurisdictions (notably Washington). This crab is a major industry on the Pacific west coast with the states of Washington, Oregon and California taking the lion's share, closely followed by BC. In 2008, US landings totaled 22,655 tonnes, valued at $118.7 million (see table). Canadian landings were 6,445 tonnes, valued at $36.5 million (see table).

COMMERCIAL USES

The Dungeness crab is sold live, cooked, whole frozen as frozen meat packs and canned. The flavor is very well received and approximately 25% of the market is in China.

LIFE CYCLE

The female can be bred only in the softshell condition and, unlike the snow crab, continues to molt throughout her life (about 8 years). She is capable of storing sperm for at least 2 batches of eggs (2 years) after being bred. Hence, the female frequently skips molts once reaching maturity. Males generally molt annually until they near commercial size, in which case, some may also skip-molt. The male may carry the female for several days before her molt. After she molts, the breeding male clasps the female so that their undersides are in close contact and sperm is released into the female's body. The sperm will remain there until the eggs are fertilized in the autumn. Fertilized eggs (estimated at 500,000 to 1 million) are extruded and attach themselves to the female's abdomen, where they are brooded until spring. After the eggs hatch, the young crabs are free swimming for about 4 months and go through 5 larval stages known as the zoea. In the final stage (the "megalops") the larvae have tiny claws and legs and become recognizable as crabs, although still have a shrimp-like tail. The male attains commercial size after 12 to 14 molts, at about four years of age. However, it will continue to grow with each molt; growth slowing after maturity. The Dungeness preys on small fish, clams, squid, worms, other crustaceans and each other. They are in turn preyed upon by halibut, dogfish, sculpins, octopus and other crabs. Salmon also feed on megalops larvae, but not adults.

CRAB, JONAH (& OTHER ROCK CRABS)

Jonah Crab, *Cancer borealis*

GENERAL

Although the large Dungeness crab is the dominate species (by far) in the rock crab fisheries, it is by no means the only commercial species. The **Jonah crab**, the Atlantic rock crab (*C. irroratus*) and the (Pacific) red rock crab (*C. productus*) are three other species in the family Cancridae (rock crabs) that are also major commercial fisheries in themselves. The yellow rock crab (*C. anthonyi*), the (Pacific) rock crab, (*C. antennarius*) and the graceful (or "slender") rock crab (*C. gracilis*) are also species of importance to recreational and commercial fishermen on the West Coast. (Also see Dungeness crab entry in this book).

PHYSICAL DESCRIPTION

Carapace width: Max. 18cm (male), 15cm (female);
Max. weight: 0.9 kg (males) , 0.5 kg (females)

The Jonah crab has a carapace that is approximately 2/3 as long as it is wide and a rough textured body surface. The pincers and snout are about the same length as its second legs. It has a red dorsal coloration with yellow-white on the ventral side. Legs are mottled yellowish-red and purple. It can be distinguished by having two curved lines of yellow spots on the posterior portion of its back that can resemble the letter "H."

The Atlantic rock crab has a carapace that is approximately 2/3 as long as it is wide and a roughly textured body surface. The pincers are moderate-sized and shorter than the second legs. Body color is yellowish, but highly concentrated with fine dots of dark purple, becoming more reddish brown after death. Unlike the Jonah crab, ventral side and appendages are brownish purple, rather than white. It is a smaller crab overall, with a smaller meat claw than the Jonah crab.

Also Known As
Atlantic
Dungeness

**SeaLifeBase
Name**
Jonah crab

**International
Recognitions**
Spain—Jaiba de
roca jonás
France—Crabe
jona
Italy—
Granciporro
atlantico

LANDINGS AND VALUES

The Jonah crab ranges from Nova Scotia to North Carolina and parts of the Caribbean in the intertidal zone to depths of 800 meters. Smaller individuals are found near shore seasonally, but larger ones are usually in deeper waters, preferring rocky bottoms. Its habitat overlaps the distribution of the Atlantic rock crab and the American lobster, *Homarus americanus*. Both crab fisheries can be a directed fishery or a bycatch of the lobster fishery. Typically, only the males are harvested.

In 2008, 4,185 tonnes of Jonah crab valued at $5.0 million was landed in the US. Most of the catches in 2008 were landed in Massachusetts (49%), followed by Rhode Island (25%), Maine (17%), and New York (6%). Small amounts were landed in New Hampshire and New Jersey. The gear used was pots and traps. Canada landed 385 tonnes, valued at $331,000, in 2008.

Jonah Crab US Landings by Year — Nominal Data Value in $US (000); Quantity in tonnes; (NMFS)					
	2004	2005	2006	2007	2008
Value	2,054	3,525	3,056	4,551	5,033
Quantity	2,024	3,255	3,036	3,893	4,185

Jonah Crab Canadian Landings by Year — Nominal Data Value in $Cdn (000); Quantity in tonnes; (DFO)					
	2004	2005	2006	2007	2008
Value	1,249	789	485	659	331
Quantity	936	642	424	503	385

Following the Dungeness crab, the (Pacific) red rock crab is the next largest commercial rock crab species on the West Coast. In 2008, 554 tonnes were landed, valued at $1.6 million (see table). Most of the landings were in California. The Atlantic (Ocean) rock crab is also a major commercial rock crab species in both the US and Canada (see table).

Atlantic Rock Crab US Landings by Year — Nominal Data Value in $US (000); Quantity in tonnes; (NMFS)					
	2004	2005	2006	2007	2008
Value	1,242	1,644	1,647	1,988	2,172
Quantity	1,348	1,707	1,681	1,959	2,176

Atlantic Rock Crab Canadian Landings by Year — Nominal Data Value in $Cdn (000); Quantity in tonnes; (DFO)					
	2004	2005	2006	2007	2008
Value	5,115	5,572	5,593	5,701	5,654
Quantity	7,469	7,987	7,255	7,545	7,111

COMMERCIAL USES

The Jonah crab is often referred to as the "Atlantic Dungeness." The meat has been described as white and succulent, although perhaps not as sweet as the Dungeness. The size is smaller than the Dungeness, but usually larger than other rock crabs. Both crabs enjoy a good restaurant trade. Rock crab is marketed whole, fresh/frozen or cooked; frozen unshelled, but eviscerated meats; and fresh (or canned) meats.

LIFE CYCLE

Similar to Dungeness crab (see entry), the female broods the fertilized eggs under her abdomen. After the eggs hatch, the young crabs are free swimming and go through several larval stages before settling to the bottom as tiny crabs. They feed mainly on molluscs, echinoderms, and other invertebrates.

Red Rock Crab (Pacific) US Landings by Year — Nominal Data Value in $US (000); Quantity in tonnes; (NMFS)					
	2004	2005	2006	2007	2008
Value	1,419	1,357	1,473	1,643	1,633
Quantity	511	498	524	582	554

CRAB, SNOW

Snow Crab, *Chionoecetes opilio*

GENERAL

Of the many crab species found off the North American coasts, the **snow crab** of the family Oregoniidae, superfamily Majoidea (spider crabs) is arguably the most important commercial species at present. This is ironic, since only a few decades ago snow crabs, in many parts of their range, were considered a nuisance by fishermen. Also known as the queen, or spider crab, snow crab is the established trade name of all genus *Chionoecetes* crabs sold in the United States. On the Pacific coast, the major species are the snow crab (*C. opilio*), the grooved "Tanner" crab (*C. tanneri*) the southern Tanner crab (*C. bairdi*) and the triangle Tanner crab (*C. angulatus*). However, the major supply of snow crab in North America is now the *C. opilio* found in Eastern Canada. The family Oregoniidae includes 4 genera and 10 species including the "toad" or lyre crabs (*Hyas* spp.), also found on both coasts and the Arctic.

Also Known As
Tanner Crab

SeaLifeBase Name
Snow crab

International Recognitions
Spain—Cangrejo de las nieves
France—Crabe des neiges
Italy—Granceola artica

A different family, Lithodidae (king and stone crabs) includes the (Alaskan) red king crab (*Paralithodes camtschaticus*) and blue king crab (*Paralithodes platypus*). These are similar in appearance to snow crabs with long, spidery-like legs except that they grow much larger. In East Coast waters, small king crab fisheries have been found for the northern stone crab* (*Lithodes maja*) (called Norway king crab in *ITIS*) and the "porcupine crab"* (*Neolithodes grimaldii*) (no common name in *ITIS*); as well as for more shallow-water toad crabs* (*Hyas araneus* and *H. coarctatus*). Toad (also "lyre") crabs are distinguished by their tubular legs, more elongated "violin-shaped" body and wider range of colors (gray to brick red). (*Not in *The Seafood List*.)

PHYSICAL DESCRIPTION

Carapace width: Max. 15cm (male), 9cm (female); Max. weight: 2.0 kg (males)

The snow crab is a crustacean with a flat and almost circular body, slightly wider in the back. It has 5 pairs of long, spider-like legs. The abdomen, which is relatively small and folded under the body, is quadrilateral in males but circular in females. Snow crabs have more slender, pincer-like, fine-toothed claws, rather than crusher-like claws. Shell color varies. Just after molting, it is reddish on the upper surface and creamy white beneath. As the shell hardens and ages, it becomes dull greenish brown above and dull yellow beneath. The full-grown male is almost twice the size of the female. Identifying snow crabs: the area above the maxillipeds dips down in a "V" on the *bairdi*, but it is straight across on *opilio*, giving the *bairdi* a sort of "buck-toothed" look.

LANDINGS AND VALUES

In the Pacific there are several species of snow crab, ranging from the Sea of Japan to Alaska and down the west coast to Oregon State. On the Atlantic side, the snow crab (*C. opilio*) is found in the Gulf of St. Lawrence and around Newfoundland and Labrador. Fishing is often done using conical traps that are 4 feet in diameter at the base and 2 feet high, covered with polypropylene netting with a plastic entrance at the top. Square traps are used in some places where fishing is done at lesser depths. Typically, only males are harvested. The US landing of snow crab

Snow Crab US Landings by Year — Nominal Data Value in $US (000); Quantity in tonnes; (NMFS)					
	2004	**2005**	**2006**	**2007**	**2008**
Value	48,636	42,761	30,454	50,403	101,157
Quantity	10,745	11,279	17,246	15,479	28,324

Snow Crab Canadian Landings by Year — Nominal Data Value in $Cdn (000); Quantity in tonnes; (DFO)					
	2004	**2005**	**2006**	**2007**	**2008**
Value	613,106	359,038	215,434	367,517	357,088
Quantity	103,372	95,455	89,640	90,664	93,866

in 2008 was 28,324 tonnes, valued at $101 million (see table). The Canadian catch in 2008 was 93,866 tonnes, valued at $357 million (see table). US snow crab landings were buttressed by a catch of 1,649 tonnes of **southern tanner crab**, valued at $6 million (not shown) and a **king crab fishery** of 12,341 tonnes, valued at $120.2 million, in 2008 (see table). On a price per pound basis then, the Alaskan king crab is arguably the second most lucrative crab fishery next to the (soft) blue crab. Canadian landings of snow crab were buttressed by 583 tonnes of **spider-toad crab**, valued at $460,000 (see table).

COMMERCIAL USES

Snow crab is available live in the shell, frozen (whole cooked in brine: meat, legs, claws), and canned. Crabmeat is lean and often used in salads, quiches, chowders, soups, casseroles and hors d'oeuvre. Japan is a major market for snow crab and Alaskan king crab (usually considered more suitable for freezing).

(Alaska) King Crab US Landings by Year — Nominal Data Value in $US (000); Quantity in tonnes; (NMFS)					
	2004	**2005**	**2006**	**2007**	**2008**
Value	93,598	91,042	67,060	97,882	120,203
Quantity	10,013	10,859	9,817	11,766	12,341

LIFE CYCLE

Mating usually takes place between a mature newly molted, soft-shelled female and a hard-shelled adult male; but older, hard-shelled females can also mate with adult males. Unlike many crabs, snow crabs do not molt throughout their lives. Females stop molting after they acquire a wide abdomen for carrying eggs and males stop after acquiring large claws. The male

(Atlantic) Spider-Toad Crab Canadian Landings by Year — Nominal Data Value in $Cdn (000); Quantity in tonnes; (DFO)					
	2004	**2005**	**2006**	**2007**	**2008**
Value	1,740	1,407	1,125	833	460
Quantity	2,046	1,804	1,444	1,254	583

usually carries the female on his back before she molts and may carry her for several days after to protect her from predation and other males during the vulnerable period before her shell hardens. A large female will produce up to 150,000 eggs that are fertilized internally and then extruded to the abdomen where they are held to incubate for up to one year. If a male is not available, the female is capable of fertilizing eggs with sperm stored from a previous mating. The eggs hatch during the warmer seasons, releasing free-swimming larvae. The larvae may spend several months and go through several molts before settling to the bottom and taking on a crab shape. Snow crabs consume a variety of small shellfish, worms and detritus; and, in turn, are prey to many groundfish.

CRAB, STONE

Golden Deepsea Crab

Florida Stone Crab, *Menippe mercenaria*

GENERAL

The Florida stone crab is a member of the family Menippidae of the superfamily Xanthoidea (*ITIS*). The family has 5 genera and about 12 species. There are 3 Atlantic Ocean species in the genus *Menippe*, including the **Florida stone crab** and the Gulf stone crab (*M. adina*), both found in *The Seafood List*. Florida's regulatory agencies consider three species of crab to be true Gulf of Mexico stone crabs; *Menippe mercenaria, M. adina*, and an unnamed hybrid of the two species. These species are fished only for their claws because the stone crab will regenerate a new limb if removed properly. Although there is a high attrition rate, stone crabs are thus "ranched" in a way.

Also Known As
Black stone crab

SeaLifeBase Name
Stone crab

International Recognitions
Spain—Cangrejo de piedra negro
France—Crabe caillou noir

PHYSICAL DESCRIPTION

Carapace width: Max. 15 cm (males) Age: estimated lifespan is 7-8 years. (MYFWC)

Adult stone crabs are recognized by their relatively oval bodies and two large, but unequally-sized claws (chelae) with black tips. Stone crabs have a large crusher claw and a smaller pincer claw with numerous small teeth used for cutting. The adult body of the Florida stone crab is tan to dark brownish-red, somewhat mottled and darkly spotted, sometimes with gray. It has a whitish underside and distinctive white bands on its legs, even as a juvenile. The Gulf stone crab is dark brown or maroon-brown and also has black claw tips. Distinguishing characteristics between the two are as follows: the Gulf stone crab is maroon brown, as compared to the Florida stone crab, which is also spotted and banded. Juvenile hybrid stone crabs can be any combination of coloration between the two pure species; their coloration is highly variable.

LANDINGS AND VALUES

The Florida stone crab ranges from North Carolina to Panama. In the US, it is concentrated around peninsular Florida and in Atlantic coastal waters. The Gulf stone crab, *Menippe adina*, overlaps this range, but is particularly concentrated in the western Gulf of Mexico from Alabama through to Texas and Mexico. Hybrids are particularly located in the Florida panhandle Big Bend area and off the coast of Georgia. Florida stone crabs prefer the bottoms of bays and grass flats. Gulf stone crabs prefer lower salinity and tend to inhabit oyster reefs and hard mud flats. Adults move into shoals just below the low tide mark and dig burrows 30 to 50 cm deep. They are harvested almost entirely in Florida, primarily from Sarasota to Fort Lauderdale.

In 2008, 2,823 tonnes of Florida stone claws, valued at $19.3 million, was landed (see table). The gear used was mostly baited pots and traps used for crab. Only the oversized claws are removed and stone crabs are returned safely to the water. It is estimated that only about 25% - 50% survive to regenerate new claws; which occurs within 18 months, but takes up to 3 years to regain 95% of the mass.

Florida Stone Claws Crab US Landings by Year – Nominal Data Value in $US (000); Quantity in tonnes; (NMFS)					
	2004	2005	2006	2007	2008
Value	27,112	21,641	24,617	26,769	19,264
Quantity	2,751	2,096	2,224	2,723	2,823

Endangered Status: stone crab population levels are estimated to be high and no overfishing is occurring. **Aquaculture:** None. The unique harvesting method helps ensure the long-term sustainability of the crab species, while providing habitat for a wide variety of other invertebrates and fishes that use their burrows for shelter.

COMMERCIAL USES

Stone crab is highly nutritious meat and often compared to lobster in appearance and flavour. The claws are cooked immediately after harvest, and sold either as fresh cooked or frozen. It is usually boiled and served in the shell with sauce.

LIFE CYCLE

Sexual maturity is reached at about 2–3 years of age in both sexes. The male Florida stone crab must wait for the female to molt before they can mate. After mating, the male will stay to protect the female for several hours to several days. Mating usually occurs in the fall and spawning in spring and summer. The female can carry the sperm for up to one year. The internally fertilized eggs are extruded and attached to the abdomen as a bright "sponge." Egg production can be up to 1 million eggs per spawning event, depending on size. The female will spawn several times per season, but can spawn all year. The pelagic larvae go through several stages over 15–30 days before settling to the bottom and metamorphosing into juveniles. Florida stone crabs prefer to feed on molluscs such as hard clams, bay scallops and conchs. Gulf stone crabs prefer to feed on oysters but will eat other molluscs. Octopi (especially), sea turtles, cobia, and grouper will feed on adult stone crab. Juvenile stone crabs can be eaten by carnivorous fish such as groupers and snappers. Adult filter-feeding fish, larval fish, and other zooplankton feed on larval stone crab. Juvenile stone crabs are more susceptible to predators than adults because they do not burrow or have the large claw of adults.

An interesting feature about the stone crab is a mark on the inside of the original large claw that resembles a thumb print. A regenerated claw will not show this "thumbprint."

**

Southern Florida is also known for another crab species landed only in that region. The golden deepsea crab (*Chaceon fenneri*) is in the family Geryonidae and is closely related to the red deepsea crab (*C. quinquedens*) found further north. Both species inhabit the continental slope and provide

Golden Deepsea Crab US Landings by Year – Nominal Data Value in $US (000); Quantity in tonnes; (NMFS)					
	2004	2005	2006	2007	2008
Value	449	597	779	645	769
Quantity	144	169	222	198	220

small, but sizeable catches; although catches of the smaller red crab have been intermittent in recent years (in both Canada and the US). In 2008, there were 220 tonnes of golden deepsea crab landed in Florida US, valued at $769,000 (see table).

CRAB

Horseshoe Crab, *Limulus polyphemus*

GENERAL

The Atlantic **horseshoe crab*** (family Limulidae) is a marine chelicerate arthropod and one of only 3 species in the class Merostomata (horseshoe crabs). It is an invertebrate more closely related to spiders and scorpions, despite its name. The name is derived from "*Limulus*," meaning odd and "*polyphemus*," referring to a giant in Greek mythology with only one eye; hence, also a previous synonym of *Limulus cyclops*, because of the myth that the horseshoe crab had only a single eye. (It actually has 10 eyes of varying complexity.) Horseshoe crabs are considered living fossils, appearing 445 million years ago and are the closest living relative to the trilobite, which existed 400 million years ago, although this current species is only about 20 million years old. Horseshoe crabs are one of the few species able to re-grow lost limbs, much like the sea star and the stone crab. [* Not on *The Seafood List*.]

Also Known As
Horsefoot Crab

SeaLifeBase Name
King crab

International Recognitions
Spain—Cangrejo cacerola
France—Limule

PHYSICAL DESCRIPTION

Max length: 60.0 cm TL male/unsexed; (Ref. 82); Max. published weight: 1,814 g (Ref. 82) Weight: Max. 5 kg; Typically the female is 16-20 in. long (including the tail) and 25% to 30% larger then the male (marinbio.org). Max. Reported Age: 20 years or more.

Horseshoe crabs get their common name from the shape of their carapace, which is rounded like a horseshoe. Their body has three main parts, the head or prosoma, the abdominal or opisthosoma and the tail or telson from which the name of the order is derived (i.e., the Greek word Xiphosura for "sword tail"). Females are larger than males and do not have the boxer glove claws that males have. Carapace coloration is usually dark green to brown and can often be covered in a variety of algae, molluscs, barnacles and other species that become attached. The underside has six paired appendages, the first of which are used to bring food to the mouth. The second pair is used as walking legs and also has claspers on males to help with reproduction. The rest are used as pusher legs. The tail is used for digging in the sand or as a lever if the animal is turned upside down. In addition, the horseshoe crab has a total of ten eyes: two compound lateral eyes located close to two rudimentary lateral eyes, two median eyes and one endoparietal eye in front (all 3 detect UV light), and two ventral eyes near the mouth of unknown utility. The last eye consists of multiple photoreceptors located on the telson. They have five pairs of "book" gills located just behind the legs, which allows them to breathe underwater. They can also breathe on land for short periods of time while the gills remain moist.

HORSESHOE CRAB

LANDINGS AND VALUES

Horseshoe crabs are found along the coast of the western Atlantic from Maine to Florida and into the Gulf of Mexico. Delaware Bay is an area for annual migration. Since the 1970s, the horseshoe crab population has been decreasing in some areas, due to several factors, including the use of the crab as bait in eel, whelk and conch trapping. However, they are now farmed for their blood. Unlike the red blood of mammals that contains iron rich hemoglobin, horseshoe crabs are "blue bloods," as oxygen transport is based on copper rich hemocyanin. This type of blood is common to many invertebrates that must survive in cold, oxygen deprived environments. More importantly, the blood contains a clotting factor that is used for the detection of bacterial endotoxins. This makes the horseshoe crab's blood highly valuable in medicine. The crabs are now often caught by hand (sometimes using rakes and trawls) and taken to labs where the blood is drawn off, and then returned to the wild. In 2008, 606 tonnes of horseshoe crab, valued at $834,000, was landed in the US. Most of the catches in 2008 were landed in New York, Massachusetts, Delaware and Virginia.

Horseshoe Crab US Landings by Year — Nominal Data Value in $US (000); Quantity in tonnes; (NMFS)					
	2004	2005	2006	2007	2008
Value	433	514	821	1,105	834
Quantity	442	645	703	787	606

COMMERCIAL USES

The crabs' blood cells release an unique clotting agent (coagulogen) called "Limilus amoebocyte lystate" (LAL) – named after the crab. This chemical reacts to bacterial endotoxins and is used in medical research and testing (e.g., testing the purity of vaccines and intravenous solutions) and the blood can be worth up to $15,000 per quart. The blood has also been used in treatments of disease that have developed a resistance to typical antibiotics such as penicillin as well as in cancer therapy and research, leukemia diagnosis and detection of vitamin B12 deficiency. Aside from medical uses, horseshoes crabs have been used as bait, a practice that is now discouraged.

LIFE CYCLE

Horseshoe crabs winter on the continental shelf and migrate near shore to spawn in the spring. Males use claspers or 'boxing gloves' to hold onto the female, often for months at a time. Females will dig nests in the sand and deposit their eggs, at which point the male will fertilize them. Females can lay between 15,000 and 64,000 eggs per season. When eggs hatch, larvae will swim for five to seven days before settling to the bottom. As they grow they move into deeper water. Before reaching maturity at about 9 years, they molt about 17 times and can live for 20-40 years.

Horseshoe crabs prey on molluscs, annelid worms, benthic invertebrates, bits of fish and other detritus. They used the middle segment of each leg, which is covered in spines, to chew their food. Because of this, they can only chew while moving. Food is then passed forward and into the mouth.

Approximately 10% of the breeding population dies each year when they are flipped over by the surf, a position from which they are not always able to recover. A "just flip 'em" campaign was started in the hopes that beach goers will right the horseshoe crabs.

CRAWFISH OR CRAYFISH

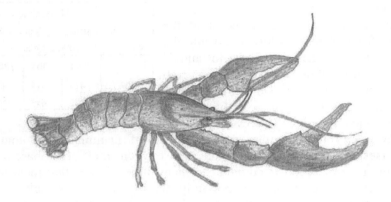

Red Swamp Crayfish, *Procambarus clarkii*

GENERAL

Crayfish (family Cambaridae) are essentially miniature lobsters, and of the same infraorder (Astacide) as those decapod crustaceans. They are abundant in North American freshwater environments, where over 300 species have been identified. However, most species are too small for human consumption. Some of these are often used as bait.

Two species are harvested extensively, for both food and bait. One is the **red swamp crayfish** or "red" crayfish and the other is the white river or "white" crawfish (*P. acutus*). Another species, the signal crayfish* (*Pacifastacus leniusculus*), is harvested on the west coast from British Columbia to California. The virile* or "northern crayfish," *Orconectes virilis,* is harvested in both the north central and the north-eastern regions of the US. Neither is farmed extensively at present. (*Not listed in *The Seafood List*.)

Also Known As
Mudbug/
Crawdad

SeaLifeBase Name
Red swamp crayfish

International Recognitions
Spain—Cangrejo de las marismas
France—Ecrevisse rouge de marais

PHYSICAL DESCRIPTION

Maximum size: up to 20cm;
Common size: 10.5–11.8 cm (35g – 36g wet weight, respectively) (FAO)

Besides size and color, it is often very difficult to tell many crayfish species apart from one another. Young red swamp crayfish are light olive green with two dark narrow stripes on both sides of the tail and a light brown stripe between, while young white river crayfish are sandy-white with many spots. The adult "red swamp" is usually red-black, while the adult "white river" is light brown with a wide black-brown stripe down the upper surface of the tail. Both are often found in the same habitat and may be darker or lighter, depending upon the water conditions. The red swamp crayfish also has no distinct separation of the carapace, while the two halves of the shell are distinct in the white river crayfish. The signal crayfish is distinguished by the distinctive red, blue and white coloration on its large claws.

LANDINGS AND VALUES

Crayfish are nocturnal and shelter-seeking animals; thus, their habitat is one that provides cover, such as vegetated areas or gravelly, stony bottoms into which they can burrow. They inhabit freshwater ponds, streams, swamps, rivers and wet meadows. They are generally omnivorous; that is, they feed on both small animal and plant life. Important natural sources of edible crayfish are the Mississippi River, the Gulf Coast and the Pacific Coast drainages. Generally crayfish are caught using baited conical or boxed traps similar to those utilized to

All Crayfish US Landings by Year — Nominal Data Value in $US (000); Quantity in tonnes; (NMFS)					
	2004	2005	2006	2007	2008
Value	4,946	8,461	1,449	9,264	9,635
Quantity	3,923	6,916	719	7,264	7,152

All Crayfish US Aquaculture Production by Year — Nominal Data Value in $US (000); Quantity in tonnes; (NMFS)					
	2004	2005	2006	2007	2008
Value	42,836	42,557	100,626	88,906	127,351
Quantity	31,926	35,171	37,972	51,992	53,285

harvest lobster. Other harvesting methods utilize drop nets or lines, but they are also caught in streams by hand. However, most are farmed. **Aquaculture:** Farming is most extensive (90% of total) in Louisiana, where vast areas of marshland are utilized for this purpose, but farming occurs in several states. The US estimated production of all crayfish (**harvested and farmed**) in 2008 was 60,437 tonnes, valued at approximately $137 million (see tables). The red swamp crayfish is the predominant farmed species. Crayfish is also imported from China. It is harvestable in Japan, but is not known to be commercially produced.

COMMERCIAL USES

The crayfish ("crawfish" or "crawdad") is a delicate- tasting shellfish that is highly valued by both North Americans and Europeans (Sweden and France are major importing countries). They are often sold live and boiled with spices. Crayfish is sometimes marketed in the United States as "écrevisses," mostly in cooked frozen form. Softshelled (molted) crayfish are also sold in vacuum-packed containers.

LIFE CYCLE

The mating period for the red swamp crayfish occurs in the late spring and early summer and involves a courtship period dependent upon tactile, visual and chemical stimuli. The reproduction process is similar to that of the lobster with the female carrying the sperm until she is ready to lay her eggs, usually in the late summer or early fall. (However, unlike the lobster, the crayfish lays only a few hundred eggs.) The fertilized eggs are carried externally on the underside of the female's body for several months. Also unlike the lobster, once the eggs are hatched, the larvae remain close to the female for several days until they have molted as many as four times. During this time, they live in a burrow which the female has constructed in the bottom sediment. The young then begin their own independent existence. The red swamp crayfish, an annual species, matures at six months and generally does not live more than two years. They are preyed on by both other fish and birds. Crayfish are omnivores, preferring fresh meat, but also scavengers of decaying animal and plant life. They are a favorite food of many fresh water fishes in their habitats.

LOBSTER

Spiny Lobster

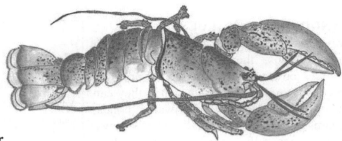

American Lobster, *Homarus americanus*

GENERAL

Also Known As
Canadian lobster/
Northern lobster

**SeaLifeBase
Name**
American lobster

**International
Recognitions**
Spain—Bogavante
Americano
France—Homard
Américain
Italy—Astice
americano

Once the "poor man's food" and sometimes used as fertilizer, the **American lobster** (family Nephropidae) has now become one of the most valuable species, pound for pound, in the world. One of the largest American lobsters ever recorded weighed more than 18 kg and measured 106 cm (tail to the tip of the largest claw) - caught off Nova Scotia in 1977. Large lobsters, or "jumbos," can achieve a lifespan of 50 years. They are usually caught far out to sea and there is a continuing controversy as to how much offshore lobsters interact with, or contribute to, inshore lobster populations. Unlike spiny lobsters (family Palinuridae) such as the Caribbean spiny lobster (*Panulirus argus*) and the California spiny lobster (*Panulirus interruptus*), the American lobster is distinguished by its large front claws.

PHYSICAL DESCRIPTION

Max length: 64.0 cm TL male/unsexed; (Ref. 4); Common length: 25.0 cm TL male/unsexed; (Ref. 4); One of the largest decapods in terms of body length.
Common weight: 0.5 to 5 lb. (0.227 to 2.27 kg) Carapace length: 2.5 to 5 in. (6.25 to 12.5 cm)
The American lobster is an invertebrate crustacean that lives under rocks or in crevices and burrows on the ocean floor. It has a hard-shelled, articulated body and, being a decapod, ten legs. The front pair is much larger than the others and is one of its distinguishing features. These legs are very strong and terminate in large claws, a "pincer" and a "crusher." The other eight legs are much smaller walking legs. The lobster also has several pairs of "swimmerets" and uses its flexible tail to swim—backwards. Much of the lobster's sensory input is obtained through long antennae located on its head. The color ranges through various camouflage shades of green and brown with the occasional blue tint. Lobsters turn their famous red color only when cooked.

LANDINGS AND VALUES

The American lobster is found along the Atlantic coastline and on the continental shelf, from the Carolinas to Northern Newfoundland. They are generally fished from small boats using baited, wooden-frame or plastic-coated steel-mesh traps that are weighted to sink to the bottom. Most of the fishery is relatively close to shore, but there is a large offshore fishery as well in some areas.

The most productive lobster beds are located in the Bay of Fundy between Maine and Nova Scotia. Although the season varies from place to place, much of the Canadian fishery is closed in summer months when the lobsters spawn. However, lobsters are maintained live in holding tanks that extends their availability year-round. The US catch of the American lobster was 39,956 tonnes in 2008, valued at $326.8 million (see table); up from 23,843 tonnes in 1989, valued at $147.2 million (not shown). The Canadian American lobster catch in 2008 was 57,921 tonnes, valued at

American Lobster US Landings by Year – Nominal Data Value in $US (000); Quantity in tonnes; (NMFS)					
	2004	**2005**	**2006**	**2007**	**2008**
Value	374,306	415,415	395,150	354,993	326,754
Quantity	40,857	39,830	42,007	35,547	39,956

American Lobster Canadian Landings by Year – Nominal Data Value in $Cdn (000); Quantity in tonnes; (DFO)					
	2004	**2005**	**2006**	**2007**	**2008**
Value	592,759	697,975	653,106	629,401	610,840
Quantity	47,595	51,616	55,010	48,904	57,921

$610.8 million (see table); up from 43,956 tonnes in 1989, valued at $266 million (not shown). US catches of spiny and slipper lobster totaled $30.6 million in 2008 (see table). **Endangered Status**: American lobster is not endangered in the main part of its range. **Aquaculture:** Full-scale lobster farming has yet <u>not</u> proven feasible, but enhancement experiments in raising larval lobster for release into the ocean appear to be successful in increasing recruitment.

COMMERCIAL USES

Vast amounts of live lobster are shipped by air worldwide. Live lobster are usually packed in seaweed or seawater-soaked paper with gel packs and shipped in 25- or 50-lb. boxes. Frozen whole-cooked lobsters are sold either as brine-filled plastic packs ("popsicle packs") or dry vacuum packs. Canned meats are either retorted and shelf

US Spiny and Slipper Lobster Landings Quantity in tonnes; value in thousand $US (NMFS)				
Type	**1989**		**2008**	
	Value	**Quantity**	**Value**	**Quantity**
Banded Spiny Lobster	N/A	N/A	120	5
California Spiny Lobster	4,051	335	8,008	336
Caribbean Spiny Lobster	28,188	4,059	22,452	1,579
Slipper Lobster	100	19	44	6
Total	**32,338**	**4,4113**	**30,624**	**1,926**

stable (hot pack) or non-retorted and require freezing (cold pack). Tails, claws and meats are also sold separately. Lobster liver ("tomalley"), a greenish-colored paste, is sometimes sold as a spread.

LIFE CYCLE

The female can mate only immediately after molting, so she has a sperm sack in which to carry injected sperm until ready to lay her eggs. After fertilization and extrusion, the female carries the eggs on her tail and swimmerets. When the eggs hatch the larvae drift up to the surface where there is lots of plankton. After three to six weeks and several moltings, the tiny lobsters drift back to the sea floor. As a lobster grows its flesh becomes compacted inside the shell and must be replaced by a new, soft one growing beneath. To do this, the lobster pulls itself into a tight "V" until the old shell membrane splits, and then crawls out, shedding the old shell. The lobster has a voracious appetite at this point, especially for calcium-rich shellfish (including other lobsters). Lobsters mature in four to five years, molting two to three times each year, decreasing to once a year as growth slows. Water temperature affects growth; however, it will likely take about seven years for a lobster to reach a 1-pound market size.

MUSSEL

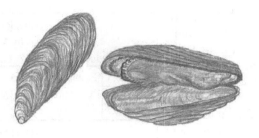

Blue Mussel, *Mytilus edulis*

GENERAL

Also Known As
Bay Mussel

**SeaLifeBase
Name**
Blue mussel

**International
Recognitions**
Spain—Mejillón
común
France—Moule
commune

Mussels have been consumed in Europe for centuries, but it is only in recent decades that North Americans have been paying attention to them. There are approximately 26 genera and about 240 species of mussels (family Mytilidae); however, three species of the genus *Mytilus* account for most of the commercial activity. The **blue mussel** is the most commonly landed and farmed mussel in North America; mostly on the East Coast and often intermingled with the foolish mussel (*M. trossulus* - not in *The Seafood List*). A small amount of Mediterranean mussel (*M. galloprovincialis*), blue mussel and foolish mussel (or "Western blue mussel") is also produced on the West Coast. These mussels can be difficult to distinguish from one another and can hybridize where their territories overlap, increasing identification difficulties.

Mussels, like clams and other filter-feeders, can accumulate potent toxins derived from the microalgae (phytoplankton) upon which they feed. The most dangerous of these to humans is paralytic shellfish poison (PSP). Other toxins of concern include diarrhoeic shellfish poisoning (DSP) and domoic acid, first found in PEI mussels in 1987. Blooms of toxic algae usually follow seasonal cycles, and in North America, shellfish are routinely monitored as part of a comprehensive sanitation programme (see "shellfish sanitation" in the glossary). Another toxic algae, azaspiracids, recently found in Irish mussels is not known in North American waters. Tunicates ("sea squirts") a type of aquatic invasive species (AIS), foul culture gear, compete for food and impede circulation, causing reduced growth rates in the smothered bivalves.

PHYSICAL DESCRIPTION
Max length: 10.0 cm male/unsexed; (Ref. 7726) (Common length: b/w 3 to 5 cm.

The blue mussel is roughly triangular in shape and has numerous fine concentric lines on the shell surface. The outer shell is blue to black in color with a shiny covering (periostracum) and the inside is white with purplish margins. Young mussels may show brown coloring and some may show radial banding of differing densities of brown pigmentation. Cultured mussels usually have a cleaner, smoother and shinier surface than those found in the wild. The foolish mussel is reported as more elongated than the blue, but in general, the three species and their hybrids can be reliably distinguished only by using diagnostic genetic markers.

LANDINGS AND VALUES

It is believed that the blue mussel was at first native to the Atlantic Ocean and was later introduced to the Pacific. It can be found in inter-tidal waters from Greenland to South Carolina, from Alaska to California and in Europe. Canadian and US landings totaled only about 5,000 tonnes in 2008 (see tables). **Aquaculture:** Although initially the blue mussel was only harvested in the wild (by hand raking, tong or use of an oyster dredge), a mussel culture industry has taken over. Mussel spat are collected on ropes deployed in spawning season (or may be collected from the

Mussel (meat wt.) US Landings by Year — Nominal Data Value in $US (000); Quantity in tonnes; (NMFS)					
	2004	2005	2006	2007	2008
Value	7,012	6,569	9,458	6,076	7,684
Quantity	2,105	1,870	1,784	1,559	1,740

Mussel (meat wt.) US Aquaculture Production by Year — Nominal Data Value in $US (000); Quantity in tonnes; (NMFS)					
	2004	2005	2006	2007	2008
Value	3,956	4,990	7,126	4,474	4,474
Quantity	269	436	457	387	387

bottom or culled from the older mussels) and transferred to culture gear such as plastic mesh tubing hung from floats. They are harvested in 12 to 24 months (depending on species, temperature and food supply), at a size of about 2 1/2 inches. Aquaculture now far outstrips commercial landings with Canadian production alone at 19,927 tonnes (live) and $27.3 million in 2008 (see table). PEI accounted for about 70% of North American culturing in 2008.

COMMERCIAL USES

Mussels handled properly can live up to 10 days out of water and most are sold fresh in the shell, although the meat is removed from some (after steaming) and canned, either plain or with sauce. Mussels can also be baked, deep-fried or pan-fried. They are also smoked, served in batter, cut for chowders, or used in hors d' oeuvre and canapés. Mussels are a nutritious, lean meat that appeals to many health-conscious consumers.

Mussel (live wt.) Canadian Landings by Year — Nominal Data Value in $Cdn (000); Quantity in tonnes; (DFO)					
	2004	2005	2006	2007	2008
Value	23,343	21,880	17,466	11,992	4,386
Quantity	17,666	16,565	13,399	9,166	3,295

Mussel (live wt.) Canada Farmed Production by Year — Nominal Data Value in $Cdn (000); Quantity in tonnes; (DFO) (StatsCan)					
	2004	2005	2006	2007	2008
Value	32,807	33,582	35,817	33,940	27,322
Quantity	22,863	22,930	23,876	23,835	19,927

LIFE CYCLE

In nature, starting in the spring, adult blue mussels produce mobile larvae resembling tiny clams that attach themselves to stones, pebbles, pilings of wharves, etc., by a series of strong "byssal" threads. At this point, a shell develops and the "spat" become permanently stationary (sessile). The mussels feed on microscopic algae which they filter-out from the surrounding water. In culturing, wild or hatchery-reared spat are collected and transferred to the mussel bed where they attach to the bottom, or are hung on lines, or in plastic mesh "socks" (primarily to keep them from dispersing). These lines or socks are attached to floats or rafts on the surface. This off-bottom culturing is highly managed and somewhat costly, but enhances growth rate and product quality; providing a cleaner, more attractive product with a high meat yield.

OCTOPUS

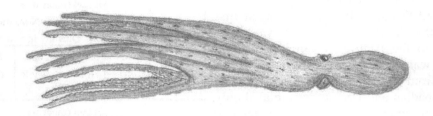

Common Octopus, *Octopus vulgaris*

GENERAL

Octopuses are cephalopod molluscs that probably evolved from snail-like creatures and are now closely related to squids, cuttlefishes and nautilus. There are hundreds of species of octopus and many of these are found in the genus *Octopus*. Consequently, it is difficult to distinguish individual species and they are often identified simply as *Octopus* spp. Two of the better known species in North America are the **common octopus** (family Octopodidae) and the North Pacific giant octopus (*Enteroctopus dofleini*).

Adult octopuses are characterized as intelligent, solitary animals that are mostly harmless, but have developed a wide array of adaptive defensives. They hide well (e.g., in crevices), but can also can quickly change their body form and color to blend with their environment. The can propel themselves quickly using their syphons to jet water and also release a disorienting ink cloud to confuse predators. Many octopuses can also detach limbs (which will later re-grow).

Also Known As
Pieuvre/ Pulpo
Común/
*Octopus
vulgaris*

**SeaLifeBase
Name**
Common
Octopus

**International
Recognitions**
Spain—Pulpo
común
France—Pieuvre
Italy—Polpo
cileno
Germany—Pulpo

PHYSICAL DESCRIPTION
Max length: 130 cm TL male/unsexed; (Ref. 275); 120 cm TL (female); Max. published weight: 10,000 g (Ref. 275)

Common octopuses have no shell or backbone (i.e., they are invertebrates), but have eight arms lined with suction cups (to hold prey) attached directly to the head, 3 hearts, a very large brain and excellent vision. An adult mantle is about 25 cm long and the arms about 1 meter long. The ventral siphon is important for swimming by jet propulsion, although crawling over the bottom is more common. With no shell, they are extremely flexible and can squeeze into small places. They do have a hard beak used for cracking the shells of molluscs and crustaceans.

North Pacific Giant Octopus, *Enteroctopus dofleini*
Max length: 300 cm TL male/unsexed; (Ref. 275); Max. published weight: 50.0 kg (Ref. 275) Common weight: 2,000 to 10,000 g (Ref. 275). Females grow larger than males (Ref. 3722). Giant octopus is largest on record.

LANDINGS AND VALUES

Octopuses are reef-associated oceanic species. The **common octopus** is found circum-globally in tropical, semitropical and it seems (occasionally at least) temperate waters from near shore to as deep as 200 meters; commonly inhabiting rocky, muddy and sandy bottoms. However, in the US, it appears it is only landed on the Atlantic Coast and in the Gulf of Mexico. The **North Pacific giant octopus** is a West Coast species, found from California to Alaska and Northern Asia.

Octopus (nei) US Landings by Year — Nominal Data Value in $US (000); Quantity in tonnes; (NMFS)					
	2004	**2005**	**2006**	**2007**	**2008**
Value	108	102	81	82	113
Quantity	31	30	18	16	21

In 2008, 21 tonnes of octopus was landed in the US, valued at $113,000 (see table). Most of the catches in 2008 were landed in Hawaii followed by the Florida (West Coast), North Carolina and Oregon. The gear used was mostly unbaited pots and traps. Canadian landings (all West Coast) totaled 19 tonnes in 2008, valued at $57,000 (see table).

COMMERCIAL USES

Octopuses are important in fisheries and are considered a delicacy on most markets. They are eaten various ways. In Japanese culture they are eaten cooked or raw, as sashimi, and may also be eaten while still alive. In Europe (e.g., Greece, Portugal, and Spain) they are often grilled and served with other dishes. They are also popular fish bait.

Octopus (nei) Canadian Landings by Year — Nominal Data Value in $Cdn (000); Quantity in tonnes; (DFO)					
	2004	**2005**	**2006**	**2007**	**2008**
Value	265	160	124	87	57
Quantity	75	48	36	27	19

LIFE CYCLE

Octopuses generally have a relatively short life span, governed by reproduction. Males will live only a few months beyond mating and females will die shortly after their eggs hatch.

O. vulgaris uses a special arm to convey sperm into the female's mantle cavity. Eggs are laid in shallow water on rocky shores or on sandy or muddy bottoms. Females find a hole, crevice or sheltered place (including using manmade objects) and often protect the nest with shells and stones. They may lay 100,000 to 500,000 eggs over a week or more. The female guards the eggs for 4-6 weeks, rarely eating, until they hatch. Eggs are cleaned with the arm tips and by directing jets of water. The eggs hatch into larvae that look like tiny octopuses. Larvae live on plankton until reaching maturity, in about 45 to 60 days of age. They use their camouflage and ink spray to envelop prey and grab them with their suckers, stunning them with a secretion of nerve toxin. They are preyed on by eels, dolphins and sharks. They live for 12 to 18 months.

After fertilization, *E. dofleini* females can lay up to 200,000 eggs, which they hang in their lair and guard as they developed. Young larval octopuses drift and feed on planktonic organisms until they descend to the bottom. They reach maturity at a mantle length of 9.5 cm for males and 15.5 cm for females. Adult giant Pacific octopuses are prey to sea otters, seals and sperm whales. They feed on mostly on benthic invertebrates such as crab, scallop, abalone, clams, but also shrimp and fish.

OYSTER

European Oyster

Olympia Oyster

Pacific Oyster

Eastern Oyster, *Crassostrea virginica*

GENERAL

Oysters are bivalve molluscs that spend their lives in one place, often cemented to a rock. The native **Eastern oyster** (family Ostreidae) is in the genus classified as a "cupped oyster" (as opposed to a "flat oyster" found in the *Ostrea* genus) and accounts for about 65% of total US production. The (flat) oyster native to the West Coast is the highly valued, but now rare, Olympia oyster (*Ostrea lurida**). The Pacific oyster (*Crassostrea gigas*) is not really native to North America, but was introduced from Japan and now typically accounts for about 34% of total US production and 99% of West Coast production. Other introduced species include the Japanese "Kumamoto" oyster (*C. gigas kumamoto*), a subspecies of *C. gigas*; and the edible oyster, also known as the European flat or "Belon" oyster (*Ostrea edulis*). Like all filter-feeders, oysters can take contaminants from the water, but danger to public health is strictly monitored (see "shellfish sanitation" in the glossary). However, infections and predators like the Japanese oyster drill *(Ocenebra japonica)* and a parasitic flatworm (*Mytilicola orientalis*) can present other challenges to native oyster growers. [*Note: the *O. conchaphila* (valid and verified in *ITIS*) is denoted as "Olympia oyster" in *The Seafood List*. Apparently both species are considered an Olympia oyster.]

Also Known As
Bluepoint/
American
Oyster

SeaLifeBase Name
American
cupped oyster

International Recognitions
Spain—Ostión
americano
France—Huître
creuse
américaine

PHYSICAL DESCRIPTION Common length: 30.0 cm TL male/unsexed; (Ref. 271)

The living soft, edible portion ("meat") of the oyster is boneless, creating an erroneous perception of a primitive creature (in fact, it is a highly evolved mollusc). The soft parts are enclosed between two rugged calcareous shells or valves. The top is fairly flat and acts as a lid, while the bottom is cupped to hold the body and a small reservoir of seawater. The shell is usually a mixture of brown, grey, green and off-white. The exterior shell tends to have a roughly sculpted appearance, oval or teardrop-shaped. The more silt or mud in the area, the longer and narrower the shell. The color of the meat varies from pearly to beige to greyish green, depending on the oyster's food supply and habitat. The gills are used for breathing and to filter food. Like the Eastern oyster, the hardy Pacific oyster is variable in shape; however, it is commonly more elongated and grows faster and larger than other varieties, up to 12 inches.

LANDINGS AND VALUES

In the US, the main harvest areas for the eastern oyster are from the Gulf of Mexico to Cape Cod. In Canada, the major beds are in the Gulf of St. Lawrence. Oysters are harvested in shallow waters with long-handled rakes, or tongs, that have long, curved tines to which a collection cage is often attached. Deeper water beds are often harvested with mechanical dredges. **Aquaculture:** Oysters of various species are highly cultured on both coasts. It is estimated that about 50 percent of wild oyster beds have been cultured at some time in their

All Oysters ~65% Eastern, 35% Pacific (meat wt.) US Landings by Year — Nominal Data Value in $US (000); Quantity in tonnes; (NMFS)					
	2004	2005	2006	2007	2008
Value	114,334	113,037	121,745	143,183	129,198
Quantity	18,143	16,257	15,626	17,034	15,779

All Oysters (meat wt.) US Aquaculture Production by Year — Nominal Data Value in $US (000); Quantity in tonnes; (NMFS)					
	2004	2005	2006	2007	2008
Value	80,075	92,602	87,658	81,536	79,666
Quantity	11,890	6,219	10,000	9,500	9,226

development. They are cultured both on and off bottom - the latter using containerized methods, either in floating arrays or on bottom racks. US landings of "wild" oysters and aquaculture production totaled approximately 25,000 tonnes (meats) in 2008, valued at more than $208.9 million; while Canadian 2008 landings and production totaled approximately 10,600 tonnes (live), valued at $17.5 million (see tables).

Endangered Status: Olympia Oyster – Special Concern (*SARA*).

COMMERCIAL USES

High-quality oysters are believed to result from the type of feed available and bottom conditions; and perhaps, quality is enhanced when the bottom is rocky sand or gravel, rather than mud. Colder waters are also believed to produce a superior, but smaller product. Oysters hibernate in winter and, kept in a cold, damp atmosphere can live out of water for nearly four months. As a result, live oysters are packed and shipped in cold storage, so they can be served fresh. Some are also shipped as frozen meats. Most are used by restaurants and hotels. High consumer demand keeps oyster prices up across North America and very little is exported.

Eastern Oyster (live wt.) ~100% Atlantic Canadian Landings by Year — Nominal Data Value in $Cdn (000); Quantity in tonnes; (DFO)					
	2004	2005	2006	2007	2008
Value	8,774	7,689	7,163	6,794	3,994
Quantity	4,299	3,276	2,405	2,357	1,613

All Oysters (live wt.) ~ 40% Atlantic, 60% Pacific Canada Aquaculture by Year — Nominal Data Value in $Cdn (000); Quantity in tonnes; (DFO)					
	2004	2005	2006	2007	2008
Value	16,740	16,521	19,063	16,726	13,502
Quantity	13,228	12,957	13,200	11,065	8,989

LIFE CYCLE

The gender of an oyster is difficult to determine and may actually change several times during its long lifespan. The gonad organ produces either eggs or sperm, which are released over a period of 4-6 weeks in the summer at water temperatures of 60°F or higher. Eggs are fertilized in the water column and then drift freely for several weeks before settling to the bottom. As part of the plankton community, they are consumed by many sea creatures, including adult oysters, and perhaps only 1% survives to cement to the bottom and metamorphosis into a tiny oyster called a spat. In northern waters, oysters reach marketable size in 4-7 years. Eastern oysters in more southern areas reach this size in 2-4 four years. Although the growth rate slows as they age, oysters continue to grow as long as they live—up to 100 years.

SCALLOP

Iceland Scallop

Bay Scallop

Calico Scallop

Sea Scallop, *Placopecten magellanicus*

GENERAL

About 300 species of scallop have been identified around the world, but only a few, like the sea scallop (family Pectinidae), are found in commercial quantities. The **sea scallop** accounts for about 99% of all scallop landings in North America and about 98% of the value. Other scallops that are fished or farmed commercially can be found in the table below. As a bivalve crustacean, the sea scallop exhibits some unique evolutionary characteristics. It can swim by "clapping" its shells together and it can see with dozens of rudimentary eyes located on the outer rim. Scallops have been photographed jumping over a fishing "dredge" or "rake" used to capture them.

Also Known As
Atlantic Sea Scallop

SeaLifeBase Name
Deep sea scallop

International Recognitions
Spain—Vieira americana
France—Pecten d'Amérique

PHYSICAL DESCRIPTION

Max length : 20.0 cm TL male/unsexed; (Ref. 7726)
The scallop has two distinct shells held together by a white adductor muscle that moves them apart. The muscle is the scallop meat that is normally abstracted. The outside surfaces of the sea scallop have a pattern of concentric growth rings and not the traditional ribs running outward from the hinge like a fan, like other scallop shells. The insides of the shells are pearly white and have a satin-like luster. The shell has distinct short corners at its hinge in the rear with the upper half of the valve slightly more rounded than the bottom half. Sea scallop shells and meats are generally larger than those of other scallops.

Common Scallops	Scientific Name	Range	US Landings (meats) 1989 MT	US Landings (meats) 2008 MT	Canada Landings (live) 1989 MT	Canada Landings (live) 2008 MT
Sea Scallop	*P. magellanicus*	Mid-Atlantic	14,974	24,286	92,188	67,406
Bay Scallop	*Argopecten irradians*	S. Atlantic	263	59	N/A	N/A
Calico	*Argopecten gibbus*	S. Atlantic	3,151	N/A	N/A	N/A
Weathervane	*Patinopecten caurinus*	N. Pacific	243	170	N/A	13
Iceland/other	*Chlamys islandica*	N. Atlantic	N/A	N/A	N/A	130
Total Scallops (includes unclassified)			**18,635**	**24,515**	**92,385**	**67,564**

LANDINGS AND VALUES

Sea scallops are found on the Atlantic coast from Newfoundland to Cape Hatteras. The catch is primarily harvested on Georges Bank, off the Virginia/New Jersey coast, the Bay of Fundy (Digby), on the Scotian Shelf and in the Gulf of St. Lawrence. In the northern part of their habitat sea scallops prefer shallow water, about 60 feet deep, while their southern counterparts live in waters of 200 feet or more. Scallops strain the water for minute plants and animals and prefer gravel or rock bottoms, where the current is reasonably swift and food

Sea Scallop (meat wt.) US Landings by Year – Nominal Data Value in $US (000); Quantity in tonnes; (NMFS)					
	2004	**2005**	**2006**	**2007**	**2008**
Value	320,039	432,514	384,758	386,047	369,896
Quantity	29,079	25,685	26,768	26,570	24,286

Sea Scallop (live wt.) Canadian Landings by Year – Nominal Data Value in $Cdn (000); Quantity in tonnes; (DFO)					
	2004	**2005**	**2006**	**2007**	**2008**
Value	112,143	75,610	84,935	88,540	92,239
Quantity	80,395	53,774	61,535	64,917	67,406

availability is high. The prime landing season is from March through to November, though they can be harvested year-round. As much as 75 percent of the total catch is taken by off-shore scallop draggers on Georges Bank. These vessels drag the ocean bottom with large rakes or dredges. The inshore fishery uses smaller dredges. US landings for sea scallop in 2008 were 24,286 tonnes (meats only), valued at $369.9 million (see table). In addition, the US landed 59 tonnes of bay scallop in 2008, valued at $1.8 million and 170 tonnes of weathervane scallop (Alaska), valued at $2.4 million (not shown). Very small catches of calico scallop in the US add to these totals in some years. In Canada, 2008 East Coast landings of sea scallop were 67,406 tonnes, valued at $92.2 million (see table); not including 130 tonnes of Iceland scallops, valued at $446,000 from the Newfoundland Grand Banks and BC landings of 13 tonnes of weathervane scallop, valued at $78,000 (not shown). **Endangered Status:** Not endangered. **Aquaculture:** Sea scallop is now being farmed, with BC and Nova Scotia producing 285 tonnes in 2008, valued at $1.3 million. Various scallop species are extensively farmed in Japan and many other countries are now experimenting.

COMMERCIAL USES

Though in North America only the scallop muscle is "shucked" and utilized (the residual tissues and shells being discarded at sea), in Europe the gonad ("roe") is considered a delicacy and typically served attached to the muscle as "coquille St. Jacques." Recently, the North American industry has begun small landings of roe for specialized markets. The meaty "rim" can also be used as a tasty addition to seafood chowders. Meats are usually graded according to size and water content. Large scallops (fewer than ten-count to the pound) bring the best price and are often individually quick frozen (IQF). Smaller scallops (40-count) may be frozen in blocks or plates for export. Scallops are often served breaded and deep fried in North America; however, in Europe they are prepared in dozens of ways. Favorite recipes often include garlic, tomato and mushroom sauces with cheese garnishes.

LIFE CYCLE

Sea scallops are either male or female, in contrast to the hermaphroditic European scallop. Spawning takes place from late August to early September. The fertilized eggs float to the surface and the resulting larvae drift considerable distances with the currents for a period of about three weeks; this accounts for their wide distribution. The larvae then settle to the bottom. The scallop's natural enemies include starfish, snails, crustaceans and fish such as cod, plaice and wolffish or wolf-eels.

SEA CUCUMBER

Sea Cucumber (California Stichopus), *Parastichopus californicus*

GENERAL

The **sea cucumber** is a marine invertebrate or "echinoderm" (spiny-skinned) animal that moves sluggishly over the sea floor in search of food. It is a close relative of the sea urchin and the sea star. At least 1,100 species have been identified worldwide. The **California stichopus** (family Stichopodidae, class Holothuroidea [sea cucumbers]) has a peculiar feature: during October and November, many stop eating, and upon examination out of water, are found to contain no internal organs. It was once thought that these organs were simply expelled, but it has since been discovered that they atrophy. Fortunately, the organs replicate themselves in six to eight weeks. A common Atlantic species is the Atlantic sea cucumber, *Cucumaria frondosa*; however, individual sea cucumber species are so difficult to distinguish they are often just referred to by a genus name such as *Parastichopus* spp.*, *Holothuria* spp. or *Cucumaria* spp. Officials of the Royal British Columbia Museum are now working on a book that is expected to assist in overcoming many identification problems. [*All sea cucumbers on *The Seafood List* are currently unnamed and referred to simply under 4 different genera.]

Also Known As
Sea Slug/
Bechedemer

SeaLifeBase Name
None

International Recognitions
Germany—
Kalifornische
Seegurke
Spain—
cohombro de
mar
Italy—cetriolo
di mare
Japan—namako

PHYSICAL DESCRIPTION
Length: average 12 in. (30 cm) Weight: over 2 lb. (0.9 kg)

The sea cucumber is a flexible, cylindrical creature that greatly resembles its namesake, the cucumber. It has been described as shaped like a "sausage with a mouth at one end and the anus at the other." The color of the California stichopus can vary a great deal, from light red to deep burgundy or even mottled brown, with a light amber ventral surface. This surface is covered with many small, tube-shaped protrusions with suckers on the ends, called tube feet. The dorsal surface is covered with stiff, conical projections, resembling the thorns of a rosebush, but larger. The mouth is ringed by feeding tentacles. Inside its body wall are five concentric muscle strips running from head to tail. It is these muscle strips that make the sea cucumber so highly valued.

SEA CUCUMBER (CALIFORNIA STICHOPUS)

LANDINGS AND VALUES

The California stichopus can be found throughout the near-shore waters of the Pacific coast, from extreme low tide levels to depths of over 300 feet. They live on all types of bottoms, from muddy sand to bedrock, although they avoid areas where waves are high. In water less than 60 feet deep, SCUBA divers gather them in large mesh bags to be hauled to the surface, where a boat waits to take them ashore. US landings of all sea cucumbers totaled 651 tonnes in 2008, valued at $2.9 million (see table). All of the landings were on the West Coast, divided between California and Washington. The Canadian catch in 2008 was 4,516 tonnes, valued at $4 million (see table). About

All Sea Cucumbers US Landings by Year — Nominal Data Value in $US (000); Quantity in tonnes; (NMFS)					
	2004	2005	2006	2007	2008
Value	2,060	3,195	3,578	2,092	2,921
Quantity	5,103	4,538	4,484	2,918	651

All Sea Cucumbers Canadian Landings by Year — Nominal Data Value in $Cdn (000); Quantity in tonnes; (DFO)					
	2004	2005	2006	2007	2008
Value	3,444	3,671	2,741	2,670	4,044
Quantity	3,409	3,862	3,459	3,152	4,516

two-thirds of the Canadian catch and value was on the West Coast as well. **Aquaculture:** Farming and ranching of sea cucumbers are common in Asia, especially China and Japan, and are under active research effort in North America. Since sea cucumbers thrive on waste material produced by other organisms, it is believed they should both thrive in, and benefit, the trophic environment surrounding other maricultured species, including finfish.

COMMERCIAL USES

The higher valued product from sea cucumber is the whole gutted and dried body wall, called "trepang" or "beche de mer." It is used in soups in parts of eastern Asia and is also considered a herbal tonic ("ginseng of the sea") for blood, kidney and intestine dysfunctions. Pharmaceutical uses in China include treating fatigue, impotence, constipation and frequent urination. There is also a strong and growing market for the five muscle strips located just inside the surface of the body wall. The muscle strips are delicious when fried quickly in butter, and as more North American consumers become familiar with this delicacy, the market is expected to grow. Other products include raw sea cucumber (served marinated in Japan), dried sea cucumber gonads (which can be priced up to $50.00/lb. in Japan), and salted, fermented intestines (which can be priced up to $30.00/lb. in Japan). However, quality is paramount and some sea cucumber species are preferred over others, especially for trepang.

LIFE CYCLE

The California stichopus spawns from April to August. Fertilization takes place when the male and female, adopting a cobra like posture with their front ends elevated off the sea floor, release sperm and eggs into the water. The larvae spend 65-125 days floating as plankton before settling to the bottom, where they become juvenile sea cucumbers. These juveniles hide much of the time among the seaweed, under rocks and in crevices. It takes four to six years for young sea cucumbers to reach their adult size of two pounds. Lifespan is 12-14 years. Moving slowly along the sea bottom, sea cucumbers look for the micro-organisms associated with sediment particles. They leave trails of nutrient materials behind them much as common earthworms do. In fact, overfishing of sea cucumbers is reported as causing hardening of the sea floor, eliminating habitat for other benthic organisms. Adult sea cucumbers have few natural predators beside some species of sea stars. An encounter with a sea star can invoke a violent, arching, back-and-forth escape response — about the only time a sea cucumber moves rapidly.

SEA URCHIN

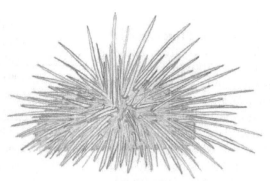

(Red) Sea Urchin, *Strongylocentrotus franciscanus*

GENERAL

Sea urchins (family Strongylocentrotidae) are close relatives of sea cucumbers and sea stars and certainly live up to the meaning of echinoderms as "spiny-skinned" animals. The fishery is unique in that it can only be harvested by divers, who usually must brave cold winter waters to pick urchins off the rocky bottom. However, their spines are sharp and if stepped on can cause a painful, but not venomous, wound.

Sea urchins of both sexes are harvested only for their gonads (collectively called "roe"). Three North American commercial varieties are the **red sea urchin*,** the green sea urchin* (*S. droebachiensis*) and the purple sea urchin* (*S. purpuratus*). (*These common name designations are not recognized in *The Seafood List*, but the scientific names are valid and verified in *ITIS*. Because of identification difficulties, often just the designation *Strongylocentrotus* spp., or other sea urchin genus names are presently used for identification.)

Also Known As
Urchins

SeaLifeBase Name
None

International Recognitions
Germany—Rote Seeigel
France—oursin rouge
Spain—erizo de mar
Italy—riccio di mare
Japan—uni

Urchin colonies are often welcomed by oyster farmers. Urchins are omnivores and attack the fouling of oyster lines by consuming mussels, barnacles, algae, sponge, tunicates, etc. — creating a symbiotic relationship that is not overlooked as an incentive for urchin culturing in this setting. Urchin colonies are also known for "clear-cutting" kelp beds and have the potential to create "barrens" in the ocean where predators or fishing does not keep them in check.

PHYSICAL DESCRIPTION

Common Diameter: 6 in. (15 cm); Maximum spine length: 3 in. (7.5 cm)

Urchins are spherical bodies encased in a hard shell called a "test" that is completely covered by sharp spines. The red sea urchin is the largest of about 30 species found on the Pacific Coast. The color varies from a solid red to red-brown to a dark burgundy and even purple. The spines are long, tapering gradually, and are much larger than those of other two species. The green and purple sea urchins grow smaller than the red sea urchin and are often identified by their respective colors; the adult purple sea urchin usually being a very strong purple color. Young red sea urchins can have a some purple coloring but usually with a red tinge and the spines are distinctive; however, juvenile purple sea urchins are often pale green (usually with some purple) and sometimes it can be difficult to distinguish these green urchins.

(Red) Sea Urchin

Landings and Values

Red sea urchins range from Alaska to Baja, California. They are found mostly in subtidal habitats from the low tide line to water 300 feet deep. They prefer rocky ground (usually near kelp beds that they primarily feed on) and avoid areas that are subject to extreme wave action or where there is sand, mud or gravel. The purple sea urchin is also a West Coast native, but green sea urchins are found on both coasts, from the Arctic to New Jersey and from Alaska to Puget Sound. Urchins generally spawn from late spring to early fall so the main harvest time is winter and early spring when roes are at their best quality. Harvesting is

All Sea Urchins US Landings by Year — Nominal Data Value in $US (000); Quantity in tonnes; (NMFS)					
	2004	**2005**	**2006**	**2007**	**2008**
Value	16,599	11,805	9,663	10,296	12,604
Quantity	9,763	7,144	6,904	6,706	6,396

All Sea Urchins Canadian Landings by Year — Nominal Data Value in $Cdn (000); Quantity in tonnes; (DFO)					
	2004	**2005**	**2006**	**2007**	**2008**
Value	13,076	10,614	8,510	7,366	7,885
Quantity	6,892	6,408	3,136	4,434	4,145

by divers who use short aluminum rakes to scoop the urchins into large mesh bags, which are then hauled to a surface vessel. Urchins are also harvested with a drag in areas where diving is not feasible, but discards from damaged urchins can be high. Harvesting focuses on the smaller animals with firmer roes. Roe content usually ranges from 5% to 15% of total weight. US landings in 2008 were 6,396 tonnes, valued at $12.6 million (see table). California is the big producer (73%) followed by Maine (20%) and Oregon and Washington. Canadian landings in 2008 were 4,145 tonnes, valued at $7.9 million (see table). BC is the big producer (45% — mostly red sea urchins) followed by New Brunswick (33% — mostly green sea urchins). **Aquaculture:** As a high value species, there is worldwide interest in farming sea urchins.

Commercial Uses

The red sea urchin roe is processed locally and usually placed fresh in sealed trays for immediate shipment, mostly to Japan where it is called "uni." There it is consumed raw, particularly as a garnish for sushi. The taste has been compared to that of a "rich oyster." Freshness, color and size (smaller preferred) are important marketing factors—the roe should be a firm bright yellow or orange. Green sea urchins are often not processed, but shipped whole and live to Japan. Other Asian and domestic markets are now developing. Sea urchins have also become important in toxicology studies.

Life Cycle

Annual spawning of the red sea urchins occurs between June and September. Together, localized groups of sea urchins simultaneously shed sperm or eggs into the water. The fertilized eggs develop into planktonic larvae and then settle on the bottom where they transform into juvenile sea urchins, which hide from predators by seeking shelter under the spines of adults. When they have reached about 1 1/2 inches in diameter, the juveniles emerge from their shelter and, using retractable feet called "podia," which lie between their spines, forage freely over the rocky sea bottom. They use their mouths, armed with 5 teeth and special jaws, to scrape off and tear up the plant, and some animals (usually small, sessile invertebrates) they consume. If unlucky, they themselves will fall prey to sea stars, crabs or lobster. Adults have few successful predators, although they may fall prey to some fish and are a favorite food of sea otters. With sea otter recovery programs now happening on the West Coast, this is expected to be a future management challenge for the fishery. Red sea urchins mature in 4 to 5 years and have a long lifespan — 100 years or more.

SHRIMP OR PINK SHRIMP (& PANDALID SHRIMPS)

Ocean Shrimp

Aesop Shrimp

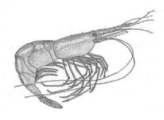

Sidestriped Shrimp

Northern (Pink) Shrimp, *Pandalus borealis*

GENERAL

In North America, the commercial shrimp fishery is comprised, for the most part, of species of the families Pandalidae and Penaeidae. **Pandalid shrimp** are coldwater species and typically account for only about 5% of all shrimp landings worldwide; but are the major shrimp fisheries in northern countries such as Canada and Denmark. Penaeid shrimp, on the other hand, are tropical or sub-tropical, with their main North American concentrations in the Gulf of Mexico. Although the word "prawn" is often used indiscriminately for all types of shrimp species, it is more often applied to large, or freshwater, species. The term "prawn," in place of "shrimp," is also favored in the UK and parts of Europe.

The **northern shrimp** or northern pink shrimp is a species of the family Pandalidae. Other pandalids fished from North America include the ocean shrimp (*P. jordani*), the Aesop* (also "striped" or "pink") shrimp (*P. montagui*), and the sidestriped (also "giant") shrimp (*Pandalopsis dispar*). Less common landings occur for the coonstriped (also "humpback" or "king") shrimp (*Pandalus hypsinotus*) and the dock* (or "coonstripe") shrimp (*P. danae*). The spot shrimp or "prawn" (*P. platyceros*) is a major fishery in itself on the West Coast, especially in BC, which catches the lion's share. The spot prawn is appreciated both for its large size and sweet flavor. (*Not listed in *The Seafood List*.)

PHYSICAL DESCRIPTION

Maximum total length: 12 cm (male), 16.5 cm (female) [FAO]
Shrimps are decapod (10 legged) crustaceans and somewhat similar in appearance to lobsters and crayfishes. Northern pink shrimp are pink or reddish in color. They have a long narrow beak, or "rostrum," in front of their eyes that is a ratio of 1:1 or 1:1.5 times longer than the length of their carapace. Unlike penaeid shrimp (see next entry), their first pair of legs is without claws. Their second pair is unequal in length but with small claws. The third pair is also without claws. Another distinguishing feature is the sharp spine or lobe that points backward from the abdomen. They are somewhat larger than the ocean shrimp, but smaller than the spot shrimp, which has a distinct white spot on the abdomen. Other common Pandalid shrimps look similar, although some may be distinguished by lateral stripes. Northern shrimp are good swimmers and can move both horizontally and vertically with ease.

Also Known As
Deep Water Prawn/
Pink Shrimp/
Northern Pink Shrimp

SeaLifeBase Name
Northern Shrimp

International Recognitions
Spain—Camarón norteño
France—Crevette nordique
Italy—Gamberetto boreale

NORTHERN (PINK) SHRIMP

LANDINGS AND VALUES

The northern shrimp is found in circumpolar waters of Asia, Europe and North America. In the Atlantic, it is especially concentrated from Greenland to the Gulf of Maine. These shrimp prefer areas with soft, muddy bottoms. Usually trawled, the principal landing seasons are spring to fall. Atlantic Canada landed 166,687 tonnes of Pandalid shrimp (mostly *P. borealis*) in 2008, valued at almost $258 million (see table). New England, (primarily Maine) landed 4,109 tonnes of unclassified shrimp in 2008, valued at $4.5 million, also thought to be northern shrimp (not shown). Ocean shrimp is the primary Pandalid fishery on the US West Coast, with 2008 landings of 15,588 tonnes in 2008, valued at $18.5 million (see table). Canada and the US also landed about 4,800 tonnes of spot prawn, valued at almost $22 million (see table). In addition, BC annually lands a variety of Pandilids including ocean, sidestriped, northern and coonstriped; in 2008, these species totaled 575 tonnes, valued at $1.7 million (not shown). **Aquaculture:** None; but interest in spot prawn.

Northern (Pink) Shrimp (includes 1-3% *P. montagui*) Canadian Atlantic Landings by Year — Nominal Data Value in $Cdn (000); Quantity in tonnes; (DFO)					
	2004	**2005**	**2006**	**2007**	**2008**
Value	249,426	257,148	234,106	257,695	257,895
Quantity	176,078	167,371	178,386	187,541	166,687

Ocean Shrimp (Pandalid) US Pacific Landings by Year — Nominal Data Value in $US (000); Quantity in tonnes; (NMFS)					
	2004	**2005**	**2006**	**2007**	**2008**
Value	7,857	10,624	6,658	11,420	18,540
Quantity	9,254	11,082	8,492	11,121	15,588

COMMERCIAL USES

Shrimp can usually be divided into two basic forms: raw (green) or cooked and then further divided into fresh or frozen. Within these broad categories, almost all shrimp sold in North America is head-off / tails, and the bulk of that is frozen. Pandalid shrimp is most often cooked, peeled and immediately frozen, so is usually only available frozen / cooked, peeled or whole. As a deep water shrimp, they do not ingest mud or sand and are not normally sold de-veined. Counts can go anywhere from 70 per pound unpeeled to 500 per pound peeled, placing northern pink shrimp in the "small" to "tiny" size categories. Pandalid shrimp are usually considered more flavorful ("sweet") than Penaeids and the smaller varieties, such as the northern shrimp, are often used as "cocktail" or salad shrimp.

Spot Prawn (Pandalid) US and Canadian Pacific Landings by Year — Nominal Value in $US/$Cdn (000); Quantity in tonnes; (NMFS/DFO)					
	2004	**2005**	**2006**	**2007**	**2008**
Value $US	2,240	2,817	3,505	2,880	3,176
Quantity US	102	123	144	117	128
Value $Cdn	28,020	40,354	37,074	25,041	18,536
Quantity Cdn	1,873	1,957	2,208	2,404	1,672

LIFE CYCLE

Northern shrimp, like other pandalids, are protandric hermaphrodites, initially functioning as males before transitioning into females. Mature shrimp breed in the late autumn or early winter. Shortly thereafter, developing eggs appear on the females' swimmerets. (Pandalids produce far fewer eggs than Penaeids.) They are carried there until hatching in the spring. The larvae swim freely for approximately 3 months and then settle to the ocean floor. They mature as males and transition to females in the third or fourth year. This is followed by mating, then spawning. Females may live and spawn for several years. They stay on the bottom during the day, feeding on worms, small crustaceans and marine plants. At night, they swim up from the bottom to feed, preying heavily on small pelagic crustaceans. They are prey for many species, including cod, halibut and seals.

SHRIMP (& PENAEID SHRIMPS)

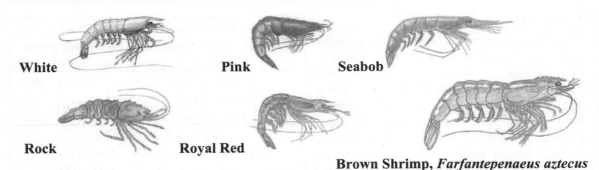

White Pink Seabob

Rock Royal Red

Brown Shrimp, *Farfantepenaeus aztecus*

GENERAL

As a product group, shrimp has traditionally been the most commercially important shellfish fishery in the United States and has lately become more important in Canada as well. Three species, known collectively as **penaeid shrimp,** or warm-water shrimp, (family Penaeidae) predominate in landings. These are the **brown shrimp,** the pink shrimp (*F. duorarum*) and the white shrimp (*Litopenaeus setiferus*).   Other less predominant Penaeid shrimps landed in the US include the Atlantic seabob (*Xiphopenaeus kroyeri*) and the roughneck shrimp* (*Rimapenaeus constrictus*). Small landings of species from other shrimp families include the rock shrimps (*Sicyonia* spp.) the royal red shrimp (*Pleoticus robustus*), the ocean shrimp (*Pandalus jordani*) and the spot prawn (*P. platyceros*) [see previous entry on pandalid shrimp]. (*not listed in *The Seafood List*)

PHYSICAL DESCRIPTION

(19.5 cm TL (male/unsexed); 23.6 cm TL (female)

The body of the shrimp consists of two distinct sections: the cephalothorax and the abdomen. Commercially, these are referred to as the head and the tail. The cephalothorax, containing the head and other vital organs, is covered by the carapace, a chitinous shell that is laterally compressed, presenting a rounded appearance. The pointed prow of the carapace, or "rostrum," extends in front of most species, above the eyes. Its size and shape are often used to distinguish the various species. The abdomen extends out from the posterior of the carapace. It is divided into six segments, the last of which terminates in a sharp point or "telson." The telson is positioned above the tail fin or tail fan. Shrimp have five pairs of walking legs or "pereiopods."

Penaeid shrimp differ from other shrimp in that they have small pincers on the front three pairs of legs, not just one (usually the first) pair. Each species of shrimp may vary considerably in color; consequently, using color to identify species may be very unreliable. A better method is to check for a groove or ridge running the length of the carapace. Brown and pink shrimp have this feature, while white shrimp do not. In addition, pink shrimp have a dark, reddish spot located between the third and fourth abdominal segments. Females are normally larger than males, and of these three species, the pink shrimp tends to grow the largest, reaching up to 11 inches.

Also Known As
Northern Brown Shrimp/
Warm-water Shrimp/
Gulf Brown Shrimp/
Redtail Shrimp
Red Shrimp
Golden Shrimp

SeaLifeBase Name
Northern Brown Shrimp

International Recognitions
France—
crevette pénaéides;
crevette royale grise
Germany—
Garnele
Spain—
quisquilla
Italy—
gamberetto

LANDINGS AND VALUES

Penaeid shrimp are found along the Atlantic coast as far north as New England. They are tropical species, however, and few are harvested north of the Carolinas. Most are trawled in the Gulf of Mexico, off Louisiana. The total US landings of Penaeid and other warm water shrimp in 2008 was almost

Total - All Shrimps (Penaeid and Pandalid) US Landings by Year — Nominal Data Value in $US (000); Quantity in tonnes; (NMFS)					
	2004	2005	2006	2007	2008
Value	404,946	392,675	430,539	410,508	421,485
Quantity	132,769	114,820	146,931	121,138	109,887

97,000 tonnes, valued at approximately $420 million (see table below). Brown shrimp and white shrimp account for most of the catch. **Aquaculture:** Penaeid shrimp traditionally account for about 70% of all wild caught shrimp and 100% of farmed shrimp worldwide. In 2008, US aquaculture produced 1,932 tonnes of shrimp, valued at $8.5 million (not shown). The success of worldwide shrimp aquaculture, that now supplies 25% of total world supply, has been depressing prices and affecting the viability of many wild shrimp fisheries.

COMMERCIAL USES

Shrimp is probably the most important commodity in the international seafood trade. Japan and the United States are the largest importers and, as such, determine how shrimp are handled, packaged and sold. Shrimp are sold live, fresh, frozen raw, frozen cooked, frozen breaded, canned or dried. Processed shrimp may be whole, headless shell-on tail, peeled tails, or peeled and de-veined tails. Almost all export shipments are either frozen or canned. Commercially, shrimp are classified by color and size rather than by species. The major classifications are brown, pink, white, red and tiger. Shrimp are also graded according to number per pound. The count for "tiny" shrimp is 70 or more per pound, whereas the more popular "jumbo" shrimp is 21 to 25 per pound and under 10 per pound for "extra colossal." In 2008, 82% of US shrimp was imported, with Thailand being the largest supplier.

LIFE CYCLE

Although specific details may vary from year to year and from one location to another, Penaeid shrimp complete their life cycle within one year. Environmental factors such as water temperature, habitat and food supply contribute to this time frame. Pink shrimp, for example, complete several migrations during their life.

Total Penaeid and Other Warm Water Shrimps US Landings by Comparison Years – Nominal Values Value in $US (000); Quantity in tonnes; (NMFS)				
	1989		2008	
Penaeid / Other	Value	Quantity	Value	Quantity
Brown Shrimp	267,006	73,402	155,114	39,086
White Shrimp	128,953	31,802	228,479	50,071
Pink Shrimp	36,029	7,805	15,142	3,809
Seabob	2,350	2,552	536	605
Penaeid nei	1,880	1,012	2,186	368
Dendrobranchiata nei	888	56	11,545	1,253
Royal Red	279	61	1,299	243
Rock, Pacific Rock	6,128	4,246	5,336	1,230
Mud, Brine, Ghost	4,525	5,354	443	103
Total	448,038	126,290	420,080	96,768

First, they move off-shore where mating occurs. Within 15 to 20 days spawning between hard-shelled males and recently molted females takes place. From 50 to 500,000 eggs are released into the sea from the female, where they drift with the currents and tides. Fertilized eggs hatch in about 14 hours. Young shrimp drift shoreward, to protective bays and estuaries that act as nurseries. Here, they grow rapidly, reaching 5 to 6 inches within the year. As the shrimp grow older and increase in size, they tend to move gradually into deeper, saltier water, returning to the ocean as they reach maturity. Their life span seldom exceeds 2 years.

SPONGE

Yellow Sponge, *Spongia barbara*

GENERAL

Sponges lack nervous, circulatory and digestive systems and have no eyes, ears, mouth or sense organs. They are rudimentary life forms, almost like plants, but unlike marine plants they are free swimming when young. Sponges occupy their own phylum, Porifera (sponges) in the animal kingdom. There are several thousand species, mostly marine, although a few are freshwater. A few species have an entirely soft fibrous skeleton with no hard elements and have been used by humans for centuries as cleaning accessories. The main species of soft sponges in North America are found in two genera, (*Hippospongia* and *Spongia*), including the **yellow sponge***, the sheepswool sponge (*Hippospongia lachne*) and the grass sponge (*Spongia gramine*). [*Sponges are not listed on *The Seafood List.*]

Also Known As
Demospongia

SeaLifeBase Name
Yellow sponge

International Recognitions (Generic)
Spain—esponja
France—éponge
Italy—spugna
Germany—Schwamm

PHYSICAL DESCRIPTION

The outer layer of a sponge is made up of flat cells, while the inside is a jelly-like mass full of holes and tunnels. Like other animals, sponge cells are differentiated, but generally not organized into distinct tissues. The outside of the sponge is usually cleaned and trimmed before sale, altering its look in nature.

Yellow sponge shape is spherical or speroidal and there are generally 10 – 20 osculum on the uppermost surface, each 7 – 10 mm in diameter. The colour in life is dark reddish-brown, almost black, when it grows at depths less than 2 meters; yellowish-grey at a depth of 10 meters. The fibers of a processed yellow sponge are more yellowish than those of other commercial sponges. Larger specimens can exceed 25 cm. It is found in relatively shallow water (2 – 15 meters).

The grass sponge is somewhat cone-shaped with very small pores on the sides that are somewhat coarse. The pores are horizontally directed to a large number of canals (1 cm. dia.) The skin is black and the interior is brown. Common size is 12 cm dia; large specimens up to 25cm. It is found in very shallow water (2 – 5 meters); specimens found deeper are small.

Sheepswool sponge is round, but with a greater horizontal than vertical dimension. The osculum is generally 12 to 18 mm in diameter, about 6 – 12 per sponge, always on the upper surface. The colour in life is a reddish-brown. Larger specimens may be over 30 cm wide and 18 cm high. It is found in relatively shallow water (2 – 10 meters).

LANDINGS AND VALUES

Yellow sponges are distributed from Newfoundland through North Carolina and live close to shore from the surface to 200 meters. Sheepswool sponges are harvested from the Florida coast and the West Indies. Grass sea sponges are found in Florida and the Gulf of Mexico.

Yellow Sponge US Landings by Year – Nominal Data Value in $US (000); Quantity in tonnes; (NMFS)					
	2004	**2005**	**2006**	**2007**	**2008**
Value	360	264	216	283	246
Quantity	102	84	60	79	72

All Sponges (incl: Grass, Yellow, Sheepswool) US Landings by Year – Nominal Data Value in $US (000); Quantity in tonnes; (NMFS)					
	2004	**2005**	**2006**	**2007**	**2008**
Value	1,072	830	657	937	772
Quantity	246	207	154	227	199

In North America, the sponge fishery developed by hand raking in the Florida Keys in the 1800s, later moving to Tarpon Springs during the Spanish-American War. An influx of experienced sponge divers from Greece brought a boom to the industry in the early 1900s, peaking in the 1930s. Overfishing, disease and new products led to a subsequent decline in harvests after World War II.

In 2008, 199 tonnes of sponges, valued at $772,000, were landed in the US. All of the catches in 2008 were landed on the Florida West Coast. The gear used was mostly hooks and diving outfits.

COMMERCIAL USES

Natural sponges are resistant to acids and tougher and easier to clean than artificial sponges. They are used in pottery production, medicine (surgery), painting, polishing, filtering, cleaning, etc. In the years of high landings, about 70% of the production was used for industrial purposes. The decline of landings combined with high prices has more recently resulted in sponges used almost exclusively for bathing. Sheepswool sponge is a fine, durable commercial sponge, and is more valuable than the yellow and grass sponge. However, many commercial users (e.g., spas and hotels) will use grass sponges in place of sheepswool sponges. The grass sponge is very soft and not very resistant, so has lower commercial value.

LIFE CYCLE

Most sponges are hermaphroditic with reproduction occurring through rudimentary forms of egg and sperm development. Sperm are expelled from the osculum of one animal and are absorbed from the medium by another, where the egg is fertilized. Usually, the fertilized eggs will hatch internally; however, some species will release them before hatching. They can also reproduce asexually through regeneration, budding or producing pods. After their larval stage, sponges attach to the bottom and become sessile. Sponges typically feed on bacteria and other minute particles by the intake of water through their pores (ostia) and, expelling waste water through their "chimney" opening (i.e., osculum). Parasites and disease appear to be their major enemies.

SQUID OR CALAMARI

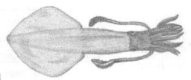

Longfin Squid

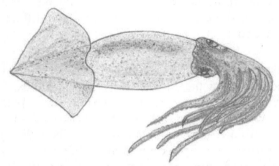

Northern Shortfin Squid, *Illex illecebrosus*

GENERAL

Squid is a cephalopod mollusc, as are octopus, nautilus and cuttlefish. Many species of squid are fished worldwide, but the **northern shortfin squid** (family Ommastrephidae) and two species of longfin squids – the "California market squid" (*Loligo opalescens*) on the West Coast and the "longfin squid" (*L. pealeii*) on the East Coast – are the main commercially important squids in North America. Two other squids accounted for small catches in recent years: the jumbo (or "Humboldt") squid (*Dosidicus gigas*) and the robust clubhook squid* (*Onykia robusta***).

Before the 1970s, the *Illex* squid was used primarily as bait and for local consumption. Spurred by foreign fishing, a large Atlantic fishery developed in the late 1970s and Canadian landings, in particular, peaked at 90,000 tonnes, only to disappear again soon after. Why this happened and whether the squid will ever return in such numbers is still debated. (* Not in *The Seafood List*; ***Moroteuthis robusta* now in *ITIS* is an apparent synonym).

PHYSICAL DESCRIPTION

Max length: 27.0 cm ML male/unsexed; (Ref. 275); 31 cm ML (female)

The squid, like the octopus, is a very distinctive fish with two tentacles and eight sucker-equipped arms (to hold prey) attached directly to the head. It has a tubular body (mantle) with two triangular-shaped swimming fins at the tail. In time of alarm, the squid can also use its siphon for "jet" propulsion. Using this siphon, and forcing water in various directions, it can also swim backwards. An internal shell, called a "pen," supports the body.

The squid is usually milky white, mottled with red or reddish brown. The *Illex* squid can be differentiated from longfin (*Loligo*) squid by its shorter fins (1/3 of mantle length, as compared to 1/2 in longfin) and shorter tentacles (1/2 of mantle length, as compared 2/3 in the longfin squids). Atlantic *Loligo* grow to 17 inches, while Pacific is usually less than 8 inches. Squid have an ink sac defense mechanism that enables them to eject dark fluids through their siphon to escape predators. They can also change color to camouflage themselves.

Also Known As
Summer Squid/
Illex Squid

**SeaLifeBase
Name**
Northern
shortfin squid

**International
Recognitions**
Spain—Pota
norteña
France—Encornet
rouge nordique
Italy—Totano
Germany—Kalmar

LANDINGS AND VALUES

The *Illex* squid ranges along the Atlantic Coast from Greenland to Florida. Large fluctuations in landings are common with this species; believed due partly to the short life span (1 to 1 1/2 years), the whims of ocean currents and perhaps over-fishing. The near-shore fishery is carried on mostly by traps and jigs. Offshore fisheries are conducted mostly by trawlers, which may use automated jigs and night lights to attract the squid. Long-finned squids are landed on both the Pacific and Atlantic coasts, with California and New Jersey accounting for the largest catches in 2008. US landings (all squid) totaled 60,321 tonnes in 2008, valued at almost $45 million (see table). The *Illex* squid accounted for about 5,300 tonnes of this total in 2008 (see table); although the almost 12,000 tonnes of unidentified squid was also landed in 2008 and no doubt included additional *Illex* landings. Canadian landings of *Illex* squid were 528 tonnes in 2008, valued at $228,000 (see table). In addition, a small amount of (mostly) *Loligo* squid is landed in BC; averaging 17 tonnes and $24,000 per year over the last 5 years (not shown). Unusual landings (Alaska) of jumbo squid, native to more equatorial currents, have ceased since 2006.

All Squids (*Illex*, *Loligo* spp., Jumbo, nei) US Landings by Year – Nominal Data Value in $US (000); Quantity in tonnes; (NMFS)					
	2004	2005	2006	2007	2008
Value	62,795	61,416	55,249	39,206	44,909
Quantity	82,313	75,641	67,793	56,012	60,321

Northern Shortfin (*Illex*) Squid US Landings by Year – Nominal Data Value in $US (000); Quantity in tonnes; (NMFS)					
	2004	2005	2006	2007	2008
Value	7,259	899	251	80	4,149
Quantity	15,210	1,361	421	115	5,335

COMMERCIAL USES

Squid is still widely used as fishing bait, but it is also valuable for food. In fact, it may be one of the most under-exploited food fisheries still widely available. It is usually processed frozen (or glazed, i.e., dipped in water), either whole, or as tubes, tentacles, or wings only. Squid has a big market in China and is a great delicacy in Japan, where it is preferred raw. Restaurant squid is often known as *calamari,* an Italian name.

Northern Shortfin (*Illex*) Squid Atlantic Canada Landings by Year – Nominal Data Value in $Cdn (000); Quantity in tonnes; (DFO)					
	2004	2005	2006	2007	2008
Value	1,480	366	2,915	108	228
Quantity	2,566	554	6,923	244	528

LIFE CYCLE

Much of the life cycle of the *Illex* squid is still a mystery. Their exact spawning ground is suspected to be somewhere near Cape Hatteras, in the Gulf Stream. By producing a jelly-like substance that surrounds the eggs, spawning squid create a large, naturally buoyant egg mass about 3 feet wide. Incubation varies with water temperature, but generally lasts about two weeks. Juvenile squid live in the Gulf Stream and are quickly carried (150 miles per day or more) northward to Canadian waters. Travelling in large schools, squid spend the day near the ocean bottom and ascend toward the surface at night. Schools are often sexually segregated, perhaps because males mature and migrate earlier. Squid quantities peak in the fall, but drop quickly as they begin to migrate southward, back to their spawning grounds, where they die after spawning. Squid feed on small crustaceans, such as euphausiids, when they are young, and on larger fish as they mature. Squid are prey to a variety of marine life (e.g., various groundfish, tuna, swordfish, whales and gulls).

WHELK (& OTHER GASTROPODS)

Periwinkles

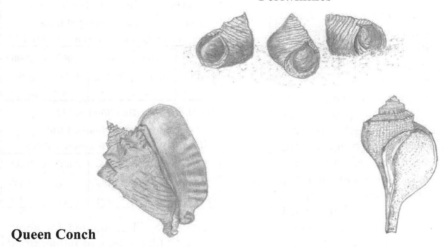

Queen Conch

Channeled Whelk, *Busycotypus canaliculatus*

GENERAL

Whelks are gastropod molluscs and related to other sea snails such as periwinkles, conchs and abalones (see previous entry on abalone). The **channeled whelk** (family Melongenidae) looks similar to the knobbed whelk, *Busycon carica** and the lightning whelk, *Busycon sinistrum,* but does not have "knobs" on its whorls. Note that these whelks are often (incorrectly) known as "conchs" or "winkles." Another whelk is the waved whelk, (*Buccinum undatum**) also known as the "North Atlantic whelk" or "Buckie," found from Newfoundland to Florida and in the Gulf of St. Lawrence. It features a thick, spiral shell that is about 3 to 6 inches in length. (* Not on *The Seafood List,* except as *Busycon* spp. and *Buccinum* spp.)

Somewhat larger than whelks and coming in many different shell-shapes, conchs (*Strombus* spp.) are gastropods of a different order (Neogastropoda) that are no longer fished in the US (except Puerto Rico and VI). However, small periwinkles, such as *Littorina littorea* (family Littorinidae), are common throughout the hemisphere. This periwinkle is actually of European origin and introduced to Nova Scotia in the mid-1800s, then spreading elsewhere. Both conch and whelk shells were used by aboriginals as ornaments and money.

PHYSICAL DESCRIPTION

Size: Up to 7 inches

The channeled whelk has five or six whorls with very small "beads" along the whorl edges rather than the large knobs that are found on the knobbed and lightning whelks. As with the knobbed whelk, and most other whelks (an exception is the lightning whelk), the channeled whelk's opening is on the right side. They are roughly pear shaped with a pale-grey "furry" periostracum. The head is yellowish-brown and the foot is whitish. It has a deep channel-like grove following each whorl and the spiral is turreted with 5 or 6 whorls. In general, the males are smaller than the females.

Also Known As
Conch/
Whelk/
Pear Whelk/
Scungilli/
Sea Snail/
Bulot Shell/
Escargot/

SeaLifeBase Name
Channeled whelk

International Recognitions
France—buccin
Germany—Wellhornschnecke
Italy—buccina
Spain—bocina
Japan—bai

CHANNELED WHELK

LANDINGS AND VALUES

Channeled whelks are found from Massachusetts to northern Florida. They live in the sand just below the low tide level. Harvesting is often accomplished by use of baited pots. Captured whelks can be held live by suspension in seawater in mesh bags or in holding pounds. The US reports whelk landings both as snails (conchs) and whelks; showing that 5 tonnes of whelks were landed in 2008, valued at $3,000 and 1,191 tonnes of snails were landed in 2008, valued at $7 million (see tables). Canadian landings of whelks were 7,219 tonnes in 2008, valued at $7.9 million (see table). Smaller landings for periwinkles were reported in each country in 2008.

Whelks (channeled, knobbed, lightning) US Landings by Year — Nominal Data Value in $US (000); Quantity in tonnes; (NMFS)					
	2004	2005	2006	2007	2008
Value	0	12	3	4,156	3
Quantity	17	17	4	678	5

Sea Snails ("Conchs") US Landings by Year — Nominal Data Value in $US (000); Quantity in tonnes; (NMFS)					
	2004	2005	2006	2007	2008
Value	1,985	3,249	7,085	821	7,054
Quantity	588	601	965	200	1,191

COMMERCIAL USES

Although you may still see conch on the menu, it is more likely to be whelk as conch is now a protected species in the US. However, some conch is imported from the Caribbean, since it is now being farmed in places like the Turks and Caicos Islands. Whelk is a darker meat than queen conch and has a stronger flavor. Italian-Americans, especially in New England, know this whelk as "scungilli" and use it in seafood

Whelk Canadian Landings by Year — Nominal Data Value in $Cdn (000); Quantity in tonnes; (DFO)					
	2004	2005	2006	2007	2008
Value	2,752	3,991	5,717	5,154	7,894
Quantity	2,805	3,826	5,786	5,290	7,219

salads and seafood marinara preparations. The foot is the edible portion of the mollusc. Often, this is tough and needs to be steamed for some time before serving. Whelk meats are generally removed from their shells and sold steamed and ready to eat - sometimes as "l'escargot." However, they may be shipped fresh/whole, canned or frozen.

LIFE CYCLE

The sexes are separate and, like other whelks, fertilization is internal. Eggs are laid in strings. Each capsule in the string can hold many eggs and each has a small hole at the top so the young whelks can escape after hatching. The string of capsules is attached to the ocean bottom at one end. Development of each embryo takes place totally within the egg capsule. At the end of the developmental period, the young emerge from the capsule looking like miniature adults. Sexual maturation will not be reached until after at least one year of growth. Whelks are carnivorous, eating small

Periwinkles US Landings by Year — Nominal Data Value in $US (000); Quantity in tonnes; (NMFS)					
	2004	2005	2006	2007	2008
Value	283	0	0	278	684
Quantity	64	0	0	64	135

Periwinkles Canadian Landings by Year — Nominal Data Value in $Cdn (000); Quantity in tonnes; (DFO)					
	2004	2005	2006	2007	2008
Value	250	248	221	46	24
Quantity	143	136	117	22	12

bivalves and other snails. In turn, they are preyed on by starfish, groundfish and crustaceans, such as crab and lobster. Conchs and periwinkles, however, are herbivores.

Bibliography

Agriculture and Agri-food Canada, March 22, 2005. *Industry Overview: All about Canada's Fish and Seafood Industry* [online]. Available from http://atn-riae.agr.ca/seafood/industry-e.htm

Auster, P. .J. and Langton, R. W. 1998. *The Effects of Fishing on Fish Habitat* [online]. Available from http://ocean.floridamarine.org/efh_coral/pdfs/Habitat_Plan/HabitatPlanAppM.pdf

Barton Warren. 1969. *American Food and Game Fishes*. New York: Dover Publications.

Biological Profiles, n.d. Ichthyology at the Florida Museum of Natural History [online]. Available from http://www.flmnh.ufl.edu/fish/Education/ bioprofile.htm

Boschung, Herbert T. Jr. et al. 1983. *TheAudubon Society Field Guide to North American Fishes, Whales and Dolphins*. New York: Alfred A. Knopf.

Bliss, D. (Ed.). 1985. *The Biology of Crustaceans,* Vol. 10, Economic Aspects: Fisheries and Culture. Orlando: Academic Press

Backus, R. H. and Bourne, D. 1987. *Georges Bank.* MIT Press

British Columbia's Fisheries & Aquaculture Sector September 2002. BC Ministry of Management Services [online]. Available from http://www.agf.gov.bc.ca/fish_stats/pdf/BC_Fisheries_&_Aquaculture_Sector_2002.pdf

Cheney, D and Mumford, T. 1986. *Shellfish and Seaweed Harvests of Puget Sound,* Seattle: Puget Sound Books

DFO 2002. *Pacific Sardine.* DFO Can Sci. Advis. Sec. Stock Status Rep. B6-07 (2002)

DFO 2003. "Why the Cod Stocks Haven't Recovered" DFO Media Room [online]. Available from http://www.dfo-mpo.gc.ca/ media/backgrou/2003/cod-3_e.htm

Dore, lan and Frimodt, Claus. 1987. *An Illustrated Guide to Shrimp of the World,* New York:: Osprey Books; Denmark: Scandinavian Fishing Year Book.

Dore, Ian. 1991. *Shellfish: A Guide to Oysters, Mussels, Scallops, Clams and Similar Products for the Commercial User,* New York: Osprey Books

Dore, Ian. 1993. *Shrimp: Supply Products and Marketing in the Aquaculture Age*, New Jersey, Urner Barry Publications

Dunfield, R. W. 1985. *The Atlantic Salmon in the History of North America.* Can. Spec. Publ. Fish. Aquat. Sci. 80: 181 p.

Eschmeyer, William N., and Herald, Earl S. 1983. *A Field Guide to Pacific Coast Fishes of North America.* Boston: Houghton Mifflin Company.

FAO. n.d. *The State of World Fisheries and Aquaculture 2004.* Rome: FAO Publishing Management Service

Feinberg, Harold S. 1979. *Simon and Schuster's Guide to Shells.* New York: Simon and Schuster Inc.

Fish Species n.d. Michigan State Department of Natural Resources [online]. Available from http://www.michigan.gov/dnr/0,1607,7-153-0364_18958---,00.html

Filisky, M. 1989. *Peterson First Guide to Fishes of North America* Boston: Houghton Mifflin Co.

Fitch, John E. and Lavenberg, Robert J. 1968. *Deep-Water Fishes of California.* Los Angeles: University of California Press.

Fletcher, Neil. *Will Atlantic cod stocks recover?* International Council for the Exploration of the Sea [online]. Available from *http://www.ices.dk/ marineworld/ recoveryplans.asp*

Froese, R. and D. Pauly. Editors. 2005. FishBase. World Wide Web electronic publication. www.fishbase.org, version (09/2005).

Gardner, Keith. 1987. *The Complete Book of Fishing, A Guide to Freshwater, Saltwater and Big Game Fishing.* New York: Gallery Books Ltd.

Goodrich, Joanne. 1993-97. *Canada's Fishery* About Canada Series. Centre for Canadian Studies at Mount Allison University in cooperation with Canadian Heritage, Canadian Studies Programme [online]. Available from http://www.mta.ca/faculty/arts/canadian_studies/english/about/fisheries/#bounty

Goodson, Gar. 1988. *Fishes of the Pacific Coast.* Stanford, California: Stanford University Press.

Gordon, Bernard Ludwig. 1977. *The Secret Lives of Fishes.* New York: Grosset and Dunlap.

Gordon, Julius and Welks, Townsend E. 1982. *Seashells of the Northeast Coast from Cape Hatteras to Newfoundland.* Blaine, Washington: Hancock House Publishers.

Gosner, Kenneth L. 1979. *A Field Guide to the Atlantic Seashore.* Boston: Houghton Mufflin Company.

Housby, Trevor. 1990. *The Concise Illustrated Book of Freshwater Fish.* Portugal: Brian Trodd Publishing House.

Hurtig, Mel et al. 1988. *The Canadian Encylopedia (Second Edition).* Alberta, Canada: Hurtig Publishing Ltd. Jordan, David Starr and Evermann,

Integrated Taxonomic Information System on-line database [online], Available from http://www.itis.usda.gov. Data retrieved as of October 1, 2005.

Kourous, George. March 7, 2005. *Depleted fish stocks require recovery effort.* Rome: FAO Newsroom [online]. Available from http:// www.fao.org/ newsroom/en/news/2005/100095/

Krane, Willibald. 1986. *Fish: Five-Language Dictionary of Fish, Crustaceans and Molluscs.* New York: Van Nostrand Reinhold.

Kurlansky, M. 1997. *Cod, A Biography of the Fish that Changed the World.* Penguin.

Lamb, Andy and Edgell, Phil. 1986. *Coastal Fishes of the Pacific Northwest.* British Columbia, Canada: Harbour Publishing.

MacKenzie, Debbie 2001 -2005. *The Starving Ocean* [online]. Available from http://www.Fisherycrisis .com/index.htm

May, A. W. et al. 2005. *Report of the Advisory Panel on the Sustainable Management of Straddling Fish Stocks in the Northwest Atlantic,* DFO Media Room Press Release [online]. Available from http://www.dfo-mpo.gc.ca/overfishing-surpeche/documents/advisory_e.htm

Martin, Roy E. and Flick, George J. 1990. *The Seafood Industry.* New York: Van Nostrand Reinhold.

McClane, A. J. (editor). 1998. *McClane's New Standard Fishing Encyclopedia,* Random House Value Publishing.

Meinkoth, Norman A 1981. *The Audubon Society Field Guide to North American Seashore Creatures.* New York: Alfred A. Knopf.

Morris, Percy A 1974. *Pacific Coast Shells.* Boston: Houghton Mifflin Company.

Morris, Percy A 1975. *Shells of the Atlantic.* Boston: Houghton Mifflin Company.

Morris, Solene. 1990. *A Concise Illustrated Book of Seashells.* Spain: Brian Trodd Publishing House.

NEFSC/NOAA (n.d.) *Brief history of the groundfishing industry of New England* [online]. Available from http://www.nefsc.noaa.gov/ history/stories/groundfish/grndfsh1.html

OECD, 1978. *Multi-lingual Dictionary of Fish and Fish Products.* Surrey: Fishing News Books Ltd.

Riccuiti, Ed. 1982. *Fish of the Atlantic.* Blaine, Washington: Hancock House Publishers.

Robins, Richard and Ray, Carleton. 1986. *A Field Guide to Atlantic Coast Fishes of North America.* Boston: Hougton Mifflin Company.

Rodger, Robin W.A. 1991. *Fish Facts: An Illustrated Guide to Commercial Species,* NY, NY, Van Nostrand Reinhold.

Rose, G. A. et al 2000. *Distribution shifts and overfishing the northern cod (Gadus morhua): a view from the ocean,* Can. J. Fish. Aquat. Sci. Vol. 57, 2000.

Rosenberg, A. et al 2005. *The history of ocean resources: modeling cod biomass using historical records.* Frontiers in Ecology and the Environment: Vol. 3, No. 2, pp. 78–84

Ryan, Shannon et al 1996. *The History of the Northern Cod Fishery,* Newfoundland and Labrador Department of Education [online]. Available from http://www.cdli.ca/cod/

Schaffner, Herbert A. 1989. *Freshwater Game Fish of North America.* New York: Michael Fried-man Publishing Group Inc.

Scott, W.B. and Scott, M.G. 1988. *Atlantic Fishes of Canada.* Toronto, Canada: University of Toronto Press.

Seafood Guide, n.d. Complete series of reports and fact sheets produced by Seafood Watch [online]. Available from http://www. mbayaq.org/ cr/SeafoodWatch/ web/ sfwfactsheet.aspx

Species Profiles n.d. *Life Histories and Environmental Requirements of Coastal Fishes and Invertebrates, USGS* at California Explores the Ocean [online]. Available from http:// ceo.ucsd.edu/ publications/ publications.html

Underwater World, n.d. Complete series of fact sheets produced by the Communications Directorate, Department of Fisheries and Oceans, Minister of Supply and Services, Ottawa, Ontario, Canada.

Voorhees, D and Pritchard, E. 2004. *Fisheries of the United States 2003.* Maryland: National Marine Fisheries Service [online]. Available from http://www.st.nmfs. gov/st1/fus/fus03/

Wasserman, Miriam, 2001, q2. *The Last Hunting Economy*, Regional Review , Boston: Federal Reserve Bank [online]. Available from http://www.bos.frb.org/ economic/nerr/rr2001/q2/lasthunt.htm

Zim, Herbert S., and Shoemaker, Hurst H. 1987. *A Golden Guide to Fishes.* Racine, Wisconsin: Western Publishing Company

New and Updated References (to the 2012 Edition)

GENERAL REFERENCES

Froese, R. and D. Pauly. Editors. 2011. *FishBase*. World Wide Web electronic publication. www.FishBase.org, version 06/2011

Guidance for Industry: The Seafood List - FDA's Guide to Acceptable Market Names for Seafood Sold in Interstate Commerce 2010 (with 2010 updates). Available from: http://www.fda.gov/Food/GuidanceComplianceRegulatoryInformation/GuidanceDocuments/Seafood/uc m113260.htm. Data retrieved as of November 1, 2011.

Integrated Taxonomic Information System on-line database [online], Available from http://www.itis.gov. Data retrieved as of November 1, 2011.

McLaughlin, P.A., et al. 2005. Common and scientific names of aquatic invertebrates from the United States and Canada: Crustaceans. American Fisheries Society Special Publication 31: 545 pp.

Nelson, J.S., et al. 2004. Common and scientific names of fishes from the United States, Canada, and Mexico. 6th ed., American Fisheries Society, Special Publication 29, Bethesda, Maryland. 386 pp.

Palomares, M.L.D. and D. Pauly. Editors .2011. *SeaLifeBase*. World Wide Web electronic publication. www.SeaLifeBase.org, version 12/2011

Rodger, R.W., 2006. The Fisheries of North America: An Illustrated Guide to Commercial Species. Canadian Marine Publications, Halifax, NS, Canada

MARINE FISHES

ALASKA POLLOCK OR POLLOCK/Walleye Pollock/*Theragra chalcogramma*
FISHWATCH
http://www.nmfs.noaa.gov/fishwatch/species/walleye_pollock.htm

AMBERJACK/Banded Rudderfish/*Seriola zonata*
NSW Dept. of Primary Industries http://www.dpi.nsw.gov.au/fisheries/recreational/saltwater-fishing/sw-species/amberjack
Florida Seafood and Aquaculture http://www.fl-seafood.com/species/amberjack.htm
World Aquaculture http://www7.taosnet.com/platinum/data/species/amberjack.html
Texas Parks and Wildlife HTTP://WWW.TPWD.STATE.TX.US/HUNTWILD/WILD/SPECIES/GRAMBERJACK/
Florida Fish and Wildlife Conservation Commission
http://www.floridaconservation.org/marine/FishID/jackgrea.html
Dept. of Marine Fisheries. 2011. Florida Fish and Wildlife Conservation Commission. World Wide Web electronic publication. http://myfwc.com/marine/FishID/jackband.html.
Publication of the South Atlantic Fishery Management Council. 2011. SAFMC. World Wide Web electronic publication.
http://www.safmc.net/FishIDandRegs/RegulationsbySpecies/BandedRudderfish/tabid/264/Default.aspx
Gulf of Maine Census. 2011. University of Southern Maine. World Wide Web electronic publication.
http://research.usm.maine.edu/gulfofmaine-census/education/media-gallery/illustrated-taxonomy-for-the-gulf-of-maine/list-of-species/detail-page/?id=83
NSW Dept. of Primary Industries. 2011. State of New South Wales. World Wide Web electronic publication. http://www.dpi.nsw.gov.au/fisheries/recreational/saltwater-fishing/sw-species/amberjack
Florida Seafood and Aquaculture.2011. Florida Department of Agriculture and Consumer Services. World Wide Web electronic publication. http://www.fl-seafood.com/species/amberjack.htm. 2004.

Jeff Batis. 2011. World Aquaculture. World Wide Web electronic publication. http://www7.taosnet.com/platinum/data/species/amberjack.html 2000.
Greater Amberjack. 2011. Texas Parks and Wildlife Department. World Wide Web electronic publication. http://www.tpwd.state.tx.us/huntwild/wild/species/gramberjack.
Food Reference Website http://www.foodreference.com/html/art-amberjack-7806.html
Florida Fish and Wildlife Conservation Commission
http://www.floridaconservation.org/marine/FishID/jackgrea.html
USFDA Seafood List http://www.cfsan.fda.gov/cgi-bin/seafd?QUERY=amberjack

BALLYHOO/Ballyhoo/*Not in TFL*
More Detail: http://fishbull.noaa.gov/1013/09mcbrid.pdf

BASS/ Largemouth Bass/ *Micropterus salmoides*
http://www.dfo-mpo.gc.ca/stats/rec/can/2005/index-eng.htm

BIGEYE/Bigeye/*Priacanthus arenatus*
http://www.gma.org/fogm/Pseudopriacanthus_altus.htm

BRUTOLA/Bearded Brutola/*Brotula barbata*
Fishes of the Great Barrier Reef and Coral Sea - Page 52

COBIA/Cobia/*Rachycentron canadum*
Aquaculture Center http://www.aquaculturecenter.com/cobia.html
Florida Museum of Natural History http://www.flmnh.ufl.edu/fish/gallery/Descript/Cobia/Cobia.html
NOAA Fishwatch http://www.nmfs.noaa.gov/fishwatch/species/cobia.htm

CROAKER/Atlantic Croaker/*Micropogonias undulatus*
Texas parks and Wildlife Dept./TPWD http://www.tpwd.state.tx.us/huntwild/wild/species/croaker/
Maryland Dept. of Natural Resources/MD DNR
http://www.dnr.state.md.us/fisheries/fishfacts/atlanticcroaker.asp
Florida Fish Identification http://indian-river.fl.us/fishing/fish/drumatla.html
http://www.asmfc.org/
USGS Species Profiles 1983 http://www.nwrc.usgs.gov/wdb/pub/species_profiles/82_11-003.pdf

CUNNER/Cunner/*Tautogolabrus adspersus*
GMA http://www.gma.org/fogm/Tautogolabrus_adspersus.htm
http://74.125.95.132/search?q=cache:ApKM21mnrs8J:maine.gov/dmr/recreational/anglerguide/doyoukn owyourcatch/documents/cunner.pdf+cunner&hl=en&ct=clnk&cd=12&gl=us

CUTLASSFISH/*Atlantic Cutlassfish/Trichiurus lepturus*
Texas Parks and Wildlife Dept/TPWD http://www.tpwd.state.tx.us/huntwild/wild/species/cutlassfish/

DORY/John Dory/*Zeus faber*
Bigelow and Schroeder, Fisheries of the Gulf of Maine, 1953
http://www.gma.org/fogm/Zenopsis_ocellata.htm
http://en.wikipedia.org/wiki/John_Dory

DRIFTFISH/Barrelfish/*Hyperoglyphe perciformis*
NOAA Ocean Explorer
http://oceanexplorer.noaa.gov/explorations/04etta/background/barrelfish/barrelfish.html
GMA http://www.gma.org/fogm/Palinurichthys_perciformis.htm
Louisiana Dept. of Wildlife and Fisheries http://www.wlf.louisiana.gov/fishing/fishid/groupers.cfm
Fish of the Gulf of Mexico http://www.rodnreel.com/gulffish/gulffish.asp?FishID=238&cmd=view

DRUM/Black Drum/*Pogonias cromis*
Smithsonian Marine Station at Fort Pierce/SMSFP http://www.sms.si.edu/IRLspec/Pogoni_cromis.htm
Maryland Dept. of Natural Resources/MD DNR
http://www.dnr.state.md.us/fisheries/fishfacts/reddrum.asp
Texas Parks and Wildlife Dept./TPWD http://www.tpwd.state.tx.us/huntwild/wild/species/reddrum/
Cornell Dept. Of Natural Resources/CDNR
http://pond.dnr.cornell.edu/nyfish/Sciaenidae/Sciaenidae.html
TPWD http://www.tpwd.state.tx.us/huntwild/wild/species/fwd/

EEL/CONGER/Conger Eel/*Conger oceanicus*
GMA http://www.gma.org/fogm/Conger_oceanica.htm
Environmental Defense Fund http://www.edf.org/page.cfm?tagID=15861

ESCOLAR/Escolar/*Lepidocybium flavobrunneum*
Field Guide to Seafood
http://books.google.ca/books?id=f1JyIFWMERUC&pg=PA53&lpg=PA53&dq=Field+Guide+to+Seafoo
d+%2B+escolar&source=bl&ots=hbDJGbfNNc&sig=Y8siSBtPSHnfJeBo-jR-
6CiV79w&hl=en&ei=jwJqTriKDeePsQK15KWkBg&sa=X&oi=book_result&ct=result&resnum=1&sqi
=2&ved=0CB0Q6AEwAA#v=onepage&q&f=false

FLOUNDER/Arrowtooth Flounder/*Reinhardtius stomias*
http://www.nmfs.noaa.gov/fishwatch/species/arrowtooth_flounder.htm
Washington Dept. of Fish and Wildlife/WDFW http://wdfw.wa.gov/fish/bottomfish/flatfish.htm
NOAA http://www.aquanic.org/publicat/usda_rac/efs/srac/726fs.pdf

FLOUNDER/Yellowtail Flounder/*Limanda ferruginea*
http://www.nmfs.noaa.gov/fishwatch/species/yellowtail_flounder.htm
Environmental Defense Fund/EDF http://www.edf.org/page.cfm?tagID=15836
http://www7.taosnet.com/platinum/data/species/flounderyellowtail.html
http://www.nefsc.noaa.gov/sos/spsyn/fldrs/yellowtail/
Not yet overfished NMFS http://www.nefmc.org/habitat/original_omnibus/yellowtail.PDF

FLOUNDER/Summer Flounder/*Paralichthys dentatus*
Fishwatch, NOAA http://www.nmfs.noaa.gov/fishwatch/species/summer_flounder.htm

GREENLING/Kelp Greenling/*Hexagrammos decagrammus*
http://nrimp.dfw.state.or.us/MRP/default.aspx?p=74
Fishery Bulletin http://www.accessmylibrary.com/coms2/summary_0286-30740198_ITM
Alaska Dept. of Fish and Game
http://www.cf.adfg.state.ak.us/geninfo/finfish/grndfish/mackerel/mackerelhome.php
Alaska Fish Science Centre: Atka mackerel; http://www.afsc.noaa.gov/species/Atka_mackerel.php

GROUPER/Red Grouper/*Epinephelus morio*
http://www.sms.si.edu/irlspec/Epinep_morio.htm

GROUPER OR GAG/Gag/*Mycteroperca microlepis*
Florida Museum of Natural History Ichthyology/FMNHI
http://www.flmnh.ufl.edu/fish/gallery/descript/gaggrouper/gaggrouper.html
Florida Fish and Wildlife Conservation Commission/FFWCC
http://myfwc.com/marine/FishID/groupgag.html
CSULB http://www.csulb.edu/depts/biology/marine/species/Graysby.html_f/Graysby.html
Reef News http://www.reefnews.com/reefnews/photos/graysby.html
http://www.nmfs.noaa.gov/habitat/habitatprotection/profile/caribbean/graysbyhome.htm

GROUPER OR HIND/Red Hind/*Epinephelus guttatus*
SAFMC http://www.safmc.net/FishIDandRegs/FishGallery/RedHind/tabid/314/Default.aspx

GRUNT/White Grunt/*Haemulon plumierii*
Smithsonian Marine Station at Fort Pierce http://www.sms.si.edu/irlspec/Haemulon_plumierii.htm
http://fishbase.com/Summary/SpeciesSummary.php?id=1126
http://www.safmc.net/FishIDandRegs/RegulationsbySpecies/Margate/tabid/304/Default.aspx
http://www.gamefishingguide.com/margate-fish.html
Fishbase http://fishbase.com/Summary/SpeciesSummary.php?id=5
TPWD Education
http://www.tpwd.state.tx.us/spdest/visitorcenters/seacenter/education/coastal_habitats/nearshore/animals/
pigfish.phtml
http://www.britannica.com/EBchecked/topic/247459/grunt

HADDOCK/Haddock/*Melanogrammus aeglefinus*
The Fish Site http://www.thefishsite.com/articles/367/haddock-culture-current-knowledge-and-
challenges
Dalhousie Univ., DFO http://oceanography.dal.ca/publications/files/Neuheimer_et_al_2008.pdf

HAGFISH/Hagfish/*Myxine glutinosa*
http://www.nefsc.noaa.gov/sos/spsyn/op/hagfish/
HOGFISH/Hogfish/*Lachnolaimus maximus*
SAFMC http://www.safmc.net/FishIDandRegs/RegulationsbySpecies/Hogfish/tabid/295/Default.aspx
FMNHI http://www.flmnh.ufl.edu/fish/Gallery/Descript/hogfish/hogfish.html

JACK/Lookdown jack /*Selene vomer*
FMNHI http://www.flmnh.ufl.edu/fish/gallery/descript/crevallejack/crevallejack.html
http://www.floridaconservation.org/marine/FishID/jackcre.html
TPWD http://www.tpwd.state.tx.us/huntwild/wild/species/crjack/

KINGFISH/Northern Kingfish/*Menticirrhus saxatilis*
Bigelow and Schroeder 1953 , NMFS 2002 , Virginia Tech Web site,
http://fwie.fw.vt.edu/www/macsis/fish.htm
NJ Department of Fish and Wildlife http://www.nj.gov/dep/fgw/artkingfish.htm

LADYFISH/Ladyfish/*Elops saurus*
Florida Conservation http://www.floridaconservation.org/marine/fishid/tarplady.html
http://myfwc.com/media/195433/ladyfish.pdf

MAHI-MAHI/Dolphin/*Coryphaena hippurus*
http://www.nmfs.noaa.gov/fishwatch/species/dolphinfish.htm

MARLIN/Blue Marlin/*Makaira nigricans*
ftp://ftp.fao.org/docrep/fao/009/ac480e/ac480e06.pdf - pg 27 Systemic Catalogue section
http://animaldiversity.ummz.umich.edu/site/accounts/information/Makaira_nigricans.html
http://www.bigmarinefish.com/marlin.html
http://en.wikipedia.org/wiki/Billfish
http://en.wikipedia.org/wiki/Atlantic_blue_marlin
NSW Fishing and Aquaculture http://www.dpi.nsw.gov.au/fisheries/recreational/saltwater-fishing/sw-
species/marlin-black-imakaira-indicai
http://www.fishbase.org/Summary/SpeciesSummary.php?id=217
MarineBio http://marinebio.org/

MUMMICHOG/Mummichog/*Fundulus heteroclitus*
http://www.dnr.sc.gov/cwcs/pdf/Mummichog.pdf

OCEAN POUT /Ocean Pout/*Zoarces americanus*
http://www.nmfs.noaa.gov/habitat/habitatprotection/profile/northeast/oceanpouthome.htm
http://maine.gov/dmr/recreational/anglerguide/doyouknowyourcatch/documents/oceanpout.pdf
NEFSC http://www.nefsc.noaa.gov/sos/spsyn/og/pout/
NMFS report
http://74.125.95.132/search?q=cache:SRXNmiBRrEQJ:www.nefmc.org/habitat/original_omnibus/ocean-pout.PDF+ocean+pout&hl=en&ct=clnk&cd=5&gl=us
Encyclopedia http://animals.jrank.org/pages/2174/Eelpouts-Relatives-Zoarcoidei-OCEAN-POUT-Zoarces-americanus-SPECIES-ACCOUNTS.html

POMPANO/Florida Pompano/*Trachinotus carolinus*
Indian River Fishing http://indian-river.fl.us/fishing/fish/pompperm.html
http://www.flmnh.ufl.edu/fish/gallery/Descript/permit/permit.html
FMNHI http://www.flmnh.ufl.edu/fish/gallery/Descript/permit/permit.html
Florida Conservation http://www.floridaconservation.org/marine/FishID/pompflor.html
TPWD http://www.tpwd.state.tx.us/huntwild/wild/species/pompano/
http://www.floridamarine.org/features/category_sub.asp?id=4689

ROSEFISH/ Blackbelly Rosefish/ *Helicolenus dactylopterus*
http://www.afsc.noaa.gov/Rockfish-Game/description/shortspine.htm

SAND LANCE/Northern Sand Lance/ *Ammodytes dubius*
DFO – Underwater World Series DFO 2122 UW-46 ISBN 0-662-92949-7

SAURY/Atlantic Saury/*Scomberesox saurus*
http://na.oceana.org/en/explore/creatures/atlantic-saury
http://www.gma.org/fogm/scomberesox_saurus.htm

SCAD/Bigeye Scad/*Selar crumenophthalmus*
Gulf of Maine Census http://research.usm.maine.edu/gulfofmaine-census/education/media-gallery/illustrated-taxonomy-for-the-gulf-of-maine/list-of-species/detail-page/?id=84
http://www.thejump.net/id/mackerel-scad.htm
http://www.gma.org/fogm/Decapterus_macarellus.htm
http://www.montereybayaquarium.org/cr/SeafoodWatch/web/sfw_factsheet.aspx?fid=155
P.M. Shiota with NOAA http://swfsc.noaa.gov/publications/CR/1986/8698.PDF

SCAMP/Scamp/*Mycteroperca phenax*
Florida Dept. of Marine Fisheries/FDMF
http://www.floridaconservation.org/marine/fishid/groupsca.html
http://www.allfishingbuy.com/Fish-Recipes/Grouper-Recepies.htm
SAMFC http://www.safmc.net/FishIDandRegs/FishGallery/Scamp/tabid/322/Default.aspx

SCULPIN/Atlantic Sea Raven – sculpin/*Hemitripterus americanus*
SOURCES: McClanes guide to freshwater fishes of North America. McClanes Guide to Saltwater fishes
of North America. BY AJ McCLANE. The New Fishing Encyclopedia. www.thejump.net/fish
GMA http://www.gma.org/fogm/Hemitripterus_americanus.htm#d0e42216

SHAD/American Shad/*Alosa sapidissima*
http://nsflyfishing.com/shadflies.html
http://www.dec.ny.gov/animals/52764.html
http://fishing.about.com/od/fishfacts/a/threadfin_shad.htm

SHARK, MAKO/Shortfin Mako Shark/*Isurus oxyrinchus*
Biology of Sharks and Rays http://www.elasmo-research.org/education/shark_profiles/i_oxyrinchus.htm

SHEEPHEAD/California Sheephead/*Semicossyphus pulcher*
CaDFG http://www.dfg.ca.gov/marine/mspcont7.asp
RBBA http://www.rbba.us/fish/sheephead.htm
Monterey Bay Aquarium/MBA
http://www.mbayaq.org/efc/living_species/default.asp?hOri=1&inhab=215
REEF http://www.reef.org/fish/pac/127

SILVERSIDE/Atlantic Silverside/*Menidia menidia*
http://www.nwrc.usgs.gov/wdb/pub/species_profiles/82_11-010.pd
http://en.wikipedia.org/wiki/Atlantic_silverside
Non-citable DFO Atlantic Canada research report

SPADEFISH/Atlantic Spadefish/*Chaetodipterus faber*
Dept. of Marine Fisheries/DMF http://www.marinefisheries.org/FishId/spadatla.html
FMNHI http://www.flmnh.ufl.edu/fish/Gallery/Descript/AtlanticSpadefish/AtlanticSpadefish.html
MarineBio http://marinebio.org/species.asp?id=428

SQUIRRELFISH/Squirrelfish/*Holocentrus adscensionis*
Science Encyclopedia http://science.jrank.org/pages/6422/Squirrel-Fish.html
 MarineBio http://www.marinebio.com/species.asp?id=42

SURFPERCH/Barred Surfperch/*Amphistichus argenteus*
http://www.surffishtackle.com/servlet/Categories?category=Grubs
http://www.aquariumofpacific.org/onlinelearningcenter/species/silver_surfperch/
http://www.psmfc.org/habitat/edu_perch_fact.html
http://www.dfg.ca.gov/marine/mspcont2.asp#barred
http://en.wikipedia.org/wiki/Amphistichus_argenteus

SWORDFISH/Swordfish/*Xiphias gladius*
http://www.fda.gov/Food/FoodSafety/Product-
SpecificInformation/Seafood/FoodbornePathogensContaminants/Methylmercury/ucm115662.htm
http://www.hc-sc.gc.ca/fn-an/securit/chem-chim/environ/mercur/merc_fish_qa-poisson_qr-eng.php#ca2
http://www.hc-sc.gc.ca/fn-an/securit/chem-chim/environ/mercur/cons-adv-etud-eng.php

SURGEONFISH OR TANG/Blue Tang/*Acanthurus coeruleus*
FMNHI http://www.flmnh.ufl.edu/fish/Gallery/Descript/BlueTang/BlueTang.html
Marine Bio http://marinebio.org/species.asp?id=277

TAUTOG/Tautog/*Tautoga onitis*
Mass. Dept of Fish and Game/MaDFG http://www.mass.gov/dfwele/dmf/recreationalfishing/tautog.htm
Delaware SeaGrant http://www.ocean.udel.edu/mas/seafood/tautog.html
NY State Dept. of Environmental Conservation http://www.dec.ny.gov/animals/9965.html

TOADFISH/Gulf Toadfish/*Opsanus beta*
http://images.google.com/imgres?imgurl=http://www.flmnh.ufl.edu/fish/gallery/Descript/GulfToadfish/g
ulftoadfish.JPG&imgrefurl=http://www.flmnh.ufl.edu/fish/gallery/Descript/GulfToadfish/GulfToadfish.h
tml&usg=__wbu6eoeVw4FtTGaKm6cbNbmvhJI=&h=286&w=380&sz=41&hl=en&start=2&sig2=Vsdc
zOLapKW8uNotzu4XHQ&um=1&tbnid=8meJZy1IGO9PpM:&tbnh=93&tbnw=123&ei=ndN4SeauKJf
0sAPD_dQW&prev=/images%3Fq%3Dgulf%2Btoadfish%26um%3D1%26hl%3Den%26rlz%3D1B3G
GGL_enUS276US276%26sa%3DN
TPWD http://www.tpwd.state.tx.us/fishboat/fish/didyouknow/amazingfish.phtml

TRIGGERFISH/Gray Triggerfish/*Balistes capriscus*
http://www.safmc.net/FishIDandRegs/FishGallery/GrayTriggerfish/tabid/292/Default.aspx
http://www.flmnh.ufl.edu/fish/gallery/Descript/Graytriggerfish/graytriggerfish.html
http://www.fishbase.us/Summary/speciesSummary.php?ID=7327&genusname=Balistes&speciesname=capriscus

TRIPLETAIL/Tripletail/*Lobotes surinamensis*
TPWD http://www.tpwd.state.tx.us/huntwild/wild/species/tripletail/
FMNHI http://www.flmnh.ufl.edu/fish/Gallery/Descript/Tripletail/Tripletail.html
Florida Fish and Wildlife Research Institute
http://www.floridamarine.org/gallery/image_details.asp?id=13324
GA DNR http://crd.dnr.state.ga.us/content/displaycontent.asp?txtDocument=444

TUNA/Albacore/*Thunnus alalunga*
http://www.nmfs.noaa.gov/fishwatch/species/pac_albacore.htm
http://en.wikipedia.org/wiki/Albacore
http://www.nmfs.noaa.gov/fishwatch/species/atl_albacore.htm
http://www.fishbase.us/Summary/speciesSummary.php?ID=142&genusname=Thunnus&speciesname=alalunga

TUNA/Bigeye Tuna/*Thunnus obesus*
http://www.nmfs.noaa.gov/fishwatch/species/pac_bigeye_tuna.htm
http://www.nmfs.noaa.gov/fishwatch/species/atl_bigeye_tuna.htm
http://www.nmfs.noaa.gov/fishwatch/species/pac_yellowfin_tuna.htm
http://www.nmfs.noaa.gov/fishwatch/species/atl_yellowfin.htm
http://www.nmfs.noaa.gov/fishwatch/species/atl_skipjack.htm
http://www.nmfs.noaa.gov/fishwatch/species/pac_skipjack.htm
http://www.fishbase.org/Summary/SpeciesSummary.php?id=146
http://www.safmc.net/FishIDandRegs/FishGallery/BigeyeTuna/tabid/266/Default.aspx

TURBOT
http://www.fao.org/fishery/topic/12356/en
http://www.nmfs.noaa.gov/fishwatch/species/green_turbot.htm

WAHOO/Wahoo/*Acanthocybium solandri*
http://www.nmfs.noaa.gov/fishwatch/species/pac_wahoo.htm
Wiki http://en.wikipedia.org/wiki/Wahoo

FRESHWATER FISHES

BOWFIN/Bowfin/*Amia calva*
Cornell http://pond.dnr.cornell.edu/nyfish/Amiidae/bowfin.html
SeaGrant Wisconsin http://seagrant.wisc.edu/greatlakesfish/fbowfin.html
NY Dept. of Environmental Conservation http://www.dec.ny.gov/animals/7014.html
http://pond.dnr.cornell.edu/nyfish/Amiidae/bowfin.html
http://www.fishbase.org/Summary/SpeciesSummary.php?id=2600
http://seagrant.wisc.edu/greatlakesfish/fbowfin.html
http://www.dec.ny.gov/animals/7014.html

BUFFALOFISH/ Bigmouth Buffalofish, *Ictiobus cyprinellus*
http://www.tpwd.state.tx.us/huntwild/wild/species/sucker/
http://identifyfish.blogspot.com/2010/11/bigmouth-buffalo-ictiobus-cyprinellus.html

BURBOT/Burbot/*Lota lota*
Cornell http://fish.dnr.cornell.edu/nyfish/Gadidae/gadidae.html
Alaska Dept. of Fish and Game/ADFG http://www.adfg.state.ak.us/pubs/notebook/fish/burbot.php
Minnesota Dept. of Natural Resources/MDNR
http://www.dnr.state.mn.us/volunteer/janfeb00/burbot_profile.html
NY Dept. of Environmental Conservation/NY DEC www.dec.ny.gov/animals/7014.html
Wisconsin SeaGrant http://seagrant.wisc.edu/greatlakesfish/burbot.html

CARPS/Common Carp/*Cyprinus carpio*
Cornell http://pond.dnr.cornell.edu/nyfish/Cyprinidae/common_carp.html
Great Lakes Information Network http://www.great-lakes.net/envt/flora-fauna/invasive/carp.html
Texas Parks and Wildlife Department/TPWD http://www.tpwd.state.tx.us/huntwild/wild/species/crp/
Minnesota Dept. of Natural Resources/MN DNR
http://www.dnr.state.mn.us/invasives/aquaticanimals/commoncarp/index.html
Gulf States Marine Fisheries Commission/GSMFC http://nis.gsmfc.org/nis_factsheet.php?toc_id=183
Minnesota Dept. of Natural Resources/MN DNR
http://www.dnr.state.mn.us/invasives/aquaticanimals/grasscarp/index.html
http://en.wikipedia.org/wiki/Cyprinid
http://en.wikipedia.org/wiki/Grass_Carp

CRAPPIE/ Black Crappie/, *Pomoxis nigromaculatus*
http://www.mnr.gov.on.ca/en/Business/LetsFish/2ColumnSubPage/STEL02_165687.html
http://www.dnr.state.mn.us/fish/crappie/index.html

GAR/Longnose Gar/*Lepisosteus osseus*
Louisiana DWF http://www.wlf.louisiana.gov/fish/longnose-gar
TPWD http://www.tpwd.state.tx.us/huntwild/wild/species/lng/
http://www.thejump.net/fishingarticles/Longnose-gar.htm
Minnesota Dept. of Natural Resources/MN DNR
http://www.dnr.state.mn.us/snapshots/fish/longnosegar.html
Florida Freshwater Fisheries/FFF http://www.floridafisheries.com/Fishes/gar.html
http://www.rodnreel.com/gulffish/gulffish.asp?cmd=view&FishID=36

SHELLFISHES

ABALONE/ Red Abalone/*Haliotis rufescens*
http://www.fishtech.com/redab.html

CLAM/ Softshell clam/*Mya arenaria*
http://webapps.marinebiodiversity.ca/BayOfFundy//taxListInfo.jsp?taxListInfo=Mya%20arenaria
http://www.marinespecies.org/aphia.php?p=taxdetails&id=140430

CLAM/ Atlantic Surfclam/ *Spisula solidissima*
Note: *Ensis* spp. – *ITIS* lists 9 species, only 3 are listed on *TSL E. directus, E. ensis, E. siliqua* - market name is razor clam; also note: *E. directus, E. minor, E. myrae* are valid/verified in *ITIS*, but the others are not.
Note: *Solen* spp. – *ITIS* lists 5 species, 4 of these are valid/verified; *TSL* recognizes *S. marginatus, S. rostriformis, S. viridis*; all 3 are marketed as razor clam .
Note: *Siliqua* spp. – *ITIS* lists 7 species; 5 valid/verified. *TSL* recognizes *S. alta, S. costata, S. patula;* all of these are marketed as razor clam.

CLAM, GEODUCK/ Pacific Geoduck/, *Panopea abrupta*
http://www.pac.dfo-mpo.gc.ca/science/species-especes/shellfish-coquillages/clam-palourde/manila-japonaise-eng.htm

http://www.pac.dfo-mpo.gc.ca/science/species-especes/shellfish-coquillages/clam-palourde/varnish-lustree-eng.htm

COCKLE OR COCKLE CLAM/Common Cockle/ Nuttall Cockle /*Clinocardium nuttallii*
Walla Walla edu
http://www.wallawalla.edu/academics/departments/biology/rosario/inverts/Mollusca/Bivalvia/Veneroida/Cardiidae/Clinocardium_nuttallii.html
http://academic.evergreen.edu/t/thuesene/bivalves/tech_key.htm#FamKey

CRAB/Dungeness Crab/*Chionoecetes opilio*
http://www.fao.org/fishery/species/2644/en

CRAB/Dungeness Crab/*Cancer magister*
http://www.dfg.ca.gov/marine/dungeness_crab.asp#rock

CRAB/Jonah Crab/*Cancer borealis*
http://www.edf.org/page.cfm?tagID=15820
http://www.dfo-mpo.gc.ca/csas/csas/status/2000/c3-68e.pdf
http://www.sealifebase.org/summary/SpeciesSummary.php?id=26783
http://www.fishbase.org/report/FAO/FAOCatchList.cfm?c_code=&areacode=&scientific=Cancer%20borealis&english=
NJ Scuba, 1994-96 .
http://animaldiversity.ummz.umich.edu/site/accounts/information/Cancer_irroratus.html
http://en.wikipedia.org/wiki/Cancer_irroratus
http://www.dfo-mpo.gc.ca/csas/csas/status/2000/c3-67e.pdf
http://animaldiversity.ummz.umich.edu/site/accounts/information/Cancer_irroratus.html
http://www.sealifebase.org/comnames/CommonNamesList.php?ID=26784&GenusName=Cancer&SpeciesName=irroratus&StockCode=1045
http://www.sealifebase.org/summary/SpeciesSummary.php?id=26783

CRAB, STONE/Florida Stone Crab/*Menippe mercenaria*
http://myfwc.com/research/saltwater/crustaceans-marine-arthropods/stone-crabs/faq/
http://collier.ifas.ufl.edu/SeaGrant/pubs/Stone_Crab__Ecology_Fact_Sheet%5B1%5D.pdf
http://www.nmfs.noaa.gov/fishwatch/species/stone_crab.htm
http://www.foodreference.com/html/art-stone-crab-7806.html
http://en.wikipedia.org/wiki/Florida_stone_crab
Conservation:
http://www.nmfs.noaa.gov/fishwatch/species/stone_crab.htm
http://www.foodreference.com/html/art-stone-crab-7806.html
Gerhart, S.D., and T.M. Bert. 2008. Life-history aspects of stone crabs genus Menippe : size at maturity, growth, and age. Journal of Crustacean Biology 28: 252–261

CRAB/Horseshoe Crab/*Limulus polyphemus*
http://marinebio.org/species.asp?id=281
http://www.essortment.com/horseshoe-crabs-miracle-blood-41662.html
http://www.sms.si.edu/IRLSpec/Limulu_polyph.htm
http://en.wikipedia.org/wiki/Horseshoe_crab

CRAWFISH or CRAYFISH/ Red Swamp Crayfish/ *Procambarus clarkia*
http://www.fao.org/fishery/species/3454/en

LOBSTER/ American Lobster/*Homarus americanus*
http://www.fao.org/fishery/species/3482/en

MUSSEL/ Blue Mussel/ *Mytilus edulis*
http://www.fao.org/fishery/species/2688/en

OCTOPUS/ Common Octopus/ *Octopus vulgaris*
http://www.wallawalla.edu/academics/departments/biology/rosario/inverts/Mollusca/Cephalopoda/Enteroctopus_dofleini.html
http://www.robinsonlibrary.com/science/zoology/mollusks/cephalopoda/octopus.htm
http://www.thecephalopodpage.org/Octopusvulgaris.php
http://www.waza.org/en/zoo/visit-the-zoo/snails-cuttlefish-octopus-and-relatives-mollusca-1254385523/octopus-vulgaris

OYSTER/ Eastern Oyster/ *Crassostrea virginica*
http://www.law.cornell.edu/cfr/text/21/161/136
http://www.dfw.state.or.us/mrp/shellfish/bayclams/about_oysters.asp
http://www.wsg.washington.edu/mas/pdfs/olyoysterlr.pdf

SEA CUCUMBERS/ California Stichopus/, *Parastichopus californicus*
http://www.royalbcmuseum.bc.ca/natural_history/invertebrates.aspx?id=264
http://www.bcarchives.bc.ca/Natural_History/Invertebrates.aspx?id=264

SHRIMP/ PANDALID/ Northern Pink Shrimp/, *Pandalus borealis*
http://www.fao.org/fishery/species/3425/en

SHRIMP/ PENAEID/ Brown Shrimp/ *Farfantpenaeus aztecus*
http://www.sealifebase.org/summary/SpeciesSummary.php?id=14595

SPONGE/Yellow Sponge/*Spongia barbara*
http://www.naturalbathandbodyshop.com/caribbean-grass-sponge.html
http://dictionary.die.net/sheeps-wool%20sponge
http://dictionary.die.net/grass%20sponge
http://www.fao.org/docrep/field/003/AC286E/AC286E01.htm
http://www.divingheritage.com/keywestkern.htm
http://www.youtube.com/watch?v=CqD_DF5jlpU&NR=1
http://www.fao.org/docrep/field/003/AC286E/AC286E01.htm
http://en.wikipedia.org/wiki/Sponge#Diseases

WHELK/ Channeled Whelk/ *Busycotypus canaliculatus*
http://www.mbl.edu/marine_org/marine_org.php?func=detail&myID=BX956
http://www.thecephalopodpage.org/MarineInvertebrateZoology/Strombusgigas.html
http://en.wikipedia.org/wiki/Knobbed_whelk

Glossary

abdomen: in finfishes, the lower portion of the body, especially that part between the pectoral fins and the anus; in arthropods, the hindmost of the two or three distinct body divisions

adductor muscles: the muscle used to draw the two valves of a bivalve mollusk together

adipose eyelid: immovable transparent outer covering, or partial covering, of the eye of some bony fishes, such as mullets and jacks

adipose fin: a small fleshy fin with no rays, located between the dorsal and caudal fins

alevin: a hatchling salmonid while still attached to the yolk mass

ambient: the encompassing environment or surrounding conditions

amphidromous: migrating between freshwater and the sea (in both directions), but not for breeding purposes

amphipods: an order of crustaceans that have no carapace and that have different forms of appendages; unlike isopods, where all the legs are alike.

anadromous: pertaining to species that mature in the ocean, then migrate to freshwater to spawn

analog products: imitation and simulated fish and shellfish products fabricated from processed fish meal; such as surimi

anal fin: a verticle fin positioned on the ventral line, on the underside of the abdomen behind the anus

antenna: a sensory appendage on the head of an arthropod

anterior: of or pertaining to the front section; as opposed to posterior

anus: the posterior external opening of the alimentary canal; also vent

appendage: any part joined to or diverging from the axial trunk; as a limb

Aristotle's lantern: the chewing mechanism of a sea urchin, consisting of five teeth operated by a complex system of levers and muscles

arthropod: an invertebrate belonging to the largest and most diverse phylum *Arthropoda,* having joined legs and segmented body parts; such as crab, crayfish, lobster, and shrimp

axillary process: a fleshy flap, usually narrow and pointed, above the pectoral or pelvic fins

barbel: a small, whisker-like sensory appendage usually about the mouth, chin, or nose

benthic: living on or near the ocean bottom

benthopelagic: Living and feeding in midwaters or near the surface as well as near the bottom.

binary fission: a method of asexual reproduction in which the body of an organism divides into two nearly equal parts

biomass: the amount of living matter, of one or more organisms, present in a particular sample habitat

bivalve: a mollusk belonging to the class *Bivalvia* within the phylum *Mollusca,* having two shells or valves which open and close as though hinged near the top; also pelecypod

book gills: type of gill in some invertebrates consisting of folds of membranous tissue arranged like the leaves of a book

brackish: slightly salty; less salty than sea water, but not drinkable

branchial pores: pores in the lateral-line canal in the gill region, especially in eels

branchiostegal ray(s): bony rays supporting the gill membranes behind the lower jaw

brine: a strong saline solution; water heavily saturated with salt

bycatch: pertaining to the incidental catch associated with a directed fishing effort of another species

bysuss: tough, silken threads secreted by certain bivalve mollusks as means of attachment to a surface; also byssal threads

carapace: the protective portion of the exoskeleton of a crustacean extending over the head and thorax, but not the abdomen

cartilage: an elastic tissue composing most embryo skeletons and skeletons of lower fish, usually turning to bone in higher orders of vertebrates

catadromous: pertaining to species that mature in freshwater, then migrate to the sea to spawn

caudal fin: the fin positioned at the hindmost portion of the body of a finfish; also tail fin

caudal peduncle: the fleshy end of the body located between the anal and tail fins; also the waist

cephalopod: the highest class of *Mollusca*, comprising squid, cuttlefishes, octopuses, nautiluses, ammonites and other related forms all having around the front of the head a group of elongated muscular arms, usually fixed with prehensile suckers or hooks

cephalothorax: the fused head and thorax of a crustacean

chicken haddie: canned haddock, cod, cusk or hake, or any combination thereof, that has not been ground, but does not include dark or sow hake

chitin: the white or colorless substance secreted by the epidermal cells that forms the exoskeleton of crustaceans and other arthropods

chondrophore: a spoonlike pit in the shell hinge of a bivalve mollusk

ciguatera: a food borne illness associated with the eating of large warm water reef fishes; usually causes acute gastrointestinal illness often followed by chronic nerve/neurological damage that can be long lasting, or even incurable

circumpolar: surrounding, lying near, or in the vicinity of a terrestrial pole

compressed: a fish that is flattened from side to side, like a flatfish; also laterally compressed;

continuous fin: referring to the condition in which the vertical fins are broadly joined to form a continuous fin around the posterior of a finfish

copepoda: a subclass of *Crustacea*; copepod crustaceans are minute marine or fresh-water crustaceans usually having six pairs of limbs on the thorax; some abundant in plankton and others parasitic on fish; a stage in crustacean larvae development

corselet: the girdle of small scales on the anterior portion of the body of mackerel-like fishes

COSEWIC: (Advisory) Committee on the Status of Endangered Wildlife in Canada

crustacean: marine invertebrates with chitinous exoskeletons and bodies divided into two or more distinct parts; such as crab, crayfish, lobster, or shrimp

ctenoid: having posterior margins with needle-like projections as with the scales of most spiny-rayed fishes

cycloid: having smooth posterior margins as with the scales of most soft-rayed fishes

deciduous scale: a loosely attached scale that is easily shed

demersal: dwelling on or near the ocean floor, as with groundfish

depensation: the effect where a decrease in spawning stock leads to reduced survival through a) increased predation per egg given constant predator pressure or b) the decreased probability of finding a mate ('Allee' effect).

depressed: said of a fish that is flattened from top to bottom so that it is wider than high

depuration: the process whereby shellfish are placed in special land-based tank systems in which they can purge themselves of microbial contaminants. This process seems to have limited efficacy for some bacteria such as *Vibrio* spp., the enteroviruses and algal toxins

detritus: dead or decaying organic matter

diadromous: pertaining to species that migrate between fresh and salt water; see anadromous and catadromous

dioecious: having separate sexes

directed fishing: fishing efforts that target specific species

diurnal: active during the day (opposite of nocturnal)

diurnal cycle: a pattern that recurs every 24 hours as a result of one full rotation of the Earth

dorsal: pertaining to the top or back

dorsally compressed: compressed from top to bottom like a skate; also dorsal-ventrally compressed

dorsal fin: the fin located on the back of fishes, and in front of the adipose fin, if it is present

dorsal spine: one of the hard rays supporting the membrane of the dorsal fin

echinoderm: a marine invertebrate of the phylum *Echinodermata* having a skin-covered skeleton of calcareous plates, often bearing spines; such as sea cucumbers and sea urchins

elongate: having a form notably long or stretched out

emarginate: notched, but not deeply forked, as in the shape of the caudal fin

epipelagic: the open ocean habitat, from the surface to a depth of 200 m

ESA: The US Endangered Species Act designates species of concern, endangered or threatened

estuary: a wide mouth of a river where its current meets the sea and is influenced by the tides; also an inlet or arm of the sea

euphausiids: an order of small malacrustaceans, resembling shrimp, and forming an important component of the world's plankton population

euryhaline: able to live in a wide range of salinities

excurrent siphon: in a mollusc, the tubular opening through which water is expelled

exoskeleton: the external skeleton or a supportive covering characteristic of all arthropods

ex-vessel price: the price received by the harvester for fish, shellfish, and other aquatic plants and animals; also ex-vessel

FADs: Fish aggregating devices

family: a grouping or category of plants or animals ranking one above the genus level and one below order level

FAS: frozen at sea

fathom: a nautical term used to describe depth or length, where 1 fathom is equal to 6 feet

fecund: refers to the capability of reproduction of the species

filament: a fine, threadlike appendage, said of certain elongated fin rays in some fishes

fingerling: a young fish, such as a salmon, usually within the first year

finlet: one of several small, isolated fin rays situated behind the dorsal or anal fin

fish: singular or plural of one species of mostly cold-blooded aquatic vertebrates usually having scales and breathing through gills

FishBase: an online global information system on fishes

fishes: refers to more than one species of fish

FL: forked length: Length of a fish measured from the tip of the snout to the posterior end of the middle caudal rays.

flatfish: any bony fish of the order *Pleuronectiformes,* characterized by a laterally compressed or flattened body, fringed with a dorsal and anal fin, eyes situated on the same side of the head, and lying on its blind side, usually on sandy or muddy ocean bottoms

foot: in mollusks, the muscular extension of the body used in locomotion; one of the numerous small appendages of an echinoderm, hydraulically operating and used in movement or feeding, or as a sense organ and often tipped with a suction disk

forked length: see FL

ganoid scales: hard, glossy, enameled scales

gape: a region of incomplete closure between the two valves of a bivalve mollusk

genus: a grouping or category of plants or animals ranking one above the species level and one below the family or sub-family level

gills: the respiratory organs for underwater breathing of fishes and other aquatic vertebrates

gill cover: the boney covering of the gill cavity; also the operculum

gill rakers: bony projections inside the gills, used to sift out solid objects from the respiratory tract

groundfish: pertaining to fishes that dwell and feed at or near the bottom of the ocean

head length: distance from the most anterior point of the head to the posterior edge of the opercle

hermaphrodite: having both male and female reproductive organs in one body

holothuroid: a class of echinoderms consisting primarily of sea cucumbers

ICCAT: International Commission for the Conservation of Atlantic Tunas

I.Q.F.: individual quick frozen

ichthyology: the scientific study of fishes

incurrent siphon: in a mollusc, the tubular opening through which water is taken in

invertebrate: an animal that lacks a spinal cord or backbone; in contrast to a vertebrate

isopods: see amphipods

ITIS: Integrated Taxonomic Information System is an authoritative database of worldwide taxonomic information with a North American focus

IUCN Red List: International Union for Conservation of Nature list of threatened species; ratings from least concern to extinct include near threatened, vulnerable, endangered, critically endangered and extinct in the wild

keel: the sharp compressed edge on the ventral surface of the body between the paired fins

kelt: a dark, thin, recently spawned-out (spent) Atlantic salmon; also a slink

keriorrhea: similar to diarrhea, only the body will expel yellowish-orange drops of oil instead of liquid bowel movements

krill: the collection of small marine crustaceans of the order *Euphausiacea* (euphausiids) that are the principal food of baleen whales and some fishes

kype: the hooked end of the lower jaw of a breeding male salmonid

larvae: immature young, which go through a more or less complete metamorphosis to reach maturity

lateral line: a thin horizontal series of pore-like openings positioned along each side of the abdomen which act as a sensory organ encompassing hearing, touch and a kind of radar

laterally compressed: flattened from side to side, as with flatfish

ligament: in a bivalve mollusc, a horny structure on the hinge area, either internal or external, connecting the valves, which acts as a spring to keep the valves open

lunate: deeply forked and narrow bladed, as in the shape of a caudal fin

mandible: of or pertaining to the lower jaw

mantle: a sheet of tissue that lines and secretes the shell of a mollusc, or covers the outside of a shell-less mollusc, and encloses the mantle cavity

mantle cavity: the space enclosed by the mantle of a mollusc, which contains the gills and the visceral mass

marginal: in reference to fins, that portion along the edge

maxilla: the bone of the upper jaw

maxilliped: one of the mouth appendages of crustacea used in feeding

median fins: the unpaired fins - anal, caudal, and dorsal; also vertical fins

megalops: larva stage following the zoea in most crabs; includes the development of legs, abdomen and eyes

membrane: a thin, pliable, sheet-like layer of tissue serving to cover or line an organ or part, separate adjoining cavities, or connect adjoining structures

milt: a milky substance containing the male sperm

mollusc: soft-bodied usually shelled invertebrate belonging to phylum *Mollusca* which includes clam, mussel, oyster, scallop, snails and squid; also mollusk

molt: to shed or cast off hair, feathers, shell, horns, or an outer layer of skin in the process of growth or periodic renewal, with the cast off parts being replaced by new ones

MSC: Marine Stewardship Council, an international body that certifies fisheries as sustainable

muscle scar: the portion on the inner surface of a bivalve shell where the muscle was attached natal: of or pertaining to one's birth

nauplius: (nauplii) a shellfish, a crustacean larvae in the first stage after leaving the egg

oceanodromous: migrating within oceans; e.g., between spawning and feeding areas

offshore zone: extend seaward from the extreme low tide mark out to the outer edge of the continental shelf, generally fished by vessels longer than 30 meters

opaque: the degree of transparency or non transparency

opercle: the large, rectangular bone of the gill cover

operculum: gill cover

otoliths: a calcareous concretion in the internal ear of vertebrates, or in the otocyst of an invertebrate, especially conspicuous in many teleost fishes where they form hard bodies and growth rings; frequently used to determine age of fishes

oviparous: pertaining to most fishes where eggs or ova are deposited, fertilized and hatched outside the body of the parent

ovoviviparous: pertaining to some fishes (some species of sharks and redfishes), where eggs are retained within the brood chamber of the parent and where development of the embryo occurs, but without the strong attachment to a placenta (as with mammals), resulting in the birth of living young

paired fins: pertaining to the symmetrical set of fins positioned on either side of the abdomen, particularly the pectoral and pelvic fins, and in contrast to vertical fins

palatine bones: make up part of the roof of the mouth of vertebrates, and some of the lower vertebrates, such as fish

pallial line: the line on the inner surface of a bivalve shell marking the location of the attachment of the mantle

parr: usually the first and second years in the life of a salmon or sea trout, when the body is marked with parr marks

parr marks: dark vertical markings on the sides of young salmonid fishes

parturition: the act of bringing forth young

pectoral fins: anterior and uppermost of the paired fins, positioned behind the gills

pelagic: pertaining to fishes that range throughout a representative sample of ocean depths known as the water column, and in contrast to groundfish

pelvic fins: posterior paired fins, located in the abdominal position or towards the rear

periostracum: a chitinous layer covering the exterior of the shell of many molluscs, serving to protect it the from corrosion

pharyngeal teeth: teeth in the pharynx or throat that are used to crush mollusks and crabs before swallowing

pigment: a substance that imparts color to animal or vegetable tissues, as melanin and chlorophyll

pincer: the nipper-like claw present on the frontmost appendages of most crustaceans

plankton: the aggregate of small marine and fresh water plant and animal organisms that drift or float with the currents, consisting of 1) phytoplankton - photosynthetic or plant constituent of plankton; mainly unicellular algae, 2) zooplankton - animal constituent of plankton; mainly small crustaceans and fish larvae.

polychaetes: small to plankton-like worms

posterior: of or pertaining to the rear section; as opposed to anterior

prosoma: the frontmost body section of certain arthropods

protandric hermaphrodites: creatures which start life as the male of the species, then later transform into the female

protogynous hermaphrodites: creatures which start life as the female of the species, then later transform into the male

PSP: Paralytic shellfish poison

ray: in finfishes, an articulated and segmented rod that supports the membrane of a fin; the arm, or radiating appendage of an echinoderm

reduction fishery: non-food fishery, a fishery for oil or meal products

redd: the spawning ground of certain fish, especially salmons and trouts

Ref.: in this book; refers to original reference source in *FishBase*

roe: unfertilized fish eggs; also caviar

rostrum: a bony extension of the snout, as in the swordfish

round weight: the weight of the whole fish or shellfish before processing

salmonid: the generic name applied to the family *Salmonidae,* which includes salmon, trout and char

SAFMC: South Atlantic Fishery Management Council. It is headquartered in North Charleston, South Carolina, and is one of eight regional fishery management councils in the United States.

SARA: Canada's Species at Risk Act, designates species as special concern, endangered, threatened, extirpated

scale: one of the thin, flat, membranous or bony outgrowths of the skin of most fishes, usually overlapping to form a nearly complete covering

scute: external bony scales or plates

SeaLifeBase: an online global information system of sea life other than fishes

sessile: not able to move; permanently attached to a solid substrate

sexually dimorphic: having observable physical differences between sexes

shellfish: any aquatic animal having a shell

shellfish sanitation: toxic and infectious health risks of shellfish are addressed and effectively mitigated by national shellfish sanitation programmes in the US and similar programs in Canada that restrict commercial harvest of bivalves to waters that have been frequently monitored and classified as approved growing waters according to very stringent standards. In the case of shellfish originating in waters of marginally acceptable microbiological quality, there are procedures for relaying harvested animals to approved clean waters for several weeks before shipment for consumption (also see **shellfish toxins** and **depuration**)

shellfish toxins: shellfish gills serve not only for "breathing," but are highly developed for collecting and sorting fine organic particles from the water, upon which they depend for nourishment. In this complex filtration process small particles, such as viruses, bacteria and toxic algae (phytoplankton) might also be collected. The accumulation of algal toxins (e.g., paralytic shellfish poison/PSP; amnesic shellfish toxin or domoic acid; diarrheic shellfish toxin; etc.) is a food risk factor almost exclusively associated with marine shellfish. Oysters, and other bivalves, such as mussels and clams, are of particular public health concern if they are collected from waters of questionable or undefined quality, e.g., contaminated with domestic sewage or naturally occurring toxic algae (also see **shellfish sanitation)**

SHL: shell

shoal: a shallow place in any body of water; a sandbank or bar; especially one that can be seen at low tide

SL: standard length: The measurement from the most anterior tip of the body to the midlateral posterior edge of the hypural plate (in fish with a hypural plate) or to the posterior end of the vertebral column (in fish lacking hypural plates)- from *FishBase*

smolt: the stage in the life cycle of a salmon or sea trout between the parr and grilse, when about two years of age and ready to migrate to sea

soft dorsal: pertaining to that portion of the dorsal fin which consists of soft rays only

spawn: the act of reproduction of fishes

species: singular or plural referring to a group of related organisms that share a more or less distinctive form and are capable of interbreeding; the basic unit of unique biological classification

spine: a fin ray that is not branched, is without obvious segments, and is more or less stiffened and sharpened at the apex

spinous dorsal: pertaining to that portion of the dorsal fin which consists of spines only

standard length: see SL

supermale: the breeding colors assumed by males of some species at the moment of breeding

swimmeret: one of the small abdominal appendages of a crustacean; also pleopods

swim bladder: a sac filled with air or other gases lying beneath the backbone often attached to the walls of the body cavity; also air bladder

symmetrical: having an exact correspondence between the opposite halves of a figure, form, line or pattern; mirror image

synchronous hermaphrodites: individual fish possess both male and female organs, producing sperm and eggs at the same time

systematics: umbrella term to describe the three processes used to describe species; the description of species (identification), naming of names (taxonomy) and description of the relationships among and between taxa (phylogenetics).

tail fan: the fanlike structure located at the tip of the tail of some crustaceans, such as shrimp, consisting of the telson and a pair of flattened abdominal appendages

tail fin: the most posterior fin, located behind the peduncle; also caudal fin

taxa: any organism or group of organisms of the same taxonomic rank (e.g., genus); plural of taxon

taxonomic: based on the principles of taxonomy

taxonomy: the scientific discipline of naming organisms.

teeth: the pointed protuberances at the hinge of a bivalve shell

telson: the unpaired terminal structure attached to the last abdominal segment of a crustacean

tentacle: the long, flexible structure, located on the head or around the mouth of some invertebrates, used for grasping or feeding, or as a sense organ

terminal: pertaining to the location of the mouth of a fish, and which is positioned at the tip of the snout

test: the skeleton of an echinoid echinoderm, consisting of rows of fused plates

thorax: the division of an animal's body between the head and the abdomen

TL: total length: straight-line measurement from the most anterior point to the most posterior point

total length: see TL

TSL: abbrev. For "The Seafood List," publ. by the US Food and Drug Administration

tubercle: a discrete lump or projection found in the surface or skin, usually a modified scale tube

umbo: in bivalve molluscs, the oldest part of the shell and situated near the hinge

unsexed: sex either not determined or not reported

valve: in a bivalve mollusc, one of the two opposite halves of the shell

varigated: marked with different colors and tints, with spots, streaks, or stripes

vent: in finfishes, the combined external opening of the digestive, urinary and reproductive tubes

ventral: pertaining to the lower portion of the abdomen; on the lower surface

vertebra: any of the segmented bones of the spinal column in vertebrates

vertebrate: any of a primary division of animals, characterized by a segmented spinal column, as fishes, birds, and mammals; in contrast to invertebrate

vertical fins: pertaining to those unpaired fins, particularly dorsal, anal and caudal and positioned on the median or center line of the body, and in contrast to paired fins; also median fins

villiform teeth: small, slender teeth forming velvety bands

visceral mass: the part of the body of a mollusc that contains the visceral organs

viviparous: pertaining to mammals and some species of sharks where the embryo becomes firmly attached to the uterine wall by a yolk-sac placenta and is nourished by the parent until gestation is complete, resulting in the birth of living young

visceral cavity: the body cavity where most of the internal organs are located **water vascular system:** the system of canals in an echinoderm that hydraulically operates the tube foot

WD: width

Weberian ossicles: a chain of small bones connecting the swim bladder with the inner ear in most freshwater fishes providing an acute sense of hearing

yolk-sac larvae: fish larvae that has already hatched from the egg but has not started feeding yet and still absorbs the yolk from a ventrally attached sac

zoea: early larval form of crabs and other decapod crustaceans such as lobster and shrimp

zygoparous: a form of oviparity, intermediate between oviparity and viviparity; eggs are fertilized internally before being released into the environment

Index to Fishes and Shellfishes

MARKET NAMES, Common Names, *Scientific names,* aliases and other

ocean perch, 192, 193, 202, 203, 204, 205
OCEAN PERCH, 192
Ocean pout, 191
OCEAN POUT, 190
ocean quahog, 330, 331, 333
ocean shrimp, 366, 368
Ocean Shrimp, 366
ocean whitefish, 260
octopus, 171, 327, 357, 372
Octopus, 324, 327, 356
Octopus vulgaris, 356
oil, 83, 85, 101, 107, 111, 113, 126, 127, 158, 159, 183, 187, 189, 203, 207, 211, 217, 218, 219, 221, 235, 237, 245, 255, 273, 291, 317
oilfish, 126, 127
OILFISH, 126
Oligoplites spp., 177
Olympia oyster, 358
Olympia Oyster, 358
Ommastrephidae, 372
omnivores, 165, 313, 351, 364
Oncorhynchus, 210, 282, 316, 318
Oncorhynchus gorbuscha, 216
Oncorhynchus keta, 212
Oncorhynchus kisutch, 214
Oncorhynchus mykiss, 316
Oncorhynchus nerka, 218
Oncorhynchus tshawytscha, 210
Onykia robusta, 372
Ophichthus rex, 124
Ophidiidae, 98
Ophiodon elongatus, 138, 170
Opsanus beta, 262
Opsanus tau, 262
Orconectes virilis, 350
Orcynopsis unicolor, 96
Oregon sturgeon, 312
Oregoniida, 340
Orthopristis chrysoptera, 148, 160
Osmeridae, 102, 310
Osmerus mordax, 310
Ostrea edulis, 358
Ostrea spp, 358
Ostreidae, 358
oviparous, 99, 165, 241, 265, 277, 289

OYSTER, 324, 358
Oyster Drum, 122
oyster toadfish, 262
oyster, cupped, 358
oyster, edible, 358
oyster, flat, 358
oyster, Japanese Kumamoto, 358
oyster, Olympia, 358
oyster, Pacific, 358
Oysterfish, 258
Oysters, 359
P. alepidotus, 100
P. burti, 100
P. paru, 100
P. simillimus, 100
Pacifastacus leniusculus, 350
Pacific barracuda, 88
Pacific Bonito, 96
Pacific butterfish, 100, 101
Pacific cod, 106, 107
Pacific creolefish, 90
Pacific giant octopus, 356
Pacific hagfish, 152
Pacific hake, 154, 278
Pacific Halibut, 156
Pacific Herring, 158
Pacific littleneck clam, 335
Pacific mackerel, 176
Pacific moonfish, 162
Pacific ocean perch, 192
Pacific sardine, 84
Pacific spadefish, 248
Pacific spiny dogfish,, 234
Pacific Whiting, 278
Pacuma toadfish, 262
Pagrus auratus, 200
Pagrus pagrus, 201
Palinuridae, 352
palmetto bass, 285
Pandalidae, 366
Pandalopsis dispar, 366
Pandalus borealis, 366, 367
Pandalus danae, 366
Pandalus hypsinotus, 366
Pandalus jordani, 366
Pandalus montagui, 366
Pandalus platyceros, 366
Pandalus platyceros, 368
Pandilids, 367
Panope bitruncata, 335
Panopea abrupta, 324, 334
Panulirus argus, 352

Panulirus interruptus, 352
Paralabrax spp., 91
Paralichthys californicus, 156
Paralichthys dentatus, 128, 132
Paralichthys lethostigma, 132
Paralithodes camtschaticus, 340
Paralithodes spp., 338
Paranthias colonus, 90
Paranthias furcifer, 90
Parapercis spp., 144
Paraplaqusia bilineata, 246
Parastichopus californicus, 324, 362
Parastichopus spp., 362
parr, 208, 209, 211, 213, 214, 215, 216, 217, 219, 319
pasta necks, 330
Patinopecten caurinus, 360
Pectinidae, *360*
pelagic, 90, 97, 113, 175, 203, 279, 281, 367
Penaeidae, *366*, *368*
Peprilus triacanthus, 100
Perca flavescens, 304
perch, 78, 90, 142, 171, 172, 192, 193, 202, 244, 284, 304, 305, 306, 308, 309, 320
PERCH, LAKE, 304
PERCH, OCEAN, 192
PERCH, YELLOW, 304
Perchaude, 304
Percichthyidae, 104
Percidae, 78, 304, 308, 320
Perciformes, 294
PERIWINKLE, 324
periwinkles, 374, 375
Periwinkles, 374
permit, 198, 199
PERMIT, 198
permits, 176
Peruvian anchovy, 84
petrale sole, 194
pharyngeal, 148, 149, 161, 166, 239, 292
Phycidae, 154
Phycine hakes, 106
pickerel, 306, 307, 320
Pickerel, 320
Picuda, 88
pigfish, 148, 149, 160

Outside Book Reviewers (2006 edition)*

General Review   Lou VanGuelpen, Gerhard Pohle
Introduction pages   Robert L. Stephenson

Featured Species Common Name	Scientific Name	Reviewers
Marine Fishes		
Walleye Pollock	*Theragra chalcogramma*	Sandra Lowe
Alewife	*Alosa pseudoharengus*	Heath Stone
Northern Anchovy	*Engraulis mordax*	Dick Beamish, Joshua Lindsay
Bluefish	*Pomatomus saltatrix*	Gary Shepherd
Pacific Bonito	*Sarda chiliensis*	Joshua Lindsay
Butterfish	*Peprilus triacanthus*	Michael Burton
Capelin	*Mallotus villosus*	Robert Trenholm, Ray Hayter
Atlantic Cod	*Gadus morhua*	Don Clark
Cusk	*Brosme brosme*	Lei Harris
Spiny Dogfish	*Squalus acanthias*	Michael Burton
Blackback / Winter Flounder	*Pseudopleuronectes americanus*	Heath Stone, Colin Levings, Paul Nitschke
Rock Grenadier	*Coryphaenoides rupestris*	Robert Trenholm, Ray Hayter
Red Grouper	*Epinephelus morio*	Michael Burton
Haddock	*Melanogrammus aeglefinus*	Lou VanEekhaute
White Hake	*Urophycis tenuis*	Robert Trenholm, Ray Hayter
Pacific Halibut	*Hippoglossus stenolepis*	Dick Beamish
Pacific Herring	*Clupea pallasii*	Mike Power, Dick Beamish
Jack Mackerel	*Trachurus symmetricus*	Joshua Lindsay
Lingcod	*Ophiodon elongatus*	Dick Beamish
Lumpfish	*Cyclopterus lumpus*	Robert Trenholm, Ray Hayter
Atlantic Mackerel	*Scomber scombrus*	Mike Power, Michael Burton
Goosefish	*Lophius americanus*	Michael Burton
Atlantic Wolffish	*Anarhichas lupus*	Michael Burton
Deepwater Redfish	*Sebastes mentalla*	Robert Trenholm, Ray Hayter
American Plaice	*Hippoglossoides platessoides*	Heath Stone
Pollock	*Pollachius virens*	Robert Trenholm, Ray Hayter
Scup	*Stenotomus chrysops*	Michael Burton
Yelloweye Rockfish	*Sebastes ruberrimus*	Sandra Lowe, Dick Beamish,
Sablefish	*Anoplopoma fimbria*	Sandra Lowe, Dick Beamish
Atlantic Salmon	*Salmo salar*	Gilles La Croix, Colin Levings
Chinook Salmon	*Oncorhynchus tshawytscha*	Colin Levings, Dick Beamish
Chum Salmon	*Oncorhynchus keta*	Colin Levings, Dick Beamish
Coho Salmon	*Oncorhynchus kisutch*	Colin Levings, Dick Beamish
Pink Salmon	*Oncorhynchus gorbuscha*	Colin Levings, Dick Beamish
Sockeye Salmon	*Oncorhynchus nerka*	Colin Levings, Dick Beamish
Black Sea Bass	*Centropristis striata*	Gary Shepherd, Michael Burton
Grey Seatrout / Weakfish	*Cynoscion regalis*	Gary Shepherd

Featured Species Common Name	Scientific Name	Reviewers
Marine Fishes (Cont'd)		
Thorny Skate	*Amblyraja radiata*	Heath Stone
Red Snapper	*Lutjanus campechanus*	Michael Burton
Rock Sole	*Lepidopsetta bilineata*	Colin Levings, Dick Beamish
Swordfish	*Xiphias gladius*	Stacey Paul, Michael Burton
Golden Tilefish	*Lopholatilus chamaeleonticeps*	Paul Nitschke, Michael Burton
Bluefin Tuna	*Thunnus Thynnus*	Stacey Paul, Michael Burton
Greenland Turbot	*Reinhardtius hippoglossoides*	Heath Stone, Robert Trenholm, Ray Hayter
Pacific Hake	*Merluccius productus*	Sandra Lowe
Freshwater Fishes		
Largemouth Bass	*Micropterus salmoides*	Philip Moy
Channel Catfish	*Ictalurus punctatus*	Philip Moy
Arctic Char	*Salvelinus alpinus*	Robert Trenholm, Ray Hayter
American Eel	*Anguilla rostrata*	Robert Trenholm, Ray Hayter
Inconnu	*Stenodus leucichthys*	Philip Moy
Northern Pike	*Esox lucius*	Philip Moy
Sauger	*Sander canadensis*	Philip Moy
Rainbow Smelt	*Osmerus mordax*	Philip Moy, Robert Trenholm, Ray Hayter
White Sucker	*Catostomus commersonii*	Philip Moy, Robert Trenholm, Ray Hayter
Lake Trout	*Salvelinus namaycush*	Philip Moy
Walleye Pike	*Sander vitreus*	Philip Moy
Lake Whitefish	*Coregonus clupeaformis*	Philip Moy
Yellow Perch	*Perca flavescens*	Philip Moy
complete		
Shellfishes		
Red Abalone	*Haliotis rufescens*	Doug Woodby
Soft-shell Clam	*Mya arenaria*	Shawn Robinson, David Robichaud
Northern Quahog / Hard-shell	*Mercenaria mercenaria*	John Kraeuter
Geoduck Clam	*Panopea abrupta*	Graham Gillespie, Claudia Hand
Blue Crab	*Callinectes sapidus*	Walt Canzonier
Snow Crab	*Chionoecetes opilio*	Robert Trenholm, Ray Hayter
Dungeness Crab	*Cancer magister*	Antan Phillips
Blue Mussel	*Mytilus edulis*	Walt Canzonier
Eastern Oyster	*Crassostrea virginica*	Walt Canzonier
Sea Scallop	*Placopecten magellanicus*	Walt Canzonier
California Stichopus	*Parastichopus californicus*	Claudia Hand
Northern (Pink) Shrimp	*Pandalus borealis*	Robert Trenholm, Ray Hayter
Northern Shortfin Squid	*Illex illecebrosus*	Robert Trenholm, Ray Hayter
Channeled Whelk	*Busycotypus canaliculatus*	Michael Burton

*Reviews were for "glaring errors and omissions" only and do not constitute an endorsement of the accuracy or completeness of the entire content. Reviewers' comments were also subject to further editing and space limitations.

New Illustrations (2012 edition)

(Minji Kim, Illustrator)

1. Alaska Pollock
2. Anchovy
3. Atlantic Blue Marlin
4. Ballyhoo
5. Barracuda
6. Barred Surfperches
7. Barrelfish
8. Bearded Brotula
9. Bigeye
10. Black Drum
11. Blackbelly Rosefish
12. Blue Tang
13. Bluefin Tuna
14. Bowfin
15. Buffalofish
16. Burbot
17. California Sheephead
18. Capelin
19. Cobia
20. Cod
21. Common Carp
22. Conger Eel
23. Crappie - Black
24. Croaker
25. Cunner
26. Cutlassfish
27. Dealfish
28. Dory
29. Escolar
30. Flounder
31. Fluke
32. Gag Grouper
33. Gar
34. Grunt
35. Gulf Toadfish
36. Haddock
37. Hagfish
38. Hind – Red Hind
39. Hogfish
40. Jack
41. Kelp Greenling
42. Kingfish
43. Ladyfish
44. Mackerel Scad
45. Mahi-mahi
46. Mojarra
47. Mummichog
48. Common (Nuttall) Cockle
49. Ocean Pout
50. Pompano
51. Sand Lance
52. Saury
53. Scamp
54. Sea Raven
55. Sea Robin
56. Shad
57. Shortfin Mako Shark
58. Silverside
59. Spadefish
60. Squirrel fish
61. Stone crab
62. Tautog
63. Triggerfish
64. Tripletail
65. Tuna (albacore)
66. Tuna (bigeye)
67. Wahoo
68. Yellow sponge